Metabolic Inhibitors

A Comprehensive Treatise

Volume II

Contributors to Volume II

W. A. ANDREAE

DANIEL I. ARNON

Z. M. BACQ

F. BERGEL

PETER BERNFELD

CLIVE BRADBEER

A. D'IORIO

Q. H. GIBSON

R. GOUTIER

E. J. HEWITT

O. HOFFMANN-OSTENHOF

JAMES G. HORSFALL

J. M. JOHNSON

WILLARD J. JOHNSON

R. M. JOHNSTONE

H. LEES

MANUEL LOSADA

N. B. MADSEN

IAN M. MILLER

BRUCE A. NEWTON

D. J. D. NICHOLAS

R. D. O'BRIEN

J. H. QUASTEL

SAUL RICH

E. C. SLATER

T. L. SOURKES

IRWIN B. WILSON

P. W. WILSON

H. BOYD WOODRUFF

E. A. ZELLER

Metabolic Inhibitors

A Comprehensive Treatise

edited by

R. M. Hochster

Biochemistry Section
Microbiology Research Institute
Canada Department of Agriculture
Ottawa, Canada

J. H. Quastel

Department of Biochemistry
McGill University and the
McGill-Montreal General Hospital
Research Institute
Montreal, Canada

Volume II

Academic Press · *New York* · *London* · *1963*

ACADEMIC PRESS INC.
111 Fifth Avenue, New York 3, New York

United Kingdom Edition published by
ACADEMIC PRESS INC. (LONDON) LTD.
Berkeley Square House, London W.1

LIBRARY OF CONGRESS CATALOG CARD NUMBER: 63-12924

PRINTED IN THE UNITED STATES OF AMERICA

2075

Contributors

Numbers in parentheses indicate the pages on which the author's contributions appear.

W. A. ANDREAE (243), *Research Institute, Canada Department of Agriculture, London, Ontario, Canada*

DANIEL I. ARNON (559), *Department of Cell Physiology, University of California, Berkeley, California*

Z. M. BACQ (631), *Département de Pathologie et Thérapeutique Générales, Université de Liège, Liège, Belgium*

F. BERGEL (161), *Chester Beatty Research Institute, Institute of Cancer Research: Royal Cancer Hospital, London, England*

PETER BERNFELD (437), *Bio-Research Institute, Cambridge, Massachusetts*

CLIVE BRADBEER (595), *National Heart Institute, National Institutes of Health, Bethesda, Maryland*

A. D'IORIO (79), *Department of Biochemistry, Medical School, University of Ottawa, Ottawa, Ontario*

Q. H. GIBSON[1] (539), *Department of Biochemistry, University of Sheffield, Sheffield, England*

R. GOUTIER (631), *Centre d'Étude de l'Énergie nucléaire, Département de radiobiologie, Mol, Belgium*

E. J. HEWITT (311), *Department of Agriculture and Horticulture, University of Bristol, Research Station, Long Ashton, Bristol, England*

O. HOFFMANN-OSTENHOF (145), *Organisch-Chemisches Institut, University of Vienna, Vienna, Austria*

JAMES G. HORSFALL (263), *The Connecticut Agricultural Experiment Station, New Haven, Connecticut*

J. M. JOHNSON[2] (161), *Chemistry Department, Chester Beatty Research Institute, Institute of Cancer Research: Royal Cancer Hospital, London, England*

WILLARD J. JOHNSON (1), *Research Laboratories, Biochemistry Department, Frank W. Horner Limited, Montreal, Quebec*

[1] Present address: Johnson Foundation, University of Pennsylvania, Philadelphia, Pennsylvania.

[2] Present address: Research Department, John Wyeth and Brother Limited, Havant, England.

R. M. JOHNSTONE (99), *McGill University and McGill-Montreal General Hospital Research Institute, Montreal, Quebec, Canada*

H. LEES (615), *Department of Microbiology, University of Manitoba, Winnipeg, Canada*

MANUEL LOSADA[3] (559), *Department of Cell Physiology, University of California, Berkeley, California*

N. B. MADSEN[4] (119), *Microbiology Research Institute, Research Branch, Canada Department of Agriculture, Ottawa, Ontario, Canada*

IAN M. MILLER (23), *Microbiology Department, Merck Sharp & Dohme Research Laboratories, Division of Merck & Co., Inc., Rahway, New Jersey*

BRUCE A. NEWTON (285), *Medical Research Council Unit for Chemical Microbiology, Department of Biochemistry, University of Cambridge, Cambridge, England*

D. J. D. NICHOLAS (311), *Chemical Microbiology Department, Long Ashton Research Station, University of Bristol, Bristol, England*

R. D. O'BRIEN (205), *Department of Entomology, Cornell University, Ithaca, New York*

J. H. QUASTEL (473, 517), *McGill University and McGill-Montreal General Hospital Research Institute, Montreal, Quebec, Canada*

SAUL RICH (263), *The Connecticut Agricultural Experiment Station, New Haven, Connecticut*

E. C. SLATER (503), *Laboratory of Physiological Chemistry, University of Amsterdam, Amsterdam, Holland*

T. L. SOURKES (79), *Allan Memorial Institute of Psychiatry, and Department of Psychiatry, McGill University, Montreal, Canada*

IRWIN B. WILSON (193), *Department of Neurology and Biochemistry, College of Physicians and Surgeons, Columbia University, New York, New York*

P. W. WILSON (595), *Department of Bacteriology, University of Wisconsin, Madison, Wisconsin*

H. BOYD WOODRUFF (23), *Microbiology Department, Merck Sharp & Dohme Research Laboratories, Division of Merck & Co., Inc., Rahway, New Jersey*

E. A. ZELLER (53), *Department of Biochemistry, Ward Memorial Building, Chicago, Illinois*

[3] Present address: Sección de Bioquimica, Centro de Investigaciones Biologicas, Madrid, Spain.

[4] Present address: Department of Biochemistry, University of Alberta, Edmonton, Alberta, Canada.

Preface

The last three or four decades have witnessed most impressive advances in biochemistry and related fields. These have led to greatly increased understanding of the details of intracellular molecular interactions. Many biochemical laboratories today display large metabolic maps, obviously prepared with great care, that depict a maze of enzymic reactions which are presumably concerned with the maintenance of processes that are involved in the life of the cell. The realization that effective control of some of these reaction mechanisms may also control cell function and cell growth makes the subject of metabolic inhibition of the greatest significance, and underlines not only its theoretical but also its practical value. Volumes I and II of "Metabolic Inhibitors" have been produced in order to document, in a comprehensive fashion, all the major advances which the judicious use of inhibitors has so far made possible. This has been accomplished at, what seems to the Editors, a crucial time in the development of the field of metabolic inhibition, for there is little doubt that the practical importance of the use of inhibitors in the control of disease is now a subject of wide and searching examination throughout the world.

"Metabolic Inhibitors" had been intended, at the outset, to be a one-volume treatise. As the subject was explored in its widest sense it became clear that, in order to provide the reader with a truly comprehensive work, at least two volumes would be necessary. The subject matter covered in these volumes involves so many aspects of biological research that only a group of highly experienced investigators can prepare truly critical and authoritative presentations. The most heartfelt thanks of the Editors go to the 52 authors who gave so much of their time, energy, and knowledge toward the preparation of these volumes.

The production of "Metabolic Inhibitors" was subject to the usual strains and delaying influences that are commonly encountered in multi-author books. Nevertheless, the authors had the opportunity to bring their contributions up to date at several stages in the production of these volumes and most authors took advantage of this opportunity. Thus, the Editors feel confident that both Volumes I and II are reasonably up to date and trust that they will fill a definite need in the field of metabolic inhibition for research workers, teachers, and graduate students.

Last, but by no means least, it remains for us to express our thanks, collectively, to the many publishers and authors for their kind permissions to reproduce some of their illustrations, to Academic Press for the excellent spirit of cooperation which prevailed throughout the production phase of these volumes, and to Dr. R. M. Johnstone for a truly fine effort in the preparation of the subject index.

Ottawa, Ontario   R. M. HOCHSTER
Montreal, Quebec   J. H. QUASTEL
Canada
October, 1963

Contents

CHAPTER 16

Dinucleotide Analogues and Related Substances

WILLARD J. JOHNSON

CHAPTER 17

Antibiotics

H. BOYD WOODRUFF and IAN M. MILLER

CHAPTER 18

Monoamine and Polyamine Analogues

E. A. ZELLER

CHAPTER 19

Inhibitors of Catechol Amine Metabolism

T. L. SOURKES and A. D'IORIO

CHAPTER 20

Sulfhydryl Agents: Arsenicals

R. M. JOHNSTONE

CHAPTER 21

Mercaptide-Forming Agents

N. B. MADSEN

CHAPTER 22

Enzyme Inhibition by Quinones

O. HOFFMANN-OSTENHOF

CHAPTER 23

Biological Alkylating Agents

J. M. JOHNSON and F. BERGEL

CHAPTER 24

Inhibition of Acetylcholinesterase

IRWIN B. WILSON

CHAPTER 25

Organophosphates and Carbamates

R. D. O'BRIEN

CHAPTER 30

Polyanionic Inhibitors

PETER BERNFELD

CHAPTER 31

Inhibitions in the Citric Acid Cycle

J. H. QUASTEL

CHAPTER 32

Uncouplers and Inhibitors of Oxidative Phosphorylation

E. C. SLATER

CHAPTER 33

Effects of Anesthetics, Depressants, and Tranquilizers on Cerebral Metabolism

J. H. QUASTEL

CHAPTER 34

Inhibitors of Gas Transport

Q. H. GIBSON

CHAPTER 35

Selective Inhibitors of Photosynthesis

MANUEL LOSADA and DANIEL I. ARNON

CHAPTER 36

Inhibitors of Nitrogen Fixation

CLIVE BRADBEER and P. W. WILSON

CHAPTER 37

Inhibitors of Nitrification

H. LEES

CHAPTER 38

Inhibition Due to Radiation

R. GOUTIER and Z. M. BACQ

Contents of Volume I

CHAPTER 16

Dinucleotide Analogues and Related Substances

Willard J. Johnson

I. INTRODUCTION

Definitions. In accordance with present-day usage, a nucleoside may be defined as the N-glycoside of a heterocyclic base, and a nucleotide as the phosphate ester of the former. A dinucleotide, as the name implies, is comprised of two nucleotides joined together by pyrophosphate linkage.[1] Thus, nicotinamide adenine dinucleotide (NAD) is the anhydride of nicotinamide mononucleotide (NMN) and adenosine monophosphate (AMP). Nicotinamide adenine dinucleotide phosphate (NADP) differs from NAD only in the possession of a third phosphate group in the 2′-position of the ribose moiety of adenosine. While usually grouped with the dinucleotide coenzymes, flavin adenine dinucleotide (FAD) is not a true dinucleotide since the ribose side chain of riboflavin is not bound through glycosidic linkage.

[1] The nomenclature used in this chapter for both DPN and TPN is that recommended by the "Report of the Commission on Enzymes of the International Union of Biochemistry, 1961"; i.e., they are referred to as NAD and NADP, respectively.

Analogues of purine and pyrimidine bases and nucleosides are relatively inert until converted to their corresponding nucleotides (1). Consequently, any meaningful discussion of the former must necessarily include their nucleotides. In other chapters of this book purine analogues have been discussed by Hitchings and Elion, and pyrimidine analogues by Brockman and Anderson.

Structural analogues of nicotinic acid and nicotinamide may become activated as antimetabolites by conversion to analogues of the dinucleotide coenzymes, NAD and NADP. There is reason to believe that the biosynthetic pathways existing for the normal metabolites are utilized in this conversion. Dinucleotide analogues are also formed *in vivo* to some extent through the NADase transfer reaction, which will be described later. Analogues of NAD have been prepared *in vitro* by modifying either the nicotinamide or adenine moiety and by replacing nicotinamide with a dissimilar heterocyclic base, or adenine with a different purine or pyrimidine base. To what extent these reactions take place *in vivo* upon administration of the precursors remains largely unclarified; in some cases the analogues have been isolated from various tissues. A large number of such analogues are now known. Those which have shown interesting antimetabolic properties will be discussed here, as will those having historical or heuristic value.

Recent developments concerning the biosynthesis of the dinucleotide coenzymes will necessitate a reinterpretation of much of the experimental data that have accumulated in this area of research. It would be of interest, therefore, to review the evidence on which the currently accepted concept is based. Certain substances which influence the metabolism of dinucleotide coenzymes will also be discussed in this chapter.

II. BIOSYNTHESIS OF NICOTINAMIDE ADENINE DINUCLEOTIDE (NAD)

A. Utilization of Nicotinic Acid

Until quite recently it had been generally accepted that the biosynthesis of NAD (I) proceeded via nicotinamide intermediates (3). This concept received further strength from the demonstration that a single large dose of nicotinamide, administered to the normal rat or mouse, gave rise to a marked increase in the liver content of NAD, while a similar dose of nicontinic acid was much less effective (4, 5).

However, conflicting evidence was obtained by Preiss and Handler

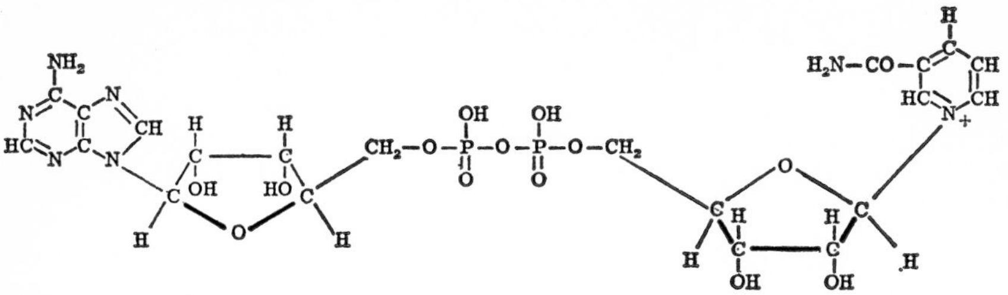

(1)

Nicotinamide adenine dinucleotide (2)

(6-8), who observed an accumulation of labeled nicotinic acid mononucleotide (NaMN) and nicotinic acid adenine dinucleotide (NaAD) when human erythrocytes (6, 7) and yeast autolyzates (8) were incubated with nicotinic acid-C^{14}. Furthermore, the appearance of labeled NaAD prior to that of NAD in rat liver following the injection of nicotinic acid-C^{14} into the intact rat suggested that NaMN and NaAD were intermediates of NAD synthesis rather than degradation products of NAD (7). Preiss and Handler's experimental results are consistent with the reaction sequence for the conversion of nicotinic acid to NAD shown in Eqs. (1–3).

$$\text{Nicotinic acid} + \text{PRPP} \rightleftharpoons \text{NaMN} + \text{PPi} \qquad (1)$$

$$\text{NaMN} + \text{ATP} \rightleftharpoons \text{NaAD} + \text{PPi} \qquad (2)$$

$$\text{NaAD} + \text{glutamine} + \text{ATP} \rightarrow \text{NAD} + \text{glutamate} + \text{AMP} + \text{PPi} \qquad (3)$$

Partial purification of the enzymes involved in reactions (1–3) has been obtained (8). A 270-fold purification from beef liver of the enzyme which catalyzes reaction (1) was recently described; the enzyme has been named "nicotinic acid mononucleotide pyrophosphorylase" (9). Its K_m for nicotinic acid was found to be approximately 1×10^{-6} M and for 5'-phosphoribosyl pyrophosphate (PRPP) approximately 5×10^{-5} M. Inhibition of the enzyme was not observed with high concentrations of nicotinic acid or nicotinamide, nor was the latter a substrate for the enzyme. NaMN, the product of the reaction, inhibited competitively with respect to both nicotinic acid and PRPP, the K_i values being 3.5×10^{-5} M and 4×10^{-5} M, respectively, and K_m, 1×10^{-6} M and 5×10^{-5} M, respectively. NaAD pyrophosphorylase, which catalyzes reaction (2) is apparently identical with Kornberg's NAD pyrophosphorylase (10):

$$\text{NMN} + \text{ATP} \rightleftharpoons \text{NAD} + \text{PPi} \qquad (4)$$

Atkinson et al. (11) have shown that reaction (4) is inhibited by

NaMN. It should be noted that K_m values of 1.2×10^{-4} M and 4×10^{-4} M for NMN and NaMN, respectively, as reported by Atkinson et al. (11), are at variance with Preiss and Handler's observations, which indicate that NaMN has the lower K_m value (8). Imsande (12) has recently reported partial purification of the enzymes involved in reactions (1–3) from an extract of Escherichia coli.

B. Utilization of Nicotinamide

NaAD, the nicotinic acid analogue of NAD, appears to be an intermediate in the synthesis of NAD whether the initial precursor be nicotinamide or nicotinic acid (13, 14). Studies by Narrod et al. (15) involving the use of nicotinamide-8-N^{15} indicate that the amide nitrogen of nicotinamide was lost prior to incorporation of the latter into NAD in the intact mouse. The presence of nicotinamide riboside or of NMN could not be detected, nor was there evidence of conversion of nicotinamide to nicotinic acid at the free base level. The synthesis of NaAD was found by Threlfall (16) to precede that of NAD in mouse and rat liver slices incubated with 10^{-2} M nicotinamide. This concentration of nicotinamide, but not nicotinic acid, gave rise to a 3–4-fold increase in the NAD content of the liver slices. In this connection Langan et al. (14) have shown that at low dosage levels, nicotinic acid is superior to nicotinamide as a precursor of both NaAD and NAD in the intact mouse, while at high dosage levels nicotinic acid, but not nicotinamide, markedly inhibits the synthesis of both dinucleotides.

Whereas the evidence is strong that NaAD is an intermediate in the conversion of nicotinamide to NAD, the stage at which the amide group is lost, whether at the free base or nucleotide level, is not clear. There is evidence for nicotinamide deamidase activity in bacteria (12, 16, 17), the green pea Pisum sativum (18), and various avian species (19), but not in mammals. However, the possibility of a low level of nicotinamide deamidase activity in mammals cannot be ruled out, since cleavage of the acid-amide linkage of salicylamide has been shown to occur in sheep kidney extracts (20) and in the rabbit in vivo (21). Sarma et al. (22) have recently reported the deamidation of NMN, but not of nicotinamide, by mouse liver extracts. On the other hand, the deamidation of nicotinamide by purified preparations from rat liver has also been reported (22a).

C. Effect of Alkylating Agents and Azaserine

Alkylating agents of the nitrogen mustard and ethyleneimino classes have been found to decrease the concentration of NAD in various normal and tumor tissues (*23, 24*). Kroger *et al.* (*23*) observed a parallelism between the carcinostatic effect of alkylating agents and the decrease in NAD levels of various rat tumor transplants. Indeed, this parallelism has been utilized as a means of gauging dosage requirements of nitrogen mustards and ethyleneimino compounds in the treatment of cancer patients (*24*).

The mechanism of this effect remains obscure. The drop in NAD levels could be due to either inhibition of synthesis or increased breakdown. Thus, Drysdale *et al.* (*25*) found that blockage of RNA and DNA formation by nitrogen mustards and sulfur mustards in various metabolizing cells led to a concomitant accumulation of adenine-containing mononucleotides, presumably due to prevention by the mustards of mononucleotide phosphorylation to the di- and triphosphates. However, the accumulated mononucleotides may also have been degradation products. Roitt (*26*) has provided evidence that inhibition of respiration and glycolysis in ascites tumor cells and rat tissues by 2,4,6-triethyleneimino-1,3,5-triazine (TEM) was due to TEM-induced breakdown of NAD. This effect appeared to be mediated by NADase, since nicotinamide protected against the inhibitory effect of TEM on glycolysis and partially restored glycolysis when added to a completely inhibited system. No evidence could be obtained that a TEM analogue of NAD was formed upon incubation of TEM with NAD in the presence of ascites cell NADase; furthermore, the breakdown of NAD by NADase *in vitro* was unaffected by TEM.

The effect of TEM on NAD in ascites tumor cells is remarkably similar to that of L-azaserine (*O*-diazoacetyl-L-serine) and DON (6-diazo-5-oxo-L-norleucine) on the liver content of NAD in the intact mouse. Narrod *et al.* (*27*) have shown that nicotinamide fails to produce an increase in mouse liver NAD when azaserine is simultaneously administered. On the other hand, when injected into the normal mouse, azaserine caused a sharp drop in the liver NAD concentration, which could be prevented by nicotinamide. Later studies (*28*) involving labeled nicotinamide revealed that azaserine induces an increased rate of NAD breakdown. The reversal of the azaserine effect by nicotinamide could be explained in terms of NADase exchange activity, which apparently is not influenced by azaserine (*28*).

Baker (*29*) has proposed that the noncompetitive inhibition of L-glutamine activity by azaserine and DON (*30*) may be due to irreversible alkylation of the phosphate groups of the pyridoxal complex formed from these inhibitors. The similarity between the effects of TEM and azaserine on NAD metabolism indicates the possibility that azaserine may function as an alkylating agent. In any event, it is apparent that the *in vivo* activity of azaserine and DON is inexplicable purely on the basis of glutamine antagonism (*29, 31*).

III. DINUCLEOTIDE ANALOGUES

A. Analogues of NAD and NADP

Various animal tissues contain an enzyme called NADase, which catalyzes the hydrolysis of NAD at the nicotinamide-ribose linkage. About 20 years ago, it was shown by Mann and Quastel (*32*) that the hydrolytic activity of NADase towards NAD could be reversibly inhibited by nicotinamide but not nicotinic acid. The mechanism of this inhibition was elucidated by Zatman *et al.* (*33, 34*), who have ostensibly shown that free nicotinamide competes with water for the active substrate-enzyme complex which remains when the nicotinamide moiety is released from NAD. Thus, in the presence of a high concentration of free nicotinamide, what is observed is an exchange reaction between free nicotinamide and the bound nicotinamide of NAD.

Analogues of nicotinamide, also, can exchange with the nicotinamide moiety of NAD in the presence of NADase to yield the corresponding analogues of NAD (*35, 36*, and reviews *37, 38*), a large number of which have now been prepared *in vitro*. Many of these have coenzyme activity (*39*), others are inert (*40*) or inhibit the coenzyme activity of NAD in dehydrogenase reactions (*41*). Analogues of nicotinamide adenine dinucleotide phosphate (NADP) can be similarly prepared (*39*).

1. ISONICOTINYLHYDRAZIDE ADENINE DINUCLEOTIDE (INH-AD)

To explain the potent antitubercular activity of isonicotinylhydrazide (isoniazid, INH) (II), Zatman *et al.* (*35*) considered the possibility that INH may exchange with the nicotinamide moiety of NAD to yield a toxic NAD analogue. The analogue (INH-AD) has been isolated from an incubation mixture containing NAD, INH, and NADase from pig brain (*36*) and from beef spleen (*42*). It does not inhibit NAD-requiring dehydrogenase reactions (*36, 42*). Although the occurrence has been reported of INH-induced pellagra in tuberculosis patients which completely responded to nicotinamide treatment (*43, 44*), there is no evidence to indicate that the deficiency symptoms were due to formation of INH-AD.

The presence of INH-AD in tissues of animals following INH administration has not been reported, nor has the analogue been detected in bacteria grown in the presence of INH. It is doubtful, therefore, that INH-AD is involved in the antitubercular activity of INH. Recent evidence (44a) suggests that INH exerts its bactericidal action by selectively inhibiting nucleic acid synthesis.

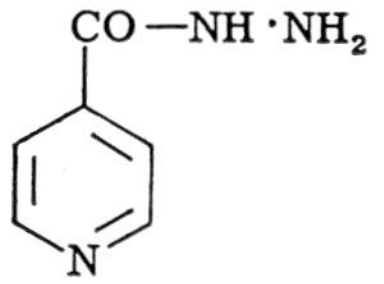

(II)

Isonicotinylhydrazide
(isoniazid, INH)

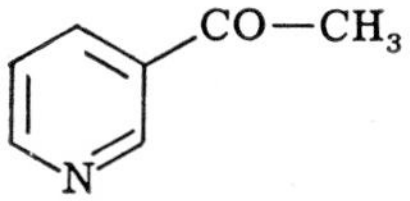

(III)

3-Acetylpyridine

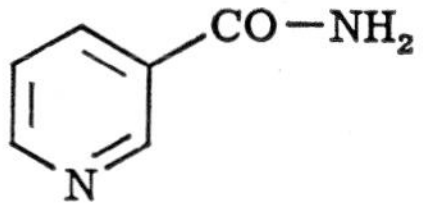

(IV)

Nicotinamide

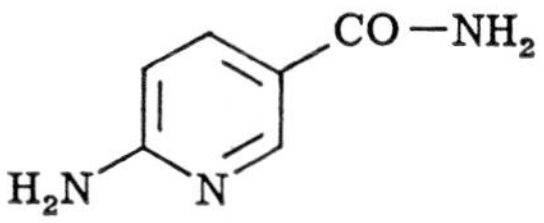

(V)

6-Aminonicotinamide

2. 3-ACETYLPYRIDINE ADENINE DINUCLEOTIDE (APy-AD)

APy-AD is an analogue of NAD (I) which differs from the latter by the presence of a CH_3 group in place of the NH_2 group of the nicotinamide (IV) moiety. This alteration in the structure of the NAD molecule does not result in loss of coenzyme activity, but changes appreciably its rate of reactivity with several different dehydrogenases (39). Kaplan and Ciotti (45) have described the preparation and properties of APy-AD. Its presence in brain and spleen of mice, but not in the liver, following 3-acetylpyridine administration has been demonstrated (46). The highest concentration of APy-AD was found in neoplastic tissue of tumor-bearing mice, which gave rise to the unrealized hope that 3-acetylpyridine might be an effective antitumor agent (46).

The first observation that 3-acetylpyridine was a vitamin antagonist was made by Woolley (47) who was able to show that both nicotinamide and nicotinic acid would annul its toxic effects. A protective effect of tryptophan, as well as nicotinamide and nicotinic acid, against 3-acetyl-pyridine toxicity in the chick embryo has also been demonstrated (48). Kaplan *et al.* (46), however, were unable to protect mice against lethal doses of the antagonist with high doses of nicotinic acid, this lack of effect being attributed to the "low exchange activity" of nicotinic acid, as observed with both pig brain and beef spleen NADase (49). Furthermore, the ability of nicotinamide, but not nicotinic acid, to counteract 3-acetyl-pyridine toxicity was adduced as evidence that APy-AD was formed *in vivo* via the NADase exchange reaction (46).

In the light of more recent findings by the Brandeis group (14) it would appear that neither of these deductions is justified. The lowest dose of nicotinic acid employed (250 mg/kg) to obtain protection against 3-acetylpyridine toxicity (46) was actually inhibitory to NAD synthesis (14), and a different result might well have been obtained if the dose of nicotinic acid found to be optimum for NAD synthesis, namely 50 mg/kg, had been used. In this regard, ability of the protecting agent to partici-pate in the exchange reaction would not seem to be an absolute require-ment, since increased synthesis of NAD, by whatever means attained, would be expected to counteract the toxic effects of the analogue. There seems to be no doubt, however, that APy-AD formation accounts for the toxicity of 3-acetylpyridine, due to concomitant depletion of NAD and inhibition of NAD-linked dehydrogenase reactions.

3. NICOTINIC ACID ADENINE DINUCLEOTIDE (NaAD)

NaAD can be formed directly from nicotinic acid (8) via reactions (1) and (2) and from nicotinamide through a modification of the same reactions not yet clearly established (14). Ballio and Serlupi-Crescenzi (50) demonstrated the formation of NaAD by the NADase exchange reaction, using beef spleen NAD nucleotidase as catalyst, following its isolation from the mycelium of *Penicillium chrysogenum*. The analogue has been prepared *in vitro* by prior formation of the ethyl nicotinate analogue from which NaAD is obtained by mild alkaline hydrolysis (51). There is no evidence to indicate that NaAD is formed by the NADase exchange reaction *in vivo*.

4. OTHER 3-SUBSTITUTED PYRIDINE ANALOGUES OF NAD

A large number of pyridine compounds substituted in the 3-position has been shown to undergo exchange with the nicotinamide moiety of NAD in the presence of pig brain NADase to yield the corresponding analogue. Analogues containing pyridine, β-picoline, 3-methylpyridylcarbinol (45), 3-aminopyridine, 3-acetamidopyridine, and 3-pyridylacryloamide (52), all of which lack a carbonyl function in position 3, were found to be void of coenzyme function. On the other hand, analogues containing pyridine-3-aldehyde (53), 3-benzoylpyridine, nicotinic acid hydrazide, pyridine-3-aldoxime, 3-isobutyrylpyridine, nicotinylhydroxamic acid, and thionicotinamide (52), all of which contain a carbonyl group, could be reduced in several dehydrogenase systems, and in some cases interfere with the enzymic reduction of NAD. The significance of these changes in the NAD molecule in relation to coenzyme function has been discussed by Anderson and Kaplan (52).

It is of interest that nicotinylhydroxamic acid, which readily gives rise to the corresponding analogue of NAD *in vitro* (52), when injected into the mouse leads to increased levels of NAD in the liver (54). Hirsch and Kaplan (55) have described a mitochondrial enzyme system which brings about the reduction of nicotinylhydroxamic acid to nicotinamide and of the nicotinylhydroxamic acid analogue of NAD to NAD. It should be noted that the conversion of salicylhydroxamic acid and its 5-bromo derivative to salicylamide and 5-bromosalicylamide, respectively, by man, mouse, and the rat had previously been demonstrated (56, 57). It is probable that the same enzyme system is responsible for the reduction of both benzoyl- and nicotinylhydroxamic acids (56).

5. 6-Aminonicotinamide Adenine Dinucleotide (6AN-AD)

6-Aminonicotinamide (6-AN) is a structural analogue of nicotinamide, differing from it only by the presence of the amino group on carbon 6. It was first studied as a competitive inhibitor of amine acetylation (58, 59), and when administered to rabbits it displayed a surprisingly high degree of toxicity. The similarity between the toxic symptoms in rabbits and those of 3-acetylpyridine in mice, as first observed by Woolley (47), suggested that 6-AN might be an antimetabolite of nicotinamide. Subsequent studies showed that the lethal toxicity of 6-AN could be completely blocked by concurrent administration of nicotinamide, nicotinic acid, or tryptophan (60, 61).

The delayed action of 6-AN when injected into animals suggested that 6-AN activity was contingent upon metabolic transformation *in vivo*, probably by incorporation into pyridine nucleotides in place of nicotinamide to give the corresponding 6-AN analogue (46). A substance was isolated from the tissues of rats and mice treated with 6-AN and from neoplastic tissues from similarly treated rats bearing the Walker 256

tumor, which proved to be the 6-AN analogue of NAD (*61*). The formation *in vitro* of 6AN-AD was obtained (*61*) by means of the pig brain
NADase exchange reaction of Zatman *et al.* (*36*). Formation of 6AN-AD
in vitro and *in vivo* was confirmed by Dietrich *et al.* (*41, 62*), who also
demonstrated that the corresponding 6-AN analogue of NADP was
formed *in vivo*. Liver, kidney, and tumor tissues of mice bearing the
mammary and adenocarcinoma 755 tumor had equal ability to synthesize
6AN-AD *in vivo*, while brain, lung, heart and skeletal muscle were able
to do so to a lesser degree (*62*). 6-AN administration does not appear to
influence appreciably the NAD levels of the tissues of treated animals
(*63, 64*), except in the chick embryo, in which an extremely high dose
(70 μg) caused a pronounced decrease in the total content of NAD (*65*).
In this connection it should be noted that a 2.5-μg dose of 6-AN in the
chick embryo is highly teratogenic and lethal when injected at 24 hours
of incubation (*66*).

Dietrich *et al.* (*41*) have studied the effect of 6-AN administration on
the activities of several NAD-linked enzyme systems in the 755 adenocarcinoma transplanted into C57BL mice. Lactic acid dehydrogenase was
unaffected, while 3-phosphoglyceraldehyde dehydrogenase, the conversion
of β-hydroxybutyrate to acetate, and α-ketoglutarate oxidase activities
were markedly inhibited. Concomitantly, there was a pronounced decrease in the levels of ATP and ADP in the tumor tissue. Similar results
were obtained with other tissues (*62*). Thus, it would appear that 6-AN
owes its biological activity to the formation of the corresponding analogues of NAD and NADP, which are unable to function as normal
hydrogen carriers, but compete with the normal coenzymes for active sites
on the enzyme (*62, 67*). Interference with nucleotide coenzyme metabolism in this manner would be expected to have a profound effect on the
over-all metabolism of tissues, since most metabolic reactions are directly
or ultimately NAD- or NADP-dependent.

The low NAD and NADP content of tumor tissues as compared with
most normal tissues (*68-70*) suggested the possibility that 6-AN might be
an effective anticancer agent. As a tumor inhibitor, 6-AN has been found
to be active against the mammary adenocarcinomas 755 (*63, 71*) and C3H
(*71*), the 6C3HED lymphosarcoma (*71*), and the Walker carcinoma 256
(*72*). The antitumor effect of 6-AN was prevented by nicotinamide given
concurrently. Martin *et al.* (*73*) have shown that the antitumor effect of
6-AN and diethylstilbestrol in combination is markedly greater than that
produced by either drug alone. Addition of testosterone to the combination decreased host toxicity without diminishing the antitumor effect.
Moreover, diethylstilbestrol greatly enhanced the ability of 6-AN to

inhibit the systems converting α-ketoglutarate and malate to citrate, and β-hydroxybutarate to acetoacetate, while testosterone had no effect in this regard nor was it able to reverse the stilbestrol effect on the three enzymic systems studied (74). Pronounced augmentation of radiotherapeutic "cure" rates against mammary adenocarcinoma 755 was obtained by combined treatment with 6-AN, 6-mercaptopurine (6-MP), and X-rays, while the "cure" rate with either chemical agent alone plus X-rays was not significantly greater than with X-rays alone (75). Under different experimental conditions, 6-AN, as the sole chemical agent, was found to augment the radiotherapeutic effect (76). In view of the radiomimetic properties of alkylating agents (77, 78), in conjunction with the depleting effect of the latter on tissue concentrations of NAD (23, 24, 79), it would seem that the attainment of synergism by means of combined therapy with 6-AN and alkylating agents is a distinct possibility.

Clinical studies with 6-AN have recently been reported (80-82). Objective evidence of tumor regression was obtained, but host toxicity was found to be a serious limitation to its use (80, 81).

6. IMIDAZOLE ADENINE DINUCLEOTIDES

Various substituted imidazoles have been shown to react irreversibly with NAD in the presence of beef spleen NADase to yield the corresponding dinucleotide analogues of NAD (83). These reactions are considered to be dissimilar to the NADase base-exchange reactions of Zatman et al. (34, 35) in that the new dinucleotide formed contains no quaternary ammonium linkage, the liberation of a H^+ ion is involved in its formation, and the dinucleotide is stable to NADase.

a. *4-Amino-5-imidazolecarboxamide Adenine Dinucleotide (AI-AD)*. The isolation of AI-AD from a reaction mixture containing NAD, 4-amino-5-imidazolecarboxamide (VI), and a soluble beef spleen NADase preparation (83) has been described by Alivisatos and Woolley (84, 85). The reaction could be completely inhibited by nicotinamide. Cleavage of the dinucleotide product by nucleotide pyrophosphatase yielded 4-amino-5-imidazolecarboxamide mononucleotide, the immediate precursor of inosinic acid (85). Further studies have shown that AI-AD could readily be converted to hypoxanthine adenine dinucleotide, and 4-amino-5-imidazolecarboxamide mononucleotide to hypoxanthine mononucleotide (inosinic acid) by pigeon liver extracts (86). As a practical measure, these reactions afford a simple and inexpensive means of obtaining imidazole mononucleotides. The possible significance of AI-AD in purine biosynthesis has been discussed by Alivisatos et al. (85, 86).

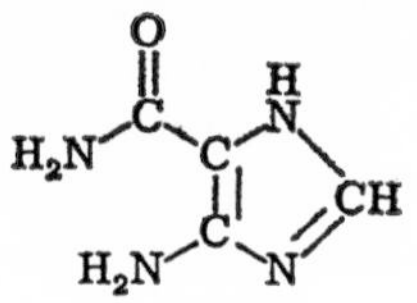

(VI)   (VII)

4-Amino-5-imidazolecarboxamide   4-(2-Aminoethyl)imidazole

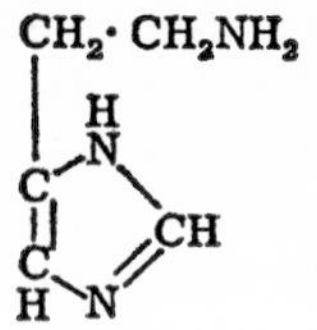

b. Histamine Adenine Dinucleotide (H-AD). Histamine, 4-(2-amino-ethyl)imidazole (VII), reacts with NAD in the presence of beef spleen NADase to yield histamine adenine dinucleotide, in which the nicotin-amide moiety of NAD is replaced by histamine *(87, 88)*. The reaction goes almost to 100% yield of the new dinucleotide, and can be inhibited by nicotinamide. The preparation and isolation of histamine adenine di-nucleotide phosphate, the histamine analogue of NADP, has also been described recently *(89)*, as has the preparation of histamine mononucleo-tide *(90)*.

Alivisatos *et al.* *(88, 91)* entertain the possibility that the histamine-NAD reaction may be involved in the mechanism of anaphylactic shock. In this connection nicotinamide has been reported to protect the adult guinea pig against a lethal dose of histamine, injected intravenously *(92)* or administered by aerosol inhalation *(93)*, but has no effect against the bronchospasm produced by acetylcholine *(93)*. More recently, it has been shown in rats and guinea pigs that both mast cell damage and histamine release in anaphylaxis could be inhibited by nicotinamide, nicotinic acid, isoniazid, and diethylnicotinamide *(94)*. Although the formation of H-AD *in vivo* has not been demonstrated, its occurrence is suggested by the presence of 1-ribosyl-4-imidazoleacetic acid in the urine of rats following histamine administration *(94, 95)*.

7. 1,3,4-THIADIAZOLE ADENINE DINUCLEOTIDE (TDA-AD)

The antitumor effects of 1,3,4-thiadiazoles were first described by Oleson *et al.* *(96)*, who observed that the 2-amino, 2-ethylamino, and 2-acetylamino derivatives (VIII, IX, X) were particularly active against a variety of animal tumors. Since both the toxicity of these compounds and their inhibitory effects on tumor growth could be reversed by nico-tinic acid or nicotinamide, they have been categorized as niacin antago-nists *(97-100)*.

Upon administration of the 2-substituted 1,3,4-thiadiazoles to human subjects a prompt increase in the serum and urinary urate levels was observed (*101*), which was subsequently shown to be due to an increase in uric acid synthesis *de novo* (*102*, *103*) but not to increased yield of uric acid from nucleic acid degradation (*102*). The uricogenic effect of 2-amino-1,3,4-thiadiazole and 2-ethylamino-1,3,4-thiadiazole as well as the oral toxicity produced by these agents could be blocked or reversed by nicotinamide (*102*). It should be noted that further substitution of the thiadiazole molecule in the 5-position leads to inactivity. Thus, 2,5-diamino-1,3,4-thiadiazole (*102*) (XI), 2-acetylamino-1,3,4-thiadiazole-5-sulfonamide (acetazolamide) (XII), and the currently employed actibacterial sulfonamides, 2-sulfanilamido-5-ethyl-1,3,4-thiadiazole (sulfaethylthiadiazole) (XIII) and its 5-methyl analogue, are not known to influence uric acid production, nor are they effective as tumor growth inhibitors.

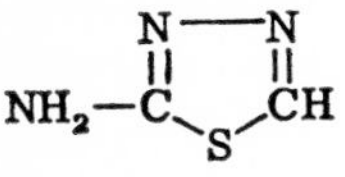

(VIII)

2-Amino-1, 3, 4-thiadiazole

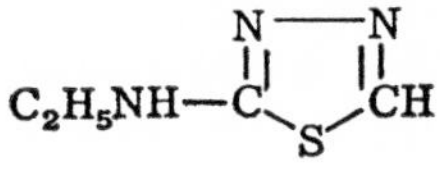

(IX)

2-Ethylamino-1, 3, 4-thiadiazole

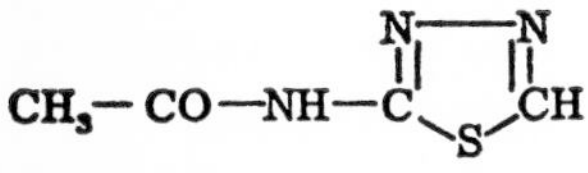

(X)

2-Acetylamino-1, 3, 4-thiadiazole

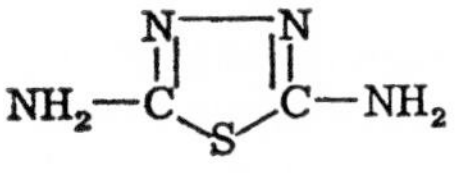

(XI)

2, 5-Diamino-1, 3, 4-thiadiazole

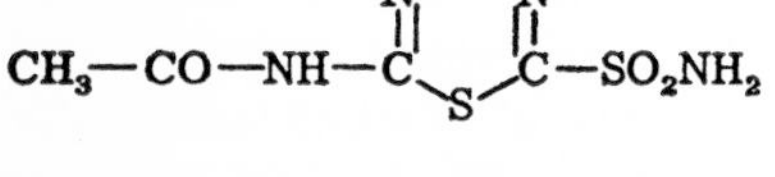

(XII)

2-Acetylamino-1, 3, 4-thiadiazole-5-sulfonamide (acetazolamide)

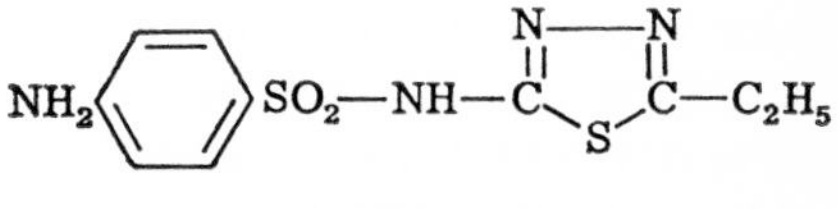

(XIII)

2-Sulfanilamido-5-ethyl-1, 3, 4-thiadiazole (sulfaethylthiadiazole)

Further studies by Krakoff *et al.* (*65*) have shown that the uricogenic effect of 2-ethylamino-1,3,4-thiadiazole in the chick embryo could be reversed by 6-aminonicotinamide and 3-acetylpyridine as well as by nicotinamide; moreover, 6-aminonicotinamide was effective at lower dosages than nicotinamide. Similarly, Oettgen *et al.* (*104*) were able to show that the antileukemic activity of 2-amino-1,3,4-thiadiazole could be reversed as effectively with 6-aminonicotinamide, 5-fluoronicotinamide, and 3-acetylpyridine as with nicotinamide and nicotinic acid, while 6-amino-5-fluoro- and 6-chloronicotinic acids were relatively ineffective as reversing agents. In this connection, Humphreys *et al.* (*105*) have recently published a detailed report on "the toxicology and antileukemic effectiveness of pyridine and thiadiazole derivatives with reference to their metabolite-antagonist relationships with nicotinamide."

Ciotti *et al.* (*100*) carried out studies on analogue formation with the object in view of providing an explanation for the antileukemic and nicotinamide antagonist activity of the 2-substituted thiadiazoles. They were able to show that 2-ethylamino-1,3,4-thiadiazole (IX) is capable of undergoing exchange, in the presence of pig brain NADase, with the nicotinamide moiety of NAD to yield the corresponding thiadiazole analogue. The new dinucleotide bears a similarity to the imidazole adenine dinucleotides (*83*), previously discussed, in that the quaternary ammonium linkage of NAD is replaced by a tertiary nitrogen (*100*). Following the injection of 500 mg/kg of 2-ethylamino-1,3,4-thiadiazole-5-C^{14} into a mouse, the radiactivity was approximately equally distributed among the various tissues, including the brain, but no evidence of analogue formation *in vivo* could be obtained (*100*).

If analogue formation via the NADase exchange reaction is responsible for the antileukemic activity of these compounds, to say nothing of their uricogenic effect, one would expect to see a decrease in NAD levels upon their administration. In fact, it has been shown (*106*) that 2-ethylamino-1,3,4-thiadiazole stimulates the synthesis of NAD from low doses of nicotinamide. On the other hand, it has been found that this compound did not alter the NAD content of the chick embryo, nor did it influence the induced synthesis of NAD by large doses of nicotinamide (*65*).

Krakoff and Balis (*102*) have suggested that the uricogenic effect of these compounds may be due to a block in polynucleotide or coenzyme formation. In this connection it should be noted that Ayvazian and Ayvazian (*107*) have pointed out that the data of Krakoff and Balis (*102*) actually indicate a decreased yield of uric acid from nucleic acids. If ethylamino-1,3,4-thiadiazole does decrease the degradation of nucleic acids, a loss of feedback inhibition could result in greatly increased *de novo* synthesis of purine nucleotides and thus account for the uricogenic effect of these thiadiazoles. Clarification of the mechanism of action of these drugs should be of some value in the elucidation of the regulatory mechanisms of uric acid synthesis *de novo*. This matter has been discussed recently by Seegmiller *et al.* (*107a*).

8. ADENINE-MODIFIED ANALOGUES OF NAD

NAD can be synthesized from NMN and ATP according to reaction (4), which is catalyzed by NAD pyrophosphorylase present ubiquitously in animal and bacterial cells.

Atkinson *et al.* (*11*) have shown that various purine riboside triphosphates can participate in reaction (4) in place of ATP to yield analogues of NAD (I) in which the adenine (XIV) moiety of the latter has been replaced by a different purine. The analogues of NAD thus formed include: nicotinamide hypoxanthine (XV) dinucleotide, nicotinamide guanine (XVI) dinucleotide, nicotinamide 8-azaguanine (XVII) dinucleotide, and nicotinamide 6-mercaptopurine (XVIII) dinucleotide. The properties of the corresponding purine riboside triphosphates involved in the synthesis of the foregoing dinucleotides have been discussed by Atkinson *et al.* (*11, 108*). Nicotinamide hypoxanthine dinucleotide had been previously prepared from NAD by chemical (*109*) and enzymic (*110*) deamination.

6-MP riboside triphosphate, but not 6-MP itself or its riboside 5′-phosphate, was found to be a competitive inhibtor of NAD pyrophosphorylase; the K_i for 6-MP riboside triphosphate was found to be 5×10^{-5} M, and the K_m for ATP, with which it competes, 7.4×10^{-5} M (*108*). Nicotinamide 6-mercaptopurine dinucleotide was prepared from its constituent nucleotides (*108*) by the method used by Hughes *et al.* (*111*) for the chemical synthesis of NAD. The properties of the chemically prepared dinucleotide corresponded to those of the enzymic preparation.

Atkinson *et al.* (*11, 108*) have postulated that the antitumor activity of 6-MP can be accounted for by inhibition of nicotinamide adenine dinucleotide synthesis. In support of this view, they have shown that 6-MP riboside triphosphate can compete with ATP to inhibit the biosynthesis of NAD from NMN *in vitro*. It should be noted that no evidence has yet been presented to indicate that 6-MP riboside triphosphate is formed *in vivo*. There is at present only indirect evidence to show that 6-MP riboside 5′-monophosphate may be enzymically phosphorylated *in vitro* (*112*). It is apparent, however, that 6-MP must be converted to the nucleotide level in order to exert its characteristic antimetabolic

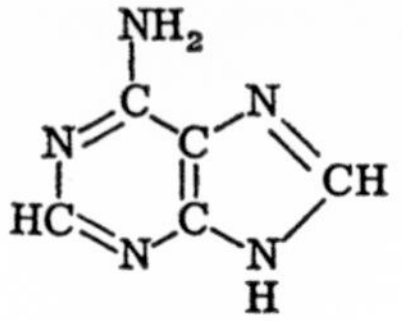

(XIV)

Adenine
(6–aminopurine)

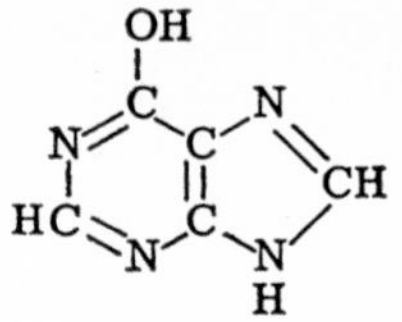

(XV)

Hypoxanthine
(6–hydroxypurine)

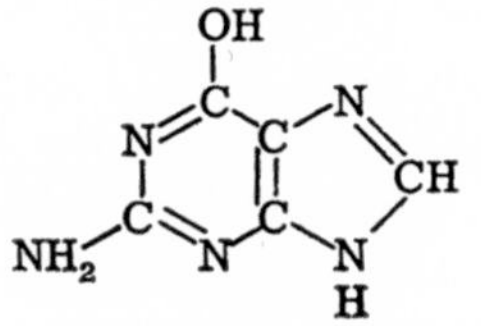

(XVI)

Guanine
(2–amino-6–hydroxypurine)

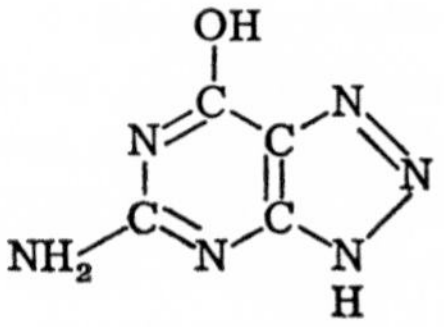

(XVII)

8–Azaguanine

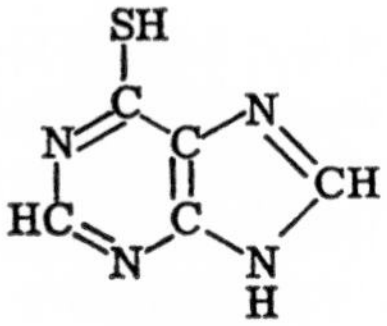

(XVIII)

6–Mercaptopurine

activity, and there is considerable evidence that 6-MP mononucleotide inhibits *de novo* purine biosynthesis (*1, 31, 113, 113a*). That 6-MP can influence NAD biosynthesis *in vivo* is indicated by studies of Kaplan *et al.* (*114*) in which it was shown that, while 6-MP had no effect on the liver NAD content in the otherwise untreated mouse, it partially prevented the increase in the level of NAD in the liver caused by injection of nicotinamide and delayed the subsequent decrease of the NAD level. The former, but not the latter effect, could be prevented by adenylic acid (*114*), which also blocks the antileukemic action and toxicity of 6-MP (*115, 116*). Kaplan *et al.* (*114*) considered the possibility that 6-MP administration might give rise to the formation of an analogue of NAD in which adenine was replaced by 6-MP, but no such analogue has been detected.

9. NICOTINAMIDE PYRIMIDINE DINUCLEOTIDE ANALOGUES OF NAD

The procedure of Hughes *et al.* (*111*), involving the use of dicyclo-hexylcarbodiimide as a condensing agent for the component nucleotides (*117*), has been utilized by Fawcett and Kaplan (*118*), for the chemical synthesis of NAD analogues in which the adenosine moiety of NAD is replaced by uridine and thymidine. The biochemical and physical properties of these analogues have been described (*118*). The thymidine analogue showed very poor coenzymic activity when tested with NAD-linked dehydrogenases, while the uracil analogue could replace NAD, but with somewhat reduced efficiency. The available evidence indicates that the poor performance of these analogues in comparison with that of NAD is due to decreased affinity of the former for the binding sites of the apoenzyme.

10. DEOXYRIBOSE ANALOGUES OF NAD

Klenow and Andersen (*119*) were able to show that deoxy-ATP, prepared enzymically (*120*), would react with NMN in the presence of NAD-pyrophosphorylase to yield the deoxyribose analogue of NAD, which differs from NAD in that the ribose of the adenosine moiety has been replaced by 2'-deoxyribose. The deoxy-NAD, when tested as hydrogen acceptor in the alcohol dehydrogenase system, reacted at a rate 50–60 times slower than NAD. However, when added along with NAD it failed to inhibit the reaction. Deoxy-NAD was inactive as a coenzyme with glucose-6-phosphate dehydrogenase and $\frac{1}{10}$ as active as NAD with glutamic acid dehydrogenase (*119*).

Deoxy-NAD has been prepared chemically by Fawcett and Kaplan (*118*), and its coenzymic capabilities have been studied with a number of NAD-linked dehydrogenases. There was considerable variation in its activity with different enzymes, but in all cases the rates of enzymic reduction were well below that of NAD, thus confirming the findings of Klenow and Andersen (*119*).

B. Analogues of Flavin Adenine Dinucleotide (FAD)

A comprehensive review on flavin coenzymes, in which was included a section on "analogues, antagonists, and other phosphorylated derivatives," was published recently by Beinert (*121*). D. W. Woolley discusses riboflavin analogues in another chapter of this treatise (Volume I, Chapter 12).

REFERENCES

1. R. E. Handschumacher and A. D. Welch, *in* "The Nucleic Acids" (E. Chargaff and J. N. Davidson, eds.), Vol. III, p. 453. Academic Press, New York, 1960.
2. M. Dixon and E. C. Webb, "Enzymes," 1st ed., p. 397. Longmans, Green, New York, 1958.
3. T. P. Singer and E. B. Kearney, *Advances in Enzymol.* **15**, 79 (1954).
4. P. Feigelson, J. N. Williams, Jr., and C. A. Elvehjem, *Proc. Soc. Exptl. Biol. Med.* **78**, 34 (1951).
5. N. O. Kaplan, A. Goldin, S. R. Humphries, and F. E. Stolzenbach, *J. Biol. Chem.* **226**, 365 (1957).
6. J. Preiss and P. Handler, *J. Am. Chem. Soc.* **79**, 4246 (1957).
7. J. Preiss and P. Handler, *J. Biol. Chem.* **233**, 488 (1958).
8. J. Preiss and P. Handler, *J. Biol. Chem.* **233**, 493 (1958).
9. J. Imsande and P. Handler, *J. Biol. Chem.* **236**, 525 (1961).
10. A. Kornberg, *J. Biol. Chem.* **182**, 779 (1950).
11. M. R. Atkinson, J. F. Jackson, and R. K. Morton, *Nature* **192**, 946 (1961).
12. J. Imsande, *J. Biol. Chem.* **236**, 1494 (1961).
13. T. A. Langan, Jr., and L. Shuster, *Federation Proc.* **17**, 260 (1958).
14. T. A. Langan, Jr., N. O. Kaplan, and L. Shuster, *J. Biol. Chem.* **234**, 2161 (1959).
15. S. A. Narrod, V. Bonavita, E. R. Ehrenfeld, and N. O. Kaplan, *J. Biol. Chem.* **236**, 931 (1961).
16. D. E. Hughes and D. H. Williamson, *Biochem. J.* **51**, 330 (1952).
17. N. Grossowicz and Y. S. Halpern, *Biochim. et Biophys. Acta* **20**, 576 (1956).
18. J. G. Joshi and P. Handler, *J. Biol. Chem.* **235**, 2981 (1960).
19. K. V. Rajagopalan, T. I. Sundaram, and P. S. Sarma, *Nature* **182**, 51 (1958).
20. M. Gonnerman, *Arch. ges. Physiol. Pflüger's* **89**, 493 (1902).
21. H. G. Bray, B. E. Ryan, and W. V. Thorpe, *Biochem. J.* **43**, 561 (1948).
22. D. S. R. Sarma, S. Rajalakshmi, and P. S. Sarma, *Biochem. Biophys. Research Communs.* **6**, 389 (1961).
22a. B. Petrack, E. A. Craston, and P. Greengard, *Federation Proc.* **22**, 233 (1963).
23. H. Kroger, B. Ulrich, and H. Holzer, *Arzneimittel.-Forsch.* **9**, 598 (1959).
24. W. Bolt, F. Ritzl, R. Toussaint, and G. Zerlet, *Klin. Wochschr.* **38**, 71 (1960).
25. R. B. Drysdale, A. Hopkins, R. Y. Thomson, R. M. S. Smellie, and J. N. Davidson, *Brit. J. Cancer* **12**, 137 (1958).
26. I. M. Roitt, *Biochem. J.* **63**, 300 (1956).
27. S. A. Narrod, T. A. Langan, Jr., N. O. Kaplan, and A. Goldin, *Nature* **183**, 1674 (1959).
28. S. A. Narrod, V. Bonavita, E. R. Ehrenfeld, and N. O. Kaplan, *J. Biol. Chem.* **236**, 931 (1961).

29. B. R. Baker, *Biochem. Pharmacol.* **2**, 161 (1959).
30. B. Levenberg, I. Melnick, and J. M. Buchanan, *J. Biol. Chem.* **225**, 163 (1957).
31. H. G. Mandel, *Pharmacol. Revs.* **11**, 743 (1959).
32. P. J. G. Mann and J. H. Quastel, *Biochem. J.* **35**, 502 (1941).
33. L. J. Zatman, S. P. Colowick, N. O. Kaplan, and M. M. Ciotti, *Bull. Johns Hopkins Hosp.* **91**, 211 (1952).
34. L. J. Zatman, N. O. Kaplan, and S. P. Colowick, *J. Biol. Chem.* **200**, 197 (1953).
35. L. J. Zatman, N. O. Kaplan, S. P. Colowick, and M. M. Ciotti, *J. Biol. Chem.* **209**, 453 (1954).
36. L. J. Zatman, N. O. Kaplan, S. P. Colowick, and M. M. Ciotti, *J. Biol. Chem.* **209**, 467 (1954).
37. N. O. Kaplan, *in* "The Enzymes" (P. Boyer, H. A. Lardy, and K. Myrbäck, eds.), 2nd ed., Vol. 3, p. 105. Academic Press, New York, 1960.
38. R. E. F. Matthews, *Pharmacol. Revs.* **10**, 359 (1958).
39. N. O. Kaplan, M. M. Ciotti, and F. E. Stolzenbach, *J. Biol. Chem.* **221**, 833 (1956).
40. B. M. Anderson and N. O. Kaplan, *J. Biol. Chem.* **234**, 1226 (1959).
41. L. S. Dietrich, I. M. Friedland, and L. A. Kaplan, *J. Biol. Chem.* **233**, 964 (1958).
42. D. S. Goldman, *J. Am. Chem. Soc.* **76**, 2841 (1954).
43. M. M. Wood, *Brit. J. Tuberc.* **49**, 20 (1955).
44. R. J. Harrison and M. Feiwel, *Brit. Med. J.* **2**, 852 (1956).
44a. P. R. J. Gangadharam, F. M. Harold, and W. B. Schaefer, *Nature* **198**, 712 (1963).
45. N. O. Kaplan and M. M. Ciotti, *J. Biol. Chem.* **221**, 823 (1956).
46. N. O. Kaplan, A. Goldin, S. R. Humphreys, M. M. Ciotti, and J. M. Venditti, *Science* **120**, 437 (1954).
47. D. W. Woolley, *J. Biol. Chem.* **157**, 455 (1945).
48. W. W. Ackermann and A. Taylor, *Proc. Soc. Exptl. Biol. Med.* **67**, 449 (1955).
49. N. O. Kaplan, M. M. Ciotti, J. van Eys, and R. M. Burton, *J. Biol. Chem.* **234**, 134 (1959).
50. A. Ballio and G. Serlupi-Crescenzi, *Nature* **180**, 1203 (1957).
51. M. Lamborg, F. E. Stolzenbach, and N. O. Kaplan, *J. Biol. Chem.* **231**, 685 (1958).
52. B. M. Anderson and N. O. Kaplan, *J. Biol. Chem.* **234**, 1226 (1959).
53. N. O. Kaplan, M. M. Ciotti, and F. E. Stolzenbach, *J. Biol. Chem.* **221**, 833 (1956).
54. B. M. Anderson, Ph.D. Thesis, Johns Hopkins University, Baltimore, Maryland, 1958.
55. P. F. Hirsch and N. O. Kaplan, *J. Biol. Chem.* **236**, 926 (1961).
56. J. Lowenthal, *Nature* **174**, 36 (1954).
57. W. M. McIsaacs and R. T. Williams, *Biochem. J.* **66**, 369 (1957).
58. W. J. Johnson, *Nature* **174**, 744 (1954).
59. W. J. Johnson, *Can. J. Biochem. and Physiol.* **33**, 107 (1955).
60. W. J. Johnson and J. D. McColl, *Science* **122**, 834 (1955).
61. W. J. Johnson and J. D. McColl, *Federation Proc.* **15**, 284 (1956).

62. L. S. Dietrich, L. A. Kaplan, I. M. Friedland, and D. S. Martin, *Cancer Research* **18**, 1272 (1958).
63. D. M. Shapiro, L. S. Dietrich, and M. E. Shils, *Cancer Research* **17**, 600 (1957).
64. N. O. Kaplan, A. Goldin, S. R. Humphreys, and F. E. Stolzenbach, *J. Biol. Chem.* **226**, 365 (1957).
65. I. H. Krakoff, C. R. Lacon, and D. A. Karnofsky, *Nature* **184**, 1805 (1959).
66. W. Landauer, *J. Exptl. Zool.* **136**, 509 (1957).
67. B. Pullman and A. Pullman, *Cancer Research* **19**, 337 (1959).
68. C. Carruthers and V. Suntzeff, *Arch. Biochem.* **45**, 140 (1953).
69. L. A. Jedeikin and S. Weinhouse, *J. Biol. Chem.* **213**, 271 (1955).
70. M. V. Branster and R. K. Morton, *Biochem. J.* **63**, 640 (1956).
71. S. L. Halliday, A. Sloboda, L. W. Will, and J. J. Oleson, *Federation Proc.* **16**, 190 (1957).
72. J. D. McColl, W. B. Rice, and V. W. Adamkiewicz, *Can. J. Biochem. and Physiol.* **35**, 795 (1957).
73. D. S. Martin, L. S. Dietrich, and R. A. Fugmann, *Proc. Soc. Exptl. Biol. Med.* **103**, 58 (1960).
74. L. S. Dietrich and D. S. Martin, *Cancer Research* **21**, 361 (1961).
75. D. S. Martin, M. M. Kligerman, and R. A. Fugmann, *Cancer Research* **18**, 893 (1958).
76. M. M. Kligerman and D. M. Shapiro, *Radiology* **69**, 194 (1957).
77. H. N. Bane, J. T. Conrad, and G. S. Tarnowski, *Cancer Research* **17**, 551 (1957).
78. P. Alexander and K. A. Stacey, *Ann. N.Y. Acad. Sci.* **68**, 1225 (1958).
79. S. Green and O. Bodansky, *J. Biol. Chem.* **237**, 1752 (1962).
80. C. P. Perlia, S. Kofman, H. Sky-Peck, and S. G. Taylor III, *Cancer* **14**, 644 (1961).
81. F. P. Herter, S. G. Weissman, H. G. Thompson, Jr., G. Hyman, and D. S. Martin, *Cancer Research* **21**, 31 (1961).
82. J. K. Wyatt and L. N. McAninch, *Can. Med. Assoc. J.* **84**, 309 (1961).
83. S. G. A. Alivisatos and D. W. Woolley, *J. Biol. Chem.* **219**, 823 (1956).
84. S. G. A. Alivisatos and D. W. Woolley, *J. Am. Chem. Soc.* **77**, 1065 (1955).
85. S. G. A. Alivisatos and D. W. Woolley, *J. Biol. Chem.* **221**, 651 (1956).
86. S. G. A. Alivisatos, L. LaMantia, F. Ungar, and B. L. Matijevitch, *J. Biol. Chem.* **237**, 1212 (1962).
87. S. G. A. Alivisatos, *Nature* **181**, 271 (1958).
88. S. G. A. Alivisatos, F. Ungar, L. Lukacs, and L. LaMantia, *J. Biol. Chem.* **235**, 1742 (1960).
89. A. A. Abdel-Latif and S. G. A. Alivisatos, *J. Biol. Chem.* **236**, 2710 (1961).
90. A. A. Abdel-Latif and S. G. A. Alivisatos, *J. Biol. Chem.* **237**, 500 (1962).
91. S. G. A. Alivisatos, *in* "Mechanisms of Hypersensitivity" (J. H. Shaffer, G. A. Lo Grippo, and M. W. Chase, eds.), p. 259. Little, Brown, Boston, Massachusetts, 1959.
92. A. Alechinsky, *Compt. rend. soc. biol.* **141**, 524 (1947).
93. I. Dainow, *Z. Vitaminforsch.* **15**, 250 (1944).
94. S. A. Karjala, *J. Am. Chem. Soc.* **77**, 504 (1955).
95. H. Tabor and O. Hayaishi, *J. Am. Chem. Soc.* **77**, 505 (1955).

96. J. J. Oleson, A. Sloboda, W. P. Troy, S. L. Halliday, M. J. Landers, R. B. Angler, K. Semb, K. Cyr, and J. H. Williams, *J. Am. Chem. Soc.* **77**, 6713 (1955).

97. W. P. Troy, A. S. Sloboda, S. L. Halliday, and J. J. Oleson, *Federation Proc.* **15**, 372 (1956).

98. D. M. Shapiro, M. E. Shils, R. A. Fugmann, and I. M. Friedland, *Cancer Research* **17**, 29 (1957).

99. M. M. Ciotti, N. O. Kaplan, A. Goldin, and J. M. Venditti, *Proc. Am. Assoc. Cancer Research* **2**, 287 (1958).

100. M. M. Ciotti, S. R. Humphreys, J. M. Venditti, N. O. Kaplan, and A. Goldin, *Cancer Research* **20**, 1195 (1960).

101. I. H. Krakoff and G. B. Magill, *Proc. Soc. Exptl. Biol. Med.* **91**, 470 (1956).

102. I. H. Krakoff and M. E. Balis, *J. Clin. Invest.* **38**, 907 (1959).

103. J. E. Seegmiller, A. I. Grayzel, and L. Liddle, *Nature* **183**, 1463 (1959).

104. H. F. Oettgen, J. A. Reppert, V. Coley, and J. H. Burchenal, *Cancer Research* **20**, 1597 (1960).

105. S. R. Humphreys, J. M. Venditti, C. J. Ciotti, I. Kline, A. Goldin, and N. O. Kaplan, *Cancer Research* **22**, 483 (1962).

106. L. Shuster and A. Goldin, *Biochem. Pharmacol.* **2**, 17 (1959).

107. J. H. Ayvazian and L. F. Ayvazian, *J. Clin. Invest.* **40**, 1961 (1961).

107a. J. E. Seegmiller, A. I. Grayzel, L. Liddle, and J. B. Wyngaarden, *Metab. Clin. Exptl.* **12**, 507 (1963).

108. M. R. Atkinson, J. F. Jackson, R. K. Morton, and A. W. Murray, *Nature* **196**, 35 (1962).

109. F. Schlenk, H. Hellstrom, and H. von Euler, *Ber.* **71**, 1471 (1938).

110. N. O. Kaplan, S. P. Colowick, and M. M. Ciotti, *J. Biol. Chem.* **194**, 579 (1952).

111. N. A. Hughes, G. W. Kenner, and A. Todd, *J. Chem. Soc.* p. 3733 (1957).

112. J. L. Way, J. L. Dahl, and R. E. Parks, Jr., *J. Biol. Chem.* **234**, 1241 (1959).

113. J. S. Salser, J. D. Hutchison, and M. E. Balis, *J. Biol. Chem.* **235**, 429 (1960).

113a. R. J. McCollister, W. R. Gilbert, Jr., and J. B. Wyngaarden, *J. Clin. Invest.* **41**, 1383 (1962).

114. N. O. Kaplan, A. Goldin, S. R. Humphreys, M. M. Ciotti, and F. E. Stolzenbach, *J. Biol. Chem.* **219**, 287 (1956).

115. A. Goldin, *J. Natl. Cancer Inst.* **14**, 1247 (1954).

116. A Goldin, J. M. Venditti, S. R. Humphreys, D. Dennis, N. Mantel, and S. W. Greenhouse. *Ann. N. Y. Acad. Sci.* **60**, 251 (1954).

117. H. B. Khorana, and A. Todd, *J. Chem. Soc.* p. 2257 (1953).

118. C. P. Fawcett and N. O. Kaplan, *J. Biol. Chem.* **237**, 1709 (1962).

119. H. Klenow and B. Andersen, *Biochim. et Biophys. Acta* **23**, 92 (1957).

120. H. Klenow and E. Lichtler, *Biochim. et Biophys. Acta* **23**, 6 (1957).

121. H. Beinert, *in* "The Enzymes" (P. Boyer, H. A. Lardy, and K. Myrbäck, eds.), 2nd ed. Vol. 2, p. 339. Academic Press, New York, 1960.

CHAPTER 17

Antibiotics

H. Boyd Woodruff and Ian M. Miller

I. INTRODUCTION[1]

"An antibiotic is a chemical compound, derived from a microorganism, which has the capacity in dilute solution of inhibiting the growth of, and even destroying, other microorganisms." This definition, devised by

[1] For the purposes of this chapter on antibiotics as metabolic inhibitors, no attempt has been made to present a complete literature survey. References have been cited for key points. Summary or review works usually have been selected in preference to the original report, as such summaries present up-to-date knowledge.

For an extension of the comments in this chapter, the reader should consult the general reviews by Verwey in *Annual Review of Microbiology,* Volume 13 (*2*); by Chain in *Annual Review of Biochemistry,* Volume 28 (*3*); and by Hahn in the *Proceedings of the Fourth International Congress of Biochemis-*

Waksman (1), serves to group several thousand compounds which may be subclassified on the basis of differences in chemical or biological properties. The complete chemical structure is known for only a few of the antibiotics, but these are of diverse nature. It is evident that microorganisms have the capacity to synthesize a variety of compounds having a wide range of inhibitory activity against other microorganisms. Frequently, the inhibitory or toxic action extends to higher plants and animals.

The word antibiotic in the above limited sense has been in use only since 1942; however, research on antibiosis is of much earlier origin. The general area of study has been defined by Waksman as existing "between true parasitism—one organism living in or upon the body of another— and true saprophytism—one organism merely destroying the waste products and the dead cells of another" (10). As the science of microbiology developed in the early 1900's, emphasis was placed on the applied areas, especially soil microbiology. Because of the complex associations among the microorganisms contained in the dynamic population of soil, antagonistic relationships became obvious to soil microbiologists and were the source of research studies and finally of review articles (11).

Antibiotics are produced with great frequency by microorganisms isolated from substrates such as the soil, air, and plant materials. Detailed descriptions of screening procedures have indicated that as many as 10% of the streptomycetes isolated from soil and grown in artificial culture produce antibiotic activity (12). Many filamentous fungi also produce antibiotics. Of 65 species isolated from soil, half have been found to form antibiotics (13). The accumulation of antibiotic activity by bacteria can be shown with ease. Sterile agar media inoculated with soil suspensions at low dilutions usually show clear zones where growth of the spreading surface bacteria is inhibited. Frequently, these zones surround colonies of sporeforming bacteria and are due to antibiotics produced by the sporeformers (14). However, critical studies demonstrate that antibiotic pro-

---

try (4). Chemotherapeutic approaches are described in "The Strategy of Chemotherapy," the Eighth Symposium of the Society for General Microbiology (5), and yearly progress in the field of antibiotic therapy has been summarized in "Antibiotica et Chemotherapia" (Volume 10 appeared in 1962) (6). Nonchemotherapeutic properties of antibiotics are discussed in "Antibiotics, Their Chemistry and Non-Medical Uses," edited by H. S. Goldberg (7). Very complete presentations concerning antibiotics and their properties are contained in the two-volume work, "Antibiotics," by Florey and his collaborators at Oxford University (8) and in the "Handbook of Toxicology," Volume II, distributed by the Division of Biology and Agriculture, National Academy of Sciences (9).

duction is limited to a rather small number of bacterial types and that the antibiotics they produce usually have a narrow spectrum.

II. REQUIREMENTS FOR OPTIMUM PRODUCTION

Antibiotics are formed readily under conditions which promote good growth of the producing microorganisms. High concentrations of available nutrients, such as digests of protein and fermentable carbohydrates, and availability of oxygen promote formation of antibiotics with most microorganisms and serve as an adequate basis for screening. Each microorganism has its own specific requirements for optimal antibiotic production. For example, streptomycin is produced in best yield if phosphate ions are restricted in the presence of excess concentrations of other nutrients (15). For maximum benzylpenicillin yields, adequate nutrients are required for formation of metabolically active mycelium of *Penicillium chrysogenum*, but thereafter penicillin formation is promoted under a condition of restricted carbohydrate supply in the presence of sources of nitrogen and sulfur, and a phenylacetic acid derivative (16). The antibiotic grisein contains iron, and maximum antibacterial potential can be realized only in a culture medium containing an excess of this element (17). Special conditions have been defined for optimum yield of each antibiotic culture studied in detail.

III. PRODUCTION IN NATURE

Studies on the significance of antibiotic formation in the natural habitat present an enigma. The high number of antibiotic-producing microorganisms found in a competitive environment, such as fertile garden soil, suggests that the ability to produce antibiotics has exerted a favorable selection pressure during the course of evolution of soil microbes. Surely, if the formation of an antibiotic represented merely a wasteful drain of carbon into a nonmetabolizable, useless compound, organisms which produce antibiotics would have great difficulty in competing with nonproducers for the relatively restricted amount of nutrients in the soil. Antibiotic-producing organisms have not died out; in fact, studies have shown that the ratio of antibiotic-producing microbes to the total population remains the same in a soil during the increase of several fold of the total microbial population resulting from the introduction of a nutrient into that soil (18).

It is tempting to speculate that antibiotic producers may be favored in the competitive environment by the formation of antibiotic activity, at least in the local microenvironment, to the extent that competition for nutrients would be lessened. All attempts to prove this hypothesis have failed. Generally, antibiotic formation under the conditions of restricted nutrients available in soil is very poor. In the soil, many antibiotics lose their activity through absorption on soil colloids, instability in the presence of soil chemicals, or by biological attack.

A number of antibiotics have been produced in sterile soil inoculated with a specific antibiotic-producing microorganism, particularly if additional nutrient supplements are added. Also, traces of the antibiotics gliotoxin, gladiolic acid, frequentin, griseofulvin, chloramphenicol, actinomycin, and certain other antibiotics derived from *Streptomyces* and *Bacillus* species have been observed in normal and nutrient-enriched soils. Although data supporting the advantage granted a microorganism by its ability to produce an antibiotic in the soil are limited and drawn primarily from studies of microbial combinations under artificial conditions, the probability is in favor of such an advantage. Brian has summarized the evidence and, on the basis of it, contends that antibiotic production is beneficial at least within microenvironments (*19*). Without question, the problem demands much further study and may be solved finally only by application of principles of quantitative genetics and the study of antibiotic formation as an evolutionary factor.

IV. SELECTIVITY OF ANTIBIOTICS

The definition of an antibiotic adequately encompasses a class of compounds and excludes unrelated forms. It is restrictive in accepting only compounds produced by microorganisms, but several of these compounds, after the original demonstrations, have been found also in higher organisms or have been made by chemical synthesis. In fact, inhibitors of microbial growth may be isolated first as normal metabolic products and confirmed as true antibiotics only later, for example, griseofulvin (*20*). Many of the recently synthesized derivatives of 6-aminopenicillanic acid are inhibitors of microbial growth which have the mode of action and properties of penicillin but which may never be strictly classified as antibiotics because microbiological synthesis has not been accomplished (*21, 22*).

Even more characteristic than the origin of antibiotics is the property of selectivity in inhibitory activity. In fact, selectivity is inherent in the biosynthesis of antibiotics, for a microorganism which produces an antibiotic must have some mechanism of protecting itself against the action of the antibiotic; that is, the producer must be resistant. One could assume that other microorganisms having biochemical similarities to the producer also will be resistant.

The selectivity crosses species and strain lines as well as class distinctions in microorganisms. Because of the selectivity of action, antibiotics have sometimes been called broad spectrum or narrow spectrum, depending on the breadth of microbial species inhibited. Broad spectrum has come to mean inhibition of many gram-positive and gram-negative microorganisms, and possibly certain of the *Rickettsia* and large viruses. The term narrow spectrum is associated frequently with inhibition of gram-positive bacteria. These terms provide a false implication, however, when one realizes that many antibiotics have a "narrow spectrum" of activity limited to the filamentous fungi, others are specific inhibitors of yeasts, still others inhibit protozoa, and some inhibit a few members of each of several large groups of microorganisms without regard to their taxonomic classification.

It is the high order of selectivity of antibiotics which gives them their commercial utility. Some can be employed as therapeutic agents because they inhibit pathogenic bacteria without harming the host plant or animal. The selectivity of action results from their selective biochemical activity. They may block formation of a structure such as the bacterial cell wall which is not present in higher organisms; they may form an inactive complex with an element required for growth by a microorganism; they may block a synthetic reaction essential for rapidly multiplying cells but not essential to the human; they may fail to penetrate into the animal cell while freely entering the microbial cell. The clinical utility of antibiotics has established them firmly as a preferred field for industrial research and has given rise to intensive screening programs which have multiplied tremendously the number of antibiotics which have been described. The selective action of the antibiotics recovered is of great concern to the medical practitioner or the plant pathologist faced with a choice among several antibiotics for treatment of a specific disease condition. A correct diagnosis is required to guide selection of an antibiotic having the appropriate spectrum. The toxicity of the antibiotic selected must be weighed against the expectation of chemotherapeutic effect.

V. BIOCHEMICAL SIGNIFICANCE OF ANTIBIOTICS

A preoccupation with the practical attributes of antibiotics has slowed appreciation of these molecules as fundamental tools in biochemistry.

Penicillin, cycloserine, bacitracin, and griseofulvin have contributed materially to our knowledge of cell wall biosynthesis; chloramphenicol, to the interrelationship of nucleic acid and protein biosynthesis; antimycin, to terminal electron transport. However, little use has been made of the many possibilties for expanding our knowledge of biochemical pathways through the study of the nonclinically effective antibiotics. The biochemist who desires to elucidate a biochemical pathway in a microorganism should have little difficulty in finding an antibiotic which will influence the pathway.

Antibiotics are of prime importance to the biochemist because they consist of unusual, even revolutionary, type structures which are significant in normal metabolic pathways. A close examination of the antibiotic structures in relation to known metabolites may give leads to the site of action of the antibiotics, but frequently this relationship is obscure. Even after the specific point of action is known, as for example in the inhibition by D-cycloserine of formation of D-alanyl-D-alanine for introduction into the cell wall peptide (23), the specificity of the antibiotic structure for the specific metabolites involved is unexpected. One immediately becomes aware that competitive antagonism within the complexities of the microbial cell is more demanding of a specific structure than was recognized by the early proponents of this method of chemotherapeutic attack upon disease microorganisms.

VI. MODE OF ACTION OF ANTIBIOTICS; CELLULAR EFFECTS

Early workers in the field of antibiotics recognized that these compounds acted by a variety of mechanisms. Differences were observed in their gross effects on microorganisms. Some of the more toxic antibiotics, such as patulin (24), are strongly bactericidal in their action. Death of the cells is rapid, and no amount of dilution or neutralization of the antibiotic allows the microorganisms to resume growth. A bacteriostatic action, or inhibition of bacterial growth without death at the lower antibiotic concentrations, is a more common characteristic of the antibiotics. Removal of the antibiotic by dilution, or loss of potency through inactivation, frequently results in renewed growth.

Plotting of the growth curve on the basis of the numbers of surviving organisms as related to time of exposure yields a variety of curves characteristic for each antibiotic tested. This observation indicates that the antibiotics differ in their attack upon microorganisms but gives little insight into specific mechanisms of action.

Two generalized properties of antibiotics which may be observed in liquid culture point to a difference in basic mechanism of action. The degree of antibiotic activity may be influenced directly by the nutrients contained in the culture medium. For example, actithiazic acid (*25*) and bacillin (*26*) do not behave as antibiotics for cells grown in complex media containing digests of animal products, as their antibiotic action is antagonized by natural products present therein. Second, the expression of antibiotic activity may be dependent on the rate of growth of the microorganism at the time it comes under the influence of the antibiotic. Penicillin and other inhibitors of cell wall synthesis are ineffective on nonmultiplying cells (*27*).

Various additional responses, which point to differing modes of action, occur with microbial colonies on agar plates exposed to a diffusing solution of an antibiotic. Some antibiotics exert their effect at any stage of microbial growth and at any density of population. The edge of the zone of inhibition with such antibiotics is indistinct, as the cultures are stopped at various intensities of growth when the advancing antibiotic front reaches the inhibitory concentration. Other antibiotics are capable of inhibiting only young cultures at a low inoculum density. In these instances, the zone of inhibition is very sharp since, as soon as the culture initiates growth, it is able to overcome further antibiotic action. Frequently, evidence of enhanced growth may be seen just beyond the inhibitory point.

Another phenomenon characteristic of antibiotics is resistance. In an agar test, resistance is evidenced by individual colonies which develop to normal size within the clear zone of antibiotic action. With most antibiotics, resistance is infrequently encountered. Resistant colonies are seldom seen within the zone of inhibition produced by penicillin. Usually, four or five colonies will be apparent within an inhibitory zone of 20-mm diameter produced by a solution of streptomycin. With the antibiotic grisein, resistance may reach the extent that over 10% of the cells within the population are capable of making growth. Resistant colonies within the inhibitory zones with this antibiotic are so frequent that individual colonies cannot be observed, but only a lessening of the density of growth within the confines of the zone is observable. Di Marco has discussed antibiotic resistance from the biochemical standpoint (*28*).

A striking measure of antibiotic activity at the cellular level may be seen by microscopic examination. Long filamentous bacterial cells are produced at partially inhibitory levels with many antibiotics. Rods of *Azotobacter* increase as much as 100-fold in length with no detectable cross walls under the influence of actinomycin. The elongated forms of sporeforming bacteria or exceptionally large bizarre staphylococci and streptococci which develop under the influence of penicillin have been described many times (29).

Nuclear abnormalities can be observed under the influence of antibiotics with appropriate staining techniques. These usually result from altered concentrations of deoxyribonucleic acid. Striking demonstrations of this effect have been produced from the action of actinomycin on HeLa cells (30).

The nuclear abnormalities suggest that antibiotics may have significance as a tool in basic genetics. This has proved to be the case. Antibiotic resistance is a convenient marker for studying the quantitative and qualitative influence of mutagenic agents on microbial cells. Furthermore, antibiotic resistance is a property associated with the transforming principle and may be carried from one cell to another during the course of transfer of deoxyribonucleic acid units (31). Certain antibiotics, which selectively kill growing cells, have been used to destroy growing protoprophs and cause the enrichment of nongrowing antibiotic-resistant auxotrophs in a population. Such antibiotics provide a strong selection pressure for isolation of new auxotrophic mutants of bacteria (32, 33).

Lysis, or dissolution of microbial cells, is a phenomenon sometimes observed with antibiotics. Lysis may be the final response to antibiotics which inhibit cell wall formation. The lytic effect can be prevented with an adequate concentration of salts or sugar to make an isotonic preparation with the cell protoplasm. Under these conditions, protoplasts may be produced (34). With certain organisms, growth in the presence of antibiotics leads to the formation of L-forms, with a change in cell size and colony morphology (35).

Antibiotics can cause lysis as a nearly instantaneous response not dependent upon growth. A lytic response of this nature can result from a direct enzymic attack on the living cells or may arise from a combination of a proteolytic enzyme with a bactericidal antibiotic which kills the microorganism and makes it susceptible to enzymic attack.

VII. MODE OF ACTION OF ANTIBIOTICS; BIOCHEMICAL SIGNIFICANCE

Numerous reports of the effects of antibiotics on the biochemical activities of microorganisms have appeared in the scientific literature. It is very difficult to correlate the biochemical abnormalities described with the initial or primary mode of action of the antibiotic. Because antibiotics act by inhibiting the growth of and eventually killing microorganisms, all biochemical activity in the cell eventually ceases. The responses which are observed following the addition of antibiotics are initiated at different time intervals. It has been assumed that the earlier responses may be the direct result of antibiotic action and that the secondary responses are the result of the death process in the cell. Even primary responses, however, may result from loss of an unstable enzyme early in the death process.

Biochemical reactions in the microbial cell are not isolated phenomena but exist as parts of chains of reactions serving to degrade nutrient materials, serving to conserve energy in the form of high energy compounds, or acting as synthetic reactions leading to the formation of complex cellular material. An antibiotic may disrupt any one of these biochemical reactions and in large measure alter many previous and subsequent steps in a reaction chain of cellular metabolism.

A microorganism which possesses multiple pathways can shift its metabolic activities with the result that life is preserved, but a completely new pattern of metabolic intermediates will accumulate, any one of which could be isolated and be claimed provisionally to be the site of action of the antibiotic. For example, an antibiotic which acts as an uncoupling agent will also be observed to prevent protein synthesis. Furthermore, it can prevent uptake of certain amino acids, as the adaptive transferase system cannot be formed or operate without transfer of energy from the respiratory pathway. Unless the facts are carefully sorted out, the claim could be made that the primary point of action of the antibiotic was on the transferase system.

Interpretations of the mechanism of antibiotic action are further complicated by the possibility that antibiotics may have multiple sites of action. The multiplicity of effects from a growth-inhibiting agent have been studied in great detail with the nonantibiotic bacterial inhibitor sulfanilamide, in which syntheses involving methionine, purines, serine, and thymine are blocked by the drug at successively higher inhibition ratios (36). Similar competition studies with antibiotics have not been as productive, but there have been reports of reversing agents for different antibiotics, each acting in a competitive fashion over a narrow range of inhibition (37). In assessing the primary point of action of an antibiotic, one must conduct such studies at approximately the growth-inhibiting concentration and not in presence of excess antibiotic.

Although the definition of the primary point of action of an antibiotic is often insecure, antibiotics can be important tools in defining biochemical pathways. No attempt will be made in this chapter to present a comprehensive listing of all of the reported activities of antibiotics. A few examples will be discussed in which the availability of antibiotics as biochemical tools has aided in our understanding of bacterial structure or bacterial metabolism.

A. The Bacterial Cell Wall

In the past 5 years, great progress has been made in elucidating the chemical nature of the bacterial cell wall. Progress has been rapid following development of techniques for separating cell wall components from the remainder of the bacterial cell. Many of the cell wall components have been identified after vigorous treatment to free them from their bound form. Some insight into the structural relationships of these components has been gained from studies of the products obtained from enzymic action. Further knowledge has been gained by metabolic inhibitors, notably antibiotics such as penicillin and cycloserine, which have been used to cause accumulation of precursors of the cell wall structure.

Analyses of cell wall constituents have revealed differences between organisms; however, there are enough similarities to make the following generalizations. Both the gram-positive and gram-negative organisms contain mucopolysaccharide in their cell walls in which have been found the amino sugars glucosamine, galactosamine, and muramic acid (3-O-lactyl-D-glucosamine); the reducing sugars glucose, galactose, mannose, arabinose, and rhamnose; and the amino acids glutamic acid, lysine or diaminopimelic acid, alanine, glycine, aspartic acid, and serine. Although the mucopolysaccharide appears to be the major wall constituent of the gram-positive organism, it amounts to only about 20% of the gram-negative cell walls, the remainder consisting mainly of lipoprotein which contains all of the normal amino acids. In addition, a group of compounds called the teichoic acids has been found in some gram-positive bacteria (38). These acids vary in composition, depending on the organism from which they were isolated, and consist of polymers of ribitol phosphate or glycerol phosphate with alanine and often glucose or N-acetylglucosamine attached to the alcohol phosphate chain.

The cell wall imparts rigidity to the bacterial cell, so that its removal exposes the osmotically fragile cell membrane with subsequent lysis of the cell in conventional media. Removal of the cell wall without injury to the rest of the cell was accomplished by Weibull (39), who exposed cells of Bacillus megaterium to the enzyme lysozyme in a hypertonic solution with the resulting liberation of bacterial protoplasts. Later, it was observed that penicillin also caused the liberation of cells free of walls in hypertonic solution (*34, 40, 41*). These observations confirmed the well-known fact that penicillin was acting only on growing cultures and indicated that the antibiotic was blocking cell wall synthesis rather than causing the destruction of pre-existing wall. Park and Strominger (*42*) quickly correlated these observations with the accumulation in penicillin-inhibited cells of the uridine nucleotides first observed by Park and Johnson (*43*). The structure of the principal nucleotide which has been isolated is shown in (I) (*44*).

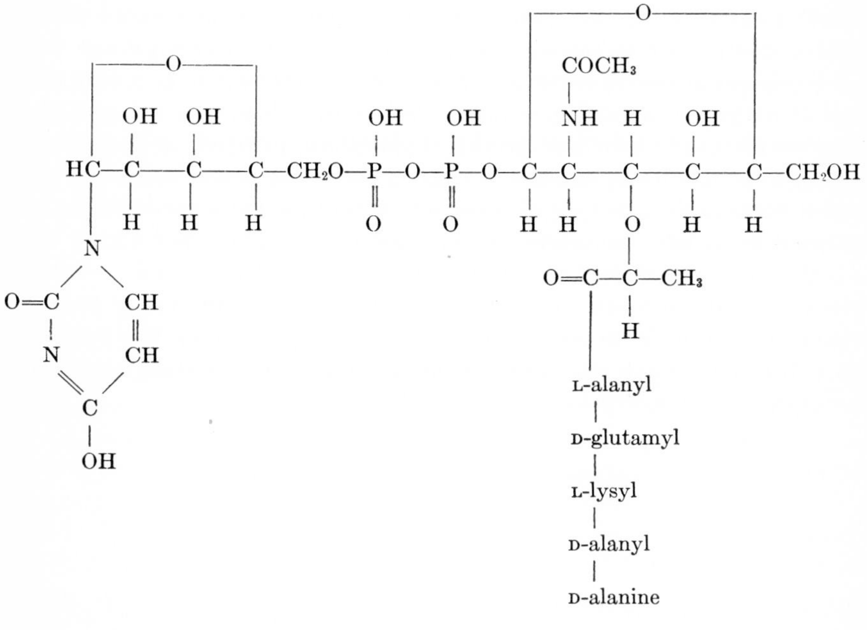

(I)

The *Staphylococcus aureus* cell wall has the same molar proportions of *N*-acetylmuramic acid, D- and L-alanine, D-glutamic acid, and L-lysine as is found in the nucleotide, suggesting that the acetylmuramic acid-peptide sequence is transferred intact into the cell wall from the uridine nucleotide. Other nucleotides have been isolated in which the peptide chain has additional amino acids, including glycine and aspartic acid (*45*).

The exact mechanism of the penicillin action is still unknown. It could be the blocking of an enzymic system concerned with the transfer of the *N*-acetylmuramic acid peptide into the cell wall, or it could be the blocking of the synthesis of an acceptor site. Quantitative studies have shown that binding of penicillin to the cell is related to the sensitivity of the cell to the antibiotic. Over 1500 molecules must be bound per cell for bactericidal action to occur; the external concentration required to prevent growth of the culture was that which would cause this amount of binding (46). The binding was specific for the penicillin structure and did not occur with inactivated penicillin. The bound material could not be removed easily by detergents or caustic. Binding occurred as readily with ruptured cells and with purified cell walls as with the intact microorganisms. Upon further degradation of the wall complex and ultracentrifugation, the bound penicillin was found to be associated with a protein fraction which possibly originated from the cell membrane (47).

D-Cycloserine also is involved in cell wall synthesis but at a step prior to that at which penicillin is implicated. When S. aureus is exposed to D-cycloserine, the nucleotide uridine diphosphate-muramic acid-L-alanyl-D-glutamyl-L-lysine accumulates (23). This is the same nucleotide that accumulates in the presence of penicillin, except for the absence of the two terminal D-alanine molecules. Strominger et al. (48) have shown that D-cycloserine is a strong competitive inhibitor of two enzymic reactions involved in the formation of the dipeptide D-alanyl-D-alanine prior to its introduction into the peptide chain of the nucleotide. These two reactions are catalyzed by the enzymes alanine racemase and D-alanyl-D-alanine synthetase as shown in Eqs. (1) and (2).

$$\text{L-Alanine} \underset{}{\overset{\text{Pyridoxal phosphate}}{\rightleftharpoons}} \text{D-alanine} \qquad (1)$$

$$\text{D-Alanine} \xrightarrow[\text{Mn}^{++}]{\text{ATP}} \text{D-alanyl-D-alanine} \qquad (2)$$

The incorporation of the dipeptide into the peptide chain is not affected by cycloserine. D-Alanine and D-cycloserine have structural similarities which probably account for the competitive relationship, and as would be expected, L-alanine does not compete with cycloserine in the dipeptide synthetase reaction.

Strominger and Threnn (49) have summarized the present knowledge of the synthesis of the S. aureus wall mucopolysaccharide in Fig. 1, which has been updated to show the inhibition point of cycloserine.

Bacitracin at growth-inhibitory levels causes S. aureus to accumulate uridine phosphate N-acetyl sugar derivatives (50). Lysis of the cells occurs at the same bacitracin concentration. Vancomycin also inhibits the synthesis of cell wall mucopeptide of S. aureus (51) and causes the accumulation of a material containing hexosamine, uracil, alanine, glutamic

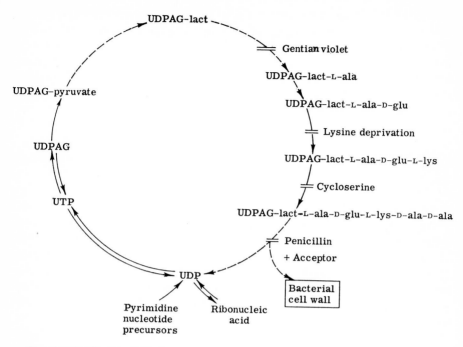

FIG. 1. Synthesis of *S. aureus* wall mucopolysaccharide. UDPAG-lact = uridine diphosphoacetylglucosamine lactic acid ether.

acid, and lysine (*52*). It will be interesting to see where these two antibiotics fit into the scheme diagramed above.

Lysozyme obtained from egg white has yielded some interesting results bearing on cell wall structure. Salton (*53*) found that the products obtained from the action of lysozyme on three gram-positive bacteria are fragments varying in size from disaccharides to materials with molecular weights of the order of 10,000–20,000. The disaccharide was composed probably of *N*-acetylglucosamine and acetylmuramic acid, and the larger fragments contained *N*-acetylhexosamines as terminal groups. These results led Salton to postulate that lysozyme was involved in breaking the amino sugar linkages. Zilliken (*54*) has found that among the products of lysozyme action on gram-positive bacteria are a number of amino sugars containing peptides which, on hydrolysis, yielded muramic acid, glucosamine, alanine, glutamic acid, and lysine. Ratios of muramic to glucosamine of 1:1 and 1:2 were both found. Based on work from a number of laboratories, Zilliken has proposed the sequence in Fig. 2 as a possible basic structure of the bacterial cell wall.

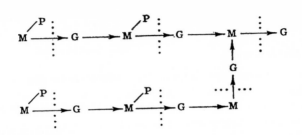

FIG. 2. Sequence proposed by Zilliken as a possible basic structure of the bacterial cell wall. M, muramic acid; G, N-acetyl-D-glucosamine; P, peptide moiety; ......, action of lysozyme; M→G, muraminidoglucosamine.

An early antibiotic named actinomycetin is capable of lysing killed gram-negative cells or living gram-positive cells. Actinomycetin has been shown to contain a number of enzymes capable of degrading the cell wall, including such enzymes as esterases, peptidases, and a lysozyme-like enzyme (55). Although the picture is complicated by the presence of a number of enzymes, actinomycetin has proved to be a tool in elucidating the structure of the cell wall.

The prevalence of N-acetyl-D-glucosamine in the wall structure suggests that it is an important compound in cell wall synthesis. Furthermore, N-acetyl-D-glucosamine serves as a precursor of muramic acid for *Lactobacillus bifidus* var. *pennsylvanicus*. This organism has a growth requirement for N-acetyl-D-glucosamine, preferably in the form of its β-glucosides or in the form of disaccharides such as N-acetyllactosamine. The *Lactobacillus* incorporated α,β-methyl-N-acetyl-D-glucosaminide-1-C^{14} directly into the muramic portion of the call wall (56). Because of the essential nature of N-acetyl-D-glucosamine in cell wall structure, one would assume that this compound should serve as a susceptible point of antibiotic inhibition. This is the case. The antibiotic bacillin derived from *Bacillus subtilis* is a competitive inhibitor of N-acetyl-D-glucosamine in greater than a tenfold range (57, 58). Even in the presence of a high concentration of the antibiotic, normal growth of a bacterial cell occurs if the culture medium is supplemented with N-acetylglucosamine. Separation of the antibiotic from N-acetyl-D-glucosamine by mild chemical treatment resulted in restoration of the antibiotic activity.

Great progress has been made in elucidating cell wall structure through the application of the antibiotics penicillin, cycloserine, actinomycetin, and bacillin. These results promise further exciting discoveries through the detailed knowledge of the intermediates accumulating with bacitracin and vancomycin, as well as with other yet undiscovered antibiotics active in the cell wall biosynthesis.

B. The Cell Membrane

The bacterial membrane immediately adjacent to the cell wall is of vital importance to the cell. In large measure, the cellular enzymes are located either in or adjacent to the membrane. It is logical to assume that the membrane would be the site of action of many antibiotics.

The membrane has been studied from a crude analytical standpoint and found to consist of as much as 20% phospholipid. Carbohydrates, the full complement of amino acids, and lipids have been isolated from the membrane, but no glucosamine is present. The membrane serves as an osmotic barrier and can maintain over 500 times increase in concentration of glutamic acid within the cell as compared with the nutrient solution external to the membrane. The internal osmotic pressure is as great as 20 atmospheres.

A number of antibiotics are known which have a destructive influence on the membrane. In gross effect, the action of several antibiotics on the cellular membrane is that of detergents. Tyrocidin is a cationic detergent. It destroys the osmotic barrier property of the membrane, and amino acids leak from the cell. The amount of lysine released from the amino acid pool in the presence of 1 μg/ml tyrocidin is equivalent to that released by boiling of the cells. Larger molecules, such as proteins, are not released, and study by electronmicroscopy shows that the cell wall has remained intact. Gramacidin S, another cyclic peptide, has similar activity in destroying the permeability of the membrane. Its molecular structure provides solvent-soluble groupings and water-soluble groupings which can be sterically oriented to fulfill the requirements for detergent action (59).

A series of antibiotics isolated from *Pseudomonas aeruginosa*, named the pyos (60), are anionic detergents, sharing in common with chemically synthesized anionic detergents the properties of action against gram-positive microorganisms and reversibility by phospholipids and steroids.

Polymyxin also causes disruption of the cell membrane. When treated with bactericidal concentrations of polymyxin B, washed cell suspensions of sensitive bacteria release 260-mμ absorbing material in a linear relation to the percentage of cells killed. With *P. aeruginosa*, this loss of purines is accompanied by equimolar release of pentose and phosphate and results from breakdown of ribonucleic acid of the cells. In the presence of excess polymyxin, the enzymic degradation of ribonucleic acid is inhibited and little 260-mμ absorbing material is liberated, although amino acids, metals, and other cytoplasmic, low molecular weight molecules may be lost.

Electron photomicrographs of cells treated with minimal concentrations of polymyxin show empty ghosts of cells that have lost intracellular material. With an excess of polymyxin, the electron-dense intracellular material remains, but a change in the surface of the cell is indicated as extraneous material agglomerates with it.

Loss of membrane permeability may be demonstrated by exposing normal and polymyxin-treated cells to N-tolyl-α-naphthylamine-8-sulfonic acid. The dye will fluoresce in ultraviolet light when combined with the negatively charged groups of proteins. No fluorescence is observed with washed cells of *Pseudomonas fluorescens*. Addition of polymyxin causes immediate fluorescence as the dye penetrates into the cell.

Polymyxin does not alter the electrophoretic pattern of most cells, indicating that it is not attached to the cell surface. Calculations show that the minimum depth to which polymyxin must penetrate in order not to affect the surface change is 100 A, indicating the possibility of membrane binding.

Polymyxin will adsorb to the membrane of protoplasts made by enzymic removal of the walls of polymyxin-sensitive gram-positive bacteria. The point of cellular attachment may be visualized with a fluorescent complex of polymyxin. Fluorescent microscopy of 1-dimethylamino-naphthalene-5-sulfonyl chloride-polymyxin treated cells, before and after removal of the cell wall with lysozyme, shows the association of the antibiotic with the cell membrane.

The specific binding loci of polymyxin have been suggested to be the polyphosphates of the membrane. There is a close correlation between the reversal of charge of phosphate colloids by specific cations and the protection of cells against the bactericidal action of polymyxin by these same cations. This interpretation is strengthened by the observation that cephalin and lipid extracted from disrupted *Pseudomonas denitrificans* form strong complexes with polymyxin.

The specificity of bactericidal action of polymyxin probably depends on the composition of the bacterial surface. The cell walls of resistant bacteria have little affinity for the antibiotic and may not allow penetration of polymyxin to the membrane. The primary difference observed in chemical composition of the wall-membrane complex of resistant gram-negative bacteria as compared to sensitive bacteria is a lower P/N ratio (*61*).

Streptomycin, at bactericidal concentrations, exerts a more subtle action on the cell membrane. Anand, Davis, and Armitage (*62*) have shown that a rapid uptake of streptomycin occurs with *Escherichia coli* cells and that the antibiotic is bound to the cell by an ionic linkage. After 10 minutes, a secondary phase of uptake is initiated, and an additional three- to fourfold amount of streptomycin is bound. The secondary uptake can be prevented by chloramphenicol, but occurs very rapidly upon addition of toluene or polymyxin B to destroy the cell membrane.

Associated with the secondary phase of binding, nucleotides and amino acids are excreted from the cell. These products arise from continued synthesis in the presence of the streptomycin, as shown by studies with isotopic carbon compounds and through quantitative measurements. Twelve times the initial intracellular amount of adenosine monophosphate is excreted after streptomycin is added. Larger molecules, such as diphosphopyridine nucleotide, are also excreted, but in smaller amounts. Damage to the cell membrane is also shown by the loss of potassium ions from the cell in the presence of streptomycin (*63*). This effect can be detected even sooner than the loss of the other cell constituents.

Streptomycin-damaged cells are impaired in ability to concentrate valine within the cell. However, the metabolism of citrate, to which the membrane of *E. coli* is relatively impermeable, is increased in streptomycin-treated cells.

The above observations have been interpreted to indicate that the primary point of action of streptomycin is on the cell membrane and that streptomycin does not damage existing membrane, but causes defects in the new membrane synthesized by antibiotic-inhibited cells (*64*). The defective membrane allows the loss of intracellular components, but also permits entry of normally impermeable compounds into the cell, including streptomycin. During the entry of streptomycin through the damaged membrane, secondary binding occurs, associated with an immediate cessation of protein synthesis and a somewhat delayed inhibition of nucleic acid synthesis.

Further studies on those constituents of the cell membrane whose synthesis is blocked by streptomycin should provide identification of vital structural components of the cell. Streptomycin-resistant cells will be valuable in this research, as these cells also show the initial binding of streptomycin but do not progress to damaged membranes, indicating a change in the membrane-forming system.

A difference in the binding capacity of other microorganisms has been shown by Hancock (*65*) with *B. megaterium*, *S. aureus*, and *B. subtilis*. With these bacteria, the initial step of membrane binding has not been found. Uptake of streptomycin parallels the increase in cell mass, and at the point of growth inhibition, over 95% of the bound streptomycin is contained in the cytoplasm in a form not easily displaced ionically. Only 1% as much streptomycin is bound by resistant cells. Hancock's studies are in agreement with those on *E. coli* in the observation that actively metabolizing cells are required for binding to occur. The uptake of streptomycin is associated with aerobic respiratory processes.

The polyene antibiotics, which are specific in their action to the fungi, serve as interesting examples for the multiplicity of actions which may be reported in the literature before the actual primary point of attack on the cell is elucidated. These agents have been reported at low concentrations to stimulate endogenous respiration and glycolysis of yeasts, whereas at high concentrations respiration and glycolysis are strongly inhibited. Further studies on isolated enzymes led to a variety of suggestions, including initiation of the destruction of the enzymes converting fructose-1,6-diphosphate to pyruvate, release of a mechanism controlling phosphorylation of reserve carbohydrates, or release of proteolytic enzymes which cause generalized destruction of the enzymes of the glycolytic system. Binding studies showed considerable similarity to penicillin in that sensitive organisms bound the agent, whereas resistant ones did not, and binding, once it occurred, could not be reversed by drastic solvent treatments.

Protoplasts prepared from *Saccharomyces cerevisiae* by enzymic removal of the cell wall have the same susceptibility to nystatin as do intact cells. It was observed that membranes treated with nystatin lose semipermeability to potassium. The enzymic effects of nystatin can be explained on the basis of a potassium deficiency caused by loss of potassium through the damaged cell membrane (*66, 67*). Furthermore, low levels of nystatin can be overcome by the addition of potassium ion to the fermentation medium. Potassium cannot reverse high concentrations of nystatin because leakage of other small molecules through the membrane occurs under these conditions.

Experiments on the mechanism of antibiotic action have not allowed elucidation of the basic structure of the microbial membrane to the same extent that studies with antibiotics have furthered our knowledge of the structure of the cell wall. These compounds do have great specificity of action, however, in their disruptive effect on the membrane. Some antibiotics primarily attack gram-positive organisms; others destroy permeability of gram-negative organisms; still others destroy permeability of yeast and filamentous fungi; and antibiotics such as streptomycin cross over usual taxonomic lines. As the reasons for these specificities are unraveled, much fundamental information should become available concerning the membrane structure.

C. Nucleic Acid Biosynthesis

Nucleic acid synthesis is an essential requirement for multiplication of bacterial cells, and one would assume it to be a sensitive point for attack. This assumption is strengthened by the fact that certain abnormal purines, for example, puromycin, nucleocidin, and nebularine, can act as antibiotics. Also, purine bases will neutralize the antibiotic psicofuranine (*68*).

Azaserine has a direct effect on the synthesis of purines and confirms a biosynthetic scheme derived by other methods. Azaserine blocks the incorporation of labeled carbon from formate-C^{14}, glycine-1-C^{14}, or β-serine-C^{14} into nucleic acid, but incorporation into only the purines is influenced, not the pyrimidines. The subsequent conversion of purine to nucleic acid is not prevented. Formation of inosinic acid is blocked, and formylglycinamide ribotide and formylglycinamide riboside accumulate in the blocked reaction. Azaserine inhibition of bacterial growth is competitively overcome by glutamine. The reaction prevented by the antibiotic is formylglycinamide ribotide + glutamine + ATP → formylglycinamidine ribotide + ADP + glutamic acid + orthophosphate. Azaserine competes with glutamine for the enzyme site, and the combination enzyme-azaserine is irreversible (*69*). Azaserine also inhibits the other reactions in the *de novo* synthesis of purines involving glutamine, but much higher concentrations of the antibiotic are required. These other sites of action are the formation of 5-phosphoribosylamine from 5-phosphoribosyl pyrophosphate and glutamine and the formation of guanylic acid from xanthylic acid and glutamine (*70*).

The antibiotic hadacidin inhibits another reaction in purine biosynthesis, namely, the formation of adenylosuccinic acid from inosinic acid and aspartic acid. The inhibition by hadacidin is competitively reversed by L-aspartate (*71*).

Recently, actinomycin has assumed considerable importance as a biochemical tool through its ability to inhibit ribonucleic acid synthesis that is directed by deoxyribonucleic acid. Actinomycin forms a complex with deoxyribonucleic acid, which can be readily dissociated, and it is thought that this is the method by which actinomycin acts (*72, 73*). The addition of actinomycin to growing cells of *S. aureus* inhibited ribonucleic acid and protein synthesis, and this inhibition was antagonized by deoxyribonucleic acid (*73*). A cell-free system capable of synthesizing ribonucleic acid from the four ribonucleoside triphosphates in the presence of deoxyribonucleic acid was inhibited by actinomycin, and the addition of excess deoxyribonucleic acid antagonized this inhibition (*74*). On the other hand, Reich *et al.* (*75*) found that deoxyribonucleic acid synthesis was not inhibited in mammalian L-cells by concentrations of actinomycin which appreciably inhibited ribonucleic acid synthesis. These authors also showed that Mengo virus, a ribonucleic acid virus, was not inhibited by 0.005 μg actinomycin per milliliter. They concluded that they were able to differentiate ribonucleic acid-directed synthesis of new ribonucleic acid, which is resistant to actinomycin, from deoxyribonucleic acid-directed synthesis of ribonucleic acid, which is sensitive to actinomycin. Recently it has been found that actinomycin is bound to deoxyribonucleic acid through the guanine residues of the nucleic acid, and the degree of inhibition of ribonucleic acid-polymerase reaction is a function of the guanine content of the deoxyribonucleic acid primer (*76*).

D. Protein Synthesis

Protein synthesis is clearly associated with nucleic acids, and lack of protein synthesis may be a secondary effect of inhibition of nucleic acid synthesis. The clearest demonstration of the action of an antibiotic on protein synthesis is the inhibition produced by chloramphenicol. This antibiotic has become a useful tool in the study of protein synthesis in bacterial, plant, and animal systems, as is shown by the rapid accumulation of literature on the subject. Some recent reviews dealing with protein synthesis have been written by Roberts *et al.* (*77*), Novelli (*78*), Jacob and Monod (*79*), and Simpson (*80*).

The available evidence suggests that there are at least three stages involved in protein synthesis. The first stage is the enzymic activation of the amino acids in the presence of adenosine triphosphate to form enzyme-adenyl-amino acid complexes. The second stage is the transfer of the activated amino acids to ribonucleic acid-amino acid complexes. These ribonucleic acids are referred to as transfer (soluble) ribonucleic acids and comprise about 10–15% of the ribonucleic acid of the cell. The third stage involves the transfer of the amino acids from the transfer ribonucleic acids to protein. It is now thought that this transfer is directed by messenger ribonucleic acid (*79*) which serves as a template for the protein. The messenger ribonucleic acid, which comprises less than 5% of the cellular ribonucleic acid, has a nucleotide composition reflecting the base composition of the deoxyribonucleic acid of the cell and may have a rapid turnover rate. The instability and small amount of the messenger ribonucleic acid has made its detection extremely difficult, and it has only been revealed by some extremely elegant experiments.

The relationship of chloramphenicol to protein synthesis was indicated by the ability of the antibiotic to block adaptive enzyme formation in *E. coli* (*81*). Growth-inhibitory levels of chloramphenicol depressed protein synthesis by 90% in washed suspensions of *S. aureus* (*82*). The same levels of chloramphenicol had no effect on respiration or the accumulation of free intracellular glutamic acid, and the rate of formation of nucleic acid was increased. The effect is reversible, and protein synthesis resumes immediately upon removal of the chloramphenicol.

The first stage of protein synthesis, the activation of the amino acids, is not affected by chloramphenicol (*83, 84*); nor is the second stage, the binding of the amino acids to the transfer ribonucleic acids (*85*). However, chloramphenicol does inhibit the synthesis of protein by cell-free extracts of *E. coli* (*86*) suggesting that the antibiotic interferes with the transfer of the amino acids from the transfer ribonucleic acids to protein. Experimental evidence for this site of action has been presented by Nathans and Lipmann (*87*). Chloramphenicol does not inhibit protein synthesis by cell-free extracts of rat liver (*88*) or rabbit reticulocytes (*89*). Relevant to these findings is the observation that the *E. coli* enzyme system which transfers the amino acids from the transfer ribonucleic acids to the ribosomes is specific for *E. coli* ribosomes, and the transfer enzyme system from liver is specific for liver ribosomes (*87*).

Several workers have observed that the ribonucleic acid formed in the presence of chloramphenicol is rapidly broken down when the chloramphenicol is removed (*90*). Aronson and Spiegelman (*91*) have indicated that the unstable ribonucleic acid formed in the presence of chloramphenicol is a normal constituent of the uninhibited cell, and Kurland, Nomura, and Watson (*92*) have found that the ribosomes made during chloramphenicol inhibition contain the same ribonucleic acid types as normal ribosomes. The principal difference between the two ribosomes is the smaller amount of protein in the inhibited ribosomes. Hahn and Wolfe (*93*) have shown that the ribonucleic acid which accumulates in the presence of chloramphenicol has the characteristic instability and base composition of messenger ribonucleic acid and suggest that the antibiotic interferes with the function of the messenger ribonucleic acid. The subject of protein synthesis is under intensive investigation at the present time, and it is certain that our knowledge of the mechanisms involved and the nature of the intermediates will be rapidly expanded.

The action of chloramphenicol depends on its structural configuration. The L(+)-*erythro* stereoisomer of chloramphenicol has less growth-inhibitory ability than the natural D(−)-*threo* form and does not affect protein synthesis. However, the L(+)-*erythro* isomer does inhibit the synthesis of D-glutamic acid polypeptide by *B. subtilis* (*94*).

Several antibiotics other than chloramphenicol have been implicated in protein synthesis, although none of them has been the subject of as much work as chloramphenicol. Chlortetracycline and oxytetracycline inhibited protein synthesis in washed suspensions of *S. aureus* at growth-inhibitory levels (*82*). There was no effect on nucleic acid synthesis, glucose fermentation, or free intracellular glutamic acid accumulation until the concentrations were increased to much higher levels. Chlortetracycline also inhibits cell wall synthesis in growing cells of *S. aureus* (*50*), but again at higher levels that it inhibits protein synthesis. Chloramphenicol has no effect on cell wall synthesis (*95, 96*).

Erythromycin inhibits protein synthesis but not nucleic acid synthesis (*97*). Several other antibiotics have been observed to inhibit protein synthesis. A partial list of these antibiotics includes streptomycin (*98*), dihydrostreptomycin (*99*), and puromycin (*100*), all of which have been shown to inhibit amino acid incorporation into protein. Cyclohexamide (*101*), gliotoxin (*102*), and viomycin (*103*) have been shown to inhibit protein and nucleic acid synthesis. Careful study of the mode of action of a number of antibiotics including those listed above should contribute materially to our knowledge of protein synthesis.

E. Uncoupling Agents; Respiration Inhibitors

Energy-generating systems are necessary to drive the reactions of protein synthesis and nucleic acid synthesis in the cell. Any uncoupling agent, therefore, should block cell development. Likewise, any inhibitor of the respiratory chain will prevent release of energy for synthetic action.

The antifungal agent antimycin is an excellent example of an antibiotic that is too toxic for clinical applications but has found a place as a powerful tool for the biochemist (*104*). It was first observed that antimycin in concentrations of less than 0.1 μg/ml inhibited oxygen uptake by yeast while carbon dioxide evolution was increased, and it was soon found that antimycin was inhibiting an essential component of the electron transport system. The exact point of attack was not clear until the discovery of the coenzyme Q system as an intermediary in the electron transport chain between succinic dehydrogenase and cytochrome c_1. The reduction of coenzyme Q is not affected by antimycin but its reoxidation is inhibited by the antibiotic (*105, 106*).

Tappel (*107*) has drawn some interesting activity-structure relationships with antimycin, showing that the presence of chelating groups and a lyophilic group are essential for the antimycin activity. Coenzyme Q is associated with lipid fractions of mammalian mitochondria (*108*).

Umbreit and his associates found that streptomycin inhibited the oxidation of pyruvate and oxalacetate by *E. coli* cells grown under anaerobic conditions (*109*). None of the known reactions involved in the oxidation of these compounds was inhibited by streptomycin. Umbreit (*110*) found that streptomycin blocked the uptake of radioactive phosphorus into a compound which was chromatographically similar to the 7-carbon compound 2-phospho-4-hydroxy-4-carboxyadipic acid and proposed that this material was an intermediate in an alternative streptomycin-sensitive pathway for pyruvate oxidation. It is doubtful that these results can be the explanation for the primary site of streptomycin action. There is a lack of correlation between the rate of killing of *E. coli* and inhibition of respiration by streptomycin (*111*), and the main oxidative pathway in *E. coli* proceeds through the oxidation of citrate which is insensitive to streptomycin.

F. Specific Enzyme Effects

Direct inhibition by antibiotics of specific enzymic reactions essential to the cell have been described and can be of great significance to biochemists. The action of D-cycloserine on alanine racemase and D-alanyl-D-alanine synthesis has been described in the section on the cell wall. Cycloserine as produced by streptomycetes is the D-isomer. Synthetic L-cycloserine also behaves as an inhibitor of microbial growth but does not cause accumulation of the UDP-muramic acid peptide of the cell wall. It is competitively neutralized by L-alanine rather than D-alanine and, at the enzymic level, the specific enzymic process inhibited is the transaminase between L-alanine, pyruvate, glutamate, and a-ketoglutarate (*112*). These findings at the enzyme level with D- and L-cycloserine point to the specificity of antibiotics for individual enzyme systems. Similar detailed knowledge of enzyme effects should be the end result of investigations of the mode of action of other antibiotics.

G. Vitamin Interrelationships

Vitamins are important as cofactors in many metabolic pathways, and excess synthesis of vitamin antagonists by microorganisms should result in a typical antibiotic response. There are few instances of clear-cut competitive relationships, however. The competitive relationship between biotin and actithiazic acid (acidomycin, mycobacidin) has led to the suggestion that the antibiotic blocks biotin synthesis (*25, 113*).

Foster and Pittillo have demonstrated that, at threshold concentrations of antibiotic in a chemically defined agar medium, physical isolation of each cell can be accomplished and complications due to resistance development or physiological factors are eliminated. Under this condition, many antibiotics may be reversed over a range of two to several fold by complex mixtures of nutrients. Purines, pyrimidines, and amino acids more commonly were the reversing agents, but in some instances vitamins served as neutralizers for antibiotics. Riboflavin not only neutralized the antibacterial activity of chlortetracycline over a sixteenfold range, but riboflavin synthesis was markedly depressed in cells partially inhibited by chlortetracycline (114).

H. Chelation

Numerous instances of metal effects in enzymic reactions have been reported, and it has been proposed that any organic compound capable of forming a stable organometallic complex is a potential enzymic inhibitor and a suitable substance for chemotherapeutic research. Streptomycin, aspergillic acid, usnic acid, and the tetracyclines all have an affinity for metallic cations and in many instances may be considered to serve as direct chelating agents. Other inhibitory compounds, especially antibiotics derived from molds, are known to have chelating properties.

Several routes whereby these chelating agents may exert their antibiotic activity have been suggested. For example, the compounds may inhibit microorganisms by depriving the cells of essential cations, or they may inhibit microorganisms in the form of the specific metal chelates. The antibiotic activity of the former compounds is suppressed by excess concentrations of the cation. The activity of the latter toxic antibiotic-chelate complexes can be neutralized by certain metallic cations which protect susceptible protoplasmic groups from the toxic chelate (115). Tetracycline is an example of an antibiotic which is more toxic to cells in a chelated form.

Metal ions may have a more generalized effect on antibiotic activity. The attachment of an antibiotic to the microbial cell may be suppressed by metal-binding agents and enhanced by metallic cations, for example, penicillin; or the antibiotic may be suppressed by metallic cations and enhanced by metal-binding agents, for example streptomycin and polymyxin.

The importance of the metal-antibiotic relationship is highlighted by studies of Saz et al. (116), who have shown that cell-free nitroreductase obtained from resistant cells is not inhibited by chlortetracycline, whereas the enzyme from sensitive cells is inhibited. It appears that the resistant cells produce altered enzymes which, in contrast to the sensitive enzymes, contain firmly bound, conjugated proflavin capable of competing successfully with chlortetracycline for the essential metallic cations.

Grisein and related antibiotics called sideromycins are examples of antibiotics which prevent access of cell enzymes to the required metal cofactor iron. In this instance, however, the antibiotics do not exert their effect by direct competition for iron but apparently prevent iron from reaching the cytoplasm. The antibiotics are most active when chelated with iron and act competitively with iron transport complexes, variously called ferrichrome, copragen, terregens factor, or sideramines (*117*). It is assumed that the sideromycins are competitive with the transport factors for binding with the specific transferases in the cell membrane.

VIII. CONCLUSION

The few examples of antibiotic activity discussed in detail indicate the complexity of conducting biochemical research with antibiotics and the complications imposed by the variety of responses reported from the action of antibiotics on the intact cells. While much spadework and many independent observations are required to accumulate a series of effects of the antibiotics, one cannot minimize the thrill which the antibiotic specialist receives from the successful dovetailing of pieces in a metabolic pathway through research on antibiotics, such as has been accomplished from studies on cell wall synthesis. With over 2000 antibiotics available as biochemical tools, we should clearly anticipate further significant advances in our knowledge of biochemical pathways as the modes of action of these abnormal biological molecules become known.

REFERENCES

1. S. A. Waksman, *Am. Scientist* 41, 8 (1953).
2. W. F. Verwey, *Ann. Rev. Microbiol.* 13, 177 (1959).
3. E. B. Chain, *Ann. Rev. Biochem.* 27, 167 (1958).
4. F. E. Hahn, *Proc. 4th Intern. Congr. Biochem., Vienna, 1958* 5, Symposium 5, p. 104. Pergamon Press, New York, 1959.
5. S. T. Cowan and E. Rowatt, eds., "The Strategy of Chemotherapy," Symposium Soc. Gen. Microbiol., No. 8. Cambridge Univ. Press, London and New York, 1958.
6. O. Gsell, "Antibiotica et Chemotherapia," Vol. 10. Karger, Basel, Switzerland, 1962.
7. H. S. Goldberg, ed., "Antibiotics, Their Chemistry and Non-medical Uses." Van Nostrand, Princeton, New Jersey, 1959.

8. H. W. Florey, E. Chain, N. G. Heatley, M. A. Jennings, A. G. Sanders, E. P. Abraham, and M. E. Florey, "Antibiotics," Vols. 1 and 2. Oxford Univ. Press, London and New York, 1949.

9. W. S. Spector, "Handbook of Toxicology," Vol. II. Saunders, Philadelphia, Pennsylvania, 1957.

10. S. A. Waksman, "Microbial Antagonisms and Antibiotic Substances," p. vii. The Commonwealth Fund, New York, 1945.

11. C. L. Porter and J. C. Carter, *Botan. Rev.* 4, 165 (1938).

12. H. B. Woodruff and L. E. McDaniel, *in* "The Strategy of Chemotherapy," Symposium Soc. Gen. Microbiol. No. 8, p. 29. Cambridge Univ. Press, London and New York, 1958.

13. E. G. Jeffreys, P. W. Brian, H. G. Hemming, and D. Lowe, *J. Gen. Microbiol.* 9, 314 (1953).

14. J. L. Stokes and C. R. Woodward, Jr., *J. Bacteriol.* 43, 253 (1942).

15. E. L. Dulaney and D. Perlman, *Bull. Torrey Botan. Club* 74, 504 (1947).

16. H. Koffler, R. L. Emerson, D. Perlman, and R. H. Burris, *J. Bacteriol.* 50, 517 (1945).

17. D. M. Reynolds and S. A. Waksman, *J. Bacteriol.* 55, 739 (1948).

18. S. A. Waksman and H. B. Woodruff, *J. Bacteriol.* 40, 581 (1940).

19. P. W. Brian, *in* "Microbial Ecology" (R. E. O. Williams and C. C. Spicer, eds.), p. 168. Cambridge Univ. Press, London and New York, 1957.

20. A. E. Oxford, H. Raistrick, and P. Simonart, *Biochem. J.* 33, 240 (1939).

21. F. R. Batchelor, F. P. Doyle, J. H. C. Nayler, and G. N. Rolinson, *Nature* 183, 257 (1959).

22. Y. G. Perron, W. F. Minor, C. T. Holdredge, W. J. Gottstein, J. C. Godfrey, L. B. Crast, R. B. Babel, and L. C. Cheney, *J. Am. Chem. Soc.* 82, 3934 (1960).

23. J. L. Strominger, R. H. Threnn, and S. S. Scott, *J. Am. Chem. Soc.* 81, 3803 (1959).

24. S. A. Waksman, E. S. Horning, and E. L. Spencer, *Science* 96, 202 (1942).

25. W. E. Grundy, A. L. Whitman, E. C. Rdzok, E. J. Rdzok, M. E. Hanes, and J. C. Sylvester, *Antibiotics & Chemotherapy* 2, 399 (1952).

26. J. W. Foster and H. B. Woodruff, *J. Bacteriol.* 51, 363 (1946).

27. G. L. Hobby, K. Meyer, and E. Chaffee, *Proc. Soc. Exptl. Biol. Med.* 50, 281 (1942).

28. A. di Marco, *in Proc. 4th Intern. Congr. Biochem. Vienna, 1958* 5, Symposium 5, p. 64. Pergamon Press, New York, 1959.

29. S. A. Waksman, "Microbial Antagonisms and Antibiotic Substances," p. 213. The Commonwealth Fund, New York, 1945.

30. M. N. Goldstein, I. J. Slotnick, and L. J. Journey, *Ann. N. Y. Acad. Sci.* 89, 474 (1960).

31. P. E. Hartman and S. H. Goodgal, *Ann. Rev. Microbiol.* 13, 465 (1959).

32. B. D. Davis, *J. Am. Chem. Soc.* 70, 4267 (1948).

33. J. Lederberg and N. Zinder, *J. Am. Chem. Soc.* 70, 4267 (1948).

34. J. Lederberg, *Proc. Natl. Acad. Sci. U. S.* 42, 574 (1956).

35. L. Dienes and H. J. Weinberger, *Bacteriol. Revs.* 15, 245 (1951).

36. W. Shive, *in* "The Biochemistry of the B_1 Vitamins" (R. J. Williams, R. E. Eakin, E. Beerstecher, Jr., and W. Shive, eds.), p. 458. Reinhold, New York, 1950.

37. J. W. Foster and R. F. Pittillo, *J. Bacteriol.* 65, 361 (1953).
38. J. J. Armstrong, J. Baddily, J. G. Buchanan, A. L. Davison, M. V. Keleman, and F. C. Neuhaus, *Nature* 184, 247 (1959).
39. C. Weibull, *J. Bacteriol.* 66, 688 (1953).
40. K. Liebermeister and E. Kellenberger, *Z. Naturforsch.* 11b, 200 (1956).
41. F. E. Hahn and J. Ciak, *Science* 125, 119 (1957).
42. J. T. Park and J. L. Strominger, *Science* 125, 99 (1957).
43. J. T. Park and M. J. Johnson, *J. Biol. Chem.* 179, 585 (1949).
44. J. L. Strominger, *Compt. rend. trav. lab. Carlsberg* 31, 181 (1959).
45. E. Ito, N. Ishimoto, and M. Saito, *Arch. Biochem. Biophys.* 80, 431 (1959).
46. H. Eagle, M. Levy, and R. Fleischman, *J. Bacteriol.* 69, 167 (1955).
47. P. D. Cooper, *Bacteriol. Revs.* 20, 28 (1956).
48. J. L. Strominger, E. Ito, and R. H. Threnn, *J. Am. Chem. Soc.* 82, 998 (1960).
49. J. L. Strominger and R. H. Threnn, *Biochim. et Biophys. Acta* 36, 83 (1959).
50. J. T. Park, *Biochem. J.* 70, 2P (1958).
51. D. C. Jordan, *Biochem. Biophys. Research Communs.* 6, 167 (1961).
52. P. E. Reynolds, *Biochim. et Biophys. Acta* 52, 403 (1961).
53. M. R. J. Salton, *Bacteriol. Revs.* 21, 82 (1957).
54. Zilliken, F., *Federation Proc.* 18, 966 (1959).
55. M. J. R. Salton, "Microbial Cell Walls." Wiley, New York, 1961.
56. P. O'Brien, M. C. Glick, and F. Zilliken, *Biochim. et Biophys. Acta* 37, 357 (1960).
57. H. B. Woodruff and J. W. Foster, *J. Bacteriol.* 51, 370 (1946).
58. R. B. Walton and E. L. Rickes, *Bacteriol. Proc. (Soc. Am. Bacteriologists)*, p. 38 (1958).
59. E. F. Gale, "Synthesis and Organization in the Bacterial Cell." Wiley, New York, 1959.
60. E. E. Hays, I. C. Wells, P. A. Katzman, C. K. Cain, F. A. Jacobs, S. A. Thayer, E. A. Doisy, W. L. Gaby, E. C. Roberts, R. D. Muir, C. J. Carroll, L. R. Jones, and N. J. Wade, *J. Biol. Chem.* 159, 725 (1945).
61. B. A. Newton, *Bacteriol. Revs.* 20, 14 (1956).
62. N. Anand, B. D. Davis, and A. K. Armitage, *Nature* 185, 23 (1960).
63. D. T. Dubin and B. D. Davis, *Biochim. et Biophys. Acta* 52, 400 (1961).
64. N. Anand, and B. D. Davis, *Nature* 185, 22 (1960).
65. R. Hancock, *Biochem. J.* 78, 7P (1961).
66. J. O. Lampen, "Third Biennial Report 1958–1960," The Institute of Microbiology, Rutgers—The State University, New Brunswick, New Jersey.
67. F. Marini, P. Arnow, and J. O. Lampen, *J. Gen. Microbiol.* 24, 51 (1961).
68. L. J. Hanka, *J. Bacteriol.* 80, 30 (1960).
69. B. Levenberg, I. Melnick, and J. M. Buchanan, *J. Biol. Chem.* 225, 163 (1957).
70. R. Abrams and M. Bentley, *Arch. Biochem. Biophys.* 79, 91 (1958).
71. H. T. Shigeura and C. N. Gordon, *J. Biol. Chem.* 237, 1937 (1962).
72. H. M. Rauen, H. Kersten, and W. Kersten, *Z. physiol. Chem.* 321, 139 (1960).
73. J. M. Kirk, *Biochim. et Biophys. Acta* 42, 167 (1960).

74. I. H. Goldberg and M. Rabinowitz, *Science* **136,** 315 (1962).
75. E. Reich, R. M. Franklin, A. J. Shatkin, and E. L. Tatum, *Science* **134,** 556 (1961).
76. E. Reich, I. H. Goldberg, and M. Rabinowitz, *Nature* **196,** 743 (1962).
77. R. B. Roberts, K. McQuillen, and I. Z. Roberts, *Ann. Rev. Microbiol.* **13,** 1 (1959).
78. G. D. Novelli, *Ann. Rev. Microbiol.* **14,** 65 (1960).
79. F. Jacob and J. Monod, *J. Mol. Biol.* **3,** 318 (1961).
80. M. V. Simpson, *Ann. Rev. Biochem.* **31,** 333 (1962).
81. F. E. Hahn and C. L. Wisseman, Jr., *Proc. Soc. Exptl. Biol. Med.* **76,** 533 (1951).
82. E. F. Gale and J. P. Folkes, *Biochem. J.* **53,** 493 (1953).
83. J. A. DeMoss and G. D. Novelli, *Biochim. et Biophys. Acta* **22,** 49 (1956).
84. J. W. Hopkins, *Proc. Natl. Acad. Sci. U. S.* **45,** 1461 (1959).
85. S. Lacks and F. Gros, *J. Mol. Biol.* **1,** 301 (1959).
86. M. R. Lamborg and P. C. Zamecnik, *Biochim. et Biophys. Acta* **42,** 206 (1960).
87. D. Nathans and F. Lipmann, *Proc. Natl. Acad. Sci. U. S.* **47,** 497 (1961).
88. R. Rendi, *Exptl. Cell Research* **18,** 187 (1959).
89. G. von Ehrenstein and F. Lipmann, *Proc. Natl. Acad. Sci. U. S.* **47,** 941 (1961).
90. F. C. Neidhardt and F. Gros, *Biochim. et Biophys. Acta* **25,** 513 (1957).
91. A. I. Aronson and S. Spiegelman, *Biochim. et Biophys. Acta* **53,** 84 (1961).
92. C. G. Kurland, M. Nomura, and J. D. Watson. *J. Mol. Biol.* **4,** 388 (1962).
93. F. E. Hahn and A. D. Wolfe, *Biochem. Biophys. Research Communs.* **6,** 464 (1961/62).
94. F. E. Hahn, C. L. Wisseman, Jr., and H. E. Hopps, *J. Bacteriol.* **67,** 674 (1954).
95. J. Mandelstam and H. J. Rogers, *Nature* **181,** 956 (1958).
96. R. Hancock and J. T. Park, *Nature* **181,** 1050 (1958).
97. T. D. Brock and M. L. Brock, *Biochim. et Biophys. Acta* **33,** 274 (1959).
98. T. Erdös and A. Ullman, *Nature* **183,** 618 (1959).
99. E. Stachiewicz and J. H. Quastel, *Can. J. Biochem. and Physiol.* **37,** 687 (1959).
100. M. B. Yarmolinsky and G. L. de la Haba, *Proc. Natl. Acad. Sci. U. S.* **45,** 1721 (1959).
101. D. Kerridge, *J. Gen. Microbiol.* **19,** 497 (1958).
102. C. J. Shepherd, *J. Gen. Microbiol.* **18,** iv (1958).
103. M. Tsukamura, *J. Biochem. (Tokyo)* **47,** 685 (1960).
104. F. M. Strong, "Topics in Microbial Chemistry." Wiley, New York, 1958.
105. A. M. Pumphrey and E. R. Redfearn, *Biochem. J.* **72,** 2P (1959).
106. D. E. Green, Y. Hatefi, and W. F. Fechner, *Biochem. Biophys. Research Communs.* **1,** 45 (1959).
107. A. L. Tappel, *Biochem. Pharmacol.* **3,** 289 (1960).
108. D. E. Green and R. L. Lester, *Federation Proc.* **18,** 987 (1959).
109. E. L. Oginsky, *Bacteriol. Revs.* **17,** 37 (1953).
110. W. W. Umbreit, *J. Bacteriol.* **66,** 74 (1953).
111. T. F. Paine, Jr., and L. S. Clark, *Antibiotics & Chemotherapy* **4,** 262 (1954).

112. P. Barbieri, A. di Marco, L. Fuoco, P. Julita, A. Megliacci, and A. Rusconi, *Biochem. Pharmacol.* **3,** 264 (1960).
113. M. Kawashima, Y. Hamada, and S. Fujii, *Pharm. Bull. (Tokyo)* **1,** 94 (1953).
114. J. W. Foster and R. F. Pittillo, *J. Bacteriol.* **66,** 478 (1953).
115. E. D. Weinberg, *Bacteriol. Revs.* **21,** 46 (1957).
116. A. K. Saz, L. W. Brownell, and R. B. Slie, *J. Bacteriol.* **71,** 421 (1956).
117. H. Bickel, E. Gäumann, W. Keller-Schierlein, V. Prelog, E. Vischer, A. Wettstein, and H. Zähner, *Experientia* **16,** 129 (1960).

CHAPTER 18

Monoamine and Polyamine Analogues

E. A. Zeller

I. GENERAL REMARKS

A. Chemical Reactivity of Amines

An attempt is made in this brief chapter to describe the biological response elicited by some amine analogues in terms of their interaction with certain enzymes. Only aliphatic and arylalkylamines, but not aromatic amines, amino acids, or amino sugars, are considered.

In aqueous media amines are capable of acting on many parts of enzyme systems. Primary as well as secondary bonds may be established as the following selection indicates: (a) Amino groups are able to share an electron pair with nucleophilic residues and tend to initiate the formation of Schiff bases and metal complexes; they are also apt to participate in transaminase reactions (Section I, B, 1). Alkylation of the amino group eliminates some of these processes, e.g., the production of Schiff bases. (b) Amino compounds are capable of taking part in the formation of hydrogen bonds, either as hydrogen donators or receptors. In every enzyme system many opportunities for hydrogen-bonding arise. The helical structure of proteins and deoxyribonucleic acids testifies to the efficiency of hydrogen bonds in which nitrogen is involved. Obviously, quaternary amines are excluded from this type of interaction. (c) According to Grimm *et al.* (1), the isosteric residues —O—, —NH—, and —CH$_2$— display such chemical and physical properties that sensitive physical and biological criteria and tests often fail to differentiate among them (2). If CH$_2$ residues adjacent to terminal amino groups are replaced by the isosteric NH groups, hydrazine derivatives are obtained. We expect, therefore, to find many similarities in the behavior of hydrazines and of their parent amines (Section II, D).

Clearly, amine analogues may and do affect enzymic systems in more than one way. If there are two or more amine residues present in one molecule, they do not necessarily affect the enzyme moiety in an identical manner. An example of the multiplicity of reaction types is given for diamine oxidase (Section I, B, 3).

Obviously, the non-nitrogen moiety of the molecule may also contribute to the binding forces between amines and enzymes. Van der Waals' forces should be mentioned in general, and the many different kinds of interaction known to exist between aromatic rings in particular. A ring-to-ring attachment has been suggested to play a role in the binding of substrates and inhibitor molecules to the active site of monoamine oxidase (Section I, B, 2).

Many drugs contain aliphatic side chains ending with dialkylated amino residues. Chlorpromazine and imipramine are two examples. Since the alkylamine forms only a relatively small part of the molecules and since some of these compounds are treated in other chapters (e.g., chapter on tranquilizers), they are omitted here.

B. Enzymology of Amine Metabolism

Mono- and polyamines are involved in many enzymic processes; to describe them all would go far beyond the allotted space and the competence of this author. The reactions include (a) the removal of the amino residue either by hydrolysis, by dismutation, by oxidative deamination, or by transamination [transamination between histamine and pyruvic acid has been observed recently (3)], (b) alkylation and dealkylation, (c) oxidation to form nitroso compounds [the nitrosamine derivative of imipramine was found in urine (4)], and (d) conversion to amides, e.g., peptides and acetylated amines. Since the biological roles of some of the processes listed are insufficiently known, they are left out here, as are the acetylation processes which are conventionally treated as a part of the field of CoA enzymes. Chemical changes that occur outside the amine residues, e.g., hydroxylation of the β-carbon of dopamine, O-methylation of catechol amines, or glucosiduronide formation, are not presented here.

Thus, we are left with the discussion of three enzymes: transglutaminase, monoamine oxidase, and diamine oxidase. Only a few points will be raised which will be required as minimal background for our discussion. Many equally, or even more, important data unfortunately have to be left out.

1. TRANSGLUTAMINASE

In the years 1954–1957 Block (5) and Sarkar et al. (6) observed that radioactively labeled amines, such as phenylethylamine and cadaverine, were incorporated into soluble proteins by covalent bonds after being incubated with liver extracts. Further analysis of this phenomenon by Waelsch and his co-workers led to the characterization of the enzyme transglutaminase (7, 8); under its influence and in the presence of Ca^{++} a number of mono- and diamines replaced the nitrogen of glutamine residues [Eq. (1)].

$$RCONH_2 + H_2NR' \rightarrow RCONHR' + NH_3 \tag{1}$$

A number of proteins, e.g., pepsin, a-globulin, and fibrinogen, serve as amine acceptors. [In insulin, the most effective protein, both glutamine residues of chain A are replaceable by cadaverine moieties.]

We may expect that the physicochemical and biological properties of the products in Eq. (1) differ markedly from those of the starting proteins.

2. MONOAMINE OXIDASES

The primary step catalyzed by monoamine oxidase (MAO) is summarized in Eq. (2) (9–11a).

$$RCH_2NH_2 + O_2 + H_2O \rightarrow RCHO + NH_3 + H_2O_2 \tag{2}$$

The enzyme is widely distributed throughout the animal organism and is found in cells derived from all three germinal layers. Intracellularly, it is located in mitochondria (9–11) and in lysosomes (12). Organs such as the brain (13, 14) and the kidney (15) display specific MAO distribution patterns. Judging from statistical data, the activity level in a given organ and species fluctuates amazingly little. In various parts of the human brain the standard deviations amounted to less than 10% (13) and in mouse liver to less than 13% (*15a*). This consistency, however, does not mean that the enzyme levels are rigidly fixed throughout the whole life-span. On the contrary, MAO changes markedly during ontogenesis (*13, 16*) and sexual maturation and responds strongly to the administration of steroid hormones (*15a*). From these data we receive the impression that the enzyme activity is regulated by an efficient and flexible feedback mechanism which adjusts the MAO level to the need of the amine metabolism.

There exist differences in MAO activity, not only among different organs of one species, but also among the same organs of different species. These variations are not entirely of a quantitative, but also of a qualitative nature. As compared with tyramine, the standard substrate, serotonin is attacked to a greater extent by brain MAO than by the liver oxidase (*17*), and *trans*-2-phenylcyclopropylamine inhibits brain enzyme *in vitro* and *in vivo* significantly better than liver MAO (Section II, C). In comparing extensively the liver oxidases of rabbit and of cattle, we are led to the conclusion that the active sites of the two enzymes differ sharply from one another (*18, 19*). MAO, therefore, is not a single entity, but comprises a whole family of closely related *homologous* enzymes.

In order to evaluate the possibility that a given amine or amine analogue can act on MAO, we have to know something about the mechanism of enzyme action and about the architecture of the active site. A considerable amount of information is summarized in Eq. (2). The general formula of a MAO substrate (disregarding N-methylation) is shown in (I). Many varied observations are compatible with the assumption of

$$RCH_2NH_2$$

(I)

an initial removal of one of the two α-hydrogens (*19–21*). In this process the substrate molecule may well be bound by covalent bond to the enzyme molecule. In the Eqs. (3–5), En and Ac are the symbols for the enzyme molecule and the hydrogen acceptor, respectively.

$$RCH_2NH_2 + EnH + Ac \rightarrow \underset{\underset{En}{|}}{RCHNH_2} + AcH_2 \tag{3}$$

$$\underset{\underset{En}{|}}{RCHNH_2} + H_2O \rightarrow RCHO + NH_3 + EnH \tag{4}$$

$$AcH_2 + O_2 \rightarrow Ac + H_2O_2 \tag{5}$$

Equations (3–5) give a more detailed interpretation of the process of oxidative deamination than Eq. (1).

The residue R of formula (I) can be substituted by aromatic, arylalkyl, and aliphatic groups, whereby in the latter case the optimal length of the aliphatic chain varies from species to species as seen in the classic paper by Alles and Heegard (*22*). As has been shown in this laboratory, the substitution of the ring of arylalkylamines by nitro, methyl, chloro, amino, and other residues deeply affects the rate of degradation of these substances by MAO, although the activity of the aliphatic amino group is only slightly influenced by these substitutions (*22a, b*).

From these and many other data it has been concluded that in the active site of MAO an aromatic ring plus a two-membered side chain is located, which favors the attachment of phenethylamine or analogous compounds to the oxidase (*23*). When the eutopic enzyme-substrate complex is achieved, the removal of one α-hydrogen gets under way according to Eqs. (3) and (4), but not after the formation of dystopic complexes.

3. Diamine Oxidases

Although diamine oxidase (DAO) (*23a*) seems to occur more diversely in the whole biosphere than MAO, it is found in fewer mammalian organs than the latter oxidases. To name one instance, DAO is lacking in the brain of man (*13*) and other mammals (*24*). Within the cell it is usually localized in the soluble fraction; in rabbit liver, however, mitochondria contain most of the DAO activity (*25, 26*).

DAO, like the other amine oxidase, undergoes marked quantitative changes during ontogenesis (*9*). In addition, it appears to be closely connected with reproduction. This is indicated by its presence in human prostatic gland, seminal plasma, placenta, and in blood plasma of pregnant women (*9*).

A number of related amine oxidases with partially overlapping substrate patterns are known. For illustration we compare the classic hog kidney DAO and spermine oxidase. The former attacks cadaverine rapidly, spermidine much less, and spermine hardly at all (*27*). Exactly the reverse is true for spermine oxidase (*28*). All these amine oxidases share a remarkable sensitivity toward acylhydrazides, e.g., semicarbazide, isoniazid, and aminoguanidine. While pI_{50} values (negative logarithm of molarity producing 50% inhibition) from 4 to 7 are found for these hydrazides, they are less than 1 or 2 for MAO. The situation is completely reversed for phenylcyclopropylamines (Section II, C) and for N-benzyl-N-methyl-2-propylamine that block MAO most efficiently (pI_{50} val-

$$H_2N(CH_2)_5NH_2$$

(II)

Cadaverine

$$H_2N(CH_2)_3NH(CH_2)_4NH_2$$

(III)

Spermidine

$$H_2N(CH_2)_3NH(CH_2)_4NH(CH_2)_3NH_2$$

(IV)

Spermine

ues from 6 to 7) without affecting appreciably the semicarbazide-sensitive oxidases. Thus, in spite of many similarities, two distinct families of amine oxidases exist. It has been proposed to separate them operationally with the help of 10^{-3} M semicarbazide (23). To the semicarbazide-sensitive enzymes which are called diamine oxidases belong a number of catalysts which display somewhat greater differences among themselves than are seen in the group of monoamine oxidases. DAO in *Mycobacterium smegmatis* (29), plant amine oxidases (30), porcine DAO [which was discovered as histaminase (31)], mescaline oxidase in rabbit liver (26, 32), and spermine oxidase in blood plasma of ruminants (33) belong to this semicarbazide-sensitive family. Spermine oxidase was isolated recently in crystalline form and contained Cu^{++} and pyridoxal phosphate (34), and pea seedling DAO was obtained in a rose red, highly purified form (35, 35a).

Since the initial steps catalyzed by MAO and DAO are covered by the same equation [Eq. (1)], by analogy the interaction between diamines and DAO may follow a sequence similar to that outlined in Eqs. (3–5). The binding of the substrate to the active site, however, is quite different from that found for MAO. Only one amine residue, called A, is released from the substrate by the enzymic process. It appears to be bound to an enzymic aldehyde residue (36, 37), presumably that of pyridoxal (receptor *a*). The second amino group, B, may be replaced by *N*-alkylated residues, by imidazole (histamine), by other heterocyclic rings, and by guanidine (agmatine) (38). Either an organic electrophilic group or a metal possibly may act as receptor for group B (receptor *b*). The distance between the receptors *a* and *b* largely determines whether a given diamine may serve as a substrate (39). Group B is not essential for the substrate-enzyme interaction, since it can be left out. The affinity, as measured by the reciprocal of K_m, however, drops sharply when the second nucleophilic residue is missing (40).

II. AMINE ANALOGUES

A. Polyamines and Mescaline

The polyamines spermine (IV) and spermidine (III) are widely distributed in biological materials, while diamines such as putrescine (1,4-diaminobutane) and cadaverine [1,5-diaminopentane (II)] have been positively identified in only a few instances. Since the two groups of amines often act in a similar fashion, albeit with different quantitative efficiency, the diamines can be considered in many cases as polyamine analogues. We still do not know the specific function of these amines, but considerable information has recently been accumulated on their biosynthesis and metabolism, as well as on a variety of physiological and pharmacological effects. Some of them serve as growth factors for certain microorganisms, and some as bactericidal substances. They produce vivid mating colors in certain fish and induce chromosomal aberrations in plants. In searching for the basis of their biological function one finds that polyamines interact with polyanions, such as nucleic acids and heparin, and that they possess the ability to influence membrane stability of bacteria, animals cells and cell particulates. Tabor, Tabor, and Rosenthal, have reviewed the field recently (41).

1. ENZYME SPECIFICITY AND BIOLOGICAL STABILITY

Hog kidney, as first shown by Zeller, rapidly oxidizes putrescine and cadaverine. It slowly degrades spermidine and spermidine analogues, also by a semicarbazide-sensitive process of oxidative deamination (27). Spermine, however, is not attacked by purified DAO; crude kidney preparations from pork, guinea pig (42), and sheep (43) display a minute capacity for deaminating spermine. In pork kidney extracts the oxidative deamination starts only after a long lag period (36, 44). A strong spermine-destroying power is observed in many bacteria, as first found in *Pseudomonas pyocyanea* by Silverman and Evans (45), and in *M. smegmatis* by Roulet and Zeller (29). In the latter case the semicarbazide sensitivity of the enzymic process was ascertained. Outside the microbiological realm the only well-defined spermine-attacking enzyme is the spermine oxidase occurring in the blood plasma of ruminants (45a) (Section I, B, 3). In searching for the origin of this plasma enzyme, Barsky could not find any appreciable spermine oxidase in the homogenates of six organs from sheep and cattle (and four other species) (43).

Why are MAO and DAO unable to deal with polyamines although

these compounds possess the basic structure of formula (I)? The same question can be asked about mescaline which, as a derivative of phenylethylamine (3,4,5-trimethoxyphenylethylamine), seems to be ideally suited to serve as a substrate for MAO. Since mescaline is susceptible to DAO (26) and spermine to spermine oxidase, the inability of MAO to catalyze the removal of certain amino residues cannot be accounted for by an abnormally high stability of the carbon-nitrogen bond. Moreover, the nonsubstrate amines compete efficiently with the ordinary substrates, indicating that the former are actually bound to the active site of MAO (22a, b). Obviously, the suitable amines form *eutopic* complexes which lead to the decomposition of the substrate, whereas the resistant substances enter into a *dystopic* complex which does not break down to the enzyme and reaction products. A model of the dystopic binding of short-chained diamines by MAO has been presented before (46). According to Zeller and his group, even good substrates of a given enzyme may produce in part dystopic complexes. The relative degree of dystopic complex formation may be evaluated with the help of a modification of the Michaelis-Menten relationship [Eq. (6)], where the subscripts d and e

$$v = \frac{\delta V_e[S]}{\delta K_e + [S]} \tag{6}$$

refer to dystopic and eutopic complexes and $1/\delta$ is defined by $(K_d + K_e)/K_d$. If $K_e = K_m$, meaning no appreciable amount of dystopic complexes is present, Eq. (6) reverts to the standard form of the Michaelis-Menten relationship. If the dystopic complexes prevail $(K_e \gg K_d)$, then v approaches zero, as in the system mescaline/MAO (22a, b).

The enzymic resistance of spermine toward MAO may well be one factor accounting for the amine's ubiquity in animal tissues. Similarly, mescaline, when taken orally (as a part of the cactus *Anhalonium*), would never get past the active MAO of the intestinal mucosa, liver, brain capillary, and brain cell, and never produce the classic hallucinations if it were not dystopically attached to this enzyme.

2. INTERACTION BETWEEN POLYAMINES AND ENZYMES

Di- and polyamines form complexes with the polyanionic nucleic acids, as evidenced by the pronounced effect of aliphatic diamines on the transition of the helix of nucleic acids to the random coil (47) and by the protective effect of spermine and other polyamines against heat denaturation of DNA (48). It seems possible that the production of these complexes is responsible for the inhibitory power of spermine on the hydrolysis of RNA and DNA catalyzed by purified nucleases (49).

Activation of a bovine testicular hyaluronidase by spermine, spermidine, and, to a lesser extent, by several other amines has been demonstrated by Miyaki *et al.* (*50*). In this study, oxidation of spermine by goat serum amine oxidase destroyed its activating ability. In view of the previous reports that hyaluronidase may play a role in the penetration of the egg cell by spermatozoa, these authors pointed out that the activation of hyaluronidase by spermine may have significance for fertilization.

When sheep plasma is incubated with spermine, a strong denaturation of plasma proteins ensues (*43*). This simple observation displays the strong biological effects of the products of the system spermine/spermine oxidase. Many more complex phenomena may have a similar basis. With *Mycobacterium tuberculosis*, for example, Hirsch and Dubos showed that the toxic agent was not spermine but rather the oxidation product of spermine that resulted from the action of beef serum amine oxidase (*33, 42*).

By no means is this kind of data restricted to the field of diamines and polyamines. To mention two examples, some products of tyramine/MAO inhibit choline oxidase (*51*) and succinodehydrase (*52*). Quastel pointed out a long time ago that products of enzymic action rather than the amines themselves may be responsible for at least some of the biological effects observed after the administration of amines.

3. INCORPORATION OF AMINES INTO PROTEINS

In Section I, B, 1 the incorporation of amines into proteins with the help of transglutaminase was discussed. The task before us remains to indicate which amines have been found to be partners in this reaction. Putrescine and cadaverine are excellent substrates and, to a lesser degree, spermine and mescaline (*7*). Whether amines are bound and stored this way, whether the incorporation of amines changes perceptibly the biological activity of specific proteins, or whether synthetic compounds can be built into cell proteins in this fashion remains to be seen. Pharmacological endeavor may one day open a rich field here.

B. *a*-Alkylamines

Amines alkylated in the *a*-position are not substrates of MAO or DAO (*9, 10*). This often-confirmed behavior of compounds such as amphetamine (V) and ephedrine (VI) is considered to be in part responsible for the long duration of their pharmacological action. As indicated by competition experiments, the *a*-alkylamines are still capable of attaching them-

$$\text{C}_6\text{H}_5-\text{CH}_2-\underset{\underset{\text{CH}_3}{|}}{\text{CH}}-\text{NH}_2 \qquad\qquad \text{C}_6\text{H}_5-\underset{\underset{\text{OH}}{|}}{\text{CH}}-\underset{\underset{\text{CH}_3}{|}}{\text{CH}}-\text{NHCH}_3$$

$$\text{(V)} \qquad\qquad\qquad\qquad \text{(VI)}$$

selves reversibly to the active site of MAO. Their *in vitro* inhibitory power, however, is rather small. Under standard conditions it takes 10^{-2}–10^{-3} M concentrations to cut down the MAO activity to half of its original value, as compared with 10^{-5}–10^{-7} M concentrations for modern inhibitors, such as iproniazid and phenylcyclopropylamines. The term inhibitor was taken much too literally and without regard to quantitative relationships by many nonenzymologists. In one instance, a one to a million dilution of ephedrine was used, which was considered to be sufficient to eliminate MAO in an isolated aortic strip. An angry glance at the enzyme, however, would have been as effective as this dilute ephedrine solution. Only a few *in vivo* inhibition experiments with α-alkylamines were carried out, and they turned out to be negative (*53*). With the coming of isotopically labeled compounds, more refined tests on the *in vivo* action of ephedrine and related sympathomimetic drugs could be designed. Schayer was the first to show that the metabolism of several radioactive amines, including epinephrine, was not greatly influenced by ephedrine and amphetamines, but quite substantially by iproniazid (*54, 55*). Since labeled amines are of necessity "exogenous" and since endogenous amines often suffer a metabolic fate different from that of exogenous substances, these experiments do not entirely preclude an effect of these α-alkyl derivatives on the metabolism of endogenous amines. This reservation was overcome by pretreating rats with amphetamine, ephedrine, or iproniazid, and by subsequent determination of their brain serotonin; of the three, only iproniazid raised the serotonin level of the brain, whereas the first two were ineffective in this respect (*56*). Furthermore, the central nervous system appears to react perceptibly only when more than half of the brain MAO activity is eliminated. While *in vivo* permeability and distribution factors may play a role, it still is very difficult to visualize ephedrine reducing brain MAO by more than 50%.

The phenylcyclopropylamines represent an impressive example of the fact that compounds closely related to amphetamine may display tremendous inhibitory power for MAO (Section II, C). A promising step in bridging the enormous gap between the blocking efficiencies of amphetamine and the phenylcyclopropylamines was made when advantage was taken of the high affinity of indole-3-ethylamine (tryptamine) for the oxidase (*57*) and when α-methyltryptamine and α-ethyltryptamine (etryptamine) were synthesized and tested. The latter compound was found to be a stronger MAO inhibitor than amphetamine ($pI_{50} \sim 4$) (*58*). At long last, a substantial *in vivo* inactivation of MAO (rat liver) with an α-alkylamine was obtained (*58*). Moreover, after treating animals with etryptamine and 5-hydroxytryptophan, Greig *et al.* noticed a marked increase in the brain levels of serotonin and epinephrine (*58*). Thus, there seems to be little doubt, at least in the case of the rat, that α-ethyltryptamine, by causing accumulation of certain amines to a high degree, can produce pharmacological effects. Etryptamine actually increases motor activity, as measured by the actophotometer, and prevents reserpine-induced depression (*58*).

In rabbits, immediately following the administration of α-methyltryptamine, the electroencephalogram (EEG) tracing resembled that of the arousal EEG produced by amphetamine. While the initial changes in the EEG occurred long before there was an accumulation of serotonin, delayed action of the amine on the EEG seemed to correlate with the increase and decrease of serotonin (*59*).

C. Phenylcyclopropylamines (PCP)

Burger *et al.* (*60*), in synthesizing phenylcyclopropylamines (VII), expected to produce substances with amphetamine-like activity. The pharmacodynamic properties of the cyclopropylamine derivatives, however, were quite distinct from that of amphetamine and were rather sug-

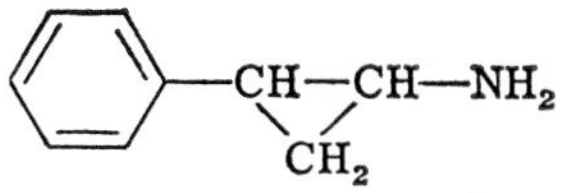

(VII)

gestive of MAO inhibition (*61*); this assumption was soon supported by the results of *in vitro* experiments (*62, 63*). Since then a large number of enzymic, metabolic, pharmacological, and clinical data concerning the great inhibitory power of phenylcyclopropylamines has been reported (*63a*).

1. *In vitro* EXPERIMENTS

Cis- and *trans-*PCP belong to the most effective *in vitro* inhibitors of MAO (*62, 63*), as indicated by the pI_{50} values, which are the highest ever recorded (*20*). From the data of Table I, one has to conclude that the

absolute and relative blocking powers of the two geometric isomers varies
with the origin of the MAO preparation. Although DAO in many ways is
closely related to MAO, the former enzyme is not affected by *cis*- and
trans-PCP (Section I, B, 3). Furthermore, another enzyme catalyzing

TABLE I

Species and Organ Specificity of MAO Inhibition by Phenylcyclopropylamines
(pI_{50} Values)

Origin of MAO	*Cis*-PCP	*Trans*-PCP
Beef liver	6.8	7.0
Rabbit liver	6.0	5.7
Rabbit brain	—	6.3

oxidative deamination, L-amino acid oxidase of snake venoms (*20*), several other dehydrogenases (*64*), and various other enzymes (*20*) turned
out to be insensitive toward PCP.

While PCP and hydrazine derivatives, e.g. iproniazid, share many
inhibitory properties, fundamental differences were discovered on closer
inspection (*19*). The data are compatible with the assumption that
iproniazid is bound to MAO by a covalent bond [see Section II, D, 1 and
formula (IX)], whereas for the binding of PCP, only secondary forces
come into play (*19*, *21*).

2. *In vivo* Experiments

In rabbits the *in vivo* inhibition of MAO by PCP can be observed
easily. The activity of the brain enzyme is reduced more strongly and for
a longer period than that of liver MAO (*20*), a fact which may be related
to the high *in vitro* sensitivity of brain MAO (Table I). It takes 5 days
for the rat brain to recover its original enzymic activity after the administration of *trans*-PCP (*24*). Apparently, the *in vivo* and *in vitro* inhibitory specificities are much the same, since 50 times the quantity of
trans-PCP which produces 50% inactivation of MAO does not alter DAO
activity in cat kidney (*24*).

Although the metabolic effects of MAO inhibition have not been thoroughly explored as yet, some decisive observations have been reported.
(*a*) In rat brain, the level of norepinephrine increases by 80–90% 5 hours
after the administration of a small amount of *trans*-PCP (*65*). (*b*) Green
et al. find brain serotonin to be consistently increased after the application of this drug (*66*, *67*). (*c*) The urinary excretion of tyramine and

epinephrine in dog (*68*) and of tryptamine in man (*69*) is enhanced by tranylcypromine (systematic name for *trans*-PCP), whereas that of 5-hydroxyindoleacetic acid is decreased (*70*). Since MAO appears to be mostly responsible for the degradation of tryptamine, we are not surprised to learn that *trans*-PCP potentiates the convulsion-producing power of this amine (*71*).

In a number of cases, a close correlation between PCP-induced metabolic changes and biological effects have been noted. Two examples are given: (*a*) The ability of PCP to arouse rats from reserpine-induced sedation was closely correlated with the restoration of the brain's capacity to accumulate serotonin without a concomitant increase of the norepinephrine level (*67*). (*b*) A rapid rise in the serotonin level of rabbits after PCP administration seems to be related to the desynchronization of the EEG (*68*).

It has to be emphasized that MAO is not necessarily the only target of the phenylcyclopropylamines, even if no other defined receptor is known as yet. One well-analyzed case will demonstrate this point. The positive inotropic action of *trans*-PCP (and other MAO inhibitors) appears primarily to be due to its capacity to release endogenous catechol amines from their cardiac stores (*72*). The duration of the response is five times longer in the rat than in the cat heart. This species difference may be explained by the fact that, in homogenates of the ventricular myocardium of the rat (and man), the catabolism of catechol amines is strongly blocked by PCP, but no such influence is seen in cat preparations. In the hearts of rat and man, therefore, *trans*-PCP seems to have a twofold function. It releases catechol amines and protects these compounds against destruction by MAO, whereas in cat heart only the former action comes into play (see also Section II, D, 4*c*).

D. Hydrazine Derivatives

When, in 1952, the hydrazine derivative iproniazid, 1-isonicotinic acid 2-isopropylhydrazide (VIII) was found to be an efficient inhibitor of

(VIII)

MAO *in vitro* (*73*) and *in vivo* (*74*), a new era in the study of the enzymology, metabolism, general pharmacology, and psychopharmacology of amine metabolism was ushered in. In 1960 Pletscher, Gey, and Zeller published a review of this rapidly growing field, based on more than 1300 references (75); the flood of investigations still does not show any sign of recession. While the period from 1952 to 1960 is thoroughly treated in Pletscher's review, unfortunately the time since 1960 can be covered here only by reference to a handful of papers, which were chosen for the purpose of demonstrating some applications of the new tool to the study of a wide variety of biological problems. Additional data are found in a more recent review (63a).

Hydrazines had to be considered as a family of purely synthetic compounds until recently, when Levenberg isolated agaritine, a phenylhydrazide of L-glutamic acid (β-N-[γ-L(+)-glutamyl]-4-hydroxymethylphenylhydrazine) from *Agaricus bisporus*, the most common edible mushroom (76). In the past, the group of hydrazine derivatives did not receive much pharmacological attention. Phenylhydrazines, however, have been used for some time to produce anemia (by an unknown mechanism), phenylalkylhydrazines to exert sympathomimetic activity similar to that of the corresponding phenylalkylamines (77), and hydrazino phthalazines to reduce blood pressure (78).

Hydrazines not only display the same chemical reactivity as amines (Section I,A) but also participate in many oxidoreductive reactions. Above all, they furnish the bulk of carbonyl reagents. They share this property with hydrazine itself and with many acylhydrazides. But neither these compounds nor potassium cyanide influence the primary step in the MAO reaction, indicating that no easily accessible carbonyl residue is present in this enzyme and that hydrazine derivatives owe their tremendous MAO-blocking effect not to their ability to react with ketones and aldehydes, but to other physicochemical properties to be mentioned in the subsequent discussion (79).

1. *In vitro* STUDIES

How do hydrazines influence MAO if not as carbonyl reagents? The answer to this question came from an investigation of the action of iproniazid. Zeller *et al.* observed that substrates compete with iproniazid (82) and that the —NHNHCH(CH$_3$)$_2$ moiety of iproniazid seems to be responsible for the action of the latter (80, 81). Furthermore, if the isosteric replacement of CH$_2$ by NH residues is kept in mind, similarities between the substrate and inhibitor patterns unmistakably appear (83, 84). Since the degree of inhibition is a function of the amount of time of preincubation of the enzyme preparation with iproniazid (before the substrate is added), and since isopropylhydrazine and other alkylhydrazines are much more effective than iproniazid, the hydrolysis of iproniazid to form isopropylhydrazine and isonicotinic acid prior to the inhibitory action has been suspected. This concept is supported by some recent observations. Labeled isonicotinic acid was isolated after the incubation of iproniazid with solubilized rat brain mitochondria (*85*), and labeled benzylhydrazine was found in rats treated with isocarboxazid (*86*). These are only a few of the many available data which lead us to believe that the hydrazine inhibitors (or some metabolic degradation products thereof) *occupy the same part on the active site of MAO as the corresponding substrates.* Once the hydrazine is attached to the active site by secondary forces, a covalent bond is perhaps established. Three sets of data favor this idea: (*a*) Davison's important observation that no inhibition of MAO by iproniazid is produced in the absence of oxygen (*19, 87*); (*b*) the inability of *N'*-disubstituted hydrazines to block the oxidase (*80, 81, 88*); and (*c*) the lack of success of every attempt to reverse the iproniazid-included inhibition (*19, 82*). All these results are consistent with the assumption that the hydrazine derivatives, after being attached to the active site by secondary forces in the manner of substrates (Eq. (3), Section I, B, 2), form a covalent bond with the enzyme (IX). The reaction sequence, however, does not proceed beyond this point, and the hydrazine remains attached to the MAO (IX). In three recent papers

R—NNH₂
|
EN

(IX)

the blocking pattern of hydrazine inhibitors has been thoroughly studied, and much new light has been thrown on the structure-activity relationships (*89–91*).

There have been many occasions when MAO inhibitors were used for enzymological studies. For example, effective inhibitors are useful when it is necessary to establish whether an unusual amine, which is oxidized by the enzyme preparation, is a substrate of MAO or of an accompanying enzyme (*63a*). With the help of iproniazid and a number of nonhydrazine agents it was proven that the oxide of *N*-dimethyltryptamine (*92*) and γ-aminobutyronitrile are really attacked by MAO.

2. *In vivo* Experiments

The term "*in vivo* inhibition" is accepted here only when the drop of MAO activity after the administration of the inhibitor has actually been determined. A rise of the serotonin level in brain may be a consequence of the MAO block, but does not per se constitute an unambiguous proof of the *in vivo* inhibition. Reactions so defined were first demonstrated by Zeller and Barsky (*74*). In addition, these authors, together with Berman, followed the recovery of MAO activity in rats until, after 96 hours, the original enzyme level was reached (*82*). This prolonged action cannot be due to the survival of iproniazid, since this compound is rapidly destroyed and disappears at a time when the level of MAO activity is at its lowest (*93*).

Another facet of *in vivo* inhibition was studied by Pletscher (*75*, p. 461) and by McGrath and Horita (*94*). These authors found that the relative degree of the MAO block in brain and liver depends considerably on the structure of the agents used and on the way they have been administered; iproniazid preferentially affects liver MAO, while phenylisopropylamine (pheniprazine) reduces brain MAO more than liver enzyme activity.

Since iproniazid appears to block MAO irreversibly (Section II, D, 1) the restoration of the enzymic activity in the course of several days may be a feedback-controlled synthesis rather than a reactivation of the inactivated enzyme molecule. This concept is supported, but not proven, by recent results obtained by Zeller, Lane, and Schweppe, who found that the rate of recovery of the MAO activity in liver after a single iproniazid injection into male mice is significantly enhanced by castration. For more data the reader is reminded of the comprehensive review given in reference *75* (p. 462).

3. MAO INHIBITORS AS TOOLS IN BIOLOGICAL RESEARCH

Amine analogues in the form of hydrazine derivatives have been used to study the biology of many organisms, from protozoa to spiders to man. The following examples can give only a rather limited view of the diversity of problems to which MAO inhibitors have been applied.

a. Lathyrism. Lathyrism, a nutritional collagen disease, can be produced experimentally with γ-aminopropionitrile. In rats the severity of the symptoms of experimental lathyrism is aggravated by iproniazid. Since γ-aminopropionitrile is deaminated by MAO, albeit slowly (Section II,D,1), this effect of iproniazid could be due to protection of the nitrile from enzymic destruction. Further investigation, however, revealed that isoniazid was also effective in potentiating the lathyrogenic effect of γ-aminopropionitrile (*95, 96*). This result all but excludes MAO from further consideration because isoniazid, differing from iproniazid only by the absence of the isopropyl residue, does not inactivate MAO. It was fortunate that iproniazid and isoniazid became available simultaneously and that the differences in MAO-blocking power was soon discovered

(*73, 74, 81, 97, 98*). Since that time they frequently have been used to decide whether MAO was involved in producing certain specific phenomena (Section II, D, 4*c*).

b. *Protection against X-Rays.* Since tryptamine and 5-hydroxytryptamine (serotonin) are "powerful radioactive amines," it should be possible to enhance their protective action by blocking MAO. A reaction of this kind may have occurred when van den Brenk *et al.* treated rats with iproniazid and reserpine (*99*). These authors observed that reserpine, if given immediately before irradiation, caused a slight protection, which could be increased by pretreating the animals with iproniazid. It would be of interest to know the results of treatment of experimental animals with a combination of MAO inhibitors and one of the indoleethylamines.

c. *Metabolism of Exogenous Dopamine.* Dopamine (3,4-dihydroxyphenylethylamine, 3-hydroxytyramine) is degraded through various channels. The selection of a given metabolic sequence may depend on the method of administration of the biogenic amine or on the individual tissue in which the transformation takes place. One may obtain a general view of dopamine metabolism by determining the radioactive urinary excretion products derived from labeled dopamine. This was done by Williams *et al.* (*100*), who repeated and extended the work of Goldstein *et al.* (*101*). The authors injected dopamine intraperitoneally into rats and determined the excretion of labeled (*a*) homoprotocatechuic acid, (*b*) dopamine, (*c*) methoxytyramine, and (*d*) homovanillic acid. One may assume that homoprotocatechuic acid, by way of the corresponding aldehyde, is a product of MAO action, that methoxytyramine is a result of catechol *O*-methyltransferase activity, and that homovanillic acid is formed with the help of both enzymes. This concept was borne out by experiments in which the animals were treated with isocarboxazid [1-benzyl-2-(5-methyl-3-isoxazolylcarbonyl)hydrazine]. The inactivation of MAO by this drug led to a threefold increase in the urinary excretion of methoxytyramine and to a tenfold reduction of the excretion of homovanillic and homoprotocatechuic acids. From these and additional data it was "concluded that both *O*-methylation and oxidative deamination are of equal importance for the metabolism of exogenous dopamine." Since pyrogallol, an inhibitor of the *O*-methylating enzyme in doses which almost completely blocked the formation of 3-methoxytyramine, did not prevent the formation of homovanillic acid, one has to assume that *O*-methylation of exogenous dopamine is not an obligatory step before the onset of oxidative deamination.

d. *Metabolism of Endogenous Serotonin in the Central Nervous System.* Serotonin, when it is attacked by MAO, is converted into indoleacetaldehyde, which in turn is oxidized by aldehyde dehydrogenases into 5-hydroxyindoleacetic acid (5-HIAA). Recently, the distribution of 5-HIAA in various parts of the rabbit brain was determined by Roos (102). Twenty hours after the administration of the MAO inhibitor nialamide (1-[2-(benzylcarbamyl)ethyl]-2-isonicotinoylhydrazine), the 5-HIAA completely disappeared. Obviously, endogenous serotonin in the rabbit brain is deaminated by MAO.

e. *Endogenous versus Exogenous Norepinephrine.* A large number of investigations have shown that norepinephrine is metabolized largely by two alternate enzymes: catechol *O*-methyltransferase and MAO. Crout *et al.* undertook a penetrating study to evaluate which of these two enzymes is of greater significance in the metabolism of norepinephrine in the brain and heart of the rat (103). Three types of experiments were performed. Initially, the enzyme activities of both methyltransferase and MAO in the brain, heart, and liver were assayed *in vitro* to evaluate the capacity of each tissue to carry out each of these metabolic steps. MAO activity was found to be greater than that of the catechol *O*-methyltransferase in the brain and in the heart, whereas the reverse was true in the liver. Secondly, inhibitors of the transferase and of MAO were administered *in vivo*, separately and together, to determine which caused a greater accumulation of endogenously formed catechol amines in the brain and in the heart. A significant increase in the catechol amine content of rat brain and heart was produced by the intraperitoneal administration of four different MAO inhibitors, whereas the injection of pyrogallol, an inhibitor of the transferase, failed to raise the level of catechol amines in these organs. Finally, the *in vivo* accumulation of injected norepinephrine by rat heart was studied in control animals and in animals treated with an inhibitor of each enzyme to determine the relative ability of each enzyme to degrade exogenous norepinephrine that penetrates into the myocardium. In animals pretreated with iproniazid the major finding was a marked accumulation of amine in the myocardium, relative to the concentration in plasma. Rats pretreated with pyrogallol, on the other hand, demonstrated a severe impairment in their ability to metabolize circulating norepinephrine. The results of these experiments suggest that MAO plays the greater role in the initial metabolism of norepinephrine in the brain and heart, while the catechol-*O*-methyltransferase is of greater significance in the liver. Since circulating norepinephrine is carried by the blood to the two organs with the highest concentration of the methyltransferase, liver and kidney, the importance of this enzyme for the destruction of the circulating and (labeled) exogenous norepinephrine becomes apparent.

f. Analysis of Drug Action: Rauwolfia Alkaloids and Chlorpromazine.
Soon after *Rauwolfia* alkaloids were known to deplete brain and other
organs of serotonin and catechol amines, the research groups of Brodie
and of Pletscher began to study these effects with the help of MAO
inhibitors. It was found that iproniazid not only counteracts the reserpine-
induced sedation, but also prevents the loss of biogenic amines from
various tissues (*75*). Since that time the pharmacological studies on
Rauwolfia alkaloids and on MAO inhibitors have become intimately
interwoven and the antireserpine effects have been used for the large scale
in vivo screening of potential MAO inhibitors. The paper by Bickel *et al.*
(*104*) is an example of a recent study of this type. These authors showed
that the single injection of two chemically fairly different inhibitors,
nialamide and I.S. 2596 [N'-(1,4-benzodioxane-2-methyl)-N'-benzyl-
hydrazine] prevented the reserpine-induced increase in the urinary
catechol amines. This action of the two inhibitors lasted for 1 week, the
same duration as their blocking effect on MAO.

Inhibitors of MAO were instrumental in the discovery of a new and
important facet of the mechanism of action of chlorpromazine. Camanni
et al. (*105*), Ehringer *et al.* (*106*), and Pletscher *et al.* (*107*) observed
that high doses of chlorpromazine prevented the protection afforded
by iproniazid against the reserpine-caused release of catechol amines in
the adrenal medulla and in the brain. A thorough analysis of this phenomenon was recently published by Gey *et al.* (*108*). Chlorpromazine
alone did not affect the levels of serotonin and norepinephrine in the
rat brain, but it counteracted the iproniazid-produced increase of the concentrations of these two amines. The authors suggest that chlorpromazine
may decrease the permeability of the storage organelles for these amines.
In this field of investigation, the usefulness of the MAO inhibitors stems
from their ability to raise the amine level far above the one caused by the
Rauwolfia alkaloids. Within the wide range of these two levels the chlorpromazine effect becomes easily discernible.

*g. Discovery of Octopamine (Norsympathol) in the Mammalian Or-
ganism.* In view of the ubiquity of MAO, it seems quite feasible that more
than one biogenic monoamine hitherto has escaped detection. Actually,
the previously doubtful existence of tyramine and tryptamine in mammals was finally confirmed with the help of MAO inhibitors by Sjoerdsma
et al. (*109*). Recently, *p*-hydroxymandelic acid was discovered in the
urine of several mammalian species, including man. Kakimoto and Armstrong suspected that this acid may have been produced from octopamine
(X) by the action of MAO (*110*). After treating rabbits with iproniazid
or phenylisopropylamine, the authors not only observed the appearance

of octopamine in the urine, but also found this compound to become the most prominent phenolic amine in the extracts of several organs. In

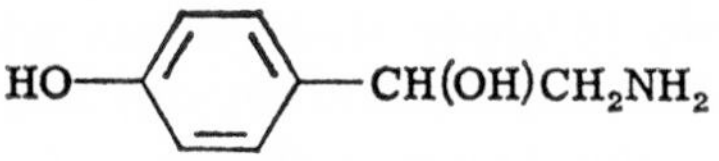

$$HO-\langle\;\rangle-CH(OH)CH_2NH_2$$

(X)

the future, when the biological effects of MAO inhibitors are evaluated, the proportionately large changes in the metabolism of phenolic amines have to be kept in mind.

4. COMPLEXITY OF BIOCHEMICAL PHENOMENA

Amines and amine analogues are capable of interacting with so many components of living organisms (Sections I, A and II, D) that one has to be cautious in the interpretation of phenomena induced by amines. Even if one limits the discussion to substances acting only on one target enzyme, a great number of parameters have to be considered. One group of factors, summarized under the term accessibility, is comprised of the pharmacon's absorption, transport, metabolic destruction, the intracellular concentration gradients, and organ and species specificity. Other complicating factors are discussed in the following sections.

a. Competition. In various biological situations probably more than one biogenic amine is inactivated by amine oxidases. Therefore, we have to expect different degrees of inhibition, depending on the substrate which at the given moment is being attacked by the enzyme. The wide range of these quantitative differences may be inferred from the pair tyramine/MAO and phenylbutylamine/MAO; the former is blocked *in vitro* 200–400 times more strongly by phenylcyclopropylamines than the latter (*19*).

There is such a close structural and isosteric relationship between iproniazid and epinephrine that another type of competition, this time for the receptor site of the effector cell, might be considered. This concept was helpful in the evaluation of the experiments of Griesemer *et al.* (*111*) and of Kamijo *et al.* (*112*). The former produced a reversible adrenergic block in the isolated rabbit aorta with the help of iproniazid, while the latter studied the effect of this drug on the response of the cat nictitating membrane to the stimulation of the sympathetic trunk.

b. Metabolic Conversion of Inert Compounds into Active Inhibitors. In view of Bovet's observation that phenylethylhydrazines display sympathomimetic activity (Section II, D, and ref. *77*), it is not surprising to find direct, amphetamine-like stimulation of the CNS by several MAO inhibitors of similar chemical structure, e.g., phenylisopropylhydrazine (pheniprazine) (*113*) and α-ethyltryptamine (*114*). The fact that iproniazid is devoid of analeptic power supports the previously mentioned assumption that iproniazid is converted to isopropylhydrazine prior to its *in vivo* action. The adrenolytic effect mentioned above (Section II, D, 4*a*) is more likely to result from the intact iproniazid molecule.

c. Membrane Effects. Since 1957 it has been suspected that iproniazid and other MAO inhibitors act on amine metabolism not only by blocking MAO, but also by preventing endogenous amines from leaving the cell. Since that time this hypothesis has been used in the interpretation of a number of experimental data (*115*). Axelrod *et al.* (*116*), on finding that three MAO inhibitors of different chemical structure and duration of action (phenylisopropylhydrazine, *N*-methyl-*N*-benzyl-2-propynylamine, and harmaline) blocked the releasing action of reserpine on norepinephrine-H^3 in the rat heart, proposed that the MAO inhibitors elevated the catecholamines in certain tissues by blocking the release of norepinephrine from its binding site. Pepeu *et al.* compared the action of iproniazid and phenylisopropylhydrazine (*117*). Whereas both compounds completely destroyed MAO of guinea pig heart atria, only iproniazid was able to counteract some of the depressant effect of reserpine. These authors explained their observations by assuming that only iproniazid presented a resistance to the release of amines in addition to being a MAO inhibitor. Spector *et al.*, however, did not believe that MAO inhibitors per se prevent the release of biogenic amines from cells (*118*). They based their conclusion on three observations: (*a*) MAO inhibitors do not prevent the release of serotonin from rabbit platelets *in vivo* or *in vitro*; (*b*) temporary blocking with harmaline, a short-acting competitive MAO inhibitor, does not block the release of brain amines by reserpine; (*c*) a variety of MAO inhibitors of various structures preserve the pharmacological action of reserpine and prevent the decline in amine level. Furthermore, whenever isoniazid was tested (*103, 105, 111, 112*), it did not influence the disappearance of amines from cells. Apparently, it has not been definitely determined whether inhibitors resist the release of amines by interacting with MAO.

III. CONCLUDING REMARKS

This short review, in spite of its obvious limitations, should demonstrate how manifold the interaction among amine and amine analogues appear to be. Biogenic amines compete with each other for chemorecep-

tors and for the binding sites of certain enzymes, and thus tend to poten-
tiate or reduce each others' biological activities. More complications are
introduced by the power of certain amines to release other compounds,
e.g. catechol amines, with ensuing interplay between releasing and released amines, or by competitive events between endogenous and exogenous amines. When we add hydrazine derivatives to our list, we find
some of these isosteric amines competing with ordinary amines for
receptor sites. In passing, the tremendous inhibitory effect of many
hydrazines on amine oxidases and amino acid decarboxylases, and thus
on amine formation and degradation, are mentioned again. With cyclo-
propylamines, not only the degree but also the type of inhibition is
changed profoundly when one substrate of monoamine oxidase is replaced
by a closely related one. We are, therefore, not too surprised when we
find that only part of the metabolic and functional network existing
between amine and amine analogues is unraveled. On the other hand,
the new tools, such as the monoamine oxidase inhibitors, have yielded
remarkable experimental results and new insights into the mode of action
of amine analogues which in turn stimulated the undertaking of many
valuable clinical studies.

REFERENCES

1. H. G. Grimm, M. Günther, and H. Titus, *Z. physik. Chem. Abt.* **B14**, 169
    (1931).
2. H. Erlenmeyer, *Bull. soc. chim. biol.* **30**, 792 (1948).
3. R. Ito, T. Ito, and K. Miyana, *Nippon Univ. J. Med.* **2**, 459 (1960).
4. V. Fishman and H. Goldenberg, *Proc. Soc. Exptl. Biol. Med.* **110**, 187
    (1962).
5. W. Block, *Z. physiol. Chem. Hoppe-Seyler's* **296**, 108 (1954).
6. N. K. Sarkar, D. D. Clarke, and H. Waelsch, *Biochim. et Biophys. Acta*
    25, 451 (1957).
7. H. Waelsch, *in* "Chemical Pathology of the Nervous System" (J. Folch-Pi,
    ed.), p. 576. Pergamon Press, New York, 1961.
8. M. J. Mycek, D. D. Clarke, A. Neidle, and H. Waelsch, *Arch. Biochem.
    Biophys.* **84**, 528 (1959).
9. E. A. Zeller, *in* "The Enzymes" (J. B. Sumner and K. Myrbäck, eds.),
    Vol. II, p. 536. Academic Press, New York, 1951.
10. H. Blaschko, *Pharmacol. Revs.* **4**, 415 (1952).
11. A. N. Davison, *Physiol. Revs.* **38**, 729 (1958).
11a. C. E. M. Pugh and J. H. Quastel, *Biochem. J.* **31**, 2306 (1937).
12. C. de Duve, H. Beaufay, P. Jacques, Y. Rahmah-Li, O. Z. Sellinger, R.
    Wattiaux, and F. de Coninck, *Biochim. et Biophys. Acta* **40**, 186 (1960).
13. H. Birkhäuser, *Helv. Chim. Acta* **23**, 1071 (1940).
14. D. F. Bogdanski, H. Weissbach, and S. Udenfriend, *J. Neurochem.* **1**, 272
    (1957).

15. M. Eder, *Beitr. pathol. Anat. u. allgem. Pathol.* **117**, 343 (1957).

15a. E. A. Zeller, R. E. Lane, and J. S. Schweppe, *Endocrinology* (to be published) (1963).

16. W. J. Novick, Jr., *Endocrinology* **69**, 55 (1961).

17. P. Hagen and N. Weiner, *Federation Proc.* **18**, 1005 (1959).

18. S. Sarkar and E. A. Zeller, *Federation Proc.* **20**, 238 (1961).

19. E. A. Zeller and S. Sarkar, *J. Biol. Chem.* **237**, 2333 (1962).

20. S. Sarkar, R. Banerjee, M. S. Ise, and E. A. Zeller, *Helv. Chim. Acta* **43**, 439 (1960).

21. B. Belleau, J. Burba, M. Pindell, and J. Reiffenstein, *Science* **133**, 102 (1961).

22. G. A. Alles and E. V. Heegaard, *J. Biol. Chem.* **147**, 487 (1943).

22a. E. A. Zeller, *Ann. N.Y. Acad. Sci.* **107**, 811 (1963).

22b. E. A. Zeller, *Biochem. Z.* (to be published) (1963).

23. E. A. Zeller, *Pharmacol. Revs.* **11**, 387 (1959).

23a. E. A. Zeller, *in* "The Enzymes" (P. D. Boyer, H. A. Lardy, and K. Myrbäck, eds.), Vol. VIII, p. 313. Academic Press, New York, 1963.

24. W. P. Burkard, K. F. Gey, and A. Pletscher, *Biochem. Pharmacol.* **11**, 177 (1962).

25. G. C. Cotzias and V. P. Dole, *J. Biol. Chem.* **196**, 235 (1952).

26. E. A. Zeller, J. Barsky, E. R. Berman, M. S. Cherkas, and J. R. Fouts, *J. Pharmacol. Exptl. Therap.* **124**, 282 (1958).

27. E. A. Zeller, B. Schär, and S. Staehlin, *Helv. Chim. Acta* **22**, 837 (1939).

28. C. W. Tabor, H. Tabor, and S. M. Rosenthal, *J. Biol. Chem.* **208**, 645 (1954).

29. F. Roulet and E. A. Zeller, *Helv. Chim. Acta* **28**, 1326 (1945).

30. R. H. Kenten and P. J. G. Mann, *Biochem. J.* **50**, 360 (1962).

31. C. H. Best and E. W. McHenry, *J. Physiol.* (*London*) **70**, 349 (1930).

32. F. Bernheim and M. L. C. Bernheim, *J. Biol. Chem.* **123**, 317 (1938).

33. J. G. Hirsch and R. J. Dubos, *J. Exptl. Med.* **95**, 191 (1952).

34. H. Yamada and K. T. Yasunobu, *J. Biol. Chem.* **237**, 1511 (1962).

35. E. Werle, I. Trautschold, and D. Aures, *Z. physiol. Chem. Hoppe-Seyler's* **326**, 200 (1961).

35a. P. J. G. Mann, *Biochem. J.* **78**, 623 (1961).

36. E. A. Zeller, *Helv. Chim. Acta* **21**, 1645 (1938).

37. E. V. Goryachenkova, *Biochemistry* (*U.S.S.R.*) (*English Transl.*) **21**, 249 (1956).

38. E. A. Zeller, *Advances in Enzymol.* **2**, 93 (1942).

39. E. A. Zeller, J. R. Fouts, J. A. Carbon, J. C. Lazanas, and W. Voegtli, *Helv. Chim. Acta* **39**, 1632 (1956).

40. J. R. Fouts, L. A. Blanksma, J. A. Carbon, and E. A. Zeller, *J. Biol. Chem.* **225**, 1025 (1957).

41. H. Tabor, C. W. Tabor, and S. M. Rosenthal, *Ann. Rev. Biochem.* **30**, 579 (1961).

42. J. G. Hirsch, *J. Exptl. Med.* **97**, 327 (1953).

43. J. Barsky, On the Reactive Site of Monoamine Oxidase, Doctoral Thesis, Northwestern University, Evanston, Illinois, 1958; *Dissertation Abstr.* **19**, 1191 (1958-1959).

44. J. R. Fouts, On the Specificity and Mechanism of the Diamine-Diamine Oxidase Reaction, Doctoral Thesis, Northwestern University, Evanston, Illinois, 1954; *Dissertation Abstr.* 14, 2194 (1954).
45. M. Silverman and E. A. Evans, Jr., *J. Biol. Chem.* 154, 521 (1944).
45a. H. Blaschko, *Advan. Comp. Physiol. Biochem.* 1, 68 (1962).
46. E. A. Zeller, *in* "Handbuch der allgemeinen Pathologie" (F. Büchner, E. Letterer, and F. Roulet, eds.), Vol. II, Part 1, p. 279. Springer, Berlin, 1955.
47. H. R. Mahler, B. D. Mehrotra, and C. Sharp, *Biochem. Biophys. Research Communs.* 4, 79 (1961).
48. H. Tabor, *Biochemistry* 1, 496 (1962).
49. D. L. Keister, Some Aspects of the Metabolic Function of the Naturally Occurring Amines, Doctoral Thesis, University of Maryland Medical School, Baltimore, Maryland, 1958; *Dissertation Abstr.* 20, 478 (1959).
50. K. Miyaki, I. Mochida, T. Wada, and T. Kudo, *Chem. Pharm. Bull.* (*Tokyo*) 7, 123 (1959).
51. C. C. Wu, *Tai-wan i-hsüeh-hui tsa-chih* 59, 862 (1960).
52. I-C. Tung, *Tai-wan i-hsüeh-hui tsa-chih* 59, 899 (1960).
53. H. Schmitt, P. Gonnard, and G. Glikman, *Bull. soc. chim. biol.* 37, 147 (1955).
54. R. W. Schayer, *Proc. Soc. Exptl. Biol. Med.* 84, 60 (1953).
55. R. W. Schayer, K. Y. T. Wu, R. L. Smiley, and Y. Kobayashi, *J. Biol. Chem.* 210, 259 (1954).
56. A. Pletscher and K. F. Gey, *Helv. Physiol. et Pharmacol. Acta* 17, C35 (1959).
57. Y. Kobayashi and R. W. Schayer, *Arch. Biochim. Biophys.* 58, 181 (1955).
58. M. E. Greig, P. H. Seay, and W. A. Freyburger, *J. Neuropsychiat.* 2, Suppl. 1, 131 (1961).
59. H. E. Himwich, *J. Neuropsychiat.* 2, Suppl. 1, 136 (1961).
60. A. Burger and W. L. Yost, *J. Am. Chem. Soc.* 70, 2198 (1948).
61. R. E. Tedeschi, D. H. Tedeschi, L. Cook, P. A. Mattis, and E. J. Fellows, *Federation Proc.* 18, 451 (1959).
62. E. A. Zeller, *Trans. 5th Conf. on Neuropharmacol., Princeton, New Jersey, May 1959*, p. 89.
63. A. R. Maas and M. J. Nimmo, *Nature* 184, 547 (1959).
63a. E. A. Zeller and J. R. Fouts, *Ann. Rev. Pharmacol.* 3, 9 (1963).
64. H. Redetzki and F. O'Bourke, *Arch. intern. pharmacodyamie* 130, 299 (1961).
65. H. Green and R. W. Erickson, *J. Pharmacol. Exptl. Therap.* 129, 237 (1960).
66. H. Green and J. L. Sawyer, *J. Pharmacol. Exptl. Therap.* 129, 243 (1960).
67. H. Green, S. M. Greenberg, R. W. Erickson, J. L. Sawyer, and T. Ellison, *J. Pharmacol. Exptl. Therap.* 136, 174 (1962).
68. G. R. Pscheidt, *Federation Proc.* 21, 417 (1962).
69. A. Sjoerdsma, J. A. Oates, and L. Gillespie, Jr., *Proc. Soc. Exptl. Biol. Med.* 103, 485 (1960).
70. M. H. Wiseman and T. L. Sourkes, *Biochem. J.* 78, 123 (1961).
71. H. Green and J. L. Sawyer, *Proc. Soc. Exptl. Biol. Med.* 104, 153 (1960).

72. N. D. Goldberg and F. E. Shideman, *J. Pharmacol. Exptl. Therap.* **136**, 142 (1962).
73. E. A. Zeller, J. Barsky, J. R. Fouts, W. F. Kirchheimer, and L. S. Van Orden, *Experientia* **8**, 349 (1952).
74. E. A. Zeller and J. Barsky, *Proc. Soc. Exptl. Biol. Med.* **81**, 459 (1952).
75. A. Pletscher, K. F. Gey, and P. Zeller, *Progr. in Drug Research* **2**, 417 (1960).
76. B. Levenberg, *J. Am. Chem. Soc.* **83**, 503 (1961).
77. D. Bovet, *Schweiz. med. Wochschr.* **73**, 127, 153 (1943).
78. W. Schuler and R. Meier, *Helv. Physiol. et Pharmacol. Acta* **13**, 106 (1955).
79. J. R. Fouts, J. Barsky, and E. A. Zeller, *Abstr. 126th Meeting, Am. Chem. Soc. New York, 1954* p. 45C.
80. E. A. Zeller, J. Barsky, J. R. Fouts, and J. C. Lazanas, *Biochem. J.* **60**, v (1955).
81. J. Barsky, W. L. Pacha, S. Sarkar, and E. A. Zeller, *J. Biol. Chem.* **234**, 389 (1959).
82. E. A. Zeller, J. Barsky, and E. R. Berman, *J. Biol. Chem.* **214**, 267 (1955).
83. E. A. Zeller, L. A. Blanksma, W. P. Burkard, W. L. Pacha, and J. C. Lazanas, *Ann. N. Y. Acad. Sci.* **80**, 583 (1959).
84. S. Sarkar and E. A. Zeller, *Federation Proc.* **20**, 238 (1961).
85. L. S. Seiden and J. Westley, *Federation Proc.* **21**, 416 (1962).
86. M. A. Schwartz, *J. Pharmacol. Exptl. Therap.* **130**, 157 (1960); **135**, 1 (1962).
87. A. N. Davison, *Biochem. J.* **67**, 316 (1957).
88. E. A. Zeller, in "Symposium on Biochemistry and Nutrition," p. 25. Cornell Univ., Ithaca, N. Y., 1956.
89. J. Szmuszkovicz and M. E. Greig, *J. Med. Pharm. Chem.* **4**, 259 (1961).
90. F. E. Anderson, D. Kaminsky, B. Dubnick, S. R. Klutchko, W. E. Cetenko, J. Gylys, and J. A. Hart, *J. Med. Pharm. Chem.* **5**, 221 (1962).
91. A. L. Green, *Biochem. J.* **84**, 217 (1962).
92. T. E. Smith, H. Weissbach, and S. Udenfriend, *Biochemistry* **1**, 137 (1962).
93. S. Hess, H. Weissbach, B. G. Redfield, and S. Udenfriend, *J. Pharmacol. Exptl. Therap.* **124**, 189 (1958).
94. W. R. McGrath and A. Horita, *Toxicol. Appl. Pharmacol.* **4**, 178 (1962).
95. K. Juva, T. Tuominen, L. Mikkonen, and E. Kulonen, *Acta Pathol. Microbiol. Scand.* **51**, 250 (1961).
96. D. N. Roy, S. H. Lipton, F. M. Strong, and H. R. Bird, *Proc. Soc. Exptl. Biol. Med.* **102**, 767 (1959).
97. E. A. Zeller, in "Histamine," Ciba Foundation Symposium, p. 339. Little, Brown, Boston, Massachusetts, 1956.
98. E. A. Zeller, J. Barsky, E. R. Berman, and J. R. Fouts, *J. Pharmacol. Exptl. Therap.* **106**, 427 (1952).
99. H. A. S. van den Brenk and K. Elliott, *Nature* **182**, 1506 (1958).
100. C. M. Williams, A. A. Babuscio, and R. Watson, *Am. J. Physiol.* **199**, 722 (1960).
101. M. Goldstein, A. J. Friedhoff, and C. Simmons, *Biochim. et Biophys. Acta* **33**, 572 (1959).

102. B.-E. Roos. *Life Sci.* 1, 25 (1962).
103. J. R. Crout, C. R. Creveling, and S. Udenfriend, *J. Pharmacol. Exptl. Therap.* 132, 269 (1961).
104. M. H. Bickel, A. Carpi, and D. Bovet, *Helv. Physiol. et Pharmacol. Acta* 19, 279 (1961).
105. F. Camanni, G. M. Molinatti, and M. Olivetti, *Nature* 184, 65 (1959).
106. H. Ehringer, P. Hornykiewicz, and K. Lechner, *Arch. Exptl. Pathol. Pharmakol. Naunyn-Schmiedeberg's* 239, 507 (1960).
107. A. Pletscher and K. F. Gey, *Med. Exptl.* 2, 259 (1960).
108. K. F. Gey and A. Pletscher, *J. Pharmacol. Exptl. Therap.* 133, 18 (1961).
109. A. Sjoerdsma, W. Lovenberg, J. A. Oates, J. R. Crout, and S. Udenfriend, *Science* 130, 225 (1959).
110. Y. Kakimoto and M. D. Armstrong, *J. Biol. Chem.* 237, 422 (1962).
111. E. C. Griesemer, C. A. Dragstedt, J. A. Wells, and E. A. Zeller, *Experientia* 11, 182 (1955).
112. K. Kamijo, G. B. Koelle, and H. H. Wagner, *J. Pharmacol. Exptl. Therap.* 117, 213 (1956).
113. J. H. Biel, P. A. Nuhfer, A. C. Conway, *Ann. N.Y. Acad. Sci.* 80, 568 (1959).
114. W. M. Anglin, *Diseases of Nervous System* 22, 456 (1961).
115. A. Pletscher, *Helv. Physiol. et Pharmacol. Acta* 14, C76 (1956).
116. J. Axelrod, G. Hertting, and P. W. Patrick, *J. Pharmacol. Exptl. Therap.* 134, 325 (1961).
117. G. Pepeu, M. Roberts, S. Schanberg, and N. J. Giarman, *J. Pharmacol. Exptl. Therap.* 132, 131 (1961).
118. S. Spector, R. Kuntzman, P. A. Shore, and B. B. Brodie, *J. Pharmacol. Exptl. Therap.* 130, 256 (1960).

CHAPTER 19

Inhibitors of Catechol Amine Metabolism

T. L. Sourkes and A. D'Iorio

I. INTRODUCTION

Epinephrine was identified as a hormone and synthesized about 60 years ago, but it is only within the last 15 years that detailed biochemical knowledge of its formation and metabolism has become available. Historically important findings have been the discovery of hydroxytyramine and norepinephrine in urine, in sympathetic nerves, and in the brain. These compounds serve as precursors of epinephrine in the biosynthetic pathway leading from phenylalanine, through tyrosine, dihydroxyphenylalanine (dopa), dopamine, and norepinephrine, but they also have additional functions. Other amino acids giving rise to catechol amines are m-tyrosine and dihydroxyphenylserine. The development of sensitive fluorometric methods for the measurement of the catecholamines and the catechol amino acids in body fluids and tissues has revolutionized the study of sympathoadrenal physiology. Detailed reviews of the biochemistry of the catechol amines have been prepared (1, 2). Many useful

79

papers on catechol amines will be found in the proceedings of a symposium held in 1958 (*3*).

In this chapter, inhibitors of catechol amine metabolism will be considered in the three categories: (*a*) biogenesis, (*b*) catabolism and "detoxication," and (*c*) binding at receptor and storage sites. The enzymes concerned in biogenesis, beginning from dopa, are dopa decarboxylase, dopamine-β-oxidase, and N-transmethylase. Information on inhibitors of the latter two enzymes is lacking, and only the first is considered.

II. SUBSTANCES INTERFERING WITH THE BIOGENESIS OF CATECHOL AMINES THROUGH INHIBITION OF DOPA DECARBOXYLASE

The amino acid precursors of the catechol amines undergo decarboxylation through the action of a pyridoxal phosphate(PLP)-linked enzyme. One of the earliest amino acid decarboxylases found in animal tissues was dopa decarboxylase, first described by Holtz, Heise, and Lüdtke in 1938 (*4*). At present this enzyme is regarded as the catalyst for the decarboxylation of 5-hydroxytryptophan also (*5*), and of some other aromatic amino acids. This section will review the literature primarily in relation to inhibitors of decarboxylase preparations which have been studied with dopa as the substrate. Hundreds of compounds have been tested for inhibition of dopa decarboxylase, but only a few of the active ones can be described here. The emphasis will be upon mechanisms of action. Further details will be found in references (*6*), (*7*), and (*8*).

A. Inhibitors Acting on the Apodecarboxylase

1. *a*-METHYLDOPA AND RELATED COMPOUNDS

a. Mechanism of Action in vitro. *a*-Methyldopa, a structural analogue of dopa in which the hydrogen atom on the *a*-carbon is replaced by a methyl group, exerts a biphasic action on dopa decarboxylase; in low concentrations it activates the enzyme, but above $10^{-5}\ M$ it displays the characteristics of a slowly reversible inhibitor competing with the substrate for sites on the enzyme surface. The mechanism of the activation has not been explained, although several experimental approaches have been tested (*6*). *a*-Methyl-3-hydroxyphenylalanine (*a*-methyl-*meta*-tyrosine) has similar properties. These compounds act as "pseudoirre-

versible" inhibitors, in the terminology of Ackermann and Potter (9);
that is, they are characterized by a relatively low apparent enzyme-
inhibitor dissociation constant. The inhibitor can be removed from the
enzyme by dialysis. The structural resemblance of these compounds to
substrates of dopa decarboxylase suggests that they inhibit by establishing a stronger bond with the apodecarboxylase through their phenolic
groups (10) than the substrate does. The *meta*-phenolic group is of special
importance in this respect because inhibitory activity is greatly reduced
in compounds lacking this group or bearing it masked by methylation.
Thus, a-methyl-*m*-tyrosine, at a concentration of 5×10^{-3} M inhibits
the dopa decarboxylase activity of an extract of pig kidney cortex 95%,
whereas a-methyl-*m*-methoxyphenylalanine and a-methyl-*p*-tyrosine at
the same concentration inhibit only 16–18%.

A series of a-methyl amino acids shows the following (descending)
order of activity against kidney dopa decarboxylase: a-methyldopa,
a-methyl-*m*-tyrosine, a-methyl-*p*-tyrosine, a-methylphenylalanine. These
compounds also inhibit tyrosine decarboxylase of *Streptococcus faecalis*,
but to a much smaller extent (6).

Like some other amino acids and amines, the a-methyl compounds are
able to sequester the coenzyme, but the inhibition of the enzyme by this
means occurs at concentrations of inhibitor where coenzyme binding is
not significantly affected (see Section II, B, 2b).

b. *Actions in vivo.* After the demonstration of the inhibitory action of
a-methyldopa *in vitro* (6), Dengler and Reichel (11) and Westermann
et al. (12) showed that this compound is also active in intact animals.
This was confirmed by the direct measurement of catechol amines and
of a-methyldopa in the tissues of rats injected with the inhibitor and with
dopa (13). This study described two biochemical effects following the
parenteral administration of a-methyldopa: (a) a decrease in the endogenous cerebral dopamine and norepinephrine, and (b) an inhibition of the
decarboxylation of exogenous dopa. The action on endogenous cerebral
amines is exemplified by the rapid fall in cerebral dopamine and norepinephrine following the injection of the a-methyl amino acid. The concentration of a-methyldopa in the brain 3 hours after the injection of the
compound is proportional to the dose administered. As soon as its concentration falls below the levels which are inhibitory toward dopa
decarboxylase, the resynthesis of the catechol amines begins; this is
achieved in less than 24 hours for dopamine but requires 2–3 days for
norepinephrine (14). Cerebral serotonin also declines in animals treated
with a-methyldopa (15); the level is restored rapidly, as in the case of
dopamine. The amine-depleting effect is not entirely specific to the

a-methyl amino acids, for other amino acids (m-tyrosine, o-tyrosine, tryptophan, 5-hydroxytryptophan) also cause a loss of cerebral catechol amines under the same conditions (16).

The second action of a-methyldopa *in vivo* is its inhibition of decarboxylation. This becomes evident when exogenous dopa or certain other amino acids are administered. The accumulation of dopamine under these conditions can be minimized by treatment of rats with a-methyldopa or a-methyl-m-tyrosine (but not a-methyl-3-methoxyphenylalanine) just before they receive a test load of L-dopa (10 mg/kg). The effect of various a-methyl amino acids upon the conversion of exogenous dopa to urinary

TABLE I

EFFECT OF α-METHYL AMINO ACIDS ON THE CONVERSION OF L-DOPA TO URINARY
DOPAMINE

Compound administered[a]	Urinary dopamine[b]
None	100
α-Methylphenylalanine	92
α-Methyl-o-tyrosine	91
α-Methyl-m-tyrosine	43
α-Methyl-3-methoxy-4-hydroxyphenylalanine	92
α-Methyl-2,5-dopa	40
α-Methyltryptophan	91
α-Methyl-5-hydroxytryptophan	10

[a] Injected intraperitoneally, in saline, 100 mg/kg, 0.5 hour before L-dopa (10 mg/kg) was given by the same route.

[b] Twenty-four-hour output expressed as percentage of output in control animals receiving only dopa.

dopamine in the rat is shown in Table I (14, 17, 18). The effect of a single injection of a-methyl-m-tyrosine in this test lasts for a few hours (18).

c. Metabolism. Although the a-methyl amino acids tested manometrically in short-term incubations were reported as resistant to the action of tissue decarboxylase (6), more sensitive fluorometric methods have shown that they are slowly acted upon by enzymes (19), with the formation of compounds bearing an isopropylamine side chain. "a-Methyldopamine" is 3,4-dihydroxyamphetamine. The decarboxylation of the a-methyl amino acids is in accord with the Westheimer model of the action of amino acid decarboxylases, which predicts that the a-hydrogen atom is not involved in this process (cf. 20).

a-Methyl-m-tyramine is a weak inhibitor of rabbit liver MAO, but a-methyldopamine is inactive (*20a*).

Subjects given 1–1.5 gm daily of a-methyldopa by mouth excrete about 10% of the compound in the urine. Upon withdrawal of the drug a-methyldopa can be detected in the urine (in diminishing amounts) for 2 days. After intravenous administration, a-methyldopa is found in the plasma for at least 2 hours; it does not appear to enter the erythrocytes (*21*).

d. Pharmacological and Clinical Effects. a-Methyldopa lowers blood pressure in hypertensive patients (*22*). Its hypotensive action has also been studied in the dog (*23*). It has a mild sedative action (*22–24*). Smith has compared its pharmacological actions in experimental animals to those of reserpine (*25*). It has now been tested widely in the treatment of hypertension (*24*), with success, and as a tranquillizer in schizophrenia, where it is ineffective (*21*). It exacerbates the tremor in Parkinson's disease (*25a*).

2. 3-Hydroxycinnamoyl Derivatives

a. Action in vitro. Many compounds based upon the structure shown in (I)

$$m\text{-OH} \cdot C_6H_4 \text{—} C = C \text{—} C \text{—} X$$
$$| \quad | \quad \|$$
$$O$$

(I)

have been synthesized and tested as inhibitors of dopa decarboxylase. Hartman *et al.* (*7*) have shown that the most active compounds possess an aryl group in the position designated by X in the above formula. These are derivatives of chalcone (II).

$$C_6H_5 \text{—} CH = CH \text{—} C \text{—} C_6H_5$$
$$\|$$
$$O$$

(II)

In compounds with X = OH (cinnamic acid derivatives) less inhibitory activity is encountered [(*7*), cf. (*6*)]. Intermediate potency is obtained with esters of cinnamic acid and with related ketones (X = an alkyl group). An additional phenolic group in the *para* position increases inhibitory activity, but not if the group is methylated. 3,4-Dihydroxycinnamic (caffeic) acid, for example, is more potent than either 3-hydroxycinnamic acid or 3-hydroxy-4-methoxycinnamic (isoferulic) acid.

Effective inhibition by members of this series is exerted upon contact with the enzyme. This contrasts with α-methyldopa, which requires a brief preincubation with the enzyme. 3-Hydroxycinnamic acid is effective *in vitro* at a concentration of 10^{-4} *M*, but other derivatives are much more potent. The most active compound in Hartman's series is 5-(3,4-dihydroxycinnamoyl)salicylic acid (*7*, *26*). It is effective at 10^{-6} *M*. These two compounds, as well as caffeic acid, act as competitive inhibitors of the enzyme (*7*).

b. Studies in vivo (*8*). Some of the 3-hydroxycinnamoyl derivatives have been examined for inhibitory action *in vivo*. The compound most active in preventing the pressor response resulting from the intravenous injection of dopa in the cat or rat is 5-(3-hydroxycinnamoyl)salicylic acid. It causes 50% inhibition *in vivo* at a dose level of 6.6 mg/kg. Its catechol analogue, the most active compound *in vitro*, is less than half as active *in vivo*. Isoferulic and 3-hydroxyphenylpropionic acids both inhibit significantly *in vivo* (cat) despite the very weak action of the former compound on dopa decarboxylase *in vitro* and the inactivity of the latter. Discrepancies of this kind introduce some difficulties in predicting inhibitory activity *in vivo* from that *in vitro*. However, the most active compounds in both tests conform to the same structural features in that they contain the 3-hydroxycinnamoyl unit.

It appears that these compounds are readily metabolized, for the pressor response to injected dopa is affected only for about 30 minutes. Injected caffeic acid disappears from blood in the same period of time. A few of the compounds have a longer duration of action, and their action can be extended by repeated administration of the drug or injection by more than one route.

3. FLAVONES

The flavones include derivatives of 2-phenylpyran-4-one and its 2,3-dihydro analogue, 2-phenylchroman-4-one (2-phenylchromone). Among the well-known natural products in this group with antidecarboxylase activity are catechin (*6*, *7*), gossypin, and rutin (*7*). They appear to be relatively more active *in vivo* than *in vitro* (*8*).

4. PHENYLPYRUVIC ACID

Phenylalanine and tyrosine are weak inhibitors of dopa decarboxylase (*26*, *27*), but their keto acids are active (*7*, *26*, *27*). Clark has shown (*8*) that 3-hydroxyphenylpyruvic and 3,4-dihydroxyphenylpyruvic acids are more effective. 4-Hydroxyphenyllactic acid has slight activity, but phenyllactic acid has none. He has also noted that 3-hydroxyphenylacetic acid has very weak activity, which is increased somewhat in its catechol analogue, dopacetic acid.

These compounds were tested using dopa decarboxylase prepared from kidney. Fellman, using extracts of beef adrenal medulla, obtained inhibitory effects with both phenylpyruvic and phenyllactic acids (28). He has suggested that inhibition of this enzyme by the excessive aromatic metabolites in the body fluids of phenylketonuric subjects plays a role in reducing endogenous catechol amine formation.

Martin et al. observed a fall in blood pressure following the injection of 4-hydroxyphenylpyruvic acid (26).

B. Interference with the Function of Pyridoxal Phosphate

1. PYRIDOXINE DEFICIENCY

Deprivation of vitamin B_6 results in diminished activity of hepatic dopa decarboxylase (29). In spite of this, young rats fed a diet deficient in this vitamin do not exhibit significant changes in the catechol amine content of the adrenal glands, liver, brain, spleen, or heart (17). The effects of the deficiency are reflected, however, in a reduced formation of urinary dopamine from injected dopa. The reduction is 35–50% when the test is performed with L-dopa. This change represents the effect of the deficiency upon the activity of dopa decarboxylase in the tissues. Urinary dopamine is also formed from injected D-dopa, probably by a pathway involving oxidative deamination, followed by asymmetric transamination of the product to L-dopa and its decarboxylation. The transamination step has been demonstrated to occur in vivo (8). Pyridoxine deficiency causes a 70–80% reduction in the rate of conversion of D-dopa to urinary dopamine in the rat. This effect sometimes appears earlier in the deficiency than the corresponding effect with L-dopa. The greater effect of the deficiency on the metabolism of D-dopa than on that of the natural isomer may signify that transaminase loses its coenzyme more readily under these conditions than the decarboxylase does (17).

Deoxypyridoxine has been tested as an antivitamin by adding it to a pyridoxine-deficient diet. After 13 days on this regime rats received D-dopa intraperitoneally as a test load. They then exhibited even greater inefficiency than the deficient controls in converting the amino acid to urinary dopamine. This may be a selective action upon transaminase, for when the rats were tested on the twenty-third day with an injection of L-dopa there was no difference in the deficient rats, whether they had been receiving deoxypyridoxine or not, although both groups excreted much less dopamine than their pyridoxine-supplemented controls (unpublished, T. L. Sourkes).

2. Agents Reacting with the Aldehyde Function

a. Carbonyl-Trapping Agents. The aldehyde group of codecarboxylase renders it susceptible to reaction with carbonyl-trapping agents such as hydroxylamine, semicarbazide, hydrazine and many of its derivatives. Holtz *et al.* in their original paper on dopa decarboxylase reported its inhibition by cyanide (4), another aldehyde reagent. This phenomenon is common to all pyridoxal phosphate(PLP)-linked enzymes. Inasmuch as many hydrazides have a blood pressure-lowering action (30, 31), the possibility has been considered that they achieve this effect by coenzyme-binding with consequent decreased rate of formation of catechol amines. At present such views are entirely speculative. Although isoniazid (isonicotinic acid hydrazide) inhibits dopa decarboxylase by forming a hydrazone with the coenzyme, this compound undergoes slow hydrolysis with the release, once again, of PLP. Addition of the hydrazide to an enzyme source permits the slow, but complete, decarboxylation of L-dopa (32).

b. Amines and Amino Acids. The applicability of the nonenzymic reaction of amines with aldehydes to problems of PLP function has also received attention. Schott and Clark have shown that derivatives of phenylalanine and of phenylethylamine react *readily* with PLP only if (a) the amino group is free; (b) the ring bears a phenolic group *meta* to the side chain; and (c) there is an active hydrogen *ortho* to the side chain (33). These generalizations bear out the findings of Schoepf and Salzer, who studied the amine-aldehyde reaction (34). The reaction of an amine (in the phenylethylamine series) with pyridoxal or PLP consists of (a) formation of a Schiff base and (b) cyclization to form a tetrahydroisoquinoline derivative (35). The examples provided in Table II show that norepinephrine and *m*-hydroxypropadrine react rapidly with PLP, but epinephrine and isoproterenol do so very slowly. Dopamine shows intermediate reactivity. Among the positional isomers of dopa, 3,4-dopa is most reactive. 2,4-Dopa, lacking a *m*-phenolic group, does not react measurably. 2,6-Dopa, which has neither *m*-hydroxyl nor free *o*-hydrogen, undergoes reaction with PLP but of an anomalous type (36). The a-methyl amino acids react with the coenzyme, but do so very slowly.

The product of reaction of PLP with 3,4-dopa has slight inhibitory activity on dopa decarboxylase *in vitro* (6). A compound with the same R_f as this adduct is found in adrenal homogenates which have been incubated with labeled dopa (37). PLP products formed with norepinephrine

TABLE II

NONENZYMIC REACTION OF PYRIDOXAL PHOSPHATE WITH AMINES AND AMINO ACIDS [

Substance	Temperature (°C)	
	38° [a]	23° [b]
Norepinephrine	4.8	—
m-Hydroxypropadrine	3.2	—
m-Tyrosine	2.2	—
3,4-Dopa	3.2	0.83
Dopamine	—	0.24
Epinephrine	0.13	—
2,5-Dopa	0.12	0.02
α-Methyl-m-tyrosine	—	0.07
α-Methyldopa	—	0.06
Isoproterenol	0.06	—
2,4-Dopa	—	No reaction

[a] Reference (33).
[b] Reference (6).

and dopamine have no effect on the cardiovascular system. Moreover, the pressor responses to norepinephrine are little affected by the intravenous administration of massive doses of PLP or pyridoxal (8). Thus, sequestering of the coenzyme by substrate or products (or both) is a cause of inhibition of dopa decarboxylase *in vitro*, but it is not known whether this reaction plays a role under physiological conditions.

C. Other Inhibitors

Other inhibitors of dopa decarboxylase have been described, but their mechanism of action is unknown. They include suramin (Naphuride) and trypan blue (38), 7-methylfolic acid and other folic acid analogues (39, 40), and isoxazolidones like cycloserine (41). An extensive list of inhibitors is given by Clark (8).

III. SUBSTANCES INTERFERING WITH THE METABOLISM OF CATECHOL AMINES

The catabolism of catechol amines has been thoroughly investigated in recent years, and these experiments are summarized in several reviews (1, 42, 43). Three major pathways have been described which can act on catechol amines to produce inactive compounds. These reactions are conjugation, oxidative deamination, and O-methylation. One or more of these processes may act on a given compound.

A. Inhibitors of Conjugation

The first studies on the metabolism of catechol amines were mainly concerned with the excretion of conjugated amines (44). It was found that the phenolic groups were substituted either with a glucuronide or a sulfate group, depending upon the species of animal. There is, however, no indication that this type of a reaction is an inactivating mechanism, for the biological activity of these conjugates has not been tested.

Some experiments have been conducted on the metabolism of epinephrine in animals pretreated with N-acetyl-p-aminophenol. The latter compound inhibits the conjugation of steroids in a competitive fashion (45). When it is injected simultaneously with epinephrine in rats, the excretion of conjugated metanephrine, which normally represents 39% of the total metabolites of epinephrine, decreases to approximately 14% of the total. This decreased conjugation is, however, not accompanied by an increase in toxicity as measured by the LD_{50} of epinephrine (0.37 mg/kg subcutaneously) (unpublished results, A. D'Iorio).

B. Inhibitors of Oxidative Deamination

1. NOMENCLATURE AND DEFINITION

Oxidative deamination of dopamine takes place according to the reaction shown in Eq. (1).

$$(OH)_2C_6H_3 \cdot CH_2CH_2NH_2 + H_2O + O_2 \rightarrow (OH)_2C_6H_3 \cdot CH_2CHO + H_2O_2 + NH_3 \quad (1)$$

The oxidation of 3-O-methyldopamine, norepinephrine, normetanephrine, epinephrine, and metanephrine proceeds analogously; the oxidation of the last two results in the formation of methylamine instead of ammonia. About 30 years ago three enzymic activities of this type were described, but in 1937 Blaschko et al. showed that "tyramine oxidase," "aliphatic amine oxidase," and "adrenaline oxidase" are identical (46). Later, Zeller gave the name "monoamine oxidase" (MAO) to the enzyme (or family of enzymes) with this unitary activity. By contrast, the name "diamine oxidase" was reserved for the enzyme acting upon short chain diamines and histamine. More recent knowledge of the substrate specificity of these enzymes shows that this nomenclature is somewhat artificial (42, 47). Nevertheless, the division into two groups is useful, as the following list of properties of the two enzymes shows.

Monoamine oxidase acts on the catechol amines, their *O*-methyl analogues, tyramine, serotonin, isoamylamine, and similar amines, as well as on long chain diamines; it is associated with the particulate material of the cell; it is inhibited by sulfhydryl reagents, octanol and iproniazid; it is not inhibited by cyanide, hydroxylamine, and other carbonyl-trapping agents; no coenzyme has been detected.

Diamine oxidase acts on short chain diamines like putrescine and cadaverine, on polyamines like spermine and spermidine, and on histamine; it is easily extracted from tissues containing it; it is inhibited by cyanide, hydroxylamine, isoniazid, and other carbonyl reagents; it is not inhibited by iproniazid, octanol, or *p*-chloromercuribenzoic acid; it is said to require both flavin adenine dinucleotide and PLP for its activity.

2. INHIBITORS OF MONOAMINE OXIDASE (MAO)

Inasmuch as inhibitors of the amine oxidases are described elsewhere in this book, the following functional classification is limited to those groups of compounds which have been tested as inhibitors of catechol amine metabolism, particularly *in vivo*. In some cases the inhibition under physiological conditions is primarily upon the *meta*-methylated derivative of the catechol amine.

a. Inhibitors Affecting Sulfhydryl Groups. The presence of an essential sulfhydryl group has been judged from the inhibition of MAO by *p*-chloromercuribenzoate *(48, 49)*, iodoacetate *(49)*, mercury salts *(48–50)*, arsenicals *(49)*, and salts of cadmium and silver *(50)*. The inhibition by mercuric ions can be reversed by glutathione and cysteine in the presence of cyanide *(48)*. MAO is also inhibited by an excess of certain sulfhydryl compounds *(50)*, by methylene blue *(51)*, and by tetrazolium salts *(52)*. It is possible that these agents interfere with a reversible oxidation-reduction of the sulfhydryl group necessary for the reaction catalyzed by MAO.

b. Riboflavin Deficiency and Riboflavin Antagonists. Riboflavin-deficient rats have a decreased concentration of hepatic MAO *(42, 53)*. The vitamin does not seem to function in a coenzyme of MAO because neither flavin adenine dinucleotide nor flavin mononucleotide reactivate extracts of the enzyme made from livers of riboflavin-deficient rats and because enzymic activity is restored to normal levels only some days after supplying the deficient rats with riboflavin. Hawkins considers that riboflavin is involved in the biosynthesis of MAO itself *(53)*.

It is nevertheless conceivable that a coenzyme does exist, in a tightly bound state within the tertiary structure of the apoenzyme.

Atabrine, a drug considered to be an inhibitor of yellow enzymes, inhibits the action of MAO on epinephrine (*54*); this anti-MAO action has been confirmed (*52*). Galactoflavin, another antimetabolite of riboflavin, does not inhibit MAO *in vitro* (unpublished data). The action of these two compounds, Atabrine and galactoflavin, on amine metabolism *in vivo* (studied with serotonin) is complex (*55*).

The recovery of MAO activity from inhibition by iproniazid is slower in the riboflavin-deficient rat (*55a*).

c. *Inhibition by Substrate Analogues.* Amphetamine and ephedrine are both competitive inhibitors of MAO (*56*), but they do not affect catechol amine metabolism *in vivo* (*57, 58*). *a*-Ethyltryptamine inhibits MAO *in vitro* and *in vivo* (*59*). All these compounds have an isoalkylamine side chain; they are not attacked by MAO.

Some amidines inhibit MAO (*60*). Propamidine has been tested in the cat and found to be without effect upon the concentration of endogenous catechol amines in various organs (*58*).

The derivatives of hydrazine include many potent inhibitors of MAO. Iproniazid, the exemplar of this series, is an irreversible inhibitor of MAO *in vitro* and *in vivo*; this property was first described by Zeller and his colleagues (*61*). The kinetics of the inhibition have been further studied by Davison (*62*). Iproniazid inhibits the metabolism of epinephrine, norepinephrine (*63–65*), and dopamine (*66*) *in vivo*. Its biological actions and those of its congeners have been extensively studied (*31, 67*) because of the significant role of MAO in intermediary metabolism and because of the therapeutic benefits derived from the use of these drugs in mental depressions and in anginal pain.

Choline phenyl ethers are competitive inhibitors for the oxidation of epinephrine by guinea pig liver slices. Derivatives with an *ortho* or *para* substituent are more active than the parent compound; *meta*-substituted derivatives decrease the activity. For example, choline *p*-tolyl ether (TM6) is more active than the *meta* isomer (TM7) *in vitro*. A chlorine substituent confers greater inhibitory activity than a methyl group does (*68*). Choline *p*-tolyl ether has been studied by several investigators for possible effects *in vivo*. Schayer and his colleagues reported it to affect the metabolism of epinephrine (*57*) and norepinephrine (*64*) *in vivo*, but Corne and Graham could not confirm this (*65*).

C. Inhibitors of 0-Methyl Transfer

In recent years the natural occurrence of the 3-*O*-methyl derivatives of catechols has been reported (*69*). The enzyme responsible for the *O*-methylation has been studied (*70*), and it has been shown to be very active for all types of catechol derivatives. It does not, however, methylate phenolic rings with only one hydroxyl in the *meta* position. A *para* substituent is apparently essential for the enzyme to react.

The enzyme is found in high concentration in liver, kidney, and brain; some activity is also present in spleen, muscle, testis, and heart (*71, 72*). Because of this wide distribution and the relatively poor pharmacological activity of the "methoxy" catechol amines (*73*) it is generally believed that the O-methylation process is one of the most active systems for the biological inactivation of catechol amines. Several inhibitors have been studied, but few kinetic studies on enzyme inhibition have been reported.

All the inhibitors presently reported in the literature are substances competing for the methyl group. These compounds are listed in Table III with a few comments on their activity. Most of them are known potentiators of the effects of catechol amines; this indicates that O-methyltransferase is important in terminating the action of these hormones in the organism. It should also be pointed out that the various substances used at present are effective only at dose levels of the order of 25–50 mg/kg *in vivo*. More recently, Belleau and Burba (*77a*) reported that tropolones act as strong inhibitors of O-methylation. Musacchio and Goldstein (*77b*) injected 4-isopropyltropolone in rats and found it to prevent O-methylation *in vivo*. The 4-methyl derivative has been tested by Mavrides *et al.* (*77c*) *in vivo* and *in vitro*, and it was found to be a competitive inhibitor with a K_i value of 1.5×10^{-5} M.

The known synergism between epinephrine and thyroxine has been studied in some detail by Thibault (*78*). Spinks and Burn (*79*) and, more recently, Zile and Lardy (*80*) have shown that thyroxine inhibits amine oxidase, and they have suggested that this impairment is the cause of the potentiation. The results presented in Table III indicate, however, that O-methyltransferase is also blocked by thyroxine. It should be pointed out that thyroxine is the only substance listed which has no effect *in vitro* on either O-methyltransferase or amine oxidase; pretreatment of animals with it is required to obtain inhibition. Since thyroxine also interferes with methionine formation (*81*) it may be assumed that the action of this hormone is related to general transmethylation processes rather than to the more specific O-methylation reaction. However, recent studies (*81a, b, c*) indicate that several iodophenolic compounds and acidic derivatives of thyroxine, triiodo- and diiodothyronine all act as inhibitors of catechol-O-methyltransferase *in vitro*. As can be seen, thyroxine can decrease the activity of both monoamine oxidase and O-methyltransferase so that these inhibitions could be partly responsible for the thyroxine potentiation of epinephrine.

TABLE III

INHIBITION OF O-METHYLTRANSFERASE

Inhibitor	Condition of assay	Dose or concentration of inhibitor	Inhibition (%)	Reference
Catechol	In vitro methylation of epinephrine by rat liver preparation (inhibitor added to incubation medium)	0.2 M	70	(77)
Catechol	In vivo half-life of norepinephrine as measured in mouse pretreated with inhibitor	3 mg	42–70	(75)
Pyrogallol	In vivo half-life of norepinephrine as measured in mouse pretreated with inhibitor	10 mg	98–100	(75)
Glycocyamine	In vivo half-life of norepinephrine as measured in mouse pretreated with inhibitor	10 mg	63–94	(75)
3,4,5-Trihydroxyphenyl-ethylamine	In vivo half-life of norepinephrine as measured in mouse pretreated with inhibitor	5 mg	63–66	(75)
Adnamine hydrochloride	In vivo half-life of norepinephrine as measured in mouse pretreated with inhibitor	1 mg	68	(75)
Nicotinamide	In vivo half-life of norepinephrine as measured in mouse pretreated with inhibitor	50 mg	15–60	(75)
Thyroxine	In vivo, metanephrine excretion by rats pretreated with inhibitor	0.5 mg	21	(76)
Thyroxine	O-Methyltransferase activity of liver preparation from rats pretreated with inhibitor	0.5 mg	50	(76)
Pyrogallol	In vivo, formation of metanephrine in mouse pretreated with inhibitor	100 mg/kg	80	(74)
Pyrogallol	In vitro methylation of epinephrine by rat liver preparation (inhibitor added to the incubation medium)	10^{-5} M	59	(74)

IV. SUBSTANCES ACTING AT RECEPTOR OR AT STORAGE SITES

The substances mentioned previously in this chapter have known metabolic effects in the sense that they block enzymes involved in the biogenesis or the catabolism of catechol amines. There are, however, many compounds which will block or enhance the effects of catechol amines without affecting their metabolic pathway. It is generally believed that such compounds act at receptor or at storage sites.

The storage of amines has been studied by many authors (82, 83), and it is well known that the catechol amines of the adrenal medulla or of nerve cells are localized in granules rich in protein and ATP. The catechol amines, ATP, and proteins presumably form a complex in these granules. One can visualize the protein as a template for the catechol ring, with the ATP molecules attached to the protein by a phosphate bond and the other phosphates linked to the amino group of the catechol amines.

The chemical morphology of receptor sites is, however, more complex than this. The existence of different types of receptor site has been postulated on the basis of the various types of activity of catechol amines and the inhibition produced by adrenergic blocking drugs. There is at present no general agreement on the diversity of these sites (84, 85). In his classic work with epinephrine and ergotamine, Dale distinguished two types of receptor (86). Ahlquist (85, 87) has attempted to classify these receptors as α and β, according to whether the response is blocked by adrenergic blocking agents or not. Furchgott (88) has recently suggested a modification of this classification: α-receptors, for contraction of smooth muscle; β-receptors, for relaxation of smooth muscle other than that of intestine, and also for increase in rate and strength of cardiac contraction; γ-receptors, for glycogenolysis; δ-receptors, for inhibition of intestinal smooth muscle.

In considering possible metabolic inhibitors the α- and γ-receptors are the only ones that are of interest. In the context of this chapter only α-receptors will be discussed. A certain number of compounds will compete with catechol amines for the reactive sites of these structures, thus preventing the effects of catechol amines on the receptors. Numerous studies in this field have been carried out on the β-haloalkylamine group of substances (84, 89). It is believed (89) that a carboxylate or phosphate anion constitutes the active center of the excitatory α-receptors with which β-haloalkylamines react to block the action of epinephrine.

Other groups of substances have also been used as adrenolytics, and it is assumed that they react in a similar fashion with the receptor sites.

The most important members of the various groups are reported in Table IV. The only common feature of the various molecules presented there is the tertiary amine function. This may indicate that the reactive center of the receptors has the character assigned to it by Belleau (89).

TABLE IV

ADRENERGIC BLOCKING SUBSTANCES

Group	Prototypes	Activity
Ergot alkalcids	Ergotamine	Prevents action of injected epinephrine or of nerve stimulation
Imidazolines	Phentolamine Tolazoline	Same
β-Haloalkylamines	Dibenamine	Prevents action of injected epinephrine and norepinephrine or of nerve stimulation (long-acting)
	Dibenzyline	Same
Dibenzazepine	Azapetine	Same, but short-acting
Benzodioxanes	Piperoxan (Benzodioxane)	Prevents action of injected epinephrine

Receptor sites and storage sites have been discussed together in this chapter because they present some obvious chemical analogy to one another. The release of catechol amines from storage can be effected by three possible mechanisms: (a) direct or central stimulation of adrenergic nerves or adrenal medulla; (b) disruption of catechol amine-containing granules by lytic agents (examples: digitonin, lecithin, Tween 80); and (c) competition by analogous substances for the catechol amine binding sites within the granules.

In the present context the only compounds of interest are those corresponding to group (c), and of the many substances reported in the literature (83) at present only tyramine may be classified in this group. It has, in effect, been reported that tyramine (90) will liberate catechol amines both in vivo and in vitro from storage granules. Since tyramine acts directly on the granules and has obvious structural analogies with catechol amines, it may be assumed that it is actually displacing catechol amines from their binding site.

Similarity of receptor and storage sites can be deduced from the action of certain adrenolytic agents (Dibenzyline, phentolamine, piperoxan, and Dibenamine) in releasing catechol amines from adrenal chromaffin granules *in vitro* (*91*).

References

1. J. Pellerin, J. Leduc, and A. D'Iorio, *Rev. can. biol.* 17, 267 (1958).
2. T. L. Sourkes, *in* "Neurochemistry" (K. A. C. Elliott, I. H. Page, and J. H. Quastel, eds.), 2nd ed., Chapter 24. Thomas, Springfield, Illinois, 1962.
3. O. Krayer, ed., "Symposium on Catecholamines." Williams & Wilkins, Baltimore, Maryland, 1959; also in *Pharmacol. Revs.* 11, 233 (1959).
4. P. Holtz, R. Heise, and K. Lüdtke, *Arch. exptl. Pathol. Pharmakol. Naunyn-Schmiedeberg's* 191, 87 (1938).
5. J. H. Fellman, *Enzymologia* 20, 366 (1959); E. Werle and D. Aures, *Z. physiol. Chem. Hoppe-Seyler's* 316, 45 (1959); A. Yuwiler, E. Geller, and S. Eiduson, *Arch. Biochem. Biophys.* 80, 162, (1959).
6. T. L. Sourkes, *Arch. Biochem. Biophys.* 51, 444 (1954).
7. W. J. Hartman, R. I. Akawie, and W. G. Clark, *J. Biol. Chem.* 216, 507 (1955).
8. W. G. Clark, *Pharmacol. Revs.* 11, 330 (1959).
9. W. W. Ackermann and V. R. Potter, *Proc. Soc. Exptl. Biol. Med.* 72, 1 (1949).
10. H. Blaschko, *Biochim. et Biophys. Acta* 4, 130 (1950); T. L. Sourkes, P. Heneage, and Y. Trano, *Arch. Biochem. Biophys.* 40, 185 (1952).
11. H. Dengler and G. Reichel, *Arch. exptl. Pathol. Pharmakol. Naunyn-Schmiedeberg's* 232, 324 (1957); 234, 275 (1958).
12. E. Westermann, H. Balzer, and J. Knell, *Arch. exptl. Pathol. Pharmakol. Naunyn-Schmiedeberg's* 234, 194 (1958).
13. G. F. Murphy and T. L. Sourkes, *Rev. can. biol.* 18, 379 (1959).
14. T. L. Sourkes, "The Extrapyramidal System and Neuroleptics," Proceedings of the International Symposium, Université de Montréal, November 1960. Éditions Psychiatriques, Montreal, 1961; also in *Rev. can. biol.* 20, 187 (1961).
15. S. M. Hess, R. H. Connamacher, M. Ozaki, and S. Udenfriend, *Pharmacol. Exptl. Therap.* 134, 129 (1961); C. C. Porter, J. A. Totaro, and C. M. Leiby, *ibid.*, p. 139.
16. T. L. Sourkes, G. F. Murphy, B. Chavez, and M. Zielinska, *J. Neurochem.* 8, 109 (1961).
17. T. L. Sourkes, G. F. Murphy, and V. R. Woodford, Jr., *J. Nutrition* 72, 145 (1960).
18. G. F. Murphy and T. L. Sourkes, *Arch. Biochem. Biophys.* 93, 338 (1961).
19. H. Weissbach, W. Lovenberg, and S. Udenfriend, *Biochem. Biophys. Research Communs.* 3, 225 (1960).
20. S. Mandeles, R. Koppelman, and M. E. Hanke, *J. Biol. Chem.* 209, 327 (1954).
20a. E. V. Heegaard and G. A. Alles, *J. Biol. Chem.* 147, 505 (1943).

21. T. L. Sourkes, G. F. Murphy, and B. Chavez, *Proc. 3rd World Congr. Psychiatry, Montreal, June 1961.* Univ. of Toronto Press, Toronto and McGill Univ. Press, Montreal, 1962, p. 649; *J. Med. Pharm. Chem.* **5**, 204 (1962).

22. J. A. Oates, L. Gillespie, S. Udenfriend, and A. Sjoerdsma, *Science* **131**, 1890 (1960).

23. L. I. Goldberg, F. M. DaCosta, and M. Ozaki, *Nature* **188**, 502, (1960).

24. Anonymous, *Brit. Med. J.* **I**, 1676 (1962).

25. S. E. Smith, *Brit. J. Pharmacol.* **15**, 319 (1960).

25a. A. Barbeau, G. F. Murphy, and T. L. Sourkes, *in* "Monoamines et Système nerveux central (J. de Ajuriaguerra, ed.). Georg, Geneva, and Masson, Paris, 1962.

26. G. J. Martin, R. Brendel, and J. M. Beiler, *Exptl. Med. Surg.* **8**, 5 (1950).

27. P. Gonnard, *Bull. soc. chim. biol.* **32**, 535 (1950).

28. J. H. Fellman, *Proc. Soc. Exptl. Biol. Med.* **93**, 413 (1956).

29. H. Blaschko, C. W. Carter, J. R. P. O'Brien, and G. H. Sloane-Stanley, *J. Physiol. (London)* **107**, 18P (1948).

30. W. von Schuler and R. Meier, *Helv. Physiol. et Pharmacol. Acta* **13**, 106 (1955).

31. G. Zbinden, L. O. Randall, and R. A. Moe, *Diseases Nervous System* **21**, Pt 2, 89 (1960).

32. D. Palm, *Arch. exptl. Pathol. Pharmakol.* **234**, 206 (1958).

33. H. F. Schott and W. G. Clark, *J. Biol. Chem.* **196**, 449 (1952).

34. C. Schoepf and W. Salzer, *Ann. Chem.* **544**, 1 (1940).

35. D. Heyl, E. Luz, S. A. Harris, and K. Folkers, *J. Am. Chem. Soc.* **74**, 414 (1952).

36. T. L. Sourkes, *Rev. can. biol.* **14**, 49 (1955).

37. J. Pellerin and A. D'Iorio, *Can. J. Biochem. Physiol.* **35**, 151 (1957).

38. H. Blaschko, *J. Physiol. (London)* **101**, 337 (1942).

39. O. Schales and S. S. Schales, *Arch. Biochem.* **24**, 83 (1949).

40. G. J. Martin and J. M. Beiler, *Arch. Biochem.* **15**, 201 (1947); P. Gonnard, *Bull. soc. chim.* **33**, 14 (1951).

41. H. J. Dengler, E. Rauchs, and W. Rummel, *Arch. exptl. Pathol. Pharmakol. Naunyn-Schmeideberg's* **243**, 366 (1962).

42. T. L. Sourkes, *Rev. can. biol.* **17**, 328 (1958).

43. J. Axelrod, *Physiol. Revs.* **39**, 751 (1959).

44. D. Richter and F. C. MacIntosh, *Am. J. Physiol.* **135**, 1 (1941).

45. G. Corte and W. Johnson, *Proc. Soc. Exptl. Biol. Med.* **97**, 751 (1958).

46. H. Blaschko, D. Richter, and H. Schlossman, *Biochem. J.* **31**, 2187 (1937).

47. J. R. Fouts, L. A. Blanksma, J. A. Carbon, and E. A. Zeller, *J. Biol. Chem.* **225**, 1025 (1957); P. Hagen and N. Weiner, *Federation Proc.* **18**, 1005 (1959).

48. J. S. Friedenwald and H. Herrmann, *J. Biol. Chem.* **146**, 411 (1942).

49. T. P. Singer and E. S. G. Barron, *J. Biol. Chem.* **157**, 241 (1945).

50. J. R. Lagnado and T. L. Sourkes, *Can. J. Biochem. and Physiol.* **34**, 1185 (1956).

51. F. J. Philpot, *Biochem. J.* **31**, 856 (1937).

52. J. R. Lagnado and T. L. Sourkes, *Can. J. Biochem. and Physiol.* **34**, 1095 (1956).

53. J. Hawkins, *Biochem. J.* 51, 399 (1952).
54. N. Allegretti and D. Vukadinovic, *Arhiv kem.* 22, 191 (1950); in *Chem. Abstr.* 46, 10449a (1952).
55. M. H. Wiseman and T. L. Sourkes, *Biochem. J.* 78, 123 (1961).
55a. M. H. Wiseman-Distler and T. L. Sourkes, *Can. J. Biochem. and Physiol.* 41, 57 (1963).
56. P. J. G. Mann and J. H. Quastel, *Biochem. J.* 34, 414 (1940).
57. R. W. Schayer, K. Y. T. Wu, R. L. Smiley, and Y. Kobayashi, *J. Biol. Chem.* 210, 259 (1954).
58. U. S. von Euler and S. Hellner-Björkman, *Acta Physiol. Scand.* 33, Suppl. 118, 21 (1955).
59. M. E. Greig, R. A. Walk, and A. J. Gibbons, *J. Pharmacol. Exptl. Therap.* 127, 110 (1959).
60. H. Blaschko and R. Duthie, *Biochem. J.* 39, 347 (1945).
61. E. A. Zeller, J. Barsky, J. R. Fouts, W. F. Kirchheimer, and L. S. Van Orden, *Experientia* 8, 349 (1952); E. A. Zeller and J. Barsky, *Proc. Soc. Exptl. Biol. Med.* 81, 459 (1952).
62. A. N. Davison, *Biochem. J.* 67, 316 (1957).
63. R. W. Schayer and R. L. Smiley, *J. Biol. Chem.* 202, 425 (1953); M. Goodall, *Pharmacol. Revs.* 11, 416 (1959).
64. R. W. Schayer, R. L. Smiley, K. J. Davis, and Y. Kobayashi, *Am. J. Physiol.* 182, 285 (1955).
65. S. J. Corne and J. D. P. Graham, *J. Physiol. (London)* 135, 339 (1957).
66. M. Goldstein, A. J. Friedhoff, and C. Simmons, *Biochim. et Biophys. Acta* 33, 572 (1959).
67. A. N. Davison, *Physiol. Revs.* 38, 729 (1958).
68. B. G. Brown and P. Hey, *Brit. J. Pharmacol.* 11, 58 (1956).
69. M. D. Armstrong, A. McMillan, and K. N. F. Shaw, *J. Biol. Chem.* 218, 293 (1956); F. De Eds, A. N. Booth, and F. T. Jones, *ibid.* 225, 615 (1957); J. Pellerin and A. D'Iorio, *Rev. can. biol.* 16, 371 (1957).
70. J. Pellerin and A. D'Iorio, *Proc. 21st Meeting, Can. Physiol. Soc., Ottawa, 1957;* J. Pellerin and A. D'Iorio, *Can. J. Biochem. and Physiol.* 36, 491 (1938); J. Axelrod, *Science* 126, 400 (1957).
71. J. Axelrod, W. Albers, and C. D. Clemente, *J. Neurochem.* 5, 68 (1959).
72. A. D'Iorio, *in* "Methods in Medical Research" (J. H. Quastel, ed.), Vol. 9, p. 208. Yearbook, Chicago, Illinois, 1961.
73. J. Champagne, A. D'Iorio, and A. Beaulnes, *Science* 132, 419 (1960).
74. J. Axelrod and M. J. Laroche, *Science* 130, 800 (1959).
75. S. Udenfriend, C. R. Creveling, M. Ozaki, J. W. Daly, and B. Witkop, *Arch. Biochem. Biophys.* 84, 249 (1959).
76. A. D'Iorio and J. Leduc, *Arch. Biochem. Biophys.* 87, 224 (1960).
77. A. M. Bacq, L. Gosselin, A. Dresse, and J. Renson, *Science* 130, 453 (1959).
77a. B. Belleau and J. Burba, *Biochem. et Biophys. Acta* 54, 195 (1961).
77b. J. Musacchio and M. Goldstein, *Federation Proc.* 21, 334 (1962).
77c. C. Mavrides, K. Missala, and A. D'Iorio, *Can. J. Biochem. and Physiol.* 41, 1581 (1963).
78. O. Thibault, *Compt. rend. soc. biol.* 142, 499 (1948).
79. A. Spinks and J. H. Burn, *Brit. J. Pharmacol.* 7, 93 (1952).
80. M. Zile and H. A. Lardy, *Arch. Biochem. Biophys.* 82, 411 (1959).

81. E. L. Oginsky, *Arch. Biochem.* **26,** 327, (1950).
81a. A. D'Iorio and C. Mavrides, *Can. J. Biochem. and Physiol.* **40,** 1454 (1962).
81b. A. D'Iorio and C. Mavrides, *Can. J. Biochem. and Physiol.* **41,** 1779 (1963).
81c. A. D'Iorio and C. Mavrides, *in* "Symposium on Regulation of Enzyme Activity and Synthesis in Normal and Neoplastic Liver," Oct. 1962, Indianapolis (G. Weber, ed.) Pergamon Press, New York (1963).
82. H. Blaschko, G. V. R. Born, A. D'Iorio, and N. R. Eade, *J. Physiol. (London)* **133,** 548 (1956); B. Falck, N. A. Hillarp, and B. Högberg, *Acta Physiol. Scand.* **36,** 360 (1956).
83. N. R. Eade, *Rev. can. biol.* **17,** 299 (1958).
84. M. Nickerson, *Pharmacol. Revs.* **1,** 27 (1949).
85. R. P. Ahlquist, *Pharmacol. Revs.* **11,** 441 (1959).
86. H. H. Dale, *J. Physiol. (London)* **34,** 163 (1906).
87. R. P. Ahlquist, *Am. J. Physiol.* **153,** 586 (1948).
88. R. F. Furchgott, *Pharmacol. Revs.* **11,** 429 (1959).
89. B. Belleau, *Can. J. Biochem. and Physiol.* **36,** 731 (1958).
90. H. J. Schümann, *Arch. exptl. Pathol. Pharmakol. Naunyn-Schmiedeberg's* **238,** 41 (1960); U. S. von Euler and F. Lishajko, *Experientia* **16,** 376 (1960).
91. A. D'Iorio and J. G. Laguë, *Can. J. Biochem. and Physiol.* **41,** 121 (1963).

CHAPTER 20

Sulfhydryl Agents: Arsenicals

R. M. Johnstone

I. INTRODUCTION

In recent years considerable work has been carried out on the active groups of proteins to determine which groups are responsible for enzymic activity (1). One of the first groups recognized, which was shown to be essential for enzyme activity, was the sulfhydryl group. The use of arsenicals, and particularly the organic arsenicals, has yielded much information on the degrees of reactivity of the sulfhydryl group in various proteins and to what extent the presence of the sulfhydryl group is essential for enzymic activity. As well as being useful in enzyme research, the organic arsenicals have proved to be valuable tools in chemotherapy. In fact, it was from the use of organic arsenicals in chemotherapy that much of the interest in the mode of action of the arsenicals has been derived.

II. CLASSIFICATION OF THE ARSENICALS

In general, the arsenicals which have been studied may be divided into five types:

(a) *Pentavalent organic arsenicals,* R — AsO_3H_2.

(b) *Trivalent arseno compounds,* R — As $=$ As — R.

(c) *Trivalent arsenoso compounds,* R — AsO.

(d) *Inorganic arsenite.* Inorganic arsenite has also been extensively used, especially in enzyme studies. However, inorganic arsenite is relatively inert compared with the trivalent organic arsenicals.

(e) *Inorganic arsenate.* Arsenate does not appear to act as a sulfhydryl reagent, but has been widely used in place of inorganic phosphate.

A. Pentavalent Arsenicals

It is now generally accepted that the active form of the organic arsenicals is the arsenoso derivative. The work of Ehrlich (*2, 3*) suggested that the pentavalent form of arsenic must be reduced to the trivalent to obtain parasiticidal activity. Hawking *et al.* (*4*) later showed that the pentavalent arsenical, tryparsamide, is reduced in the body to a highly trypanocidal trivalent arsenical. Although the trivalent arsenoso compounds were at first considered too toxic for use, Tatum and Cooper (*5*) demonstrated that Mapharsen (2-amino-4-arsenosophenol) can be used successfully in place of the less toxic pentavalent compounds.

B. Trivalent Arsenicals

1. ARSENO COMPOUNDS

Considerable confusion existed for some time as to whether the arseno compounds are active as such. Voegtlin and Smith (*6*) showed that with arseno compounds there is a latent period before trypanosomes disappear from the blood, whereas with the arsenoso compounds there is an immediate effect. Other workers claimed that arseno compounds are active without further modification (*7, 8*). Eagle (*9*) resolved the discrepancy by showing that certain arseno compounds, the arsphenamines, are considerably less active against *Treponema pallidum* if precautions are taken to dissolve and test the arseno derivative under anaerobic conditions. Under aerobic conditions the arseno compounds are readily oxidized, and their activity is therefore due to the formation of the arsenoso derivatives. The trivalent arsenoso compounds are therefore the active form of this class of compounds.

2. ARSENOSO COMPOUNDS

In the majority of the compounds studied, both in enzyme research and in chemotherapy, the R is benzenoid. Many of the arsenical war gases, however, have aliphatic side chains (*10*). The aliphatic and polycyclic arsenicals are generally less active than the benzenoid derivatives.

III. REACTIONS OF ARSENICALS WITH SIMPLE THIOLS

The evidence accumulated so far indicates that the arsenicals owe their toxic effects to their ability to combine with thiol groups. Ehrlich (*2, 3*) originally suggested that arsenicals exert their effects by combining with sulfhydryl groups. Later, Voegtlin and associates (*11*) postulated that the toxic action of arsenoso compounds toward trypanosomes is due to a combination with thiol groups in the protoplasm (they suggested glutathione), leading to an inhibition of respiration. Barber (*12*) demonstrated that arsenosobenzenes may combine with organic sulfhydryl compounds such as thiolacetic and thioglycolic acid to form a thioarsenite according to Eq. (1).

$$C_6H_5AsO + 2RSH \rightarrow C_6H_5As \begin{matrix} \nearrow SR \\ \searrow SR \end{matrix} + H_2O \tag{1}$$

It was also shown (*12*) that thiol compounds in sufficient concentration will reduce a phenylarsonic acid to the arsenosobenzene. Gough and King (*13*) concluded from an examination of the properties of the arylthioarsenites that these compounds are slowly hydrolyzed to yield highly toxic arsenoxides at ordinary temperatures and in neutral solution. The dissociation of a thioarsenite may be controlled by pH, a higher pH leading to dissociation of the thioarsenite (*14*).

It thus appears that the reaction of a trivalent arsenoso compound with simple thiol compounds is a reversible one and that, as suggested by Gordon and Quastel (15), in neutral solution an equilibrium can exist between an arsenoso and a thiol compound, as shown in Eq. (2).

$$C_6H_5 \cdot AsO + 2RSH \rightleftharpoons C_6H_5As \underset{SR}{\overset{SR}{\big<}} + H_2O \qquad (2)$$

IV. ENZYMES AS THIOL COMPOUNDS

The knowledge that trivalent arsenicals can combine with thiol compounds did not immediately lead to a realization that the toxic effect of the arsenicals may be due to their ability to combine with thiol groups present in essential enzymes. Prior to 1920, it was known that the nitroprusside test for sulfhydryl groups is given by a variety of tissues. The work of Hopkins and Dixon (16) drew attention to two types of thiol compounds, "soluble," like glutathione, and "fixed," meaning associated with cellular protein. It was not until later that thiol groups were shown to be an integral part of certain enzymes and that the enzymic activity often depends on the presence of these groups.

Sumner and Poland (17) in 1933 first demonstrated the presence of sulfhydryl groups in crystalline urease. In the next few years, it was shown that several hydrolytic enzymes contain sulfhydryl groups (18–20) and that the enzymic activity depends on these groups. The presence of sulfhydryl groups in oxidizing enzymes was demonstrated in 1938 by Hopkins and Morgan (21), by Morgan et al. (22) in succinoxidase, and by Rapkine (23) in phosphoglyceraldehyde dehydrogenase. Thus, it became apparent that a number of widely different enzymes contain thiol groups as integral parts of their active centers.

A. Effects of Arsenicals on Enzyme Systems

1. PYRUVATE

a. *Pyruvate Metabolism.* It is now well established that the oxidation of pyruvate in many types of cells, animal as well as bacterial, is markedly inhibited by organic trivalent arsenicals and inorganic arsenite. As early as 1911, it was shown (24) that biological oxidations are inhibited by arsenite. Subsequent observations confirmed these findings

(*25, 26*), and it was shown (*27*) that keto acid oxidations are particularly sensitive to the action of arsenite. Peters and co-workers (*28*) found that pyruvate oxidation in brain is much more affected by the arsenical war gas, lewisite, than by inorganic arsenite at equivalent concentrations.

The work of Barron and Singer (*29*) and of Gordon and Quastel (*15*) showed that several organic arsenicals are powerful inhibitors of pyruvate metabolism. A number of trivalent arsenicals, derivatives of arsenoso-benzene, inhibit the pyruvic oxidase activities in brain, liver, and micro-organisms (*15, 29*). Not only is the oxygen uptake with pyruvate as substrate inhibited, but the synthesis of a number of substances, such as acetoacetate, α-ketoglutarate, acetylmethylcarbinol, citrate and glycogen, is inhibited (*30*). The concentration of arsenical required to obtain complete inhibition of pyruvate metabolism varies from one arsenical to another but is usuallly considerably less than 1 mM (*15, 29*). γ-(p-Arsenosophenyl)butyrate at a concentration of $5 \times 10^{-6} M$ causes complete inhibition of pyruvate utilization and citrate formation in rat heart sarcosomes (*31*).

The oxidation of α-ketoglutarate as well as other intermediates of the citric acid cycle, such as malate and succinate, is also inhibited by organic arsenicals (*15, 29*).

b. Pyruvate Decarboxylation and Alcohol Oxidation. An enzyme derived from two different sources does not necessarily respond to thiol reagents in the same way. Lutwak-Mann (*32*) showed that yeast alcohol dehydrogenase, but not liver alcohol dehydrogenase, is inhibited by iodoacetate. These findings were confirmed by Barron and his colleagues using arsenicals as thiol reagents (*29, 33*). Stoppani and his colleagues (*34–36*) showed that yeast pyruvic decarboxylase is sensitive to the action of a number of organic arsenicals.

c. Aldehyde Dehydrogenase. Not only the oxidation of keto acids, but the oxidation of aldehydes, such as glycoaldehyde, acetaldehyde (*36a, b, c*), succinic semialdehyde (*36d*), and xanthine (*36e*), is inhibited by inorganic arsenite.

2. SUCCINATE OXIDATION

The succinoxidase system and succinic dehydrogenase have been extensively studied with respect to the inhibitory activity of arsenicals. Although Peters *et al.* (*28*) reported that lewisite does not affect succinic dehydrogenase activity, later work has shown that this system is appreciably inhibited by a variety of organic arsenicals, including lewisite. Thus, Gordon and Quastel (*15*) showed that complete inhibition of succinic dehydrogenase activity in rat liver slices is obtained with $10^{-3} M$

2-amino-4-arsenosophenol. Similar results were obtained by Barron and Singer (29). Slater (37) compared the effects of p-arsenosoaniline on succinic dehydrogenase and on the succinoxidase system and found that the inhibition of succinic dehydrogenase by p-arsenosoaniline can account for the observed inhibition of the succinoxidase system. A highly purified preparation of succinic dehydrogenase is also sensitive to the action of arsenicals (38).

In chick liver homogenates, succinic dehydrogenase may be inhibited by inorganic arsenite (38a). Malic and lactic acid dehydrogenases are also markedly inhibited by arsenite (38b).

3. GLUCOSE UTILIZATION

Van Heyningen (39) has suggested that hexokinase depends on sulfhydryl groups for metabolic activity, and it was shown (40) that crystalline yeast hexokinase is completely inhibited by 10^{-3} M lewisite. Gordon and Quastel (15) observed that glucose oxidation in brain tissue is inhibited by trivalent organic arsenicals. Marshall (41) and Chen (42) suggested that in certain trypanosomes, hexokinase is inhibited by arsenosobenzene and 2-amino-4-arsenosophenol.

Glock and McLean (43) found that glucose-6-phosphate dehydrogenase and 6-phosphogluconate dehydrogenase in rat liver are inhibited by p-chloromercuribenzoate, whereas p-arsenosoaniline at 2.5×10^{-4} M has no effect. In most cases (29), where the arsenicals have been compared with p-chloromercuribenzoate, both reagents inhibit metabolic activity, although p-chloromercuribenzoate is effective at lower concentrations.

Respiration and glycolysis are inhibited by arsenite in the Jenson sarcoma (43a, b), the former being considerably more affected than the latter.

4. EFFECTS OF ARSENICALS ON AMINO ACID METABOLISM

Singer and Barron (44) in their systematic study of sulfhydryl enzymes in cell metabolism showed that the oxidation of D-alanine in rat kidney tissue is completely inhibited by (p-aminophenyl)dichloroarsine hydrochloride at 5×10^{-5} M. Singer (45) showed similar inhibitions of pig-kidney D-amino acid oxidase with p-aminophenylarsine oxide. Using a variety of D-amino acids as substrate, Singer found that the extent of inhibition by the arsenical is independent of the amino acid used as substrate. The arsenical, γ-(p-arsenosophenyl)butyrate, is also an effective inhibitor of D-alanine oxidation with a purified D-amino acid oxidase (45).

The DPN-linked oxidation of glutamic acid in liver is inhibited by trivalent arsenicals as well as the glutamate-pyruvate and glutamate-oxaloacetate transaminase activities (44). In many cases where the organic arsenicals are effective inhibitors, inorganic arsenite or iodoacetate has little effect (15, 29, 44).

The enzymes of *Clostridium sporogenes*, which catalyze the anaerobic oxidation and reduction of amino acids (46), are highly sensitive to the action of organic arsenicals such as arsenosobenzene and 2-amino-4-arsenosophenol. The enzyme system in *C. sporogenes* activating molecular hydrogen is particularly sensitive to the action of arsenicals, being completely inhibited at a concentration of 4×10^{-5} M 2-amino-4-arsenosophenol. This concentration of 2-amino-4-arsenosophenol inhibits the reduction of amino acids by approximately 50% (47).

The oxidation of monoamines, including adrenaline, is inhibited by arsenicals (44), in agreement with the observation of Friedenwald and Herrmann (48) that tyramine oxidase is a thiol enzyme. Diamine oxidase (44), however, is not inhibited by arsenicals.

5. Fatty Acid Oxidation

Many of the enzymes catalyzing the oxidation of fatty acids have been shown to be inhibited by arsenicals. Stearate, oleate, and β-hydroxybutyrate oxidation in animal tissues, as well as acetate oxidation in yeast and bacteria, are inhibited by arsenicals (44). β-Hydroxybutyrate oxidation is highly sensitive to organic arsenicals, being completely inhibited by 5×10^{-4} M p-arsenosobenzoic acid (44).

The breakdown of acetoacetate in guinea pig kidney slices is nearly completely inhibited by inorganic arsenite (48a), and the formation of acetoacetate from fatty acids is largely prevented by atoxyl (48b).

6. Hydrolytic Enzymes

A wide variety of hydrolytic enzymes have been shown to be inhibited by organic arsenicals. Indeed, the hydrolytic enzymes were the first in which the presence of free thiol groups was associated with enzyme activity (17–20). Rona and György (49) found that arsenosobenzene, and arsenosomethane cause appreciable inhibition of urease activity, and Rona, Airila, and Lasnitski (50) found that maltase and a-methyl-glucosidase are also inhibited by arsenosomethane. Hellerman (18) had shown that urease is inhibited by thiol reagents, and these findings were confirmed (15) by showing that low concentrations of 2-amino-4-arsenosophenol and other arsenicals are capable of inhibiting urease activity.

Some of the hydrolytic enzymes are relatively insensitive to arsenicals. High concentrations of 2-amino-4-arsenosophenol have to be used to inhibit liver esterase activity (15). Gordon and Quastel (15) could obtain no inhibition of pancreatic lipase with arsenicals, whereas Singer and Barron (44) obtained a 50% inhibition of this enzyme with the same arsenicals. The discrepancy in these results may perhaps be due to the different incubation periods used by the authors. The former authors (15) used a very short incubation period (15 minutes), whereas the latter (44) used an incubation period of 6 hours. Slater (37) has shown that the inhibition of succinoxidase activity by p-arsenosoaniline takes approximately 15 minutes to become established. Wheat germ lipase (45) is sensitive to low concentrations of p-arsenosoaniline. Singer (45) has further shown that with this enzyme preparation the extent of inhibition by the arsenical depends on the substrate used, oxidation of substrates of higher molecular weight being more inhibited than those of low molecular weight.

Acid phosphatase and liver arginase are inhibited by relatively high concentrations of lewisite (33).

Cholinesterase and choline dehydrogenase have both been shown to be thiol enzymes inhibited by arsenicals (15, 33, 51, 52).

Mounter and Whittaker (51) have compared the sensitivity of cholinesterase to arsenicals with that of other thiol enzymes and have found it to be relatively insensitive.

B. Effects of Pentavalent Arsenicals on Enzyme Systems

The pentavalent arsenicals, unlike the trivalent ones, have little effect on enzymic activities (15, 47).

C. Comparison of the Reactivities of Different Arsenicals with Various Enzymes

The extent of inhibition of a given enzyme often depends on the type of arsenical used. This is clearly shown by the fact that arsenite is a much poorer inhibitor of enzyme activities than are organic trivalent arsenicals (15, 29). However, even among the organic arsenicals, there are many differences in their inhibitory effects on enzyme systems.

Yeast carboxylase, D-amino acid oxidase (kidney), and urease are not inhibited by lewisite (33) although all three enzymes are appreciably inhibited by derivatives of arsenosobenzene (15, 35, 44). On the other hand, pyruvate oxidation in brain preparations is markedly inhibited by lewisite (*28*). Stoppani *et al.* (*36*) compared the effects of arsenoso-methane and 2-amino-4-arsenosophenol on purified yeast decarboxylase. They showed that nearly 7 times as much arsenosomethane as 2-amino-4-arsenosophenol is required to obtain 50% inhibition of decarboxylase activity. The respiration of brain and kidney slices is far more sensitive to lewisite than to *p*-arsenosobenzoic acid (*33*), an inhibition of 66% of the respiration being obtained with the former and 10% with the latter at equimolar concentrations.

D. Reversal by Monothiols of Enzyme Inhibitions Caused by Arsenicals

Since the thiol group can be destroyed by a number of means, e.g., oxidation, alkylation, mercaptide formation, it is important to demonstrate that the loss of enzymic activity observed in the presence of arsenicals is due to the formation of a thioarsenite complex with enzyme thiol groups. It has been shown (*13, 14*) that the linkage of an arsenical with a thiol is a dissociable one; therefore, addition of excess thiol should bring about a reversal of the inhibitions and toxic reactions caused by arsenicals.

Voegtlin *et al.* (*11, 53*) have shown that an excess of thiol compounds, such as glutathione, may delay or prevent the action of arsenicals on trypanosomes. The inhibitions produced by a number of arsenicals and on a variety of enzymes can in every instance be largely prevented by the presence of excess thiol compound, such as glutathione and cysteine. In most cases, a large excess (a hundredfold) is required for complete protection (*15, 29, 44*).

It is obvious, however, that protection against inhibition is not identical with reactivation. The experiments of Barron and Singer (*29*), Singer and Barron (*44*), and Gordon and Quastel (*15*) showed that reactivations of enzyme inhibition do occur after the inhibition has set in; for example, cholinesterase may be completely reactivated by thiols even after a 2-hour exposure to arsenicals (*15*). In many cases, however, the extent of reactivation decreases after prolonged contact with the arsenical. Thus, Barron *et al.* (*33*) demonstrated that glutathione will reverse by 50% the lewisite inhibition of anaerobic glycolysis if added to the system 10 minutes after the addition of the arsenical. If the glutathione is added 30 minutes after the arsenical, only 20% reversal is observed.

The nature of the monothiol used also plays a role in determining the extent of reactivation. The succinoxidase system, inhibited by *p*-arsenoso-benzoic acid (5×10^{-5} M), can be completely reactivated by 10^{-3} M glutathione but only 25% reactivated with 10^{-2} M cysteine (*29*). Similarly, Gordon and Quastel (*15*) and Barron and Singer (*29*) obtained reversals of pyruvate oxidation with glutathione after inhibition with arsenosobenzene derivatives, but Stocken *et al.* (*54, 55*) could not obtain a reversal of Mapharsen-inhibited pyruvate oxidation with 2-mercapto-ethanol. It is apparent, therefore, that the thiol used for reactivation greatly influences the extent of reactivation.

E. Reactivation with Dithiols

It is now well established that dithiols are more effective than mono-thiols in reversing the inhibitions caused by arsenicals. Curiously enough, it was the inability to demonstrate reversal with monothiols of inhibitions produced by lewisite (*54, 55*), which eventually led to the synthesis of British Anti-Lewisite (BAL).

To obtain information on the nature of the arsenical-protein complex, Stocken and Thompson (*56*) studied the effects of adding lewisite to the protein kerateine, which has a large number of thiol groups. Rosenthal (*57*) had shown that when trivalent arsenicals are combined with proteins, the arsenicals cannot be separated from the protein by ultrafiltration. Stocken and Thompson (*56*) demonstrated that the addition of lewisite to kerateine causes a disappearance of the free thiol groups. Moreover, 75–90% of the arsenic bound to protein is combined in a molar ratio of one arsenic to two thiols. If kerateine is pretreated with mild oxidizing agents which destroy thiol groups, there is no combination with lewisite. These data provide additional evidence that free thiol groups are required for combination with the arsenicals.

The ratio of arsenical to thiol in the kerateine-lewisite complex sug-gested to Stocken and Thompson (*56*) that lewisite combines with adjoin-ing thiols in this protein and that simple dithiols might reverse or prevent the toxic actions of the arsenicals more effectively than monothiols. The results of these experiments show that a number of low molecular weight dithiols form relative stable complexes with lewisite (*55*). Stocken and Thompson (*55*) measured the dissociation of the lewisite-thiol complex by estimating the time required for the reduction of porphyrindin with various thiol-lewisite complexes. The reaction proceeds according to Eqs. (3) and (4).

The thioarsenites were used at equimolar concentrations and the porphyrindin at a concentration one-half that of the thioarsenites. Thio-arsenites from monothiols reduce porphyrindin much more quickly than do thioarsenites formed from dithiols (Table I).

Moreover, the dithiols, ethane-1,2-dithiol, 2,3-dimercaptopropanol

$$\begin{array}{c} \text{R---S} \\ \diagdown \\ \text{As---CH}{=}\text{CHCl} + H_2O \rightleftarrows \text{ClCH}{=}\text{CHAsO} + 2\text{RSH} \\ \diagup \\ \text{R---S} \end{array} \qquad (3)$$

$$2\text{RSH} + \text{porphyrindin} \rightarrow \text{R---S---S---R} + \text{leucoporphyrindin} \qquad (4)$$

(BAL), 1,3-dimercaptopropanol, propane-1,3-dithiol, a,β-dimercaptopropionic acid, are capable of reversing the inhibition by lewisite of pyruvate oxidation where simple monothiols are not effective. A number of dithiols such as β,β'-dimercaptodiethyl sulfide and pentane-1,5-dithiol do not

TABLE I

HYDROLYSIS RATES OF THIOARSENITES PREPARED FROM LEWISITE AND THIOLS (55)

Thiol	Decolorization time (minutes)
Cysteine	0.25
Thioacetic acid	0.50
Aminothiophenol	0.83
Glutathione	2.5
2-Mercaptoethanol	3.5
2,3-Dimercaptopropanol (BAL)	>180
Ethane-1,2-dithiol	>180
1,3-Dimercaptopropanol	>180
Propane-1,3-dithiol	>180
β,β'-Dimercaptodiethyl ether	>180

overcome the lewisite-produced inhibition of pyruvate oxidation. These results prompted Stocken and Thompson (55) to conclude that a 5- or 6-membered ring between arsenical and dithiol is the most stable thioarsenite complex and that this property of the dithiols can be used to advantage to liberate a free thiol from another less stable thioarsenite. Whittaker (58), however, has shown that a number of dithiols are effective in reversing lewisite inhibitions. The least effective in this group are butanedithiol and pentanedithiol. Whittaker (58) has concluded that these results are consistent with the hypothesis that a cyclic structure is formed between arsenicals and dithiols and that the ring need not be limited to five or six members. Eagle and Doak (59), however, suggest that there is insuffcent evidence to support the hypothesis that cyclic thioarsenites are more stable than the straight chain compounds.

Nevertheless, there is no doubt that many dithiols are more effective in reversing the inhibitory actions of arsenicals than are monothiols (53–55). Stocken and Thompson (55) have shown that a concentration of British Anti-Lewisite three times that of arsenosobenzene is capable of reversing the arsenosobenzene inhibition of pyruvate oxidation. Considerable excess of monothiol (up to a hundredfold excess) is required to reverse the inhibitions caused by arsenosobenzene derivatives on the pyruvate oxidation system (15, 29).

Of all the dithiols prepared, BAL has proved to be the most effective and easiest to use for many practical reasons, such as solubility, relative lack of toxicity, and nonvolatility. The clinical use of BAL in cases of arsenical poisoning and poisoning by other heavy metals has been very extensive (59–61). Although originally prepared as an antidote to the war gas lewisite, it has found its greatest use in accidental arsenical poisoning.

V. INHIBITION OF LIPOIC ACID-DEPENDENT REACTIONS

Although there is much evidence to suggest that many of the inhibitions caused by the arsenicals are due to combination with the thiol groups of enzymes, recent evidence suggests that a site of action of arsenicals may also be the sulfhydryl groups of lipoic acid. The data already given show that α-keto acid oxidation is particularly sensitive to the action of trivalent arsenicals. It is now well established that lipoic acid is a cofactor in α-keto acid oxidation (62). Reiss and Hellerman (31) and Reiss (63) have found that arsenicals inhibit all lipoic acid-dependent reactions. Moreover, Sanadi et al. (64, 65) have shown that the biological oxidation of α-ketoglutarate by ferricyanide, which is lipoic acid independent, is insensitive to arsenite. The oxidation of α-ketoglutarate in the absence of an artificial hydrogen acceptor is well known to be arsenite sensitive (29).

The inhibition by γ-(p-arsenosophenyl)butyrate of pyruvate utilization and citrate formation in rat heart sarcosomes can be reversed more effectively with dihydrolipoic acid than with BAL (31). These results have given support to the belief that lipoic may be a site of action of arsenicals.

It is interesting to note that there is some structural similarity between BAL and lipoic acid.

$$
\begin{array}{ccc}
\text{SH} & \text{SH} & \qquad\qquad \text{SH} \qquad\qquad \text{SH} \\
| & | & \qquad\qquad | \qquad\qquad\quad | \\
\text{CH}_2\text{—CH—CH}_2\text{OH} & & \text{CH}_2\text{—CH}_2\text{—CH—(CH}_2)_4\text{—COOH}
\end{array}
$$

BAL   Dihydrolipoic acid

It has also been suggested that the sulfhydryl group of coenzyme A may be a site of action of arsenicals.

VI. FACTORS INVOLVED IN THE STABILITY OF THIOARSENITES AND THEIR APPLICATION TO THE INHIBITION OF ENZYME ACTIVITIES

Thioarsenites formed from dithiols are relatively stable complexes and dissociate at far lower rates than do thioarsenites from monothiols (55). This fact no doubt accounts for the greater ease with which dithiols reverse the inhibitions produced by arsenicals. However, thioarsenites formed from a given dithiol and a variety of arsenicals may have different rates of dissociation; for example, the Mapharsen-BAL complex dissociates to a greater extent than does the lewisite-BAL complex (66). (A positive nitroprusside test is obtained with Mapharsen-BAL but not with lewisite-BAL.) The lewisite-BAL complex has less than one-fifth the toxicity of lewisite itself, whereas Mapharsen-BAL is at least as toxic as the free arsenical (66). However, other authors have reported a diminished toxicity of the Mapharsen-BAL complex (67–69).

With a given arsenical, the dissociation rate of its monothioarsenites is greatly affected by the nature of the monothiol; for example, the rate of dissociation of the lewisite-cysteine complex is 10 times as great as that of the glutathione complex. Such factors no doubt account for the fact that glutathione is better able to reverse the effects of the arsenicals than is cysteine (15, 29). It no doubt accounts also for the observations that thioarsenites, such as arsenosobenzene thioglycolate (15) and other thioarsenites (70–72) may be nearly as toxic as the parent compound (see also reference 59).

The data described indicate that reactivation by a given thiol may depend on the dissociation rate of the thioarsenite formed. The reverse is probably also true; the extent of inhibition by a given arsenical may depend on the dissociation rate of the thioarsenite formed with cellular thiol compounds. Thus, appreciable differences exist in the extents of inhibition of various enzymes by a given arsenical (15, 29, 44, 47). In the pyruvic oxidase system, the thiol groups affected appear to be those of lipoic acid (31, 63). It is conceivable that the dissociation rate of the thioarsenites formed with lipoic acid may be appreciably lower than those formed from a protein thiol and an arsenical. The formation of cyclic thioarsenites has previously been proposed to explain the increased stability of dithiol arsenicals (54, 56, 58). The possibility of ring forma-

tion between enzyme thiol groups and arsenicals has not obtained support
(*37, 59*), although ring formation between arsenicals and lipoic acid has
obtained support (*31, 63*).

The nature of the arsenical may also influence the dissociation rate of
the thioarsenite formed, be it monothiol or dithiol. Such an interpretation
may explain the observations that different arsenicals inhibit the same
enzymes to appreciably different extents; for example, urease, which is
inhibited by 1.6×10^{-4} M Mapharsen (*15*), is not affected by 10^{-3} M
lewisite (*33*). Yeast carboxylase is inhibited by (p-aminophenyl) dichloroarsine hydrochloride (*29*) and Mapharsen (*35*) but not by lewisite (*33*).
Similarly, D-amino acid oxidase is inhibited by (3-amino-4-hydroxy-
phenyl) dichloroarsine hydrochloride (*44*) and by p-arsenosoaniline (*45*)
but not by lewisite (*33*). In many cases, enzymes inhibited by the
arsenosobenzene derivatives are also inhibited by lewisite (*15, 29, 33*).
Such observations indicate that in studies of the inhibitory effects of
organic arsenicals and the reversal of the inhibitions, the nature of the
arsenical as well as the thiol compounds may influence the degree of
inhibition and the extent of reversal.

VII. EFFECTS OF ARSENICALS ON PHYSIOLOGICAL ACTIVITY

There can be little doubt that the inhibitions of tissue respiration and
glycolysis observed in presence of arsenicals are due to an inhibition of
specific enzymes involved in these processes (*15, 33, 73, 74*) Müller has
shown that mitosis in epithelial cells is disturbed by diphenylarsine (*75*).
Trivalent, but not pentavalent, arsenicals inhibit the growth of mammalian cells cultured *in vitro* (*76*). Inorganic arsenite will abolish the
effect of ACTH on steroid synthesis in adrenals (*77*). In plants, arsenite
prevents the response to auxins (*78*). Virus reproduction is inhibited at a
concentration of arsenite which has no effect on bacterial growth or virus
adsorption (*79*).

These experiments illustrate the wide variety of physiological activities
that may be affected by arsenicals in many types of cells.

VIII. SOME EFFECTS OF ARSENICALS ON TUMORS

Lacassagne *et al.* (*80*) have reported that the application of organic
arsenicals to mouse skin does not initiate tumor growth. Beck (*81*) showed

that of 39 pentavalent arsenicals, aliphatic and aromatic, only sodium cacodylate produced gross histological damage to mouse sarcoma S $_{37}$ at maximum tolerated doses. Twenty-four trivalent arsenicals did produce gross histological damage to mouse tissue. With some arsenicals, e.g. phenyldichloroarsine, the toxic response to the arsenical is decreased in tumor-bearing animals. With Mapharsen the toxicity of the arsenical is identical in normal and tumor-bearing mice (81). Further studies by Beck and Gillespie (82) on the toxicity of arsenicals on tumor-bearing mice showed that the decreased toxicity occurs only in animals bearing small tumors (82). Cortisone and ACTH protect the animal against sublethal doses of arsenicals (83).

Mapharsen has recently been shown to reduce the mitotic index of 6C3HED lymphosarcoma (84). A single injection kept the mitotic index at a low level over a prolonged period of time. The addition of 6-mercaptopurine appears to offset the effects of Mapharsen (84).

IX. STRUCTURE OF ARSENICALS IN RELATION TO PARASITICIDAL ACTIVITY

Much of the work on the biological activity of the arsenosobenzenes had been done in relation to parasiticidal activity. Prior to the advent of penicillin, the arsenicals were extensively used in the treatment of trypanosomal infections. A large number of derivatives of arsenosobenzene were synthesized in an attempt to enhance the parasiticidal activity of the arsenosobenzene without increasing the toxicity to the host. A review of the structural changes of the arsenosobenzenes in relation to biological activity has appeared (59). An attempt will be made here to summarize how the changes in the structure of the arsenosobenzenes affect the parasiticidal activity.

Unsubstituted arsenosobenzene is highly toxic to every cell type and is too toxic to be used therapeutically. Substitution on the benzene ring by —Cl, —NO$_2$, —OH, —CH$_3$, —F and the position of these substituents do not appreciably alter the activity of arsenosobenzene and have no selective action (59).

Acidic substituents, such as —COOH, —SO$_3$H, and R—COOH, markedly depress both the treponemicidal and trypanocidal activities without decreasing the toxicity to the animal to the same extent (59). Substitution by fatty acids to give the γ-(p-arsenosophenyl)butyric acid, δ-(p-arsenosophenyl)valeric acid, and ε-(p-arsenosophenyl)caproic acid enhances the parasiticidal activity relative to the toxicity to the host.

The first two compounds are actively trypanocidal against *Trypanosoma equiperdum* both *in vivo* and *in vitro*, although they have no significant effect against *Treponema pallidum*. Conversely, the caproic acid derivative has considerable treponemicidal activity but is almost inert against *T. equiperdum*. Evidently, highly specific factors are involved in producing the enhanced parasiticidal activity or diminished parasiticidal activity.

Eagle and Doak (*59*) have concluded that the nonionized forms of acid-substituted arsenosobenzenes are the active forms. With some of the acid-substituted arsenosobenzenes, a hundredfold difference in parasiticidal activity is observed in the pH range 8.5–5.5.

Substitution of arsenosobenzenes with acid amide groups results in a remarkably uniform toxicity and parasiticidal activity. Sixteen compounds of this general structure are described by Eagle and Doak (*59*). The activity of the acid amide-substituted arsenosobenzene lies midway between the free arsenosobenzene and the acid-substituted substance; for example, the *in vitro* parasiticidal activity of *p*-arsenosobenzamide is about half of that of the arsenosobenzene, while *p*-arsenosobenzoic acid has less than 1% the parasiticidal activity of arsenosobenzene.

An important property of the acid amide-substituted compound is a marked decrease in the toxicity to the host relative to the parasiticidal activity. The toxicity of *p*-arsenosobenzamide is 10% that of arsenosobenzene, but as mentioned previously it has 50% of the parasiticidal activity of arsenosobenzene. The integrity of the amide group is essential for a favorable effect on toxicity, but the position of the substituent group on the benzene ring has little effect. The favorable therapeutic effect of amide-substituted arsenosobenzene has been used to advantage in chemotherapy (*71, 72, 85–87*).

Esterification of the acid-substituted arsenosobenzene enhances both toxicity and parasiticidal activity (*59*).

Numerous other monosubstituted arsenosobenzenes have been synthesized. Few, however, have proved of great value in chemotherapy. Melarsen oxide (*p*-[2,4-diaminotriazinyl-6]aminoarsenosobenzene) is an exception to this rule, being highly effective against trypanosomal infections (*88*).

The effects of multiple substituents on the benzene ring have not been studied so extensively as those of the monosubstituents. With few exceptions, the compounds studied are not much more useful than the parent compound, arsenosobenzene (*59*). Mapharsen, 2-amino-4-arsenosophenol, is one of the exceptions. Eagle *et al.* (*89*) tested the activity of a number of aminophenol-substituted arsenosobenzenes, $RR' \cdot C_6H_3 \cdot As\,O$, where

R and R′ are NH$_2$ and OH, respectively: 3-NH$_2$, 4-OH (Mapharsen); 3-OH, 4-NH$_2$; 2-NH$_2$, 3-OH; 2-OH, 5-NH$_2$; 3-OH, 5-NH$_2$; and 2-OH, 3-NH$_2$. Only Mapharsen in this group possesses high parasiticidal activity and relatively low toxicity, and has been used successfully in chemotherapy.

It is therefore apparent that substituents may greatly modify the biological activities of an arsenical. Compounds have been obtained that have high parasiticidal activity combined with low toxicity to the animal. While certain substituted arsenosobenzenes are active against one type of parasite, they may be considerably less active against another organism. Clearly, in assessing the effects of substituents, specific factors must be considered, such as rate of penetration of the arsenical into a particular cell and its affinities for different thiol enzymes or thiol constituents of the cell.

REFERENCES

1. D. E. Koshland, Jr., *Advances in Enzymol.* 22, 45 (1960).
2. P. Ehrlich, *Ber.* 42, 17 (1909).
3. P. Ehrlich and A. Bertheim, *Ber.* 43, 917 (1910).
4. F. Hawking, T. J. Hennelly, and J. H. Quastel, *J. Pharmacol. Exptl. Therap.* 59, 157 (1937).
5. A. L. Tatum and G. A. Cooper, *J. Pharmacol. Exptl. Therap.* 50, 198 (1934).
6. C. Voegtlin and H. W. L. Smith, *J. Pharmacol. Exptl. Therap.* 15, 475 (1920).
7. J. F. Shamberg, G. W. Raizess, and J. A. Kolmar, *J. Am. Med. Assoc.* 78, 402 (1922).
8. W. Yorke and F. Murgatroyd, *Ann. Trop. Med.* 24, 449 (1930).
9. H. Eagle, *J. Pharmacol. Exptl. Therap.* 66, 423 (1939).
10. M. J. Sartori, "The War Gases." Churchill, London, 1943.
11. C. Voegtlin, H. A. Dyer, and C. S. Leonard, *U.S. Public Health Repts.* 38, 1882 (1923).
12. H. J. Barber, *J. Chem. Soc.* p. 1020 (1929).
13. G. A. C. Gough and H. King, *J. Chem. Soc.* p. 669 (1930).
14. A. Cohen, H. King, and W. I. Strangeways, *J. Chem. Soc.* p. 3043 (1931).
15. J. J. Gordon and J. H. Quastel, *Biochem. J.* 42, 337 (1948).
16. F. G. Hopkins and M. Dixon, *J. Biol. Chem.* 54, 527 (1922).
17. J. B. Sumner and L. O. Poland, *Proc. Soc. Exptl. Biol. Med.* 30, 553 (1933).
18. L. Hellerman, *Physiol. Revs.* 17, 454 (1937).
19. T. Bersin, *Ergeb. Enzymforsch.* 4, 68 (1935).
20. T. Bersin, *Z. physiol. Chem. Hoppe-Seyler's* 222, 177 (1933).
21. F. G. Hopkins and E. J. Morgan, *Biochem. J.* 32, 611 (1938).
22. F. G. Hopkins, E. J. Morgan, and C. Lutwak-Mann, *Biochem. J.* 32, 1829 (1938).
23. L. Rapkine, *Biochem. J.* 32, 1729 (1938).
24. M. Onada, *Z. physiol. Chem. Hoppe-Seyler's* 70, 433 (1911).

25. A. Szent-Györgyi, *Biochem. J.* **24**, 1723 (1930).
26. C. Voegtlin, S. M. Rosenthal, and J. M. Johnson, *U.S. Public Health Repts.* **46**, 339 (1931).
27. H. A. Krebs, *Z. physiol. Chem. Hoppe-Seyler's* **217**, 191 (1933).
28. R. A. Peters, L. A. Stocken, and R. H. S. Thompson, *Nature* **156**, 616 (1945).
29. E. S. G. Barron and T. P. Singer, *J. Biol. Chem.* **157**, 221 (1945).
30. E. S. G. Barron and T. P. Singer, *Science* **97**, 356 (1943).
31. O. K. Reiss and L. Hellerman, *J. Biol. Chem.* **231**, 557 (1958).
32. C. Lutwak-Mann, *Biochem. J.* **32**, 1364 (1938).
33. E. S. G. Barron, Z. B. Miller, G. R. Bartlett, J. Meyer, and T. P. Singer, *Biochem. J.* **41**, 69 (1947).
34. A. O. M. Stoppani and A. S. Actis, *Anales asoc. quím. arg.* **40**, 128 (1952).
35. A. O. M. Stoppani, A. S. Actis, J. O. Deferrari, and E. L. Gonzalez, *Biochem. J.* **54**, 378 (1953).
36. A. O. M. Stoppani, A. S. Actis, J. O. Deferrari, and E. L. Gonzalez, *Nature* **170**, 842 (1952).
36a. W. B. Jacoby, *Arch. Biochem. Biophys.* **70**, 625 (1957).
36b. W. B. Jacoby, *Proc. Natl. Acad. Sci. U. S.* **46**, 206 (1960).
36c. H. R. Mahler, B. Mackler, D. E. Green, and R. M. Bock, *J. Biol. Chem.* **210**, 465 (1954).
36d. R. W. Albers and G. J. Koval, *Biochim. Biophys. Acta* **52**, 29 (1961).
36e. B. Mackler, H. R. Mahler, and D. E. Green, *J. Biol. Chem.* **210**, 149 (1954).
37. E. C. Slater, *Biochem. J.* **45**, 130 (1949).
38. T. P. Singer, E. B. Kearney, and H. Zastrow, *Biochim. et Biophys. Acta* **17**, 154 (1955).
38a. V. R. Potter and C. A. Elvehjem, *J. Biol. Chem.* **117**, 341 (1937).
38b. N. B. Das, *Biochem. J.* **31**, 1116 (1937).
39. R. Van Heyningen, Report to the Ministry of Supply, Great Britain, by M. Dixon, No. 10, 1942.
40. K. Bailey and E. C. Webb, *Biochem. J.* **42**, 60 (1948).
41. P. B. Marshall, *Brit. J. Pharmacol.* **3**, 8 (1948).
42. G. Chen, *J. Infectious Diseases* **82**, 26 (1942).
43. G. E. Glock and P. McLean, *Biochem. J.* **55**, 400 (1953).
43a. B. Z. Dresel, *Biochem. Z.* **192**, 35 (1927).
43b. B. Z. Dresel, *Biochem. Z.* **178**, 70 (1926).
44. T. P. Singer and E. S. G. Barron, *J. Biol. Chem.* **157**, 241 (1945).
45. T. P. Singer, *J. Biol. Chem.* **174**, 11 (1948).
46. L. H. Stickland, *Biochem. J.* **28**, 1746 (1934).
47. R. Mamelak and J. H. Quastel, *Biochim. et Biophys. Acta* **12**, 103 (1953).
48. J. S. Friedenwald and H. Herrmann, *J. Biol. Chem.* **146**, 411 (1942).
48a. J. H. Quastel and A. H. M. Wheatley, *Biochem. J.* **29**, 2773 (1935).
48b. M. Jowett and J. H. Quastel, *Biochem. J.* **29**, 2189 (1935).
49. P. Rona and P. György, *Biochem. Z.* **111**, 115 (1920).
50. P. Rona, Y. Airila, and A. Lasnitski, *Biochem. Z.* **130**, 582 (1922).
51. L. A. Mounter and V. P. Whittaker, *Biochem. J.* **53**, 167 (1953).
52. R. H. S. Thompson, *Biochem. Soc. Symposia* (*Cambridge, Engl.*) **2**, 28 (1948).

53. C. Voegtlin, H. A. Dyer, and C. S. Leonard, *J. Pharmacol. Exptl. Therap.* 25, 297 (1925).

54. L. A. Stocken, R. H. S. Thompson, and V. R. Whittaker, *Biochem. J.* 41, 47 (1947).

55. L. A. Stocken and R. H. S. Thompson, *Biochem. J.* 40, 535 (1946).

56. L. A. Stocken and R. H. S. Thompson, *Biochem. J.* 40, 529 (1946).

57. S. M. Rosenthal, *U.S. Public Health Repts.* 47, 251 (1932).

58. V. P. Whittaker, *Biochem. J. 41*, 56 (1947).

59. H. Eagle and G. O. Doak, *Pharmacol. Revs.* 3, 107 (1951).

60. H. Eagle, H. J. Magnuson, and R. Fleischman, *J. Clin. Invest.* 25, 451 (1946); J. Wexler, H. Eagle, H. J. Tatum, H. J. Magnuson, and E. B. Watson, *ibid.* 25, 467 (1946); M. B. Sulzberger, R. L. Baer and A. Kanof, *ibid.* 25, 474 (1946); 25, 488 (1946); W. Modell, H. Gold, and McK. Cattell, *ibid.* 25, 480 (1946); A. B. Carleton, R. A. Peters, L. A. Stocken, R. H. S. Thompson, and D. I. Williams, *ibid.* 25, 497 (1946); W. T. Longcope, J. A. Luetscher, Jr., M. M. Wintrobe, and V. Jäger, *ibid.* 25, 528 (1946); J. A. Luetscher, Jr., H. Eagle, and W. T. Longcope, *ibid.* 25, 534 (1946); W. F. Hughes, Jr., *ibid.* 25, 541 (1946); A. Gilman, R. P. Allen, F. S. Philips, and E. St. John, *ibid.* 25, 549 (1946); W. T. Longcope and J. A. Luetscher, Jr., *ibid.* 25, 557 (1946).

61. L. A. Stocken and R. H. S. Thompson, *Biochem. J.* 40, 458 (1946).

62. L. J. Reed, *in* "The Enzymes" (P. D. Boyer, H. Lardy, and K. Myrbäck, eds.), Vol. 3, p. 222. Academic Press, New York, 1960.

63. O. K. Reiss, *J. Biol. Chem.* 233, 789 (1958).

64. D. R. Sanadi, M. Langley, and F. White, *Biochim. et Biophys. Acta* 29, 218 (1958).

65. D. R. Sanadi, M. Langley, and F. White, *J. Biol. Chem.* 234, 183 (1959).

66. R. A. Peters and L. A. Stocken, *Biochem. J.* 41, 53 (1947).

67. E. A. H. Friedheim and H. J. Vogel, *Proc. Soc. Exptl. Biol. Med.* 64, 418 (1947).

68. W. F. Riker, *J. Pharmacol. Exptl. Therap.* 87, Suppl. 66-67 (1946).

69. J. L. Sawyers, B. Burrows, and T. H. Maren, *Proc. Soc. Exptl. Biol. Med.* 70, 194 (1949).

70. F. Murgatroyd, *Ann. Trop. Med.* 31, 473 (1937).

71. G. F. Otto and T. H. Maren, *Science* 106, 105 (1947).

72. G. F. Otto and T. H. Maren, *Am. J. Hyg.* 50, 92 (1949).

73. W. Hughes and G. A. Levy, *Biochem. J.* 41, 8 (1947).

74. R. H. S. Thompson, *Biochem. J.* 40, 525 (1946).

75. H. H. Müller, *Naturwissenschaften* 33, 253 (1946).

76. W. B. Savchuck, H. W. Loy, and S. S. Schiaffino, *Proc. Soc. Exptl. Biol. Med.* 105, 543 (1961).

77. E. Shonbaum, M. K. Birmingham, M. Saffran, and E. Kurlents, *Can. J. Biochem. and Physiol.* 34, 527 (1956).

78. G. S. Christiansen, L. J. Kunz, W. D. Bonner, Jr., and E. V. Thimann, *Plant. Physiol.* 24, 178 (1948).

79. D. E. Dolby, *J. Gen. Microbiol.* 12, 406 (1955).

80. A. Lacassagne, R. Royer, and G. Sudall, *Comp. rend. soc. biol.* 145, 1451 (1951).

81. L. V. Beck, *Cancer Research* **9**, 626 (1949).
82. L. V. Beck and R. L. Gillespie, *J. Natl. Cancer Inst.* **12**, 1223 (1954).
83. L. V. Beck, *Proc. Soc. Exptl. Biol. Med.* **78**, 392 (1951).
84. R. A. Roosa and E. D. DeLamater, *Cancer Research* **20**, 1543 (1960).
85. J. D. Fulton and W. Yorke, *Ann. Trop. Med.* **37**, 80 (1943).
86. H. H. Anderson, V. P. Bond, and B. E. Abreu, *Federation Proc.* **5**, 162 (1946).
87. H. H. Anderson and E. L. Hansen, *Am. J. Trop. Med.* **27**, 153 (1947).
88. E. A. H. Friedheim, *Schweiz. med. Wochschr.* **71**, 116 (1941); *J. Am. Chem. Soc.* **66**, 1775 (1944); *Ann. Trop. Med. Parasitol.* **42**, 357 (1948); *Am. J. Trop. Med.* **29**, 173 (1949).
89. H. Eagle, G. O. Doak, R. B. Hogan, and H. G. Steinman, *J. Pharmacol. Exptl. Therap.* **74**, 210 (1942).

CHAPTER 21

Mercaptide-Forming Agents[1]

N. B. Madsen

I. INTRODUCTION

Mercaptide formation is one of the chief reactions used in research on sulfhydryl groups. The whole question of the role of —SH [2] groups in enzymic catalysis appears just now to be going through a period of doubt and uncertainty, whereas in the early part of the last decade it appeared to be firmly fixed on a course whose ultimate destination was thought to be known. At that time the generally accepted criteria for the recognition of a "sulfhydryl enzyme" were its inhibition by PCMB and its reactivation by cysteine or other thiols. The satisfaction of these criteria usually led to speculation about the role of the —SH groups in the

---

[1] Contribution No. 511, from the Microbiology Research Institute, Research Branch, Canada Department of Agriculture, Central Experimental Farm, Ottawa, Canada.

[2] The following abbreviations are used: —SH, sulfhydryl; PCMB, p-chloro-mercuribenzoate; NEM, N-ethylmaleimide; EDTA, ethylenediaminetetraacetate; PCMPS, p-chloromercuriphenylsulfonate; DPN, diphosphopyridine nucleotide; DPNH, reduced form of DPN; Tris, tris(hydroxymethyl)aminomethane.

mechanism of catalysis. Recent research has indicated, however, that the problem is more complex than was formerly thought; for example, evidence of the direct transfer of hydrogen in reactions involving pyridine nucleotides has rendered untenable certain postulated reaction sequences. Sulfhydryl groups have also been demonstrated to have important roles in the maintenance of protein structure. Many of the results which were interpreted as indicating a participation of —SH groups in the mechanism of enzyme action can also be explained by postulating changes in protein configuration. Keeping this rather unsettled stage of development in mind, the present chapter will attempt to evaluate the advantages and limitations of mercaptide-forming agents in promoting our knowledge of this important subject.

The subject of the —SH groups of enzymes has been the theme of many excellent reviews, which have, naturally, discussed mercaptide formation. Among these, Barron (1) may be consulted for an insight into the literature and prevailing opinions prior to 1950. "A Symposium on Sulfur in Proteins," edited by R. E. Benesch et al. (2), presents a good picture of the remarkable scope of biological processes in which —SH groups play an important role, as well as a critical appraisal of modern methods and results. Boyer (3) has given an account of the chemistry of mercaptide formation and has dealt capably with the application of this and other phenomena to the problem of enzyme action. Cecil and McPhee (4) have delved extensively into the sulfur chemistry of proteins, and their review is recommended for its thoughtful discussions of analytical methods.

Because of the extensive recent reviews available, and in keeping with the emphasis which this book places on the inhibitor rather than on the biological system under investigation, this chapter will confine itself mostly to discussions of the principles and applications of the methodology now available. The limitations of space and purpose have dictated a highly selective rather than inclusive approach. For this reason, it has been possible to choose only a few enzymes for detailed examination to illustrate various points. Similarly, work with crude biological preparations has been excluded because of space and because it is difficult to interpret the results of such work.

II. METAL CATIONS

A. Chemistry of Mercaptide Formation

Gurd and Wilcox (5) have presented a comprehensive review on the binding of metallic cations by proteins, peptides, and amino acids, in which they discuss the chemistry of mercaptide formation in detail. Table I is presented to give a rough idea of the relative affinities of metal

TABLE I

FIRST ASSOCIATION CONSTANTS (LOG k_1) FOR THE COMBINATION OF SOME CATIONS AND SMALL MOLECULES

Cation	Sulfide[a]	RS⁻	NH₃	Imidazole	Acetate	Glycinate
Hg^{++}	53.5	>20	8.8	—	4.0	10.3
Ag^+	50	15	3.2	—	0.7	3.7
Cu^{++}	41.5	—	4.2	4.4	2.2	8.2
Pb^{++}	27.5	11	—	—	2.0	5.5
Cd^{++}	27.2	8	2.7	2.8	1.3	3.9
Ni^{++}	27.0	—	2.8	3.3	—	5.8
Co^{++}	26.7	9	—	—	—	4.6
Zn^{++}	25.2	7	2.8	2.6	1.0	4.8

[a] pK of the solubility product, taken from Kolthoff (6). The remainder of the data are abstracted from the data collected by Gurd and Wilcox (5). Many of the constants, particularly those for the mercaptides, should be regarded as approximations.

ions for various groups typical of those found in proteins. As noted before by Klotz (7), there is a rough correlation between these affinities and the order of the solubility product constants of the metal sulfides. It may be seen also that the specificity of mercury and silver for —SH groups is only relative. Thus, one might expect that when these metals are added to a protein solution they will saturate the —SH binding sites first but that any excess will immediately begin associating with other groups. The first association constants only are listed in Table I, with the exception of the association constants for the formation of sulfides, because metals bound to proteins may not be able to form higher complexes, as they would with smaller molecular weight analogues. A small anion from the medium would usually be bound to the metal.

The constants given in Table I are for the reaction given in Eq. (1),

$$\text{Metal} + \text{ligand} \rightleftharpoons \text{metal} - \text{ligand} \qquad (1)$$

whereas, under experimental conditions, hydrogen ion competes with the metal for the ligand, while anions from the medium compete with the ligand for the metal. If we use the formation of a mercaptide from mercuric chloride and a protein-bound —SH group as an example [Eq. (2)], the over-all equation is:

$$\text{R—SH} + \text{HgCl}_2 \rightleftharpoons \text{R—S—HgCl} + \text{H}^+ + \text{Cl}^- \qquad (2)$$

but this contains two dissociations, namely:

$$R\text{—}SH \rightleftharpoons R\text{—}S^- + H^+ \tag{3}$$

$$HgCl_2 \rightleftharpoons HgCl^+ + Cl^- \tag{4}$$

plus the actual formation of the mercaptide, for which the equation analogous to Eq. (1) is Eq. (5).

$$R\text{—}S^- + HgCl^+ \rightleftharpoons R\text{—}S\text{—}HgCl \tag{5}$$

The equilibrium constant for Eq. (2) does not appear to have been determined, but a rough estimate may be calculated if we assume that the association of $HgCl^+$ to a protein-bound —SH group is similar to that of mercury to small molecular weight thiols where the "log association constant"[3] is a minimum of 20 (8, 9). The logarithms of the association constants for R—SH and $HgCl_2$ [reverse of Eqs. (3) and (4)] are taken as 8.5 (10) and 6.5 (11), respectively. This leads to a log equilibrium constant for Eq. (2) of 5, which indicates that the equilibrium is still far to the right.

It should be noted that one of the important factors in determining the equilibrium of Eq. (2) is the dissociation of an anion from the mercury [Eq. (4)]. The relative affinities of various anions for mercury are $CN^- > I^- > Br^- > Cl^- > NO_3^-$. It may be calculated from the data of Sillen (11) that the logs of the association constants for the reaction shown in Eq. (6),

$$HgX^+ + X^- \rightleftharpoons HgX_2 \tag{6}$$

where X is a halogen, are 11.0, 8.3, and 6.5 for I^-, Br^-, and Cl^-, respectively. Thus, the equilibrium of Eq. (2), as well as the specificity of the reaction of mercury with —SH as opposed to other available groups, can be influenced by the type of small anions present. This theme will be taken up again in relation to one of the organic mercurials.

It is also seen readily that the pH will have a great influence on the equilibrium of Eq. (2). What may not be so apparent is that pH will affect the specificity of the reactions of metals with various protein groups because of the different pK's of the latter. For example, at pH 7.0, all of the carboxyl groups and approximately half of the imidazole groups of a protein are free of protons and may therefore react readily with metal

---

[3] The term "log association constant" is used here to mean the same as "log k_1" as defined by Gurd and Wilcox (5) on p. 316 of their review.

cations. On the other hand, only a small fraction of the —SH and ϵ-amino groups (perhaps of the order of 1% and 0.1%, respectively) are available.

Although the association constants listed in Table I indicate that several of the protein-bound groups would not be expected to be very effective in binding metals, the binding by glycinate ion shows that chelation would increase affinities to a significant extent. Tanford and Epstein (12) showed that the tight binding of zinc to insulin would be consistent with the chelation of each Zn^{++} to two imidazole groups. Ingram (13) has found that native horse hemoglobin will bind four Ag^+ per molecule, as measured amperometrically, but X-ray analysis indicates only two silver spots. Furthermore, only two Hg^{++} or PCMB molecules were bound. The results have been interpreted as indicating that there are two clusters of two —SH groups each, the two —SH groups in each cluster lying so close together that they can chelate the Hg^{++}. The PCMB bound to one of the —SH groups in a cluster would block a second mercurial by steric hindrance.

Vallee and associates (14) have recently made some very interesting observations on bovine pancreatic carboxypeptidase, a zinc metalloenzyme containing 1 gm atom of zinc per mole of protein. The enzymic activity is abolished by removing the zinc with chelating agents and is restored upon adding zinc. No —SH groups are found in the native enzyme, but one group per mole of protein can be titrated in the zinc-free enzyme. Furthermore, the addition of silver or PCMB to the zinc-free enzyme prevents the restoration of activity by adding zinc. The authors suggest that zinc is bound as a mercaptide but that it is also bound by a second linkage; the chelation thus produced would explain the relatively high affinity of zinc for this enzyme. These results open up several new possibilities in connection with sulfhydryl enzymes. First, a chelation of a metal involving an —SH group may occur in nature. Second, this chelation may prevent any normal reactivity of the —SH group. A new type of sulfhydryl enzyme is introduced which can be detected only with special techniques. Third, one may speculate on the possibility that such a chelated metal may act as a structural link serving to maintain an enzyme in a conformation necessary for activity.

B. Application to Estimation of Thiols

Mercaptide formation with silver and mercury ions has been the basis of a number of amperometric procedures, which have been developed to a large extent by Benesch and Benesch and by Kolthoff and Stricks. Silver nitrate has been used extensively, being added to a solution of the thiol containing ammonium ions which serve to complex the silver (15–17).

The conditions required were not suitable for most proteins, but Benesch
et al. (*18*) introduced the use of Tris buffer as the complexing ion, thus
making it possible to carry out the titrations at neutral pH. Their method
could be used to estimate the speed of reaction of various classes of —SH
groups. Urea was used as a denaturing agent to determine the total sulfhydryl content of a protein. Some of their results, however, are considerably higher than those obtained by other methods. Cecil and McPhee
(*4*) review the whole question of the use of silver to titrate —SH groups.
They note that silver ion forms complexes with the mercaptides of a
stability comparable to the mercaptides themselves, and high results are
obtained. Ammonia does not complex the silver strongly enough to prevent this, and Tris appears to be still less effective. It is on this basis that
Cecil and McPhee explain the high titration value for —SH groups in
hemoglobin compared to the values obtained by titration with mercury
or organic mercurials. Ingram (*13*) presents an ingenious alternative
explanation, discussed in Section II, A.

One may note, however, that the amount of PCMB bound to hemoglobin, as measured by equilibrium dialysis, agreed with the amperometric
silver titration (*18*). Here again, as in so many instances, at least some
of the discrepancies in results from different laboratories may be due to
the different rates of reaction of various types of —SH groups on the
same protein. This reviewer believes that the method of Benesch *et al.*
(*18*) has, in general, yielded results in excellent agreement with those
obtained by other methods and that those discrepancies so far found are
not yet numerous enough or sufficiently well documented to justify dis-
carding this procedure.

Mercuric ion is, in some respects, more suitable for the titration of
thiols because the mercaptides formed are considerably more stable than
the complexes between the mercaptides and mercury (but see Section
II, C, where it is pointed out that silver may be more effective than
mercury in reacting with certain "masked" —SH groups). The latter
complexes can be suppressed by a high concentration of suitable anions,
such as chloride (*8, 9*). Mercuric chloride has been used as the basis of
various amperometric titrations (*19*), but the stoichiometry of the
mercaptide formation tends to vary under different conditions because of
the divalency of mercury. Cecil and McPhee (*4*) advise that it may be
difficult to tell if the end point of a titration corresponds to $RSHgX$,
$(RS)_2Hg$, or $(RS)_2Hg_2$. They feel that certain organic mercury derivatives fulfill the need for a univalent reagent with some of the advantages
of mercuric ion. The use of organic mercurials will be discussed in a later
section.

C. Inhibition of Enzymes

Heavy metals were at one time used widely for inhibitory studies, but they fell into disfavor after the development of the more specific organic mercurials. The use of metals for inhibitions is subject to the limitations of specificity and reaction conditions which were discussed earlier.

Those enzymes which possess —SH groups should form complexes with mercuric ion, and such complexes would be expected to be less soluble (5). Several enzymes have been isolated as crystalline mercury complexes, including enolase (20), rat lactic dehydrogenase (21), papain (22), and lysozyme from papaya latex (23). The papain crystallizes as a dimer with one molecule of mercury, in a manner reminiscent of the crystalline mercury complex of mercaptalbumin (24). The lysozyme has no —SH groups, and it is believed that the mercury is bound to an imidazole group.

Urease has been the subject of considerable experimentation with regard to inhibition by metals. Jacoby (25) showed that it could be inhibited by mercuric ion, and Bersin (26) found that H_2S would reverse this inhibition. The data of Hellerman et al. (27), when recalculated for the molecular weight of 483,000 given by Sumner et al. (28), indicate that the first 22 moles of PCMB added per mole of urease produce no inhibition, while there is a linear titration of the activity with the next 22 equivalents. It is therefore interesting that Ambrose et al. (29) found that as little as 6 equivalents of silver ion were sufficient to cause complete inhibition. Shaw (30) investigated the relative efficiency of inhibition by a number of metal ions and found that it was directly related to the logarithm of the solubility constant of the metal sulfides. Silver, however, was considerably more efficient as an inhibitor than mercury, which may be related to the greater ability of silver to react with masked —SH groups, as discussed below. There is also the possibility, as suggested by Hellerman (31), that PCMB causes structural changes, such as a dissociation of the urease molecule. Urease shows many interesting facets and it might be interesting to reinvestigate the inhibition by mercaptide-forming agents, using the more recent methods discussed above and below.

Hellerman et al. (32) employed silver in an interesting series of experiments on crystalline glutamic acid dehydrogenase. If their results with the enzyme from calf liver are expressed on the basis of a molecular weight of 1×10^6, then 40 gm atoms of silver may be added without any inactivation. Further addition of silver produces a proportional inhibition which is complete at a total of 80 gm atoms per mole of protein. An additional 40 —SH groups can be titrated with silver only after denaturation. Organic mercurials can react with the first 40 —SH but only with

difficulty with the second 40, as they produce little inhibition. Amperometric titration with silver agrees with the enzymic titration in yielding a
total of 80 —SH groups per mole of native protein. The authors suggest
that the organic mercurials fail to inhibit because of steric hindrance. The
—SH groups are believed to play a direct role in the catalytic function
of the enzyme.

Cecil and McPhee (4) have criticized the above interpretation on the
grounds that if steric hindrance prevents the organic mercurials from
approaching the —SH groups there would also be difficulty in the approach of the glutamic acid molecule. They suggest that the —SH groups
are present in some form of combination which is broken more easily by
silver ion than by the mercurials or mercury, as is apparently the case
with disulfides. This suggestion would imply that the —SH groups are
more concerned with maintenance of protein structure than directly with
the catalytic function.[4]

This reviewer agrees with Cecil and McPhee, but would also like to
point out that PCMB was allowed to react with the glutamic dehydrogenase for only 2 minutes before enzymic activity was measured. At
the low concentration of protein-bound —SH groups employed ($5.6 \times
10^{-7} M$), the extent of inhibition reported with varying concentrations
of PCMB is consistent with the occurrence of a second-order reaction
having a rate constant similar to those reported for other enzymes and
proteins which react slowly with PCMB (see Section III, A and Table
III). That PCMB is capable of reacting with all of the groups available
to silver is shown in the same paper by amperometric measurement of
the —SH groups after reaction with the mercurial. Here the reaction went
to completion because of the much higher concentrations of both protein
and mercurial which were used in this experiment. This paper presents
some fascinating contrasts in the effectiveness of silver versus organic
mercurials as inhibitors of certain types of sulfhydryl enzymes and again
illustrates the fact that slowly reacting or masked —SH groups react very
much more quickly with silver than with organic mercurials or even with
mercuric ion.

Heavy metal inhibition of sulfhydryl enzymes may occur when it is
undesirable and, possibly, undetected. Hoch *et al.* (33) have recently
presented evidence that the inhibition of yeast alcohol dehydrogenase by
N'-methylnicotinamide is caused by silver present in the chemical as

---

[4] *Note added in proof:* A more recent communication indicates that silver
ion does cause glutamic dehydrogenase to dissociate. Eighty equivalents of
Ag^+ per 10^6 gm of protein changed the $s_{20,w}$ from 24.4 to 10.5. [K. Rogers, T.
E. Thompson, and L. Hellerman, *Biochim. Biophys. Acta* 64, 202 (1962).]

supplied. The inhibition by hydroxylamine is also due to contaminating metals. Another facet of the dangers of contamination of chemicals by heavy metals may possibly be illustrated by the same enzyme. The results of Barron and Levine (34), when recalculated for a molecular weight of 150,000 indicate that the addition of DPN causes the disappearance of 8 —SH groups per mole of enzyme, an average of two per DPN bound (35). This has led to speculation on the role of the —SH groups in this enzyme; but if the DPN used has been contaminated with metals, the results may be in error.

III. ORGANIC MERCURIALS

A. Chemistry of Mercaptide Formation

PCMB is the most commonly used compound of this type and was introduced by Hellerman and his associates (27). p-Chloromercuriphenyl-sulfonate was recommended by Velick (36) because of its greater solubility. Cecil and McPhee (4) prefer phenylmercuric hydroxide, while compounds of methylmercury have been used extensively by Hughes (37) and co-workers. Other organic mercurials which have been used include mersalyl and 4-(p-dimethylaminobenzeneazo)phenylmercuric acetate. The latter compound must be used in a two-phase system with heptanol and is chiefly useful for quantitative measurements (38).

The reaction of an organic mercurial with an —SH group may be depicted as in Eq. (7).

$$R—HgX + R'—SH \rightleftharpoons R—Hg—S—R' + H^+ + X^- \tag{7}$$

The nature of the anion attached to the mercurial, here denoted by X^-, may have a significant effect on the equilibrium and specificity of the reaction. Boyer (3, 39) has pointed out that, when PCMB is solubilized in base, the chloride is probably replaced by OH^-. Pyrophosphate or glycylglycine increase the solubility of PCMB, presumably by displacing the chloride. Harris and Hellerman (40) have found that EDTA may overcome the inhibition of some enzymes by PCMB, and certainly the interaction of the two reagents is shown by the shift in the ultraviolet absorption spectrum of the PCMB (39). Chinard and Hellerman (41) caution about the use of chelating agents in conjunction with PCMB, but in at least one case the presence of EDTA does not affect the inhibition by PCMB (42). Hughes (43) has found that methylmercury hydroxide will combine in nonspecific fashion in great excess of the number of protein —SH groups, but methylmercury iodide is much more specific because only the —SH groups can overcome the strong affinity between the mercurial and iodide. Boyer (*39*) has contributed a detailed and systematic study of the effect of various anions on the reaction between PCMB and certain model proteins. This should be of considerable benefit in guiding future studies, but caution will still be needed when using new systems. Hoch and Vallee (*44*), for example, found a significant difference in the number of —SH groups titratable in alcohol dehydrogenase by PCMB in different buffers (16 vs. 31 —SH groups per protein molecule in Tris versus phosphate buffer).

The equilibrium of Eq. (7) is generally considered to be far to the right, but the actual value has seldom been determined. An indication that PCMB is bound tightly to protein —SH groups is given by the adherence to stoichiometry when the latter are titrated. Ingram (*13*) has shown that the order of tightness of binding is $HgCl_2 > PCMB > AgNO_3$. This would place the association constant for PCMB with —SH groups between 10^{15} and 10^{20} M, since these are the approximate association constants for silver and mercury (Table I). Hughes (*37*) determined the equilibrium constant for the reaction of methylmercury iodide with mercaptalbumin [Eq. (8)] and found that it corresponded to a pK of 4.45.

$$CH_3HgI + \text{albumin-SH} \rightleftharpoons \text{albumin-S-HgCH}_3 + H^+ + I^- \qquad (8)$$

If we assume that the association constant of CH_3Hg^+ and I^- is the same as for HgI^+ and I^-, namely 10^{11} [from Sillen (*11*)], and that the association constant of albumin-S^- and H^+ is equivalent to that of $-OOC\cdot CH(NH_3^+)CH_2\text{-}S^-$ and H^+, taken as 3.4×10^8, then it may be calculated that

$$K_{assoc} = \frac{(\text{albumin-S-HgCH}_3)}{(\text{albumin-S}^-)\,(CH_3Hg^+)} = 1.2 \times 10^{15} \qquad (9)$$

This result is in fair agreement with that estimated for PCMB above. It may be noted that pH will have a considerable effect on the equilibrium of Eq. (8), and Hughes found that a pH of 7.3 or more was necessary to obtain a quantitative reaction. Table II gives a few of the association constants which have been estimated.

A few estimations of the binding of PCMB to protein have been made. Benesch *et al.* (*18*) found association constants of 4.6×10^4 and 2.4×10^4 with sheep and human hemoglobins by the method of equilibrium dialysis. Madsen and Gurd (*48*), using the ultracentrifugal separation method,

TABLE II

FIRST ASSOCIATION CONSTANTS (LOG k_1) FOR THE FORMATION OF SOME MERCAPTIDES

Ions	Cysteine	Thiogly-colate	Gluta-thione	Mercaptal-bumin
(1) Hg^{++} [a]	20	22	20	—
(2) RS—Hg$^+$ [a]	20	22	20	12.6,[b] 13.2[c]
(3) RS—Hg—R′—Hg$^+$ [d]	—	—	—	17.2[e]
(4) CH$_3$Hg$^+$ [f]	15	—	—	15

[a] The values of log k_1 for the small molecular weight thiols are estimated by taking half of the pK_I for the dissociation of the mercaptide Hg(RS)$_2$ given by Stricks, et al., (9) i.e., the sum of lines (1) and (2) add up to the pK_I. RS—Hg$^+$ in line (2) is the respective mercaptide formed in the first step of the complex formation.

[b] Calculated by Gurd and Wilcox (5) from the data of Edelhoch et al. (45) for human mercaptalbumin.

[c] Calculated from the data of Kay and Edsall (46) for bovine mercaptalbumin.

[d] R is mercaptalbumin; R′ is 3,6-bis(acetatomethyl)dioxane.

[e] Calculated by Gurd and Wilcox (5) from the data of Edsall et al. (47) for human mercaptalbumin

[f] see text for the calculation based on the data of Hughes (37) for human mercaptalbumin.

found an association constant of 1×10^6 for PCMB and phosphorylase, but this result is complicated by the accompanying dissociation of the protein. The data so far accumulated, sketchy and preliminary though they may be, already show some intriguing differences and suggest that a systematic study might provide an additional parameter of considerable value in assessing the effects of these inhibitors.

Slightly more information is available about the rates of reaction between organic mercurials and —SH groups. Cysteine and other simple thiols apparently react "instantaneously" in the sense that the reaction is complete as soon as it can be measured by present methods. Protein-bound —SH groups vary considerably in their rate of reaction with PCMB and other inhibitors. PCMB reacts with the first —SH groups of papain, causing complete inhibition in less than 2 minutes, but the reaction with the remaining five groups is very slow (49). Swenson and Boyer (50) have found that adolase exhibits at least three classes of —SH groups with respect to rate of reaction with PCMB. The first 5–7 groups react in less than 15 seconds and another 3–4 in about 90 minutes, full activity still being maintained. On more prolonged standing at 37° an additional 4–5 groups react, accompanied by a progressive loss of activity. Finally, the remaining —SH groups, to a total of 28 per molecule, can be titrated only in 5 M urea. Benesch *et al.* (*18*) found 29 groups per molecule with their amperometric silver titration. It is now usually considered that those protein-bound —SH groups which are "masked," "sluggish," or not "freely reacting" are protected by either steric hindrance or some type of weak bonding, and the latter explanation is gaining favor. Swenson and Boyer (*50*) have pointed out the possible significance of their results in relation to the role of —SH groups in maintaining the structural integrity of aldolase.

Various factors have been found to influence the rate of reaction of PCMB with a given class of protein-bound —SH group. Boyer (*39*) showed that increasing the sulfate concentration increased the rate of reaction with egg albumin. He suggested that the sulfate would displace an undissociated hydroxyl group from the mercury. Another contributing factor could, however, be an effect on protein configuration of intermolecular association, since these are influenced by the salt concentration. Boyer (*39*) also showed that pH had a considerable effect on both the rate and extent of reaction. For example, at pH 4.6 in 0.33 M acetate, 4.0 moles of PCMB reacted rapidly with 1 mole of egg albumin; at pH 7.0 in 0.05 M phosphate, only 3.2 moles reacted in 24 hours. Further increases in the pH had little effect.

Boyer (*39*) was the first to establish that the reaction between PCMB and protein-bound —SH groups follows second-order kinetics. This is true of the reaction with egg albumin at pH 7.0 and leads to the conclusion that the three —SH groups are essentially homogeneous with respect to their reaction with PCMB. Under certain conditions, however, an increase in reaction rate can be observed after one-third of the —SH groups have been titrated. It is possible that the formation of the first mercaptide initiates a slow change in protein configuration which, when complete, facilitates the reaction of the other —SH groups. A somewhat similar hypothesis has been advanced for the "all-or-none" reaction of PCMB with phosphorylase, which nevertheless also follows second-order kinetics (*48*). This will be discussed in more detail later.

Shukuya and Schwert (*51*) showed that the reaction between PCMB and glutamic acid decarboxylase follows second-order reaction kinetics, as does that of PCMB and lactic dehydrogenase [Takenaka and Schwert (*52*)]. The data of Neilands (*53*) for the latter reaction may also be analyzed to show adherence to second-order kinetics for both the mercaptide formation and the inhibition. Some data on the rates of reaction between PCMB and proteins are tabulated in Table III. Perhaps not too much significance can yet be attached to the fact that the enzymic inhibition, in the few cases where data are available, is slower than the

TABLE III

RATES OF REACTION BETWEEN PCMB AND SOME SULFHYDRYL PROTEINS[a]

Protein	Mercaptide formation[b]	Enzymic inhibition
β-Lactoglobulin[c]	7.5	—
Egg albumin[d]	20.9	—
Glutamic acid decarboxylase[e]	18.8	—
Lactic dehydrogenase of heart[f]	61.4	—
Lactic dehydrogenase of heart[g]	45	12
Phosphorylase a[h]	51	43
Phosphorylase b[i]	82	8

[a] Values are second-order velocity constants in liters moles^{-1} sec^{-1}.

[b] Measured by the spectrophotometric method of Boyer (39).

[c] Boyer (39); 0.33 M acetate, pH 4.6, 28°.

[d] Boyer (39); 0.05 M phosphate, pH 7.0, 28°.

[e] Shukuya and Schwert (51); 0.1 M phosphate, pH 6.5, 25°.

[f] Takenaka and Schwert (52); 0.1 M phosphate, pH 6.8. The enzyme used was the resolved fraction A, and the figure of 4.4 —SH groups per mole of protein was used in the calculation.

[g] Estimates calculated by the reviewer from the data published in graphical form by Neilands (53); 0.1 M phosphate, pH 7.0, 25°. The unresolved enzyme was used, which has been shown to contain 3 —SH groups per mole of protein reacting uder these conditions (54–56).

[h] Madsen and Cori (42); 0.02 M sodium glycerophosphate, pH 6.7, 21°.

[i] Madsen and Cori (42). Conditions as in h.

mercaptide formation. Nevertheless, one is tempted to speculate that the mercaptide formation is not directly responsible for the inhibition but that an intermediary step is required. It is hoped that more such data will become available in the future so that this idea may be either documented or refuted.

B. Methods Employing Organic Mercurials

1. INHIBITORY STUDIES

The use of PCMB for the inhibition of enzymes was introduced by Hellerman and his co-workers. Methods for synthesizing and handling the compound have been given by Chinard and Hellerman (41). Further useful information is found in the article by Boyer (39). In determining the effect of PCMB on an enzyme or enzyme system, the mercurial should be preincubated with the enzyme for various lengths of time and at various concentrations before the substrate is added for the determination of enzymic activity. The necessity for varying the concentration and time is dictated by the second-order nature of the reaction with many —SH groups. In the past, several enzymes which have now been shown to be dependent on intact —SH groups for activity were classed as non-sulfhydryl enzymes because the investigator did not allow sufficient time for the reaction. A study of the effect with time has the further advantage that the data may, in some cases, be used to calculate rate constants, which may then be compared with the rate of mercaptide formation. Of course, if the reaction is of the "instantaneous" type, this will soon be apparent and an elaborate study of the effect with time may not be necessary or possible.

The use of a single concentration of inhibitor can be criticized not only on the basis of the effect on reaction rate but also because, in order to make sure of demonstrating any possible inhibition, the concentration chosen may be so high that nonspecific interaction may occur. Nonspecific binding of PCMB to phosphorylase began to occur at 2.4×10^{-4} M PCMB (48). Benesch et al. (18) had previously demonstrated nonspecific binding.

It is advisable to add the inhibitor before the substrate even when the mercaptide formation is extremely rapid because the presence of substrate may protect the enzyme against inhibition. For example, acetyl phosphate prevents PCMB from reacting with two to three —SH groups of glyceraldehyde-3-phosphate dehydrogenase in spite of the fact that the mercurial should be able to cleave a thio ester bond (57).[5] This will be discussed further in Section IV, A.

As indicated in Section III, A, the composition of the solution with regard to pH concentration and type of anions can have a considerable effect on the reaction between PCMB and proteins. After suitable conditions for time and concentrations have been established for the inhibition of an enzyme by an organic mercurial, it is advisable to try to reactivate the enzyme by adding a thiol such as cysteine or glutathione. Since mercaptide formation is a reversible reaction, the addition of an excess of thiol should regenerate the —SH groups of the enzyme and restore activity. Failure to achieve this indicates that more than simple mercaptide formation must have occurred. While it has been said that protein denaturation could account for such results, this only raises the question as to why such denaturation should have occurred. If, for example, the

[5] *Note added in proof:* Data published recently indicates that PCMB does not split thio esters at neutral pH. [T. Sanner and A. Pihl, *Biochim. Biophys. Acta* **62**, 171 (1962).]

—SH groups of the enzyme were concerned directly with substrate activation or binding, it is difficult to see why tying them up as mercaptides should lead to irreversible denaturation. On the other hand, the reversal of inhibition with a thiol, while it can no longer be considered conclusive evidence of specificity or function, does eliminate certain troublesome complications.

The prevention of inhibition by substrate or cofactors has been investigated fairly extensively, but only a few positive results have been obtained (3). Since a test of this relationship requires incubation of inhibitor, substrate, and enzyme together, it is obvious that certain technical difficulties are presented when a single substrate is involved, particularly if the reaction with the mercurial is slow. In the latter case it might be possible to determine the effect of substrate on the rate of mercaptide formation, as measured by the spectrophotometric method of Boyer (39). The effect of substrates can more easily be determined where two are involved, since one can be preincubated with the inhibitor and the enzyme, and the reaction can be started with the second substrate. Some investigators have determined the effect of the presence of substrate on the titration of enzyme-bound —SH groups by amperometric or spectrophotometric means. Caution must be observed here that the results are not caused by contaminating metals, as discussed in Section II, C.

The failure of a substrate to protect an enzyme against inhibition by a mercurial does not necessarily mean that the —SH groups are not directly concerned with substrate binding because the mercurial will usually have a greater affinity. Where negative results are obtained it might be profitable to devise a more sensitive test, such as the effect on the rate of either inhibition or mercaptide formation. Where the binding of substrate or cofactor to enzyme can be detected by spectrophotometric of fluorometric means, the effects of mercurials on these phenomena should be investigated. The results of using the latter techniques have been reviewed by Shifrin and Kaplan (58).

This chapter is concerned only with mercaptide-forming agents, but consideration of the effects of quinones, arsenicals, and alkylating agents, treated elsewhere in this volume, in conjunction with the results from mercaptide formation, can be very valuable in differentiating the functions of —SH groups. Thus, Strittmatter (59) used both PCMB and NEM to study the —SH groups of microsomal cytochrome reductase. He found that PCMB reacts with three —SH groups per protein molecule, as measured spectrophotometrically, and with a fourth group after denaturation with Duponol. Inactivation began during addition of the first equivalent of PCMB but was not completed at one equivalent, although the curve could be extrapolated to 100% inactivation at one equivalent. The presence of DPNH afforded partial protection at low PCMB concentrations. NEM reacted quickly with two —SH groups, causing 100% inactivation, and more slowly with a third —SH group. In the presence of DPNH, however, NEM reacted quickly with only one —SH group and more slowly with a second, producing a derivative which was fully active. This derivative was now completely inactivated by one equivalent of PCMB, and DPNH afforded no protection. By these experiments the four —SH groups [lettered (a)–(d)] have been completely differentiated:

Group (a) reacts quickly with PCMB and NEM and appears to be intimately related to enzymic activity and DPNH binding in particular. DPNH protects it against reaction with NEM.

Group (b) reacts almost as quickly with NEM as does (a) but somewhat more slowly with PCMB, and does not appear to be related to activity.

Group (c) reacts slowly with NEM and is not essential for activity.

Group (d) can only be titrated with PCMB when the enzyme is denatured.

Sometimes, different types of organic mercurials will yield different results. Halsey (60) found that the first two equivalents of methylmercuric nitrate caused only a small inhibition of yeast glyceraldehyde-3-phosphate dehydrogenase and that a total of four equivalents were required for complete inhibition. Two equivalents of PCMB produced complete inhibition.

2. ESTIMATION OF THIOLS

Mercaptide-forming agents are widely used to measure sulfhydryl groups quantitatively, and organic mercurials are achieving more popularity for this purpose. Chinard and Hellerman (41) discussed the methods used up to 1953 for the titration of —SH groups by PCMB. The end point of the titration has been determined with nitroprusside as an outside indicator. Cecil and McPhee (4) suggest that amperometric titration is probably the best method for determining the end point. Hughes (37) investigated the use of methylmercury iodide with mercaptalbumin as a model thiol. The mercurial in toluene was equilibrated with the protein in an equal volume of buffer, and excess mercurial was titrated with dithizon. Horowitz and Klotz (38) introduced an azomercurial which was used in much the same manner but which would be determined directly by colorimetry.

Boyer (39) observed that when PCMB reacts to form a mercaptide there is an increase in its absorption spectrum, this increase being maximal at 250 mμ at pH 7.0 and at 255 mμ at pH 4.6. Based on this phenomenon, he has worked out quantitative methods for the titration of —SH groups in proteins. Since the total spectral shift accompanying mercaptide formation varies slightly with different thiols, it is necessary to titrate a known quantity of PCMB with increasing amounts of the thiol until there is no further increase in absorbancy (after suitable corrections have been made for the reactants). Care must be exercised to ensure that none of the reagents used cause spectral changes, as EDTA and iodide ion were found to interfere. The spectral shift was shown, however, to be quite specific for —SH groups, and this fact enables the investigator to demonstrate that an inhibition by PCMB is really caused by mercaptide formation. Careful use of high concentrations of urea have been employed to determine the total —SH content of a protein, with results that agree well with amperometric methods. The Boyer technique has by now been used successfully in many different laboratories. For the enzymologist it offers the considerable advantages of not requiring specialized equipment and of being simple and rapid.

Boyer also showed that the method was applicable to kinetic studies of mercaptide formation, and the results so obtained have been reviewed in Section III, A.

Equilibrium dialysis (18) and the ultracentrifugal separation method (48) have also been used to determine the binding of mercurials to proteins. These methods are more cumbersome and time consuming than most, but they appear to be accurate and apparent dissociation constants may be calculated from the data.

3. ESTIMATION OF STRUCTURAL CHANGES

Edelhoch et al. (45) may have been the first to introduce physical methods to measure the effect of mercaptide formation on protein structure when they used light scattering to study the dimerization of mercaptalbumin with mercury salts. Light scattering also made it possible to determine the equilibria and kinetics of the reactions involved. Madsen et al. (42, 48, 61) used the analytical ultracentrifuge and light scattering to demonstrate the effects of PCMB on the structure of phosphorylase. The ultracentrifuge, which has also been used elsewhere (62), makes it possible to demonstrate gross changes only, such as occur on dimerization or dissociation of protein units. Light scattering may make it possible to observe more subtle changes, in addition to kinetic studies. The introduction of the charged PCMB molecule into a protein should result in a change of electrophoretic mobility, but the application of electrophoretic techniques to the phosphorylase problem did not meet with much success.

It might be more useful where a protein has a higher ratio of —SH groups to weight.

Elödi (*63*), in studying the effect of PCMB on the structure of swine muscle glyceraldehyde-3-phosphate dehydrogenase, was able to show that configurational changes, of a finer detail than had hitherto been found, could be demonstrated by measuring the specific optical rotation $[\alpha]_D^{20}$ and the intrinsic viscosity. This is discussed in Section IV, A.

The two methods used by Elödi, as well as optical rotatory dispersion, should prove to be of great value in determining the effects of organic mercurials on the configuration of proteins. No doubt, as newer techniques of greater sensitivity to slight changes in protein configuration are developed, they will be applied with profit. Those methods which make possible a kinetic analysis of structural changes will probably yield the most significant information.

IV. TWO INDIVIDUAL ENZYMES

Results obtained with several enzymes have been reviewed above in the course of discussing the effects of inhibitors. Because of space, only two more of the many possible choices can be reviewed here. The first is chosen because of the large amount of data which has accumulated about it, and because it appears to fulfill most closely the original and classic concept of a sulfhydryl enzyme. The second was chosen because of the reviewer's personal familiarity with it and because it is representative of a second class of sulfhydryl enzymes in which the —SH groups are involved in the maintenance of protein structure.

A. Glyceraldehyde-3-phosphate Dehydrogenase

This enzyme has been studied intensively, and the experiments with sulfhydryl reagents are particularly instructive for the variety of both experimental techniques and the results obtained, as well as the manner in which the latter have been fitted into a general reaction mechanism. The enzyme has been crystallized from yeast with a molecular weight of 122,000. The enzyme crystallized from rabbit muscle contains two moles of DPN which can be removed by charcoal. Its molecular weight was taken as 120,000 in earlier studies, but is now considered to be 137,000 (*64, 65*). Both enzymes catalyze reaction (*10*) in which the normal aldehyde substrate is glyceraldehyde-3-phosphate. Rapkine and his coworkers

$$RCHO + DPN^+ + HPO_4^{2-} \rightleftharpoons RCOOPO_3^{2-} + DPNH + H^+ \qquad (10)$$

showed that the yeast enzyme is inhibited by iodoacetate (*66*) and that DPN protected the enzyme against inhibition by certain oxidizing agents (*67*). Velick (*36*) found that the addition of PCMPS to the muscle enzyme caused a proportional loss of activity until inactivation was complete at 3 moles of PCMPS per mole of enzyme. Ultracentrifugal separation analysis indicated that the combination of inhibitor with enzyme was accompanied by a release of the 2 moles of bound DPN and was complete when three moles of inhibitor had been bound. Both effects were reversed instantaneously upon addition of cysteine. In the case of the yeast enzyme, two equivalents of PCMB were sufficient to produce complete inactivation, and the activity was restorable with cysteine. The inhibitor-enzyme complex could be crystallized, and it would not bind DPN. Thus, the evidence would appear to point to participation of —SH groups in the binding of the nucleotide, but Velick pointed out that steric hindrance or configurational changes provide alternative explanations. More recently, he has presented evidence that conformational changes in the protein do occur upon inhibition (*68*).

Considerable evidence, both kinetic and chemical in nature, has accumulated that an acyl enzyme is an intermediate in Eq. (10) and that an —SH group on the enzyme provides the protein-bound part of this compound. Equation (10) may thus be formulated in the steps (adapted from the schemes of Racker and of Boyer) shown in Scheme I.

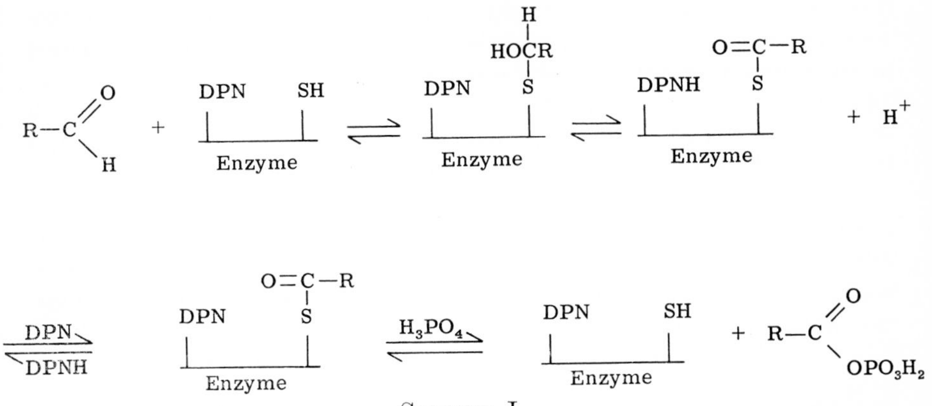

SCHEME I

Observations on the relationships between substrate and sulfhydryl reagents are among the evidence favoring the participation of —SH groups as shown in Scheme I. Segal and Boyer (*69*) showed that glyceraldehyde-3-phosphate gives almost complete protection against inactivation by iodoacetate. Amperometric iodosobenzoate titration gave 15 —SH groups per mole of enzyme, 5 of which disappeared after treatment with iodoacetate, but only 3 disappeared when the aldehyde was present along with the iodoacetate. That two —SH groups react with the substrate was corroborated by the later finding (*70*) that acetyl phosphate blocks the reaction of two —SH groups with PCMB. Spectrophotometric titration with PCMB indicates that 11 groups react rapidly and three more slowly at pH 4.6. Acetyl phosphate decreases the number of titratable groups by two. The acyl-enzyme compounds formed from acetyl phosphate or 1,3-diphosphoglycerate have the properties of thiol esters [Krimsky and Racker (*71*)].

The apparent involvement of two —SH groups in the binding of both nucleotide and substrate is further substantiated by the results of Racker and Krimsky (*72*), who showed that the absorption at 360 mμ resulting from the binding of DPN to the muscle enzyme can be abolished by 1,3-diphosphoglycerate, acetyl phosphate or acetyl glutathione, as well as by PCMB or iodoacetate. They favor an aldehydolysis of a DPN-sulfhydryl bond with the concomitant formation of a thiol ester during the first stage of the enzymic catalysis.

Elödi (*63*) has recently presented evidence that the role of —SH groups in the swine muscle enzyme may be more extensive than is suggested above. He showed that the addition of successive increments of PCMB to the enzyme cause proportionate changes in both the specific optical rotation and the intrinsic viscosity. This suggests that pronounced structural changes had occurred, probably involving a considerable unfolding of the α-helical structure. Both properties ceased changing at a total of 14 equivalents of inhibitor. There was no lag in commencing changes with the first increment, suggesting that even the first 2 or 3 —SH groups reacting, which are generally considered to be involved in the enzymic reaction, may also be involved in maintaining structural integrity. It might be interesting to attempt to find out if structural changes occur during the enzymic process. Boyer and Schultz (*73*) did find that there was a slight, reversible change in optical rotation on removing DPN from the rabbit muscle enzyme.

B. Phosphorylase

The studies on the interaction of PCMB with crystalline muscle phosphorylase (*42*, *48*, *61*) are another example of the application of several techniques differing widely in principle to ascertain the nature of the reaction and the effect on the protein. Phosphorylase a has a molecular weight of 495,000 (74). Approximately 18 equivalents of PCMB were required for complete inactivation of the enzyme, a figure which agrees well with the amino acid analysis of 9 cystine equivalents (75), as well as with titrations of the —SH groups by the spectrophotometric method of Boyer, and the binding of PCMB as measured by the ultracentrifugal separation technique. Ultracentrifrugal analysis indicated that the inhibited enzyme had a molecular weight one-quarter that of the native enzyme and that during the course of reactivation by cysteine the reassociating protein passed through a dimeric stage. Enzymic reactivation proceeded more slowly than the return to the original molecular weight. The kinetics of the reaction were studied by spectrophotometry, enzymic activity, and light scattering. The spectrophotometric method indicated that the reaction of PCMB with the —SH groups followed second-order kinetics. The enzymic inactivation also followed second-order kinetics but was slightly slower than the mercaptide formation. The light scattering showed that the dissociation of the protein molecule followed first-order kinetics and was very much slower than the other two processes. Thus, the inactivation is not caused by the dissociation.

The reaction of PCMB with phosphorylase was shown to be an "all-or-none" process because partially inhibited enzyme showed two molecular species in the ultracentrifuge, the ratio of monomer to total protein being the same as the ratio of PCMB added to total —SH content. This was substantiated by chemical analysis of the two molecular species separated by ultracentrifugation; the monomer fraction contained sufficient mercurial to saturate all its —SH groups, whereas the tetramer contained only a little mercurial. Thus, whereas the 18 —SH groups of phosphorylase a have not yet been differentiated by kinetic means, the preceding experiment suggests that the reaction of the first few —SH groups on a protein molecule increases the reactivity of the remainder. Finally, the binding of PCMB to phosphorylase was measured by the ultracentrifugal separation method. This showed that the first approximately 19 equivalents of mercurial were bound tightly to the protein (apparent association constant of 10^6), while a further larger number of equivalents were bound more loosely and, presumably, to groups other than sulfhydryl.

The results obtained with phosphorylase prompt a certain amount of speculation about the sequence of events during inhibition. The first —SH groups of a protein molecule to form mercaptides facilitate the reaction of the remainder, so that all the —SH groups of a molecule form mercaptides very quickly. The inhibition appears to be slightly slower than the mercaptide formation, although the difference in rate is small enough that it may not be significant. If it is assumed to be significant, then some factor other than mercaptide formation must account for the inhibition. Local structural changes may be the cause. Finally, after inhibition, the protein molecule dissociates. One of the remaining problems, the events occuring immediately upon mercaptide formation which lead to inhibition, might prove amenable to study by a method which is rapid and sensitive to small changes in protein configuration, such as optical rotation.

The experiments with phosphorylase provided decisive evidence that the blocking of —SH groups may lead to pronounced changes in protein structure and, by implication, that —SH groups may be important in the maintenance of a given protein configuration. Similar results have since been found for other proteins, but the nature of the linkages in which the —SH groups might be involved remains unknown and the subject of considerable speculation (3, 4, 76, 77). Mercurials can be of considerable use in detecting those cases where —SH groups may be involved in protein structure, since a slow reaction of a mercurial with —SH groups appears to be associated with such involvement.

V. SUMMARY

The chemistry of mercaptide formation has been discussed from the standpoint of specificity in comparison to other possible reactions. Reaction conditions which may affect the application of mercaptide formation have been considered. After appraisal of the analytical use of mercaptide-forming agents in estimating the —SH groups of proteins, it was concluded that an amperometric silver titration method and a spectrophotometric method employing PCMB are the most suitable among those currently available. The use of silver and mercuric ions for inhibitory studies offer certain advantages, but care must be exercised that the results obtained are specifically due to mercaptide formation. Organic mercurials, and PCMB in particular, are the most generally useful and specific agents available for inhibitory studies designed to delineate the relationships between —SH groups and the mechanism of enzyme action.

As research continues, an increasing number of phenomena are observed to result from mercaptide formation in enzymes. Some of these phenomena and their significance with respect to enzyme action have been discussed briefly. Considerable further data must be assembled, however, before truly sound deductions can be made about the role of —SH groups in enzymic catalysis and protein structure. Fortunately, the present techniques appear adequate for achieving much of this objective.

REFERENCES

1. E. S. G. Barron, *Advances in Enzymol.* 11, 201 (1951).
2. R. E. Benesch *et al.*, eds., "Sulfur in Proteins." Academic Press, New York, 1959.
3. P. D. Boyer, *in* "The Enzymes" (P. D. Boyer, H. Lardy and K. Myrbäck, eds.), 2nd ed., Vol. I, p. 511. Academic Press, New York, 1959.
4. R. Cecil and J. R. McPhee, *Advances in Protein Chem.* 14, 255 (1959).
5. F. R. N. Gurd and P. E. Wilcox, *Advances in Protein Chem.* 11, 311 (1956).
6. I. M. Kolthoff, *J. Phys. Chem.* 35, 2711 (1931).
7. I. M. Klotz, *in* "The Mechanism of Enzyme Action" (W. D. McElroy and B. Glass, eds.), p. 257. Johns Hopkins Press, Baltimore, Maryland, 1954.
8. W. Stricks and I. M. Kolthoff, *J. Am. Chem. Soc.* 75, 5673 (1953).
9. W. Stricks, I. M. Kolthoff, and A. Heyndrickx, *J. Am. Chem. Soc.* 76, 1515 (1954).
10. R. E. Benesch and R. Benesch, *J. A. Chem. Soc.* 77, 5877 (1955).
11. L. G. Sillen, *Acta Chem. Scand.* 3, 539 (1949).
12. C. Tanford and J. Epstein, *J. Am. Chem. Soc.* 76, 2170 (1954).
13. V. M. Ingram, *Biochem. J.* 59, 653 (1955).
14. B. L. Vallee, T. L. Coombs, and F. L. Hoch, *J. Biol. Chem.* 235, PC 45 (1960).
15. I. M. Kolthoff and W. E. Harris, *Ind. Eng. Chem. Anal. Ed.* 18, 161 (1946).
16. R. Benesch and R. E. Benesch, *Arch. Biochem. Biophys.* 19, 35 (1948).
17. I. M. Kolthoff and W. Stricks, *J. Am. Chem. Soc.* 72, 1952 (1952).
18. R. E. Benesch, H. A. Lardy, and R. Benesch, *J. Biol. Chem.* 216, 663 (1955).
19. I. M. Kolthoff, W. Stricks, and L. Morren, *Anal. Chem.* 26, 366 (1954).
20. O. Warburg and W. Christian, *Biochem. Z.* 310, 384 (1942).
21. F. Kubowitz and P. Ott, *Biochem. Z.* 314, 94 (1943).
22. E. L. Smith, J. R. Kimmel, and D. M. Brown, *J. Biol. Chem.* 207, 533 (1954).
23. E. L. Smith, J. R. Kimmel, D. M. Brown, and E. O. P. Thompson, *J. Biol. Chem.* 215, 67 (1955).
24. W. L. Hughes, Jr., *J. Am. Chem. Soc.* 69, 1836 (1947).
25. M. Jacoby, *Biochem. Z.* 181, 194 (1927).
26. T. Bersin, *Ergeb. Enzymforsch.* 4, 68 (1935).
27. L. Hellerman, F. P. Chinard, and V. R. Deitz, *J. Biol. Chem.* 147, 443 (1943).
28. J. B. Sumner, N. Gralén, and I.-B. Eriksson-Quensel, *J. Biol. Chem.* 125, 37 (1938).
29. J. F. Ambrose, G. B. Kistiakowski, and A. G. Kridl, *J. Am. Chem. Soc.* 73, 1232 (1951).
30. W. H. R. Shaw, *J. Am. Chem. Soc.* 76, 2160 (1954).
31. L. Hellerman, Personal communication; also see Boyer (*3*).

32. L. Hellerman, K. A. Schellenberg, and O. K. Reiss, *J. Biol. Chem.* **233**, 1468 (1958).

33. F. L. Hoch, R. G. Martin, W. E. C. Wacker, and B. L. Vallee, *Arch. Biochem. Biophys.* **91**, 166 (1960).

34. E. S. G. Barron and S. Levine, *Arch. Biochem. Biophys.* **41**, 175 (1952).

35. J. Van Eys and N. O. Kaplan, *Biochim. et Biophys. Acta* **23**, 574 (1957).

36. S. F. Velick, *J. Biol. Chem.* **203**, 563 (1953).

37. W. L. Hughes, Jr., *Cold Spring Harbor Symposia on Quant. Biol.* **14**, 79 (1950).

38. M. G. Horowitz and I. M. Klotz, *Arch. Biochem. Biophys.* **63**, 77 (1956).

39. P. D. Boyer, *J. Am. Chem. Soc.* **76**, 4331 (1954).

40. J. Harris and L. Hellerman, *Federation Proc.* **12**, 215 (1953).

41. F. P. Chinard and L. Hellerman, *Methods Biochem. Anal.* **1**, 1 (1954).

42. N. B. Madsen and C. F. Cori, *J. Biol. Chem.* **223**, 1055 (1956).

43. W. L. Hughes, Jr., *in* "The Mechanism of Enzyme Action" (W. D. McElroy and B. Glass, eds.), p. 286. Johns Hopkins Press, Baltimore, Maryland, 1954.

44. F. L. Hoch and B. L. Vallee, *Arch. Biochem. Biophys.* **91**, 7 (1960).

45. H. Edelhoch, E. Katchalski, R. H. Maybury, W. L. Hughes, Jr., and J. T. Edsall, *J. Am. Chem. Soc.* **75**, 5058 (1953).

46. C. M. Kay and J. T. Edsall, *Arch. Biochem. Biophys.* **65**, 354 (1956).

47. J. T. Edsall, R. H. Maybury, R. B. Simpson, and R. Straessle, *J. Am. Chem. Soc.* **76**, 3131 (1954).

48. N. B. Madsen and F. R. N. Gurd, *J. Biol. Chem.* **223**, 1075 (1956).

49. B. J. Finkle and E. L. Smith, *J. Biol. Chem.* **230**, 669 (1958).

50. A. D. Swenson and P. D. Boyer, *J. Am. Chem. Soc.* **79**, 2174 (1957).

51. R. Shukuya and G. W. Schwert, *J. Biol. Chem.* **235**, 1658 (1960).

52. Y. Takenaka and G. W. Schwert, *J. Biol. Chem.* **223**, 157 (1956).

53. J. B. Neilands, *J. Biol. Chem.* **208**, 225 (1954).

54. A. P. Nygaard, *Acta Chem. Scand.* **9**, 1048 (1955).

55. A. P. Nygaard, *Acta Chem. Scand.* **10**, 397 (1956).

56. G. Pfleiderer, D. Jeckel, and Th. Wieland, *Arch. Biochem. Biophys.* **83**, 275 (1959).

57. F. Lynen, E. Reichert, and L. Rueff, *Ann.* **574**, 1 (1951).

58. S. Shifrin and N. O. Kaplan, *Advances in Enzymol.* **22**, 337 (1960).

59. P. Strittmatter, *J. Biol. Chem.* **234**, 2661 (1959).

60. Y. D. Halsey, *J. Biol. Chem.* **214**, 589 (1955).

67. N. B. Madsen, *J. Biol. Chem.* **223**, 1067 (1956).

62. P. J. Snodgrass, B. L. Vallee, and F. L. Hoch, *J. Biol. Chem.* **235**, 504 (1960).

63. P. Elödi, *Biochim. et Biophys. Acta* **40**, 272 (1960).

64. W. B. Dandliker and J. B. Fox, *J. Biol. Chem.* **214**, 275 (1955).

65. J. B. Fox and W. B. Dandliker, *J. Biol. Chem.* **218**, 53 (1956).

66. L. Rapkine, *Biochem. J.* **32**, 1329 (1938).

67. L. Rapkine, S. M. Rapkine, and P. Trpinac, *Compt. rend. acad. sci.* **209**, 253 (1939).

68. S. F. Velick, *J. Biol. Chem.* **233**, 1455 (1958).

69. H. L. Segal and P. D. Boyer, *J. Biol. Chem.* **204**, 265 (1953).

70. O. J. Koeppe, P. D. Boyer, and M. P. Stulberg, *J. Biol. Chem.* **219**, 569 (1956).
71. I. Krimsky and E. Racker, *Science* **122**, 319 (1955).
72. E. Racker and I. Krimsky, *J. Biol. Chem.* **198**, 731 (1952).
73. P. D. Boyer and A. R. Schultz, *in* "Sulfur in Proteins" (R. Benesch *et al.*, eds.). p. 199. Academic Press, New York, 1959.
74. P. J. Keller and G. T. Cori, *Biochim. et Biophys. Acta* **12**, 235 (1953).
75. S. F. Velick and L. F. Wicks, *J. Biol. Chem.* **190**, 741 (1951).
76. K. U. Linderstrøm-Lang and J. A. Schellman, *in* "The Enzymes" (P. D. Boyer, H. Lardy, and K. Myrbäck, eds.), 2nd ed., Vol. I, p. 511. Academic Press, New York, 1959.
77. E. L. Smith, *J. Biol. Chem.* **233**, 1392 (1958).

CHAPTER 22

Enzyme Inhibition by Quinones

O. Hoffmann-Ostenhof

I. INTRODUCTION

Although quinones are closely related to certain aromatic compounds, namely, *p*- and *o*-dihydroxybenzene (catechol and hydroquinone) and their homologues, to which they can easily be transformed by reduction, their properties differ very strongly from those of aromatic substances. Their oxidizing capacities, their unsaturated character, and also their carbonyl groups explain their great reactivity. Therefore, it is understandable that quinones exert various actions on living cells and whole organisms.

In the literature numerous reports are to be found on more or less specific bactericidal, fungicidal, antimitotic, and cytostatic effects of quinones. Attempts to use these actions for practical purposes, e.g., by using certain quinones as fungicidal agents or in the chemotherapy of malaria and cancer have been made with some success.

On the other hand, a great variety of quinones are known to be formed by microorganisms, plants, and animals (*1*). Most of these quinones appear to be final metabolic products, but quinones are also formed as intermediates in some processes, e.g., in melanin formation. Quinones also seem to play an important role in the respiratory chain. Although the exact mechanism of the participation of quinoid compounds in this process is not yet completely elucidated, it seems to be established that the naphthoquinone derivatives of the vitamin K series as well as the so-called ubiquinones ("coenzyme Q"), and perhaps some other quinones, like α-tocopherylquinone and—in plants only—plastoquinone, act as carriers in the respiratory chain and may also have some function in oxidative phosphorylation. An interesting discussion of the development in this field can be found in the proceedings of a recent symposium (2).

Most of the mentioned biological effects of the quinones are probably caused by their action on certain enzymes. This reasoning has induced many workers to investigate quinone inhibition of various enzymes with the purpose of establishing correlations between these effects and the biological actions of the quinones.

II. QUINONE INHIBITION OF ENZYMES BY INTERACTION WITH SH GROUPS

In very many, but not in all, cases quinone inhibition of enzymes must be considered an attack of the quinone on sulfhydryl groups essential for the catalytic function of the enzyme. Interaction with such SH groups is apparently the only mechanism responsible for quinone inhibition of nonoxidative enzymes. Usually, the enzymes can be protected against quinone inhibition by SH compounds like cysteine, glutathione, and BAL; by addition of these substances to an already inhibited enzyme, partial reversal of the inhibition can frequently be obtained.

Quinone interaction with SH groups of enzymes must be considered a much more complex and, on the other hand, less specific effect than the action of some of the classic reagents for sulfhydryl groups of enzymes, such as iodoacetate, iodoacetamide, arsenicals, or p-chloromercuribenzoate. From studies of the interaction of quinones with low molecular sulfhydryl compounds, it may be deduced that several modes of action are possible.

By virtue of their oxidizing power, quinones can oxidize two SH groups to an S—S linkage [Eq. (1)].

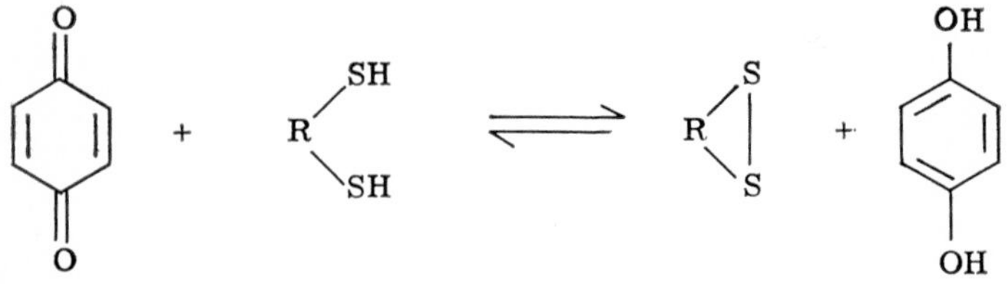

$$\text{(1)}$$

This action, which originally was considered the only explanation of enzyme inhibition by quinones (3), is probably predominant with quinones in which all four positions of the quinone ring are substituted, and should produce an enzyme inhibition which can easily be reversed by addition of SH compounds.

A mode of action frequently encountered when studying the reaction of low molecular sulfhydryl compounds with quinones is the addition of the sulfhydryl group to the reactive double bond of the quinone. The primary step seems to be 1,4-addition. With equivalent amounts of quinone and sulfhydryl compound and in the absence of oxygen, the formation of a monosubstituted hydroquinone can be observed [see Eq. (2)] (4).

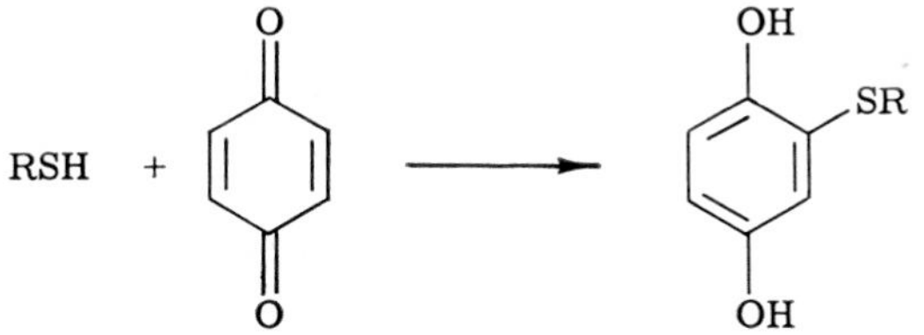

$$RSH \quad + \qquad \qquad \longrightarrow \qquad \qquad \tag{2}$$

Zuman and Zumánová (5) have shown that 2,3-dimercaptopropanol (BAL) and benzoquinone can react in a 1:2 ratio according to Eq. (3).

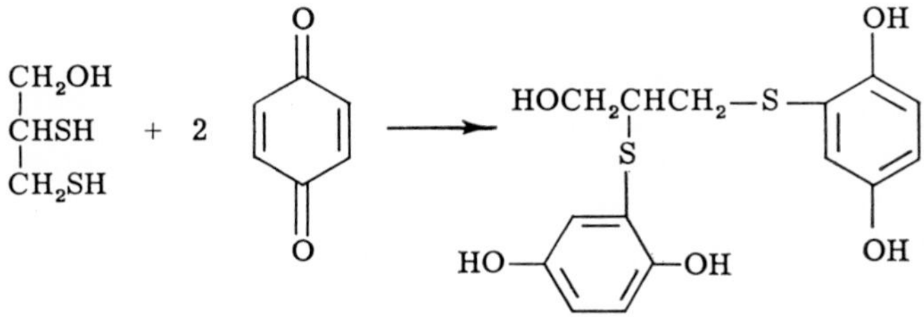

$$\begin{matrix} CH_2OH \\ | \\ CHSH \\ | \\ CH_2SH \end{matrix} \quad + \quad 2 \qquad \qquad \longrightarrow \qquad \qquad \tag{3}$$

In most cases, however, secondary processes take place which frequently lead to unidentifiable polymerization products. Schubert (6), who studied the interaction of p-benzoquinone with thioglycolic acid, observed the formation of a tetraalkylthio derivative of the quinone and explains the formation of this compound by a sequence of reactions. The originally formed monosubstituted hydroquinone is oxidized to a quinone, and the 1,4-addition is repeated. This reaction cycle goes on until all free positions of the quinone are substituted.

Closer examination of the interactions of quinones with cysteine (7–9), which lead mainly to the formation of insoluble polymer products, have shown that bicyclic quinone imide compounds can be isolated from the reaction mixtures and may be considered as intermediates. Using cysteine ethyl ester with p-xyloquinone and 1,4-naphthoquinone, respec-

TABLE I

SOME EXAMPLES OF QUINONE INHIBITIONS OF NONOXIDATIVE ENZYMES

Enzyme tested	Source of enzyme	Remarks
Cholinesterase	Horse serum	p-Benzoquinone inhibits very strongly; no protection by 3,4-dihydroxyphenylalanine (10).
Alkaline phosphatase	Kidney, lung, serum, milk, yeast (11-13)	Benzoquinone derivatives inhibit much more strongly than naththoquinones (12, 13).
Acid phosphatase	Kidney, prostate, gland, yeast (11-13)	
Fructose-1,6-diphosphatase	Liver (14)	
Urease	Plants (15, 16), Helix pomatia (17)	Some benzoquinones and naphthoquinones, especially 1,2-naphthoquinone, inhibit very strongly (18). 2-Methyl-1,4-naphthoquinone partly reverses the inhibition by other naphthoquinones (19).
Glutaminase	Dog kidney	p-Benzoquinone inhibition cannot be reversed by excess substrate. SH agents protect the enzyme (20).
Papain	Carica papaya (21)	Inhibition by benzoquinones and naphthoquinones very similar to urease. 1,2-Naphthoquinone and chlorinated benzoquinones inhibit very strongly (22).

Proteinase	Yeast	Very similar to papain (23).
Proteinase	Potato	Benzoquinone inhibits this SH enzyme (24).
Deoxyribonuclease	Pancreas	1,4- and 1,2-Naphthoquinones inhibit, whereas some benzoquinones, as well as polyphenols transformable into quinones, show a slight activating effect (25).
Hyaluronidase	Bovine testicles	Inhibition by p-benzoquinone and related quinones. Alkali-treated quinone solutions inhibit much more strongly than quinone itself (26).
Pyruvate carboxylase	Yeast (27), fungi (28)	Various benzoquinones, 1,2- and 1,4-naphthoquinones, anthraquinones inhibit very strongly (27). The enzyme can be protected by SH compounds.
Carbonic anhydrase	Plants	Quinones inhibit by attack on essential SH groups (29, 30).
Xylose isomerase	*Pseudomonas hydrophila*	p-Benzoquinone inhibits this SH enzyme (31).

tively, Kuhn and Hammer (8) have isolated compounds to which they ascribe structures (I) and (II).

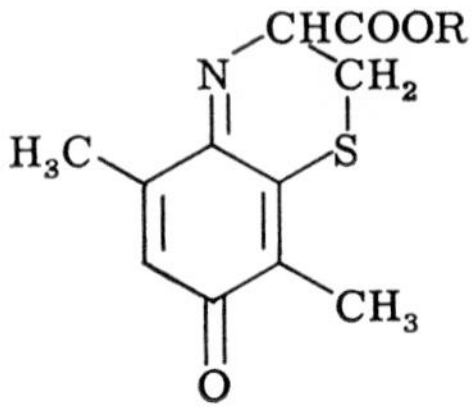

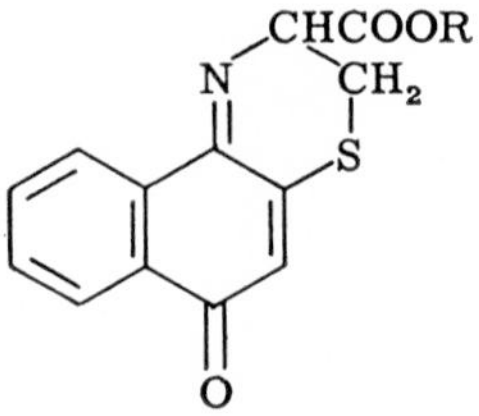

Finally, although no evidence for such a reaction can be derived from experiments with low molecular weight sulfhydryl compounds, the possibility of a reaction of the SH group with the two carbonyl groups of the quinones should not be overlooked. Considering the ease with which the carbonyl groups of aldehydes and quinones react with SH groups, it is hard to imagine why the otherwise very reactive carbonyl groups of quinones should be completely unable to undergo such an addition reaction. By carbonyl addition mono- or dithiohemiacetals could be formed.

It is still impossible with our present knowledge to decide which of the mentioned reaction mechanisms may be predominant in the interaction of SH groups of an enzyme protein with a given protein, causing an inhibition of enzyme activity. Of course, the structure of the quinone must play an important role in determining which of the reactions will take place. Thus, quinones with no free positions in the ring, like the vitamins K_1 and K_2, the ubiquinones, or duroquinone, will not participate in 1,4-addition reactions. But other factors, such as the concentration of the quinone, the pH conditions, and also the steric position of the SH groups in the polypeptide chains of the enzyme, may have a major influence.

In Table I, which is not intended to be complete, some representative examples of quinone inhibition of nonoxidative enzymes are given. Although it has not been established in all cases listed that interactions with SH groups is the underlying mechanism, this must be considered probable, and almost all the enzymes mentioned in Table I are known to be SH enzymes.

III. QUINONE INHIBITION OF ENZYMES OF OXIDOREDUCTION

Even more complex than the mode of action of quinone inhibition of nonoxidative sulfhydryl enzymes is the mechanism of quinone action on enzymic oxidoreduction processes.

The first observations of a quinone inhibition of oxidative processes were made by workers who wanted to use p-benzoquinone as a hydrogen acceptor instead of methylene blue in experiments with the Thunberg technique (*32, 33*). Since then, many reports on the inhibitory actions of quinones on various oxidoreductases and enzyme systems involving oxidoreduction have been published; a list of some representative examples is given in Table II.

In some cases, the enzymes acted upon are also sulfhydryl enzymes and therefore attacked by one or more of the mechanisms discussed above. However, other modes of action must also be considered.

As already mentioned in the introduction, some quinones are believed to have an important function in the respiratory chain. Although neither the exact mechanism of their participation nor their localization in the respiratory chain has been definitely established, it must be assumed that these quinones act as hydrogen and/or electron carriers in a way which is comparable, e.g., to that of the flavins. It also has been postulated by several authors that quinones participate in the phosphorylation processes of the respiratory chain, and various attractive theories about the mechanism of this action have been suggested. A profound discussion of this problem is to be found in an article by Slater, Copla-Boonstra, and Links (59).

Some of the effects of quinones on oxidoreductases or oxidative enzyme systems can possibly be explained by a competition between the quinone inhibitor and the quinone endogenous to the respiratory chain. But even without such competition with a quinone carrier of the system, it could be imagined that the added quinones serve as electron carriers which bypass some essential participants of the respiratory chain. By such a shunting action, the uncoupling of phosphorylation by quinones, a frequently observed phenomenon, can be explained.

The older work on quinone effects on enzymic oxidation reactions (cf. Table II) did not take into account the carrier function of quinones endogenous to the respiratory chain. Some more recent papers, however, deal especially with the action of inhibitory quinones on respiratory systems requiring ubiquinones or vitamin K for their function and are therefore of special interest.

We shall first discuss the studies of quinone action on ubiquinone-requiring systems. Crane (*46*) investigated the ability of some quinones to restore the antimycin-sensitive succinate cytochrome c reductase and succinate oxidase activities in mitochondrial systems which were deprived of ubiquinone by solvent extraction. He found that only quinones very closely related to the endogenous ubiquinone, namely, ubiquinones with

TABLE II

SOME EXAMPLES OF QUINONE INHIBITION OF OXIDOREDUCTASES AND OXIDOREDUCTIVE ENZYME SYSTEMS

Enzyme tested	Source of enzyme	Remarks
Triose phosphate dehydrogenase	Bacteria (34)	Menadione inhibits.
Glucose dehydrogenase	Bovine liver (35)	o- and p-Quinones inhibit.
Glycollate dehydrogenase	Plants (36)	p-Benzoquinone inhibits while being partly reduced.
Estrone reductase	Yeast (37)	The reduction of estrone to 17β-estradiol is inhibited by p-benzoquinone, whereas the reverse process is not affected.
3-Hydroxyanthranilate oxygenase	Kidney, liver (38, 39)	Menadione inhibits the transformation of 3-hydroxyanthranilate to quinolinic acid.
Pyrocatechol oxygenase	Bacteria (40)	o-Benzoquinone inhibits the reaction—probably through interaction with SH groups—and cannot be considered an intermediate of the conversion of pyrocatechol to cis,cis-muconic acid.
Catalase	Blood, liver (41, 42)	The action is inhibited by several p-benzoquinones derivatives and naphthoquinones, and also by meriquinoid amines.

NADH-oxidase system	Lupine mitochondria, (43), *Tetrahymena puriformis* (44), animal mitochondrial systems (45)	SN 5949 inhibits; it appears that the NADH-cytochrome c reductase part of the system is mainly attacked (44). See also text.
Succinate oxidase system	Various sources (32, 46–56)	The system is attacked by quinones, apparently at several places; the substrate reducing part (succinate dehydrogenase), probably by interaction with essential SH groups of the enzyme; in the later stages of electron transport the quinones may interfere with ubiquinone- or vitamin K-requiring steps (cf. also text).
Glycolytic system	Ascites tumor cells (57, 58)	E39 Bayer [2,5-dipropoxy-3,6-bis(ethylenimino)-*p*-benzoquinone] and related cancerostatic substances inhibit glycolysis but not respiration (58).

from 3 to 10 isoprenoid units in the side chain in the 6-position (UQ_3–UQ_{10})[1] were able to restore the mentioned activities completely, whereas several other quinones acted as strong inhibitors. Of these, the action of the diethoxy analogue of UQ_{10} can be reversed by addition of UQ_{10}; the diethoxy analogue seems to act as a competitive inhibitor of the system. The inhibiting action of other quinone inhibitors on the system, however, cannot be reversed by addition of ubiquinone. They include naphthoquinones such as SN 5949 [2-hydroxy-3-(2-methyloctyl)-1,4-naphthoquinone], the vitamins K_1 and K_2, lapachol, and norlapachol, whereas 2-hydroxy-1,4-naphthoquinone, 2,3-dimethyl-1,4-naphthoquinone, 2-undecyl-1,4-naphthoquinone, a-tocopherylquinone, and p-xyloquinone do not influence the system at all.

The influence of duroquinone and some lower homologues of the ubiquinones on the P/O ratios of the oxidation of added NADH by a mitochondrial system has been studied by Jacobs and Crane (60). UQ_0 (the ubiquinone molecule without a polyisoprenoid chain in the 6-position), UQ_2, and also duroquinone showed marked uncoupling effects on the system.

According to Smith and Lester (47), who studied the influence of UQ_0 and its bromo derivative (2,3-dimethoxy-5-methyl-6-bromo-p-benzoquinone) on succinate oxidase and on pyruvate oxidase activities and the accompanying phosphorylation in beef heart mitochondria and active preparations derived from them, the observed inhibitory effects of these ubiquinone analogues are not competitive, since the inhibitions could not be reversed with any of the ubiquinone homologues. The authors explain their results by suggesting two modes of action of the inhibiting quinones: (a) These quinones react with vital sulfhydryl groups in the electron transport and phosphorylation systems, which is indicated by the fact that cysteine and glutathione are capable of protecting the systems against the effect and even of partially reversing them when added later, and (b) the inhibiting quinones serve as electron carriers which bypass some carriers endogenous to the electron transport and phosphorylation system.

Naphthoquinones of the vitamin K group seem to play a role in respiration and phosphorylation systems similar to that of the ubiquinones. However, all evidence existing seems to prove that these two groups of quinones are not interchangeable or, in other words, that their localiza-

---

[1] Following the rules of the Enzyme Commission (45), the abbreviation UQ for ubiquinone is used in this chapter. The index, e.g. UQ_{10}, denotes the number of monounsaturated isoprenoid units in the side chain in the 6-position of the ubiquinone molecule.

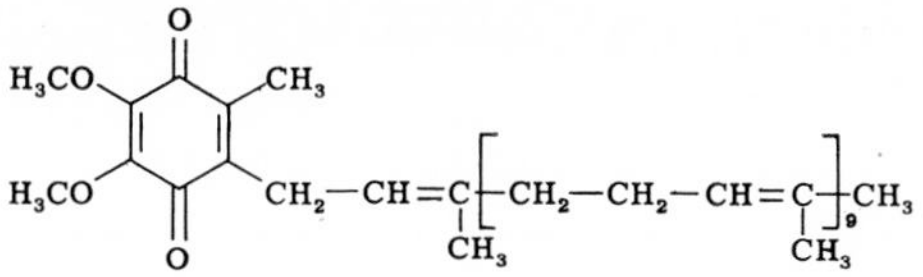

Ubiquinone with 10 isoprenoid units in the side chain (UQ$_{10}$)

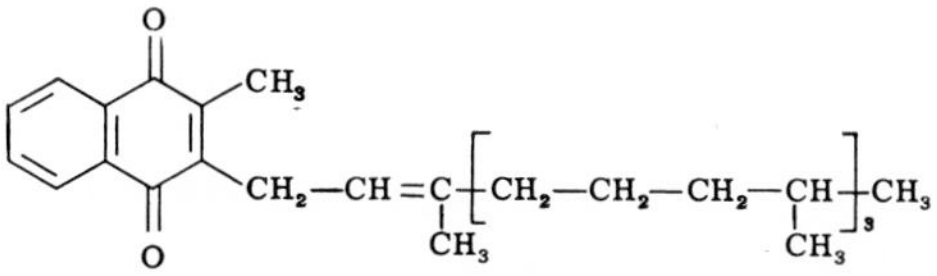

Vitamin K$_1$

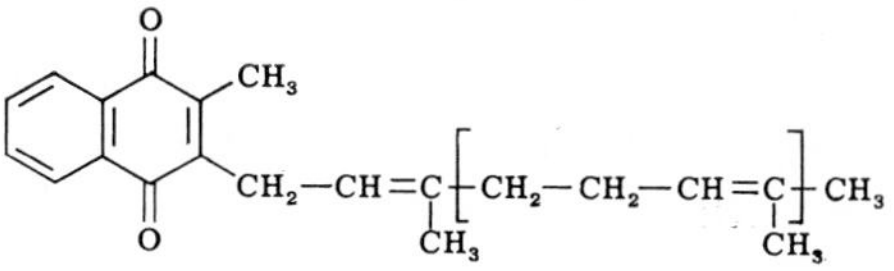

Vitamin K$_2$

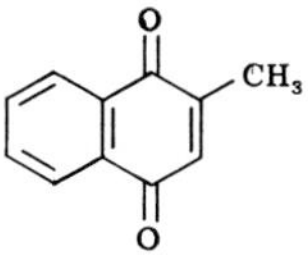

Menadione

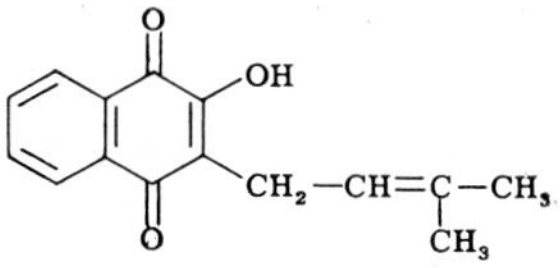

Lapachol

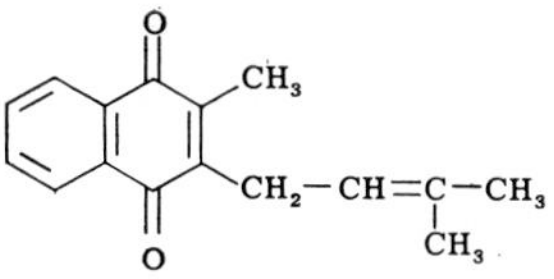

" Methyllapachol"

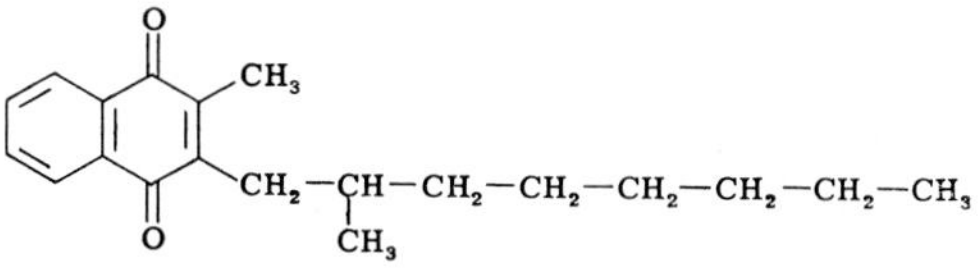

SN 5949

tion in the respiratory chain is different. There are indications that some species contain both types of quinones as participants of the respiratory chain, whereas in others only one is present.

In the case of the action of exogenous quinones on respiration and phosphorylation systems, it is frequently very difficult to distinguish between attacks on the ubiquinone and the vitamin K-dependent parts of the systems. As the vitamins K have already been known for some time and the participation of these compounds in the respiratory chain was considered possible before the ubiquinones were discovered, many workers investigated the action of various presumable vitamin K antagonists on oxidative systems without knowing that another quinone carrier may be involved in the reactions studied. Therefore, the conclusions drawn from some of these earlier experiments are at least partly invalidated, and in all these cases, the question of which of the presumable vitamin K antagonists are in fact attacking the system at the site of vitamin K participation needs reassessment. We have seen previously that one of the most typical vitamin K antagonists, namely, the so-called SN 5949, is capable of interfering with a system requiring ubiquinone rather than vitamin K.

In order to study the specific role of vitamin K in a bacterial system, Brodie and Ballantine (*61, 62*) have devised a very ingenuous method. In a bacterial phosphorylating NADH-oxidase system, all bound vitamin K can be specifically destroyed by irradiation at 360 mμ. It is possible to restore the oxidative, but not the phosphorylating, capacities of the system by addition of riboflavin phosphate. For the restoration of phosphorylation, however, the addition of vitamin K or some closely related compounds proved to be necessary. Napthoquinones which are active in this system contain a methyl group in the C-2 position and an unsaturated side chain of at least five carbon atoms in the C-3 position of the quinone ring. Other quinones restored only oxidation, whereas phosphorylation was either very low or completely suppressed. The authors (*62*) also investigated the action of some uncoupling agents on the complete system, i.e., without previous destruction of vitamin K by irradiation, and found that dicoumarol and also lapachol (2-hydroxy-3-butenyl-1,4-naphthoquinone) act as competitive inhibitors of phosphorylation, whereas oxidation is not inhibited. In this context, the interesting suggestion of Russell and Brodie (*63*) that only such compounds which can be transformed by reduction to β-chromans can participate in phosphorylation, must be mentioned.

Enzymes capable of reducing quinones have been recognized for several years (*64*). They appear not to be highly specific with regard to the quinone substrate, as several quinones are reduced at about the same rate. Quite recently, however, Märki and Martius (65) have isolated and purified a flavin protein from beef liver which catalyzes hydrogen transfer from reduced pyridine nucleotides to vitamin K_2 and some other naphtho- and benzoquinones, but not to vitamin K_1 or to UQ_{10}. The authors consider it a part of the respiratory chain involving vitamin K_2. The enzyme is highly sensitive to small concentrations of dicoumarol, but no experiments on the action of naphthoquinone analogues of vitamin K on its activity are reported. It would be highly desirable to know whether compounds like lapachol or SN 5949 inhibit the vitamin K_2 reductase of Martius and Märki and whether this action is competitive.

In conclusion, it may be said that the study of quinone inhibitions of oxidoreductive systems has already proved to be a valuable tool for the investigation of the role of quinone carriers participating in the respiratory chain and in the concomitant phosphorylation system. Our knowledge of these systems is still far from complete. Some other quinones, like the plastoquinones in photosynthesizing plants (66–68) or α-tocopheryl-quinone, may also function in respiration and phosphorylation systems, and it may be hoped that the use of quinone analogues will help to get a closer insight into the intimate mechanisms of respiratory systems. But the study of quinone inhibitions of oxidative systems may also be of use for practical purposes. It is not improbable that some specific quinone inhibitors acting on respiratory systems will prove to be of therapeutic value.

REFERENCES

1. R. H. Thomson, "Naturally Occurring Quinones." Academic Press, New York, London, 1957.
2. G. E. W. Wolstenholme and C. M. O'Connor, eds., "Quinones in Electron Transport," Ciba Foundation Symposium. Little, Brown, Boston, Massachusetts, 1961.
3. L. Hellerman and M. E. Perkins, *J. Biol. Chem.* 107, 241 (1934).
4. G. H. Meguerrian, *J. Am. Chem. Soc.* 77, 5019 (1955).
5. P. Zuman and R. Zumánová, *Tetrahedron* 1, 289 (1957).
6. M. Schubert, *J. Am. Chem. Soc.* 69, 712 (1947).
7. R. Kuhn and H. Beinert, *Ber.* 77, 606 (1944).
8. R. Kuhn and I. Hammer, *Ber.* 84, 91 (1951).
9. H. Burton and S. B. David, *J. Chem. Soc.* p. 2193 (1952).
10. W. K. Berry, K. P. Fellows, P. J. Fraser, J. P. Rutland, and A. Todrick, *Biochem. J.* 59, 1 (1955).
11. I. W. Sizer, *J. Biol. Chem.* 145, 405 (1942).
12. O. Hoffmann-Ostenhof and E. Putz, *Monatsh. Chem.* 79, 421 (1948).
13. O. Hoffmann-Ostenhof and E. Putz, *Monatsh. Chem.* 81, 703 (1950).
14. E. O. F. Walsh and G. Walsh, *Nature* 161, 976 (1948).
15. J. H. Quastel, *Biochem. J.* 27, 1116 (1933).

16. L. Hellerman, M. E. Perkins, and W. M. Clark, *Proc. Natl. Acad. Sci. U.S.* **19**, 855 (1933).
17. R. Russ, *Z. vergleich, Physiol.* **38**, 284 (1956).
18. O. Hoffmann-Ostenhof and W. H. Lee, *Monatsh. Chem.* **76**, 180 (1946).
19. W. H. Schopfer and E. C. Grob, *Helv. Chim. Acta* **32**, 829 (1949).
20. F. W. Sayre and E. Roberts, *J. Biol. Chem.* **233**, 1128 (1958).
21. T. Bersin and W. Logemann, *Z. physiol. Chem. Hoppe-Seyler's* **220**, 209 (1933).
22. O. Hoffmann-Ostenhof and E. Biach, *Monatsh. Chem.* **78**, 53 (1948).
23. O. Hoffmann-Ostenhof and H. Moser, *Monatsh. Chem.* **79**, 570 (1948).
24. A. Niemann, *Z. physiol. Chem. Hoppe-Seyler's* **305**, 196 (1956).
25. O. Hoffmann-Ostenhof and W. Frisch-Niggemeyer, *Monatsh. Chem.* **83**, 1175 (1952).
26. S. Roseman and A. Dorfman, *J. Biol. Chem.* **199**, 345 (1952).
27. R. Kuhn and H. Beinert, *Ber.* **80**, 101 (1947).
28. M. W. Foote, J. E. Little, and T. J. Sproston, *J. Biol. Chem.* **181**, 481 (1949).
29. K. Kondo, H. Chiba, and F. Kawai, *Bull. Research Inst. Food Sci. Kyoto Univ.* **13**, 12 (1954).
30. K. Kondo, H. Chiba, and F. Kawai, *Bull. Research Inst. Food Sci., Kyoto Univ.* **13**, 23 (1954).
31. R. M. Hochster, *Can. J. Microbiol.* **1**, 589 (1955).
32. H. Wieland and K. Frage, *Ann.* **477**, 1 (1929).
33. H. Wieland and A. Lawson, *Ann.* **485**, 193 (1932).
34. H. Schreiber, *Med. Klin. (Munich)* **48**, 747 (1953).
35. M. Nakamura, *J. Biochem. (Japan)* **41**, 67 (1954).
36. W. Franke and I. Schulz, *Ann.* **578**, 147 (1952).
37. K. Repke, *Arch. exptl. Pathol. Pharmakol., Naunyn-Schmiedeberg's* **230**, 178 (1957).
38. S. Auricchio, M. Piazza, and E. Quagliarello, *Boll. soc. ital. biol. sper.* **33**, 1211 (1957).
39. S. Auricchio, M. Scotto, and M. Piazza, *Boll. soc. ital. biol. sper.* **33**, 1223 (1957).
40. O. Hayaishi, A. A. Batchett, and B. Witkop, *Ann.* **608**, 158 (1957).
41. O. Hoffmann-Ostenhof and E. Biach, *Monatsh. Chem.* **76**, 319 (1946).
42. L. Horner and C. Betzel, *Ann.* **571**, 225 (1951).
43. T. E. Humphreys and E. E. Conn, *Arch. Biochem. Biophys.* **60**, 226 (1956).
44. H. J. Eichel, *J. Biol. Chem.* **222**, 121 (1956).
45. "Report of the Commission on Enzymes of the International Union of Biochemistry," Pergamon Press, New York, 1961.
46. F. L. Crane, *Arch. Biochem. Biophys.* **87**, 198 (1960).
47. A. L. Smith and R. L. Lester, *Biochim. et Biophys. Acta* **48**, 547 (1961).
48. H. Bergstermann and W. Stein, *Biochem. Z.* **317**, 217 (1944).
49. E. G. Ball, C. B. Anfinsen, and O. Cooper, *J. Biol. Chem.* **168**, 257 (1947).
50. H. Heymann and L. F. Fieser, *J. Biol. Chem.* **176**, 1359 (1948).
51. W. W. Ackerman and V. R. Potter, *Proc. Soc. Exptl. Biol. Med.* **72**, 1 (1949).
52. A. E. Reif and R. Potter, *J. Biol. Chem.* **205**, 279 (1953).

53. H. W. Clark, H. A. Neufeld, C. Widmer, and E. Stotz, *J. Biol. Chem.* **210**, 851 (1954).
54. C. Widmer, H. W. Clark, H. A. Neufeld, and E. Stotz, *J. Biol. Chem.* **210**, 861 (1954).
55. A. Herz, *Biochem. Z.* **325**, 83 (1954).
56. K. Okunuki and J. Sekutsu, *J. Biochem. (Japan)* **42**, 397 (1955).
57. W. Remmele and W. Rick, *Z. Krebsforsch.* **61**, 449 (1957).
58. H. Holzer, P. Glogner, and G. Sedlmayr, *Biochem. Z.* **330**, 59 (1958).
59. E. L. Slater, J. P. Copla-Boonstra, and J. Links, *in* "Quinones in Electron Transport," Ciba Foundation Symposium (G. E. W. Wolstenholme and C. M. O'Connor, eds.), p. 161. Little, Brown, Boston, Massachusetts, 1961.
60. E. E. Jacobs and F. L. Crane, *Biochem. Biophys. Research Communs.* **2**, 218 (1960).
61. A. F. Brodie and J. Ballantine, *J. Biol. Chem.* **235**, 226 (1960).
62. A. F. Brodie and J. Ballantine, *J. Biol. Chem.* **235**, 232 (1960).
63. P. J. Russell and A. F. Brodie, *in* "Quinones in Electron Transport," Ciba Foundation Symposium (G. E. W. Wolstenholme and C. M. O'Connor, eds.), p. 205. Little, Brown, Boston, Massachusetts, 1961.
64. W. D. Wosilait and A. Nason, *J. Biol. Chem.* **206**, 255 (1954).
65. F. Märki and C. Martius, *Biochem. Z.* **333**, 111 (1960).
66. R. L. Lester and F. L. Crane, *J. Biol. Chem.* **234**, 2169 (1959).
67. N. I. Bishop, *Proc. Natl. Acad. Sci. U.S.* **45**, 1696 (1959).
68. N. I. Bishop, *in* "Quinones in Electron Transport," Ciba Foundation Symposium (G. E. W. Wolstenholme and C. M. O'Connor, eds.), p. 385. Little, Brown, Boston, Massachusetts.

CHAPTER 23

Biological Alkylating Agents

J. M. Johnson and F. Bergel

I. INTRODUCTION

Biological alkylating agents belong to a group of compounds which, chemically speaking, attack nucleophilic (electron-rich) centers. The details of these mechanistic aspects have been fully discussed by Ross (*1, 2*). In contrast, the mechanistic aspects of their biological action, a summary of which will be given later in this review, have been only partly elucidated during recent years. The fact will emerge that these compounds are only in an indirect way "metabolic antagonists," for on the whole they do not participate in biochemical processes of the cell in the same manner as true antimetabolites, i.e, as "fraudulent" substrates, products, or coenzymes, but seem to achieve their effects by interacting chemically with certain constituents of living cells and altering them in such a way that the change in the structure and functional properties of these constituents leads finally to cell death. However, it should be mentioned here that some alkylating agents appear to influence amino acid incorporation and thus may, under certain conditions, act as metabolic inhibitors (*3*).

A great number of reviews and papers read during symposia have been

CHART I—ALKYLATING AGENTS

A. Sulfur-mustards

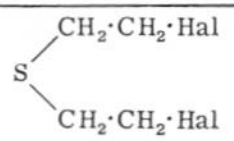

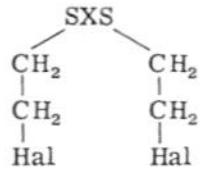

$$S \big\langle \begin{matrix} CH_2 \cdot CH_2 \cdot Hal \\ CH_2 \cdot CH_2 \cdot Hal \end{matrix}$$

$$SXS \quad \begin{matrix} CH_2 & CH_2 \\ CH_2 & CH_2 \\ Hal & Hal \end{matrix} \quad (122)$$

B. Nitrogen-mustards
Aromatic

$$M = -N \big\langle \begin{matrix} CH_2-CH_2-Cl \\ CH_2-CH_2-Cl \end{matrix}$$

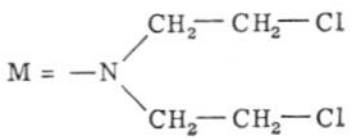

1. Purely aromatic

e.g., CB 1048

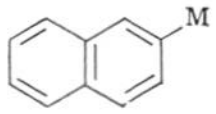

M (naphthalene) active (140)

2. Aromatic aliphatic

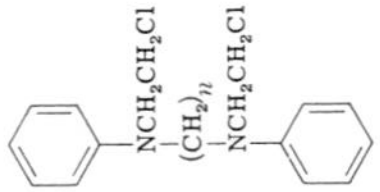

$$\begin{matrix} NCH_2CH_2Cl \\ (CH_2)_n \\ NCH_2CH_2Cl \end{matrix} \quad (141)$$

n = 1, 2, 3, 4
⟶ Decr. act. ⟶

3. With latent activity

(a) Azobenzenes

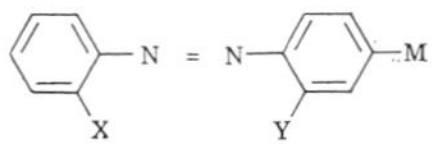

M—N=N— (benzene with X, Y)

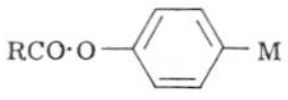

X = CO₂H, Y = Me; CB 1414, highly active (59)

(b) Acyl groups

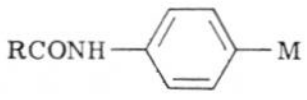

RCONH—M   RCO·O—M   R = Me or Ph (149)

R = Cl₃C, CB 1431, active (58)

(c) Aminoacyl groups

(c₁) RCHCONH—M / NH₂   R = H, PhCH₂, inactive (150)

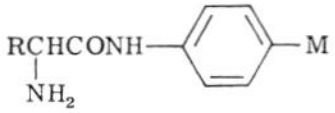

(c₂) (CH₂)ₙ CH—NH CO / CO N R

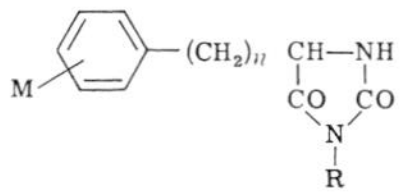

e.g., CB 1655; n = 0, R = H, M is *meta*; active (40)

4. Nitrogen mustards
Aromatic + substituent

(a) Fatty acid or O-fatty acid

(a₁) M—(CH₂)ₙCO₂H

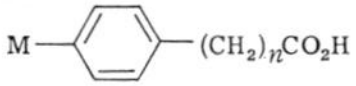

e.g., Chlorambucil, n = 3, highly active (145)

(a₂) M—O(CH₂)ₙCO₂H

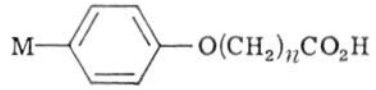

n = 2, highly active (144)

(b) Amino acids

(b₁) M—(CH₂)ₙCHCO₂H / NH₂

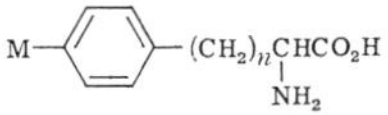

n = 1
L- CB 3025, highly active; D- CB 3026, much less active; DL- CB 3007 = Sarcolysine, active (142,143)
n = 0
less active; n = 2 or 3, highly active; CB 1385, 1494 (144)

(b₂) M—O— —CH₂CHCO₂H / NH₂

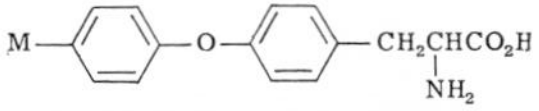

CB 3051, inactive (146)

(c) Alkylamines

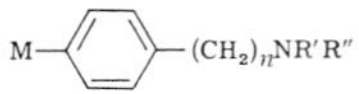

M—(CH₂)ₙNR'R"

R' = R" = H, highly active; R' = Me, R" = H, highly active; R' = R" = Me, active (23);
⁺NR₃, n = 2, inactive

(d) Peptides

(d₁) M—CH=CCONHCHR / NH / COPh   CO₂H   inactive

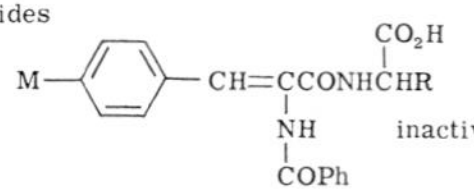

(d₂) M—CH₂CH·CO·NHCH₂ / NH / COPh   CO₂H   inactive

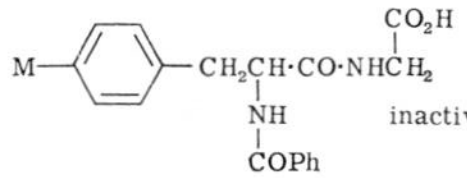

CB 3084

(d₃) M—CH₂CHCO·NHCHR / NH₂   CO₂H   (148)

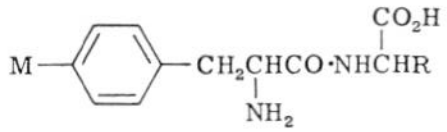

(d₄) M—CH₂CH·NH·COCHR / NH₂   COOEt (L)   (47)

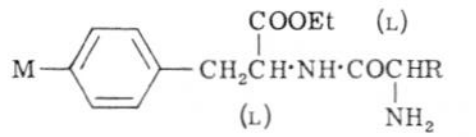

e.g., CB 3262, R = CH₂CH(CH₃)₂, active

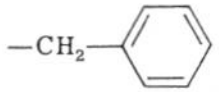

(d₅) M—CH₂CH·NH·COCHR / NHCOCH₃   COOEt (L), CB 3224; R = —CH₂— active (147)

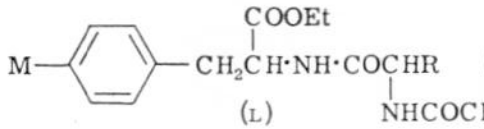

C. Nitrogen mustards; Aliphatic

1. MeM, HN2, active

2. ClCH₂CH₂M, HN3, active

3. MeN(CH₂CH₂Cl)₂, active

4. RCH M, R = H, Me, active
   COR'·R' = OH or N< (53)

CHART I (*Continued*)

5. $M(CH_2)_n \cdot CHCO_2H$
   NH_2 (*56, 57a*)

6. 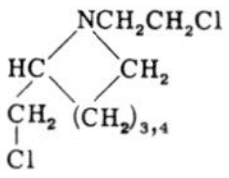 (*123*)

7. Carbohydrates
   NH—CH$_2$—CH$_2$—Cl
   |
   CH$_2$
   |
   (CHOH)$_4$
   |
   CH$_2$
   |
   NH—CH$_2$—CH$_2$—Cl
   BCM, active (*124*)

D. Nitrogen mustards; Amides RCOM

1. R = Organic acid res. (*125*)
2. R = EtO—, active (*126*)
3. R = 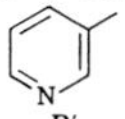 (*127*)
4. R = $-P$ (*63b*)
5. R = $NH_2CHCH_2O^-$
   COOH
   CB 3159, active (*128*)

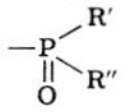

E. Nitrogen mustards; Heterocyclics

1. Pyridine
   (*151*) 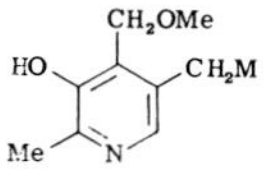

2. Pyrimidine 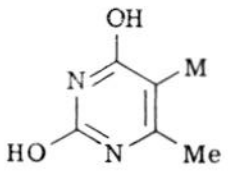
   Dopan (*152*)

3. Antimalarial structures

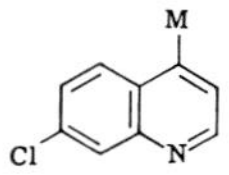

CB 3117, inactive (*66*) 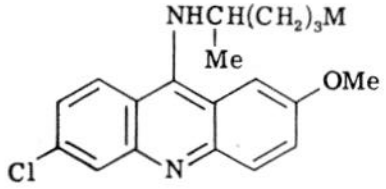   Quinacrine M (*153*)

F. Other alkylating agents

1. Tosyl derivatives
   $CH_2 \cdot CH_2 \cdot Tos$
   Ph—N
   $CH_2 \cdot CH_2 \cdot Tos$
   active (*129*)

2. Methanesulfonoxy
   X
   MeSO$_2$O $\diagdown$ OSO$_2$Me

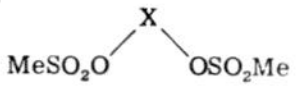

   (a) X = (CH$_2$)$_n$
       $n = 4 =$ Myleran (*70*)
   (b) X = $-CH_2CH=CHCH_2-$
   (c) X = $-CH(CH_2)_2CH-$
       Me   Me
   (d) $n = 2 =$ Dimethyl Myleran
       X = $-CH_2(CHOH)_2CH_2-$
       CB 2511, active (*130*)

3. Ethylenimines

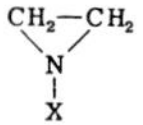

(a) Phosphoramides
    TEPA, active; ThioTEPA, etc. (*131*) 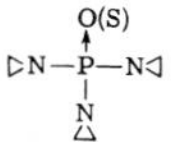

(b) Quinones 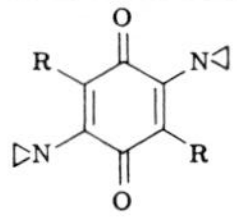
    R = OPr = E 39, active (*86, 135, 136*)

(c) Triazines 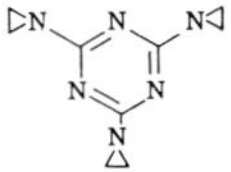
    TEM, active (*137, 138, 139*)

(d) Amides and Ureas

   (d$_1$) e.g. $\diagup$NCONH(CH$_2$)$_6$NHCON$\diagdown$
          active (*90*)

   (d$_2$) RCON$\diagdown$
          R = CH$_3$(CH$_2$)$_{16}$ (*91*)

4. Epoxides 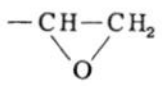 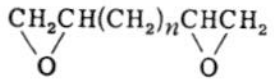
   $-CH-CH_2$
        O
   CH$_2$CH(CH$_2$)$_n$CH$_2$
     O   O
   $n = 1, 2, 3, 4, 5, 6$ (*133, 134*)
   ⟶ Decr. act. ⟶

5. Methylolamides
   X·NH·CH$_2$OH
   e.g. 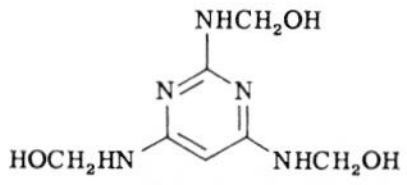
   active (*90*)

published, and it would only be a waste of precious space to attempt to summarize these here. One could perhaps start with a reference to some of this published material and then concentrate in the main on newer developments so far not available in a predigested form. A symposium (4) on biological alkylating agents was presented at the New York Academy of Science in 1957. A table presented there by Bergel (5), showing the various groups and subgroups of alkylating agents, has been brought up to date (Chart I). In addition to this report on the 1957 symposium, there are reviews by Haddow (6), Davis (7), Montgomery (8), Timmis (9), and R. B. Ross (10), which adequately cover the older work. More recently, and principally from a clinical point of view, the use and function of these agents was discussed during a conference in Washington (11). Of course, reviews (12) are being prepared in increasing numbers, and some will become available not very much later than this article. Even textbooks on medicinal chemistry (13) allow space for this group of chemotherapeutic compounds.

II. NEWER DEVELOPMENTS

During the last few years, the search for improved alkylating agents has been carried out with reference to the following cytotoxic groups: (A) nitrogen mustards, (B) dimethanesulfonates, (C) ethylenimines, and (D) epoxides and others.

A. Nitrogen Mustards

Due to the fact that simple dichloroethylamine derivatives such as HN2 [(I), R = CH_3], nor-HN2 [(I), R = H], do not possess any pronounced selectivity of action vis-à-vis normal and abnormal dividing cells, work in this field has revolved around the modification of the "carrier" part of the drug molecules, consisting in the first place of aromatic residues (II). These aromatic rings can be substituted by side chains R which may be (a) acidic, (b) basic, or (c) of an amino acid-

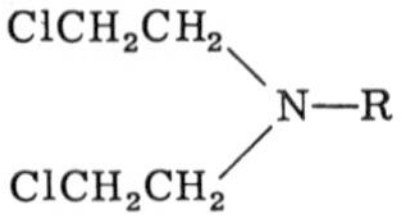

"Warhead"   "Carrier"

(I) 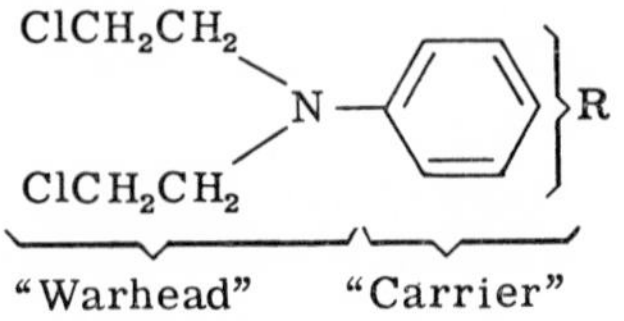   (II) peptide character. In addition, a brief reference will be made to so-called "latent compounds" (*58* and *59*).

1. WHERE THE SUBSTITUENT R IS AN ACIDIC RESIDUE

Work in this field led to the development of the butyric acid derivative called CB 1348, chlorambucil, or Leukeran [(III), $n = 3$, M = $(ClCH_2CH_2)_2N$— here and in all succeeding formulas], which was found to be active against the Walker carcinoma 256 (*14*) and produced a fall in circulating neutrophiles and more so of lymphocytes (*15*). The higher and lower homologues of chlorambucil [(III), $n = 0, 1, 2,$ and 4] were

M—⟨ ⟩—(CH₂)ₙCOOH   M—⟨ ⟩—O(CH₂)ₙCOOH

(III)   (IV)

found to be less active against the same experimental tumor. It has found use in clinical medicine against lymphocytic leukemia and lymphosarcoma.

The introduction of an oxygen atom between the aromatic ring and the fatty acid side chain, gave rise (*16*) to a series of compounds of the general formula (IV). The compound in which $n = 2$ was found to be twice as active as CB 1348, but also twice as toxic, whereas the homologues in which $n = 0, 1, 3,$ and 4 were again less active. It is interesting to note that both these compounds with pronounced antitumor activity are isosteric, which suggests that their activity is in some way connected with the length of the side chain.

Another series of closely related, but nonacidic compounds of general formula (V) has recently been studied (*17*) because of their relation to schistosomicidal drugs (*18–20*). Only the compound (V) ($n = 7$) was

M—⟨ ⟩—O—(CH₂)ₙ—O—⟨ ⟩—M

(V)

slightly active when tested against the Walker carcinoma, whereas the compound (V) ($n = 6$) was inactive at the same dose level. In addition to this, Baker *et al.* at the Stanford Research Institute have begun a study (*21*) of a wide range of analogues of chlorambucil, which includes, for example, such compounds as (VI, VII, and VIII), as well as the *ortho* and *meta* mustard isomers of chlorambucil. The cinnamic acid isomers (VIII) have shown encouraging antitumor activity against the mouse tumor sarcoma 180, adenocarcinoma 755, and leukemia L 1210, the standard test tumors of the Cancer Chemotherapy National Service Center, Bethesda. Their effects, however, are more like phenylalanine mustard than chlorambucil (*22*).

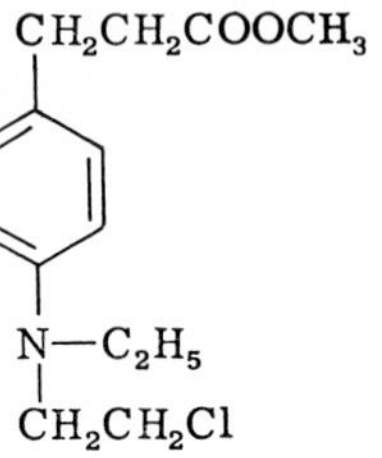

$CH_2CH_2COOCH_3$

$N-C_2H_5$
CH_2CH_2Cl

(VI)

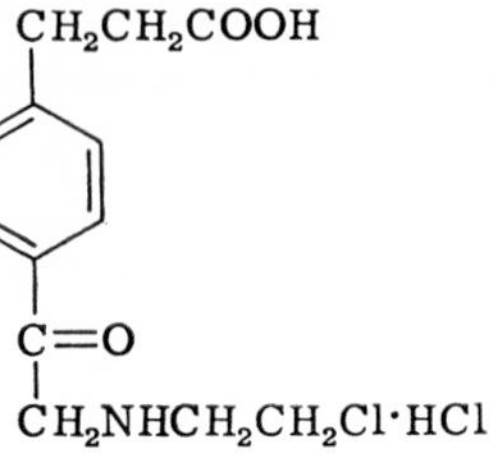

CH_2CH_2COOH

$C=O$
$CH_2NHCH_2CH_2Cl \cdot HCl$

(VII)

$CH=CHCOOH$

CH_2CH_2Cl
$-N$
CH_2CH_2Cl

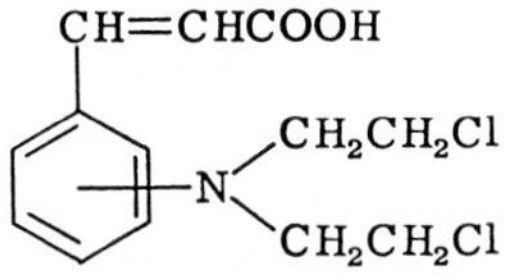

o-, *m-*, and *p-*Isomers

(VIII)

2. WHERE THE SUBSTITUENT R IS A BASIC RESIDUE

Some compounds of the general formula (IX) have been prepared and tested against the Walker carcinoma 256 (*23*). The compounds (IX),

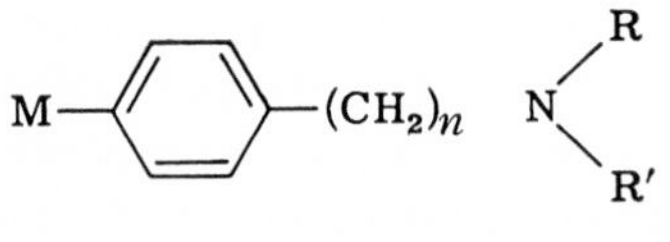

$$M-\langle\text{benzene}\rangle-(CH_2)_n \quad N\begin{array}{c}R\\\\R'\end{array}$$

(IX)

$$M-\langle\text{benzene}\rangle-(CH_2)_n \quad \begin{array}{c}Me\\N^+-Me\\Me\end{array} \Big\} \ I^- \text{ or } Br^-$$

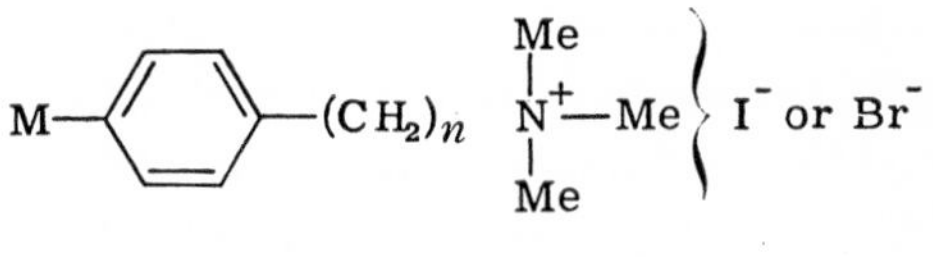

(X)

$n = 2$, $R = R' = H$ and $n = 2$, $R = H$, $R' = Me$ were found to be active, while compound (IX), in which $n = 2$, $R = R' = Me$ was less active, and (X), $n = 1$ and 2, a quaternary derivative, was found to be ineffective.

3. WHERE THE SUBSTITUENT R IS OF AN AMINO ACID-PEPTIDE CHARACTER

From the recent literature it appears that more attention has been paid to this group of compounds than to the two groups already mentioned, the reason being that the amino acid moiety might become involved in the metabolic processes of the cancer cell and thus act as an efficient carrier of the mustard "warhead." One of the first representatives of this class which had an appreciable antitumor activity (24) was the DL-phenyl-alanine mustard called merphalan (XI), which was also independently

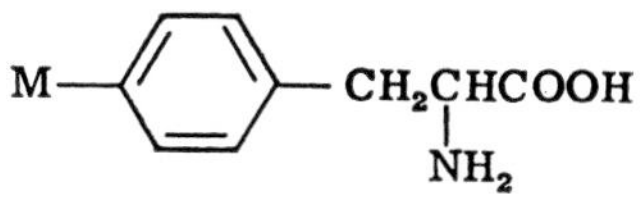

$$M-\langle\bigcirc\rangle-CH_2\underset{\underset{NH_2}{|}}{C}HCOOH$$

(XI)

synthesized by Russian workers (25) and called sarcolysine. Due to the interesting properties of merphalan and sarcolysine, it was decided to prepare the L- and D-enantiomorphs, which have become known as melphalan (name derived from *m*ustard-L-*p*henyl*alan*ine) and medphalan, respectively. Biological tests of these three optical forms on the Walker tumor and on the rat sarcoma 45 (26) have shown the highest activity to be produced by the L-isomer, with the D-isomer being the least active compound. These differences among the sterically related compounds have also been verified by other workers (27–30) using other biological systems. On the other hand, when Zamenhof et al. (31) used the three phenyl-alanine mustards *in vitro* on the transforming DNA of *Hemophilus influenzae*, there was no difference among them in their inactivating power. These findings suggest that the differences in the biological activity of each isomer may be due to transport or permeability properties, in that the L-enantiomorph may more effectively penetrate the cells. The use of labeled L- and D-forms would test this hypothesis.

Another modification of the phenylalanine molecule carrying the mustard residue involved the length of the chain between the aromatic ring and the *a*-amino acid end group (16), giving rise to compounds of general formula (XII). To cite one example, called aminochlorambucil [(XII), $n = 2$], it was found to be less toxic and less active than merphalan, but

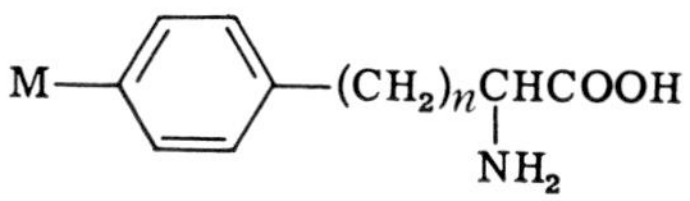

$$M-\langle\bigcirc\rangle-(CH_2)_n\underset{\underset{NH_2}{|}}{C}HCOOH$$

(XII)

its more favorable effect on circulating blood elements warranted its clinical study. The resolution of aminochlorambucil by Smith and Luck (32) and the subsequent biological testing of the isomers on the S 91 Cloudman mouse melanoma showed that one of the isomers was more

effective than the other, and by analogy with the phenylalanine series
it was assumed that this had the L-configuration. However, the measurement of the optical rotations of the isomers under acidic conditions [Lutz
and Jirgensons' rule (33)] indicated that the more active compound,
surprisingly, possessed the D-configuration. Further evidence by Bergel
et al. (34) supported this interesting difference between the phenylalanine
and phenylaminobutyric acid series.

Until 1959, all these compounds carried the mustard group in the *para*
position to the other residues of the aromatic ring. However, a number of
laboratories (35–38) have now synthesized the *meta* isomer of merphalan
or sarcolysine [(XIII), $n = 1$], which showed an improved antitumor
activity (39) and therapeutic index as compared with the compounds
belonging to the *para* series. This also applies to the *para* and *meta*
isomers of phenylglycine [(XII), $n = 0$] prepared by Ross *et al.* (40)
and Connors (41). The same workers (41, 42) have even taken this story

(XIII)   (XIV)

a stage further by preparing the *ortho* isomer of merphalan or sarcolysine
(XIV), which is more active than either the *meta* or *para* isomers but
has a somewhat greater toxicity.

Another possible way of varying structural changes on the phenylalanine molecule is to produce compounds in which the α-amino group is
transferred to the β-position. This was first suggested by Professor J.
Murray Luck of Stanford University, and taken up by Bergel *et al.* (43),

(XV)

who prepared the *para*-mustard derivative of β-phenyl-β-alanine (XV)
which was found to be less effective than melphalan, but at the same time

less toxic. The difference in biological activity among the *para*, *meta*, and *ortho* isomers in the β-phenyl-α-alanine series prompted the synthesis (*38, 44*) of the *meta*-mustard in the β-alanine series (XVI), which was found to be more biologically effective than the corresponding *para* isomer, while the toxicity was about the same. It seems therefore that in

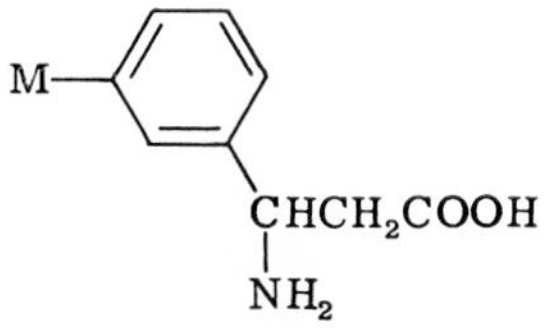

CHCH₂COOH

M—⟨benzene ring⟩

$$\text{M}-\overset{}{\underset{\underset{\text{NH}_2}{|}}{\text{C}}}\text{HCH}_2\text{COOH}$$

(XVI)

both the α- and β-amino series the general trend is toward increased activity, but about the same or slightly diminished toxicity, as the mustard group is moved from the *para* position of the aromatic ring to the *meta* position and thence to the *ortho* position. The future preparation and testing of the *ortho* isomer in the β-alanine series would, so one hopes, prove this specific activity-structure relationship. The last kind of modification of the prototype amino acid derivative which should be mentioned here refers to both simple acyl or peptide derivatives of the α-amino group and esters, amides, or peptides of the carboxyl group. The two N-acyl compounds which first received attention were N-formyl [(XVII), R = CHO] (*45, 46*) and N-acetyl derivatives of merphalan and sarcolysine [(XVII), R = COCH₃] (*45*). The investigators in Russia claimed that antitumor activity was not abolished in these compounds, although a very much higher dose was required to produce the same effect as with merphalan or sarcolysine. The corresponding N-formylmelphalan has been reported in the literature (*47*), but due to the method of preparation the product was apparently partly racemized. Turning to the carboxyl end of the molecule, one finds that the ethyl and isopropyl esters of merphalan or sarcolysine have been prepared by the Russian workers (*45*), and biological tests showed that there was very little difference between the esters and the original amino acid as far as antitumor activity (rat sarcoma 45) was concerned. The corresponding ethyl ester of melphalan has now been prepared (*47*) and also shown to be similar in activity to melphalan itself, although when used in a regional perfusion of a cancerous limb it proved to be more vigorous in its side effects than the free amino acid (*48*). The same group (*47*) in England have prepared melphalan amide hydrochloride [(XVIII), R = NH₂, R′ = H] as well as *N*-formylmelphalan amide [(XVIII), R = NH$_2$; R′ = CHO] and the ethyl amide [(XVIII), R = NHEt, R′ = CHO].

M—⟨benzene⟩—CH$_2$CHCOOH
                       |
                      NHR

(XVII)

M—⟨benzene⟩—CH$_2$CHCOR
                      |
                     NHR′

(XVIII)

From their results one can pick out two points of interest, viz., (*a*) the general toxicity, hemotoxicity, and antitumor activity are greatest in compounds carrying a free amino group and (*b*) acylation of the free amino group reduces the biological activity although, in most cases, the ratio between the toxic and effective antitumor dose (the therapeutic index) remains roughly the same.

Focusing attention on some peptides containing merphalan (sarcolysine) or melphalan, two separate investigations may be considered. First, there are the contributions by the Russian group with the general tendency towards the use of sarcolysine (merphalan) and other DL- or racemic amino acids (*46, 49, 50*). All of their peptides of sarcolysine (merphalan) to date[1] are *N*-formyl derivatives, for instance, *N*-formylsarcolysylphenylalanine ethyl ester (XIX). Other peptides recorded are those where the amino acid residue is valine, glycine, tryptophan, *S*-chloroethylcysteine, methionine, *S*-benzylhomocysteine, and leucine. It was claimed that all of these peptides have a favorable therapeutic index with low hemotoxicity. It is interesting to note here that some peptides of chlorambucil of general formula (XX) have been prepared (*50, 51*), and biological tests showed that when R was represented by a natural amino acid the compounds possessed strong carcinostatic activity, whereas when R was an unnatural amino acid activity was low or absent.

COOC$_2$H$_5$
                                |
M—⟨benzene⟩—CH$_2$CHCONHCHCH$_2$—⟨benzene⟩
                      |
                     NHCHO

(XIX)

M—⟨benzene⟩—(CH$_2$)$_n$CONHR

(XX)

Turning now to the peptide work carried out in England (*47*), with the tendency towards the use of melphalan and other optically active amino acids, a series of dipeptides of melphalan was prepared of general

---

[1] *Note added in proof:* The preparation of sarcolysine peptides (with valine) in which the amino group is free has recently been recorded. [I. L. Knunyants, K. I. Karpavichus, and O. V. Kil'disheva, *Izv. Akad. Nauk. S.S.S.R. Otd. Khim. Nauk.* p. 1024 (1962).]

formula (XXI), where R was such that the amino acid residue was L-valine, L-leucine, L- and D-alanine, and L- and D-phenylalanine.

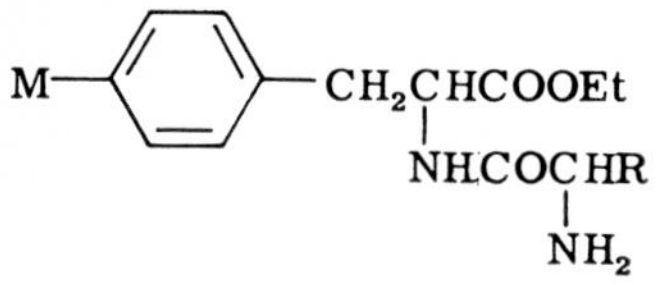

M⟨benzene⟩CH₂CHCOOEt
|
NHCOCHR
|
NH₂

(XXI)

CH₃
\
CHCHCONHCHCONHCH₂COOC₂H₅
/ |
CH₃   NH₂·2HCl

with CH₂⟨benzene⟩M above

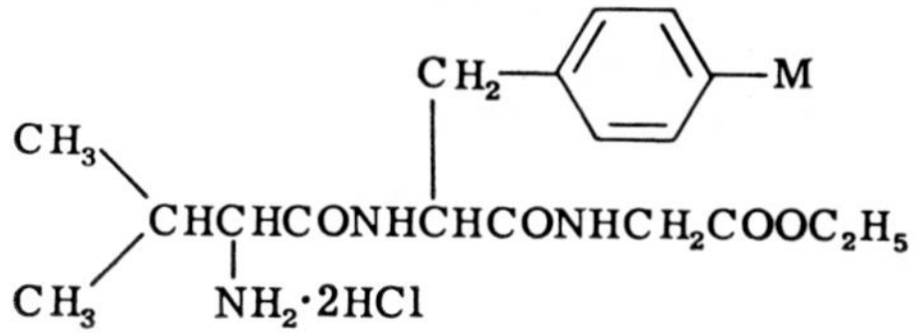

(XXII)

In addition to this, three tripeptides have been prepared, viz., L-valylglycylmelphalan ethyl ester dihydrochloride, L-alanyl-L-leucylmelphalan ethyl ester dihydrochloride, and the interesting L-valylmelphalanylglycine ethyl ester dihydrochloride (XXII), where the cytotoxic amino acid is in the center of the molecule. One tetrapeptide, viz., L-valylglycylglycylmelphalan ethyl ester dihydrochloride (XXIII) has also been prepared.

CH₃
\
CHCHCONHCH₂CONHCH₂CONHCHCH₂—⟨benzene⟩—M
/ | |
CH₃   NH₂·2HCl   COOC₂H₅

(XXIII)

M—⟨benzene⟩—CH₂CHCOOEt
|
NHCOCHCH₂—⟨benzene⟩
|
NHCOCH₃

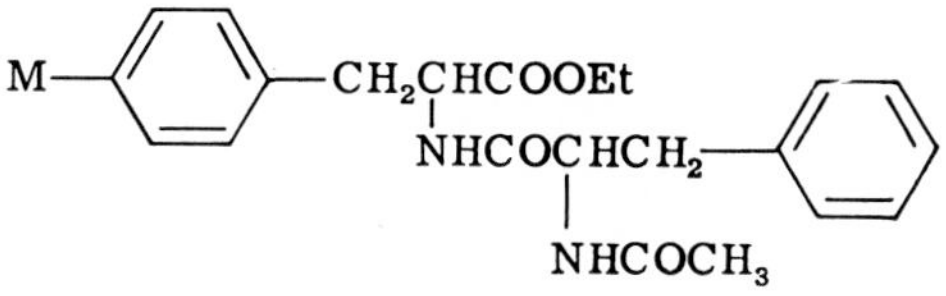

(XXIV)

Biological testing of these compounds has shown that in general they have no great advantage over melphalan, as their activity is approximately equivalent to that of the melphalan they contain. However, so far with the L-leucyl dipeptide it appears that the compound is effective against a wider range of experimental tumors than the parent substance. Whether this proves to be the case under clinical conditions, particularly in view of the usefulness of melphalan in regional perfusion (52) of patients with malignant melanoma, remains to be seen. On the other hand, in parallel with the Russian claim that their compounds containing formyl- or acetylsarcolysine (merphalan) possessed a better therapeutic index, the English workers (47) found in preliminary tests with representative dipeptides of melphalan (similar to those above) in which the terminal amino group was blocked by an acetyl residue that, for instance, N-acetylphenylalanylmelphalan ethyl ester (XXIV) had a substantially more favorable therapeutic index than melphalan itself. One may perhaps ask why all this tedious work on modifications of the original phenylalanine mustard has been undertaken. The reason is obviously that all the groups engaged in this work tried to produce a compound possessing the very desirable antitumor properties of melphalan, but with a very much lower toxicity and hemotoxicity.

Before concluding this section on amino acid derivatives as carriers of the nitrogen mustard group, two further sets of compounds could be mentioned briefly: first, those where the mustard moiety replaces the α-amino group of the amino acid, as reported by Ishidate and his co-workers (53, 54) and more recently by Nyhan and Busch (55), e.g., the mustard derivative of alanine (XXV) which was found to be active on the Yoshida sarcoma; and second, those in which the nitrogen mustard moiety replaces the ω-amino group in diamino acids (XXVI), produced by Japanese (56) and Russian (57) teams.

$$CH_3CHCOOH \qquad\qquad M(CH_2)_nCHCOOH$$
$$| \qquad\qquad\qquad\qquad\qquad |$$
$$M \qquad\qquad\qquad\qquad\qquad NH_2$$
$$(XXV) \qquad\qquad\qquad\qquad (XXVI)$$

4. Compounds with Latent Activity

Another line of approach in the nitrogen mustard field concerns the concept of "latent activity," which means the preparation of compounds possessing low chemical and biological activities, but which would undergo degradation under physiological conditions to form a moiety with high alkylating power and consequently pronounced antitumor effects. With this end in view a series of practically inert azo mustards was synthesized by Ross and Warwick (58, 59), who put forward the suggestion that these compounds might become activated by a process of *in vivo* reduction of the azo link by enzymes, and that certain substituents on the aromatic ring might facilitate this reduction. This was demonstrated *in vitro* with purified xanthine oxidase and most readily with compound CB 1414 (XXVII), which also proved to be the most active member of this series against the Walker rat carcinoma 256. The effective molecular species was considered to be (XXVIII), the end product of the complete reductive fission.

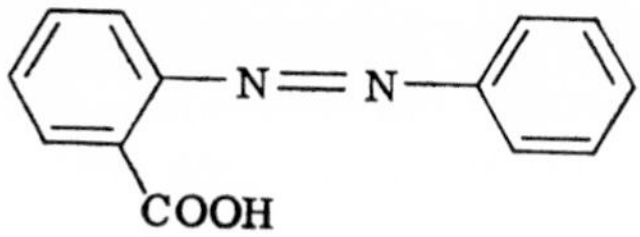

(XXVII)

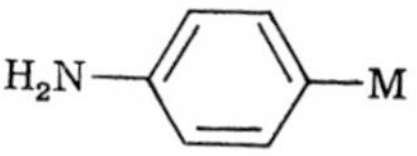

(XXVIII)

A different group of latent compounds was synthesized and examined by Ross et al. (40, 42) and Connors (41), viz., mustard derivatives of aryl- and arylalkylhydantoins. The two compounds in this series which were most active are represented by formulas (XXIX and XXX), the former being the precursor of the meta-mustard of phenylglycine already mentioned [(XIII), $n = 0$].

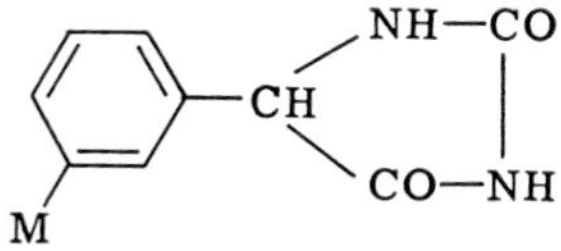

(XXIX)

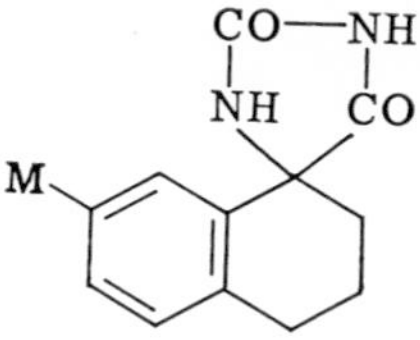

(XXX)

The next group with amino acids as carrier includes O-carbamoyl derivatives of serine and threonine (60). Here the mustard radical is attached in the form of an amide (XXXI), and the proximity of an electron-attracting carbonyl group weakens the reactivity of the chlorine atoms. It was rather surprising to find that the threonine derivative [(XXXI), $R = CH_3$, $R' = CH(NH_2)COOH$] showed no biological activity, in contrast to the serine compound referred to as mercasin or

$$M \cdot CO \cdot O \cdot \overset{\overset{\displaystyle R}{|}}{C}H \cdot R'$$

(XXXI)

CB 3159 [(XXXI), $R = H$, $R' = CH(NH_2)COOH$], which with low toxicity exerted similar antitumor effects to those of the urethane derivatives [(XXXI), $R = H$, $R' = CH_3$] (61), as studied by Bushby (62).

When using phosphoric acid with $\equiv P = O$ as a carrier of the mustard group, another interesting compound endoxan, cytoxan, or cyclophosphamide (XXXII) (63a) was developed from original work by Friedman and Seligman (63b). One of the reasons for the preparation of this drug was the possibility that it might be split by phosphoramidases of the organism to release the unsubstituted nitrogen mustard [(I), R = H]. Indeed, its inactivity in tissue culture and its activity against various

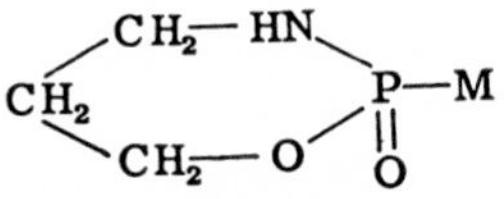

$$\begin{array}{c} CH_2-HN \\ CH_2 \qquad\qquad P-M \\ CH_2-O \qquad \overset{\|}{O} \end{array}$$

(XXXII)

animal tumors strongly supports the working hypothesis just mentioned.

Although, in the space of this article, one cannot enumerate all possible variations of carriers of the mustard group, brief mention should be made of heterocyclic systems. A large number of compounds of this type have been prepared and tested, one of which, called dopan (XXXIII), has been found by the Russians (64) to be worthy of clinical use.

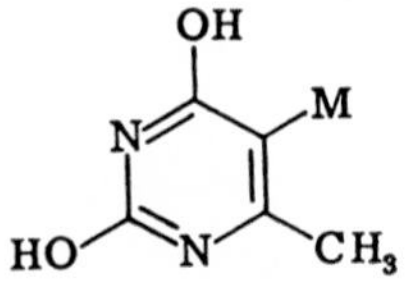

$$\begin{array}{c} OH \\ N \qquad M \\ HO \qquad N \qquad CH_3 \end{array}$$

(XXXIII)

The corresponding uracil mustard was prepared and studied in America (65). Other heterocyclic agents belonging to the class of antimalarial structures have been mentioned in previous reviews and papers (66–68), and other types with references can be found in a list (69) published by the Cancer Chemotherapy National Service Center, Bethesda.

B. Dimethanesulfonates

Some years ago a series of methanesulfonic acid esters of the general formula (XXXIV) was developed by Timmis (70), two members of which have found clinical use: the C_4-compound called Myleran [(XXXIV), $n = 4$] and the C_9-compound [(XXXIV), $n = 9$], known as nonane (70, 71). Myleran was shown to have selective action on the circulating

$$CH_3SO_2O(CH_2)_nOSO_2CH_3 \qquad\qquad CH_3SO_2O\overset{\overset{\displaystyle CH_3}{|}}{C}HCH_2CH_2\overset{\overset{\displaystyle CH_3}{|}}{C}HOSO_2CH_3$$

(XXXIV)   (XXXV)

blood elements of rats. In contrast to the mustards, which depress the lymphocytes rather than the neutrophiles, Myleran has the reverse effect (70). Since then, it has become the drug of choice for the treatment of chronic myelogenous leukemia. Dimethyl Myleran (XXXV), which turned out to be more water soluble than the parent compound, was prepared and tested (72). Its neutrophile-depressing activity was about three times greater than that of Myleran itself (72), and as it also showed a quicker response it was tried in cases of acute leukemia (73).

In view of the biological properties of a bischloroethylamino derivative of dideoxy-D-mannitol, degranol (74), the preparation of a series of dimethanesulfonyl esters of sugar alcohols was undertaken (75, 76). The compound of formula (XXXVI), also a dideoxy-D-mannitol derivative, known as mannitol Myleran, was found to be an effective tumor inhibitor with a wide animal tumor spectrum (75) but had relatively little effect on bone marrow. Just as among the amino acid mustards, steric conditions in this series of polyols plays an important part, e.g., the L-mannitol diesters proved to be ineffective.

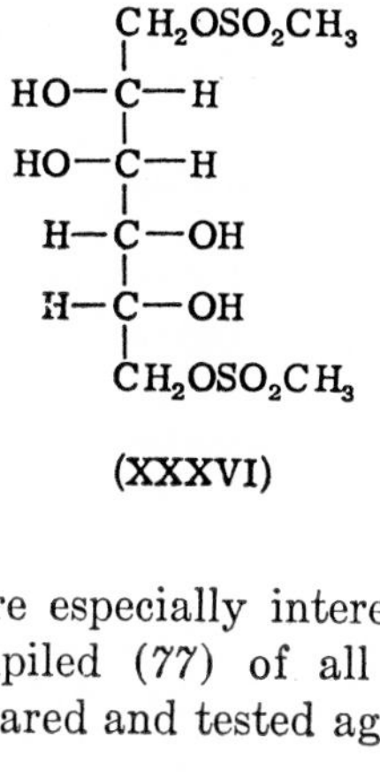

$$
\begin{array}{c}
CH_2OSO_2CH_3 \\
HO-C-H \\
HO-C-H \\
H-C-OH \\
H-C-OH \\
CH_2OSO_2CH_3
\end{array}
$$

(XXXVI)

For those readers who are especially interested in the methanesulfonates, a list has been compiled (77) of all the methanesulfonic acid esters which have been prepared and tested against experimental tumors.

C. Ethylenimines

Three of the earlier compounds in this series (13) were triethylenemelamine (TEM) (XXXVII), triethylenephosphoramide (TEPA) (XXXVIII), and triethylenethiophosphoramide (TESPA) (XXXIX), TEM is effective against chronic leukemia, but appears to be more toxic than the nitrogen mustard HN2 [(I), R = CH₃], whereas TESPA is the most widely used, being more stable than TEPA and also effective on

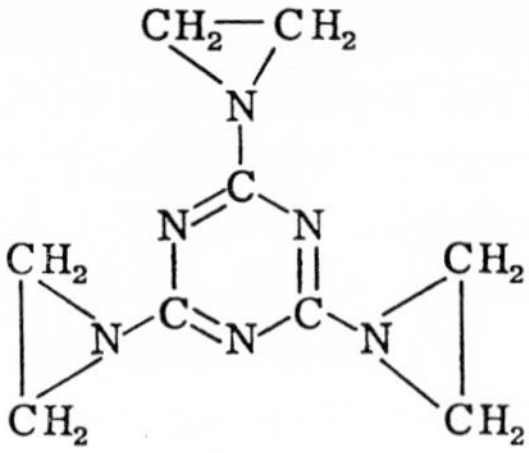

$$CH_2-CH_2$$

(XXXVII)

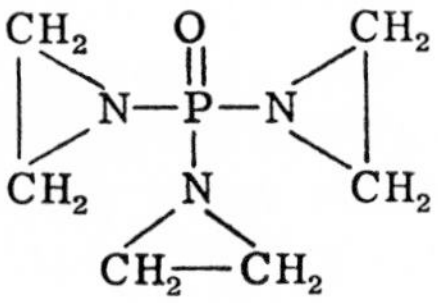

(XXXVIII)

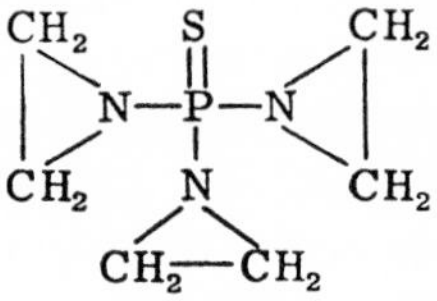

(XXXIX)

some solid tumors. A compound which is structurally related to TESPA has now been developed (78) and is known as OPSPA (XL). Biological

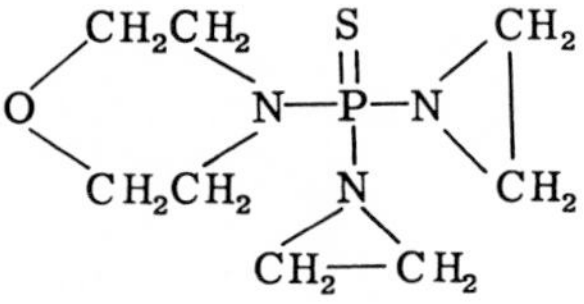

(XL)

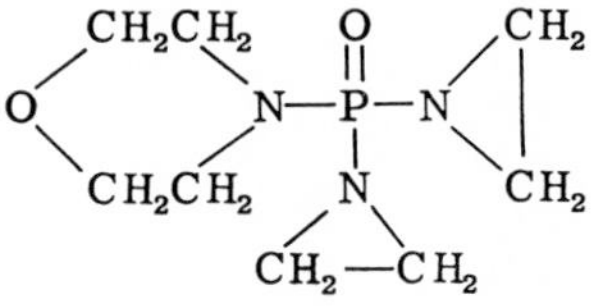

(XLI)

tests have shown this compound to be active against the Flexner-Jobling carcinoma in rats, a result which is also produced by its major sulfur-free metabolite MEPA (XLI). This activity can be enhanced by simultaneous administration of azaserine, aminonucleosides, or 6-mercaptopurine. Very recently, two new compounds have been reported which are structurally similar to MEPA. They were considered to be "duel antagonists," incorporating in one molecule two different chemotherapeutic moieties, viz., the bis(ethylenimine) phosphoro and carbamic acid residues. The first of these [(XLII), R = $-C_2H_5$] (79) has shown significant activity against various animal tumors (80–82). The second compound [(XLII), R = $CH_2C_6H_5$] has been found to possess a more pronounced antitumor activity both in animals and man (81). In fact, it was reported (79, 80)

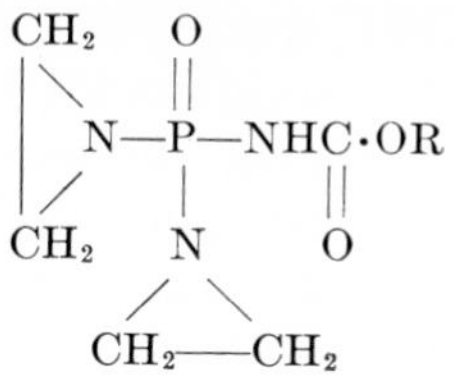

(XLII)

that the benzyl analogue [(XLII), R = $CH_2C_6H_5$] produced complete cures in some DBA/2 mice inoculated with leukemia L 1210, a result which has never before been obtained by the same workers with other agents. A further report has also appeared (83) of encouraging results obtained with this drug in the treatment of bronchogenic carcinoma. Work on ethylenimino derivatives of quinones (84–86) has led to two interesting compounds, one designated Bayer E 39 [(XLIII), R = —$CH_2CH_2CH_3$] and the other Bayer A 139 [(XLIII), R = —$CH_2OC_2H_5$]. These gave some interesting results in biological and biochemical investigations and are now undergoing extensive clinical trials. The same applies to a third and later addition to this series, represented by formula (XLIV) and known as Bayer 3231 (87–89).

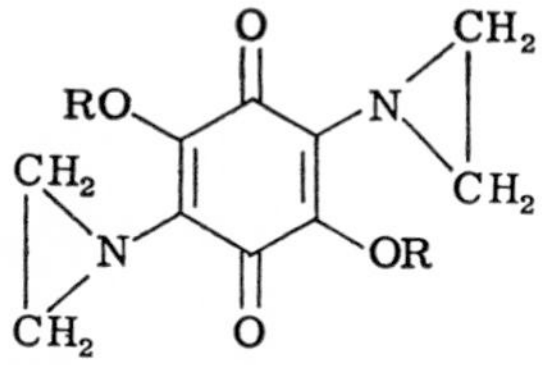

(XLIII)

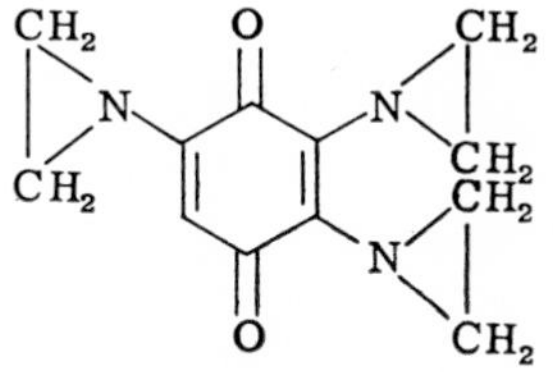

(XLIV)

Not all ethylenimine derivatives are predominantly antitumor agents. It will be remembered that among a series of mono- and polyfunctional ethylenimines developed by Walpole et al. (90), it was demonstrated that the monofunctional derivatives (XLV), in contrast to the polyfunctional ones (e.g., XLVI and XLVII), possessed no antitumor activity, but were carcinogenic (91, 92). The conclusion was reached that neither polyfunctionality, nor cross-linking, nor the formation of a polyreactive polymer or micelle was necessary for the carcinogenic action of ethylenimines. That the various biological effects of alkylating agents, viz., antitumor activity, carcinogenicity, mutagenic action, and chromosome damage do not always run parallel is shown by the differences in antifertility activity of some of their representatives, including ethylenimines (93). It was found that Myleran [(XXXIV), $n = 4$] interfered with spermatogenesis in rats for several weeks, while melphalan (XI) was ineffective in this respect; TEM (XXXVII) also rapidly induced infertility. This infertility was also produced by other ethylenimine derivatives, being greatest in trifunctional and least in monofunctional compounds. While the alkylating agents tested were carcinogenic, other chemical types of carcinogenic agents did not produce sterility. A recently published review (94) lists the synthetic substances which are known to interfere with animal reproduction.

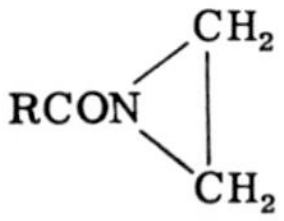

(XLV) 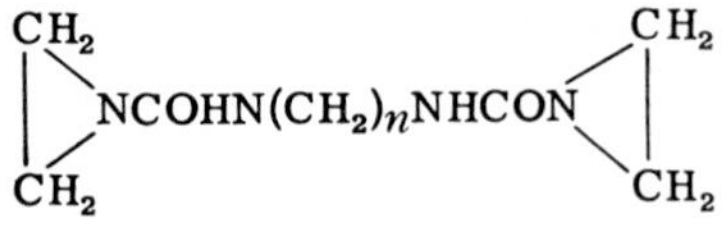   (XLVI)

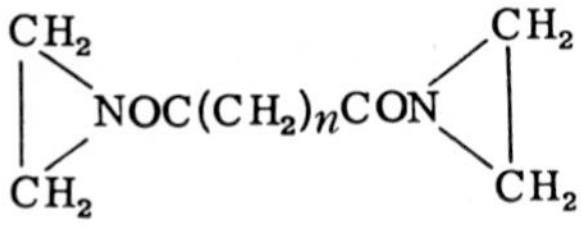

(XLVII)

D. Epoxides and Others

During recent years activity in this field has not been very great, but one might mention the work of two different laboratories. Firstly, Walpole (92) et al. found that on testing various epoxides, for example (XLVIII–L), certain monofunctional members (XLIX) were carcinogenic. This phenomenon is similar to that observed with the ethylenimines previously mentioned. Secondly, Gerzon et al. (95) established that the compound (LI) possessed high chemotherapeutic activity when tested against the mouse leukemia P 1534, and later that compound (LII) was even more active. Both these compounds are now undergoing clinical trials.

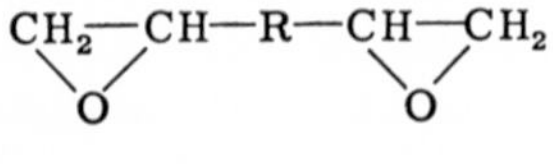

(XLVIII) 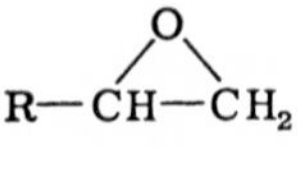   (XLIX) 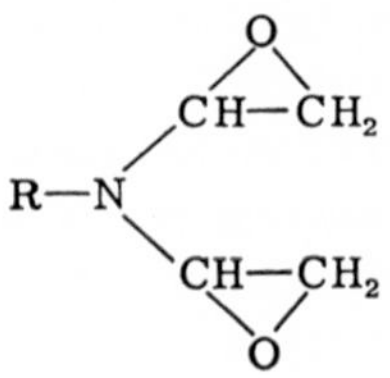   (L)

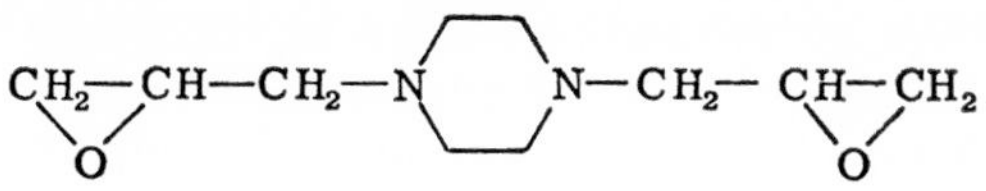

CH₂—CH—CH₂—N⟨ ⟩N—CH₂— CH—CH₂ (structure)

(LI)

CH₂—CH—CH₂—N⟨ ⟩⟨ ⟩N—CH₂— CH—CH₂ (structure)

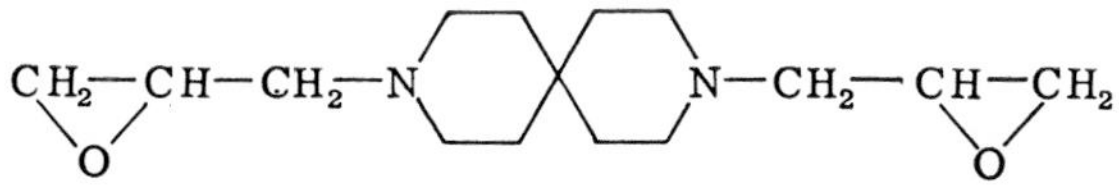

(LII)

A completely different type of alkylating agent in the form of dimethyl-nitrosamine, DMN (LIII), was recently reported by Magee and Barnes (*96*), who found that rats, when fed on a diet containing 50 ppm of DMN, developed primary hepatic tumors and that protein synthesis was inhibited. Further work by Farber and Magee (*97*) using DMN-C^{14} led to the belief that rat liver RNA was methylated, probably by diazomethane

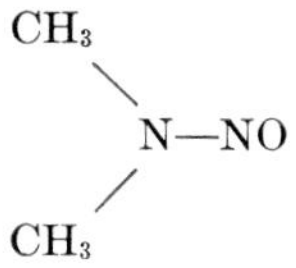

$$CH_3 \diagdown N—NO$$
$$CH_3 \diagup$$

(LIII)

as an intermediate, to produce chemically abnormal products. These results support the idea (*98*) that alkylation of cell constituents (in the first instance DNA) is an important factor in carcinogenesis by alkylating agents, but there exists also some evidence for the role of altered RNA in the early stages of cancer production (*99, 100*).

III. MECHANISM OF ACTION

The preceding sentences connect the foregoing section on newer representatives of the family of alkylating agents with the important problem of how such agents may bring about their *in vivo* effects. It is safe to assume, as mentioned in the introduction, that these chemically reactive compounds interact with nucleophilic centers of receptor molecules of the cell. But first, ignoring tissue culture or ascites tumor cells *in vitro*, how do the drugs arrive at the receptor sites in the whole animal or man without getting lost on the way? The ideal conditions are obviously that their transport should be as smooth as possible and that few side reactions should take place, particularly with water or any irrelevant tissue constituents (competition factors). Then there should be a satisfactory concentration of the agents in the target area, which depends to a large extent on the degree of its vascularization. But granted that such blood supply would serve tumors at least as well as the corresponding healthy host tissue, it is still highly desirable to have a better drug permeability of cancer cells, a lower degradation rate, and a greater number of receptor molecules than with normal cells. However, it is only too well known that by what ever detailed mechanisms these compounds achieve their effects (in the end irreversible cell damage in the case of antitumor drugs), the ideal conditions described just now, never exist all at the same time.

Focusing attention on the "receptor molecules," the two alternatives are first, proteins, including enzymes, and second, the nucleic acids, especially DNA [a number of observations mainly by Ambrose *et al.* (*101, 102*) extend these possibilities to the lipoproteins of the cell surface]. Within these macromolecules the most favored centers for reaction under specified ionic conditions [cf. Ross (*2*)] are —COOH, —NH_2, —SH, —PO_3H and, as will be seen below, tertiary nitrogen atoms of heterocyclic systems. It was thought that the outcome of such reactions was fatal alterations of either (*a*) enzymic activities, (*b*) reduplication processes, (*c*) surface properties of the cell, or any combination of these effects. On the other hand, in view of the mutagenic activity of some of the alkylating agents, and also considering the role of DNA as a genetic controlling factor (see transforming principles), the most widely accepted idea was that the difunctional alkylating agents interacted with certain groups within the DNA molecule and caused cross-linking and a change in steric configuration; yet there was no absolute certainty as to the true connection between this mechanism of action and the biological effects.

However, during the last few years, some very interesting results have been obtained giving rise to three well-supported hypotheses. One school believed, at least at the beginning, that the important reaction was the esterification of phosphate groups in nucleoprotein [Alexander *et al.* (*103*)]. Another school came to the conclusion that the major interaction was that with the nitrogen atoms of purine or pyrimidine bases in nucleic acids [Skipper; Lawley and Wallick; Butler and Press (*104–108*)], while the third school defended the hypothesis of an interaction with sulfhydryl groups of essential proteins [Roberts and Warwick (*109–112*)]. Considering first the evidence for the interaction with nitrogen atoms of the bases, Lawley and Wallick (*105*) showed that the action of the nitrogen mustard HN2 on DNA at pH 7 and at a temperature of 37° changed the shape of the DNA absorption curve, indicating alkylation of purine or pyrimidine rings. Similar reactions with nucleotides suggested that the guanine residue was most susceptible to alkylation, which was also confirmed by acid hydrolysis of the alkylated DNA. A new component was found, the spectrum of which was compared with those of alkylguanines and found to resemble that of a 7-alkylguanine. This led the authors to believe that the intermediate of the alkylation was a quaternary salt. Support for this was obtained by comparing the alkylation of 1,7-dimethylguanine (LIV) by methyl sulfate, as a model agent, with that of guanylic acid (LV).

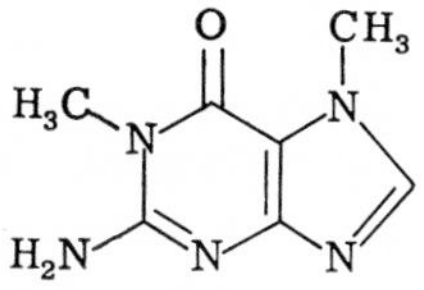

(LIV)

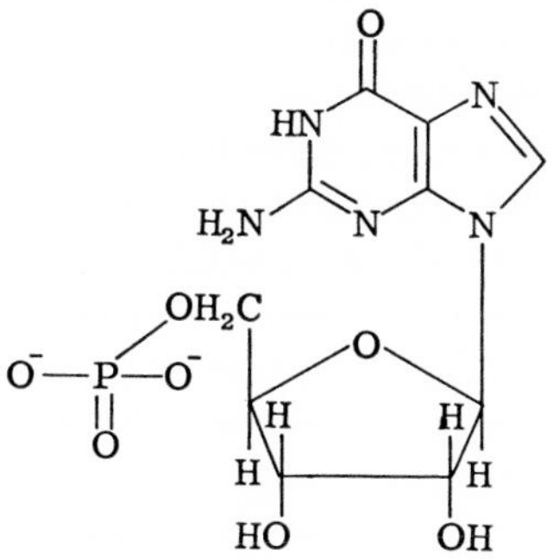

(LV)

The outcome of this study was that the products obtained from guanylic acid were 7-methylguanosinium-9-ribotides [(LVI), R = ribose phosphate].

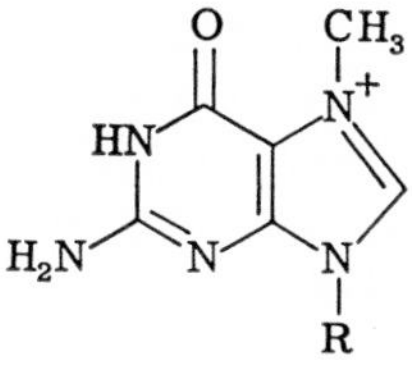

(LVI)

In alkaline solution at 23°, the quaternary salt underwent a reaction leading to products with different spectra, which were thought to be ring fission products in which the ribose residue was still retained. It is interesting to note here that when Hems (*113*) subjected a solution of guanylic acid to ionizing radiation by X-rays the main product obtained was (LVII), from which it was inferred that splitting of the imidazole ring had taken place. This establishes a link between the effects of X-rays

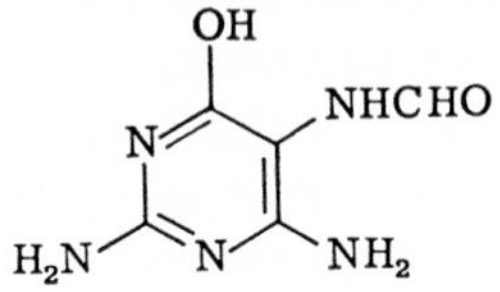

(LVII)

and of alkylating agents which have been termed "radiomimetic compounds" in the past.

In continuation of his work, Lawley (106) estimated the relative reactivities of deoxyribonucleotides towards methyl sulfate at pH 7 and at a temperature of 37°. He showed that guanine was more readily attacked than cytosine, which behaved similarly to adenine, and that thymine was the most resistant base. The same set of experiments also brought to light the fact that alkylation of sugar phosphate residues only took place to a small extent (but see below) and that the main reaction was directly with the bases. The same author also established that these bases still possessed the same order of reactivity when present as constituents of DNA, and that attack by alkylating agents could be expected to be greater on nucleic acids containing a preponderance of guanine and cytosine residues rather than of adenine and thymidine units. In addition, when deoxyguanylic acid was methylated with methyl sulfate at pH 7.2 and at a temperature of 37° (107), 7-methylguanine was again obtained by hydrolysis, but under much milder conditions than for the guanylic acid product, degradation being appreciable at pH 7. Unless a rearrangement accompanied its hydrolysis, the intermediate product would be of the same type as formula (LVI), but with R = deoxyribose phosphate. All of this demonstrated that alkylation of the guanine residues of DNA could lead to considerable changes in the characteristics of the macromolecule due to the quaternization of nitrogen groups, as well as to cleavage of the sugar phosphate residue from the alkylated guanine moieties. This does not mean that some adenine units were not attacked at the same time. Brookes and Lawley (114) showed that methylation of adenosine or adenylic acid under neutral conditions gave mainly the 1-methyl derivative together with 3-methyl and probably 1,3-dimethyl derivatives. In this respect, alkylating agents differ from ionizing radiation in that the latter, according to Hems (113), causes a ring-opening of the imidazole part of adenine, its nucleoside, and nucleotide like that of the guanine derivatives.

Coming back to the claim that the biological alkylating agents esterified the phosphate or other acidic group in nucleoprotein, it was reported by Stacey, Alexander et al. (103) that when they treated bovine serum albumin with representative alkylating agents, viz., epoxides, nitrogen mustards, and esters of methanesulfonic acid, they were able to confirm certain evidence for the esterification of carboxyl groups of native proteins. They also discovered that it was only epoxides which reacted to any great extent with protein amino groups, the other agents reacting only to a small extent. Some further work using ovalbumin disclosed that alkylating agents appear to react readily with —SH groups of protein, but only when denatured, for with native proteins most of these sulfhydryl groups were inaccessible. Experiments in which DNA was treated with melphalan (XI) showed that by far the most reactive center was the primary phosphate group. Using conditions where DNA was in excess, as is the case *in vivo*, it was claimed that the phenylalanine mustards esterified only the phosphate groups. With synthetic polymers, proteins, and DNA, in solution of less than 1%, the bifunctional agents produced cross-linking within the same molecule, whereas at higher concentrations cross-linking occurred between different molecules, leading in some instances to the formation of gels. Alexander et al. (103) speculated at that time that the alkylation of the phosphate groups of DNA resulted in the formation of unstable triesters, which was confirmed by the hydrolysis of treated and untreated samples of DNA. Fission of the triester occurred at the mustard link [Eq. (1)] which provided further evidence for the

$$=\overset{|}{\underset{|}{P}}-OCH_2CH_2R + H_2O \rightarrow \overset{|}{\underset{|}{P}}-O^-H^+ + RCH_2CH_2OH \qquad (1)$$

view that the mustards do not react with amino groups when DNA is in excess, because an alkyl bond with amino nitrogen is much more stable and would not be affected by the 20 minutes' heating at 90°. Indeed, all of the combined mustard was released by this treatment. More recently, Alexander (115) and his colleagues have obtained further results which they believe could reconcile the hypothesis of nitrogen alkylation as the cause of nucleic acid changes with their original belief in the phosphate groups as a primary target of nucleophilic substitution. In some cases, when using monofunctional alkylating agents, they observed two effects on DNA, the first consisting of a gelation of DNA without change of molecular weight, the second of more pronounced alterations. This could be explained only by assuming that esterification of phosphate groups took place initially followed by a transfer, particularly of methyl groups, to base nitrogen. While there is still a considerable gap between the views of the different schools, it looks as if the whole pattern of events following the application of alkylating agents is becoming more orderly. Whether these observations, culminating in the isolation of cross-linked bases [Brookes and Lawley (114)], are relevant to the biological events has to be seen.

A similar consideration applies to yet another completely different investigation which centers around the possible mode of action of Myleran [(XXXIV), $n = 4$]. As an introduction to this study, Roberts and Warwick (109, 110) studied the *in vivo* metabolic products of a typical monofunctional alkylating agent, viz., ethyl methanesulfonate ("half Myleran," LVIII). Ethyl-C^{14} methanesulfonate, labeled on the *a*-carbon

$$CH_3 \cdot SO_2 \cdot O \cdot C_2H_5$$

(LVIII)

atom, was injected into Wistar rats, in the urine of which radioactive compounds were subsequently detected. The bulk of the radioactivity was found to be carried by *S*-ethyl-*N*-acetylcysteine (LIX) and a smaller amount by a keto acid (LX). No labeled products were found of the type

$$C_2H_5 \cdot S \cdot CH_2 \cdot CH \cdot COOH \qquad\qquad C_2H_5 \cdot S \cdot CH_2 \cdot CO \cdot COOH$$
$$| $$
$$NHCO \cdot CH_3$$

(LIX)   (LX)

which would have been formed had the "half Myleran" reacted with acids or amino groups *in vivo*, although the possibility of their formation was not precluded since they could have been metabolized before excretion. This work was then repeated using Myleran-2,3-C^{14} in place of the mono-functional compound (111). By analogy it was thought that Myleran would react *in vivo* with the thiol group of cysteine or cysteine-containing compounds, resulting in the formation of metabolites of *S*-dicysteinyl-butane (LXI) or *S*-(4-hydroxybutyl)-cysteine (LXII), but this was not the case. It was also demonstrated that Myleran was not metabolized to

$$HOOC \cdot CH \cdot CH_2 \cdot S \cdot (CH_2)_4 \cdot S \cdot CH_2 \cdot CH \cdot COOH \qquad HO \cdot (CH_2)_4 \cdot S \cdot CH_2 \cdot CH \cdot COOH$$
$$| \qquad\qquad\qquad\qquad | \qquad\qquad\qquad\qquad\qquad\qquad |$$
$$NH_2 \qquad\qquad\qquad\qquad NH_2 \qquad\qquad\qquad\qquad\qquad\qquad NH_2$$

(LXI)   (LXII)

carbon dioxide as was the case with 1,4-butanediol and ethyl methane-sulfonate. In fact, after its injection, the one major metabolite obtained was stable to hot mineral acid and gave no positive test on paper with ninhydrin or platinic iodide. When Myleran was allowed to react with cysteine *in vitro*, the major product of the reaction was the S-β-alanyl-tetrahydrothiophenium salt (LXIII). The urine obtained from rats in-

$$
\begin{array}{c}
\text{CH}_2\text{—CH}_2 \\
| \hspace{2.5cm} \\
\text{CH}_2\text{—CH}_2
\end{array}
\diagup\hspace{-0.3cm}\diagdown
\text{S}^{+}\text{— CH}_2\cdot\underset{\underset{\text{NH}_2}{|}}{\text{CH}}\cdot\text{COOH}
\qquad \text{CH}_3\text{SO}_3^{-}
$$

(LXIII)

jected with this sulfonium salt, contained one major metabolite which was identical with that obtained with Myleran itself. This sulfonium salt, under a variety of conditions, was nearly quantitatively converted into tetrahydrothiophene; this led Roberts and Warwick (*112*) to suspect that the major urinary metabolite was a derivative of this heterocyclic system. Further evidence was obtained when tetrahydrothiophene-S^{35} and its oxidation product, injected into rats, gave a metabolite of tetrahydro-thiophene-S^{35} 1,1-dioxide (LXIV) which was identical with that obtained from Myleran and the sulfonium salt (LXIII).

Analytical and synthetic experiments showed finally that the structure of the urinary metabolite was that of 3-hydroxytetrahydrothiophene 1,1-dioxide (LXV).

$$
\begin{array}{c}
\text{CH}_2\text{—CH}_2 \\
| \hspace{1.2cm} | \\
\text{CH}_2 \hspace{0.8cm} \text{CH}_2 \\
\diagdown \hspace{0.3cm} \diagup \\
\text{S} \\
\diagup\hspace{-0.25cm}\diagdown \\
\text{O} \hspace{0.6cm} \text{O}
\end{array}
\qquad\qquad
\begin{array}{c}
\hspace{1.6cm}\text{OH} \\
\hspace{1.6cm}| \\
\text{CH}_2\text{—CH}_2 \\
| \hspace{1.2cm} | \\
\text{CH}_2 \hspace{0.8cm} \text{CH}_2 \\
\diagdown \hspace{0.3cm} \diagup \\
\text{S} \\
\diagup\hspace{-0.25cm}\diagdown \\
\text{O} \hspace{0.6cm} \text{O}
\end{array}
$$

(LXIV)   (LXV)

Roberts and Warwick then put forward the hypothesis that Myleran *in vivo* could react with either the thiol groups of glutathione or of larger molecules, such as proteins, including enzymes. To test this, Myleran was made to react separately with glutathione, denatured egg albumin, and reduced keratin; in each case, after degradation, tetrahydrothiophene was obtained, together with dehydropeptides or lanthionine derivatives. It appears that if this "dethiolation reaction" of essential cellular constituents can be connected with the biological effect of Myleran, then the differences between the Myleran type of alkylating agent, on the one hand, and the nitrogen mustard type, on the other, may be explained on the basis of a different mode of action. Of course, it cannot be excluded at present that under *in vivo* conditions the different groups of alkylating agents may follow simultaneously several pathways of interaction; and while one mode may be predominant under certain circumstances, the one responsible for antitumor or antileukemic action could be identical with one or the other proposed previously.

IV. SUMMARY AND OUTLOOK

It is hoped that this brief article may have brought to light some of the more recent advances in the field of biological alkylating agents. These drugs, though not true metabolic antagonists and not representing a major answer to the urgent question of a satisfactory chemotherapy of human cancers and leukemias, have proved to be a fruitful subject for the study of antitumor, carcinogenic, and mutagenic effects, for the investigation of structure-activity relationships inside this group, and for the possible mechanism of action by which this family of compounds may achieve their biological effects. The reader could object to the emphasis on chemistry and biochemistry of the alkylating agents, whereby a great number of biological results have been left unmentioned.

What further developments lie ahead in this field, if any? It is true that all attempts to prepare compounds with new carrier moieties have led to only moderate improvements in the ratios of toxicity and hemotoxicity to experimental antitumor activities. None of the more recent representatives has proved to be as effective as modern antimicrobial drugs in human medicine, although some of them have been used with some degree of success in "regional perfusion," a novel surgical technique (*52, 116–120*) which, together with the systemic treatment of neoplastic diseases, requires better and more selective compounds. Will it be possible for the chemist, in collaboration with the biochemist, experimental pathologist, and clinician, to deliver improved alkylating agents, or has he rung all the possible changes in combining alkylating groups with different carriers, some of which may by themselves be physiologically important. The results with the peptidic derivatives point to the use of proteins or protein-like moieties, and a comparable series could be started with nucleotides and polynucleotides. Some of the ideas expressed by Baker (*121*) could be pursued in different directions, and our advancing knowledge of immunological properties might open up new pathways. But whether alkylating groups attached to anything reasonable will be forgotten in time to come depends largely on advances with other types of biologically active compounds, whether they belong to metabolic antagonists, enzymes, antibodies, or compounds which are capable of exercising control over cell growth, cell division, and cell aging.

REFERENCES

1. W. C. Ross, *Advances in Cancer Research* 1, 397 (1953).
2. W. C. J. Ross, *Ann. N. Y. Acad. Sci.* 68, 669 (1958).
3. W. L. Nyhan, *J. Pharmacol. Exptl. Therap.* 130, 268 (1960).
4. O. V. St. Whitelock, ed., "Comparative Clinical and Biological Effects of Alkylating Agents," *Ann. N. Y. Acad. Sci.* 68, 657–1266 (1958).
5. F. Bergel, *Ann. N. Y. Acad. Sci.* 68, 1238 (1958).
6. A. Haddow, *in* "The Physiopathology of Cancer" (F. Homburger, ed.), 2nd ed., p. 602. Hoeber, New York, 1959.
7. W. Davis, *Mfg. Chemist* 31, 233, 289 (1960).
8. J. A. Montgomery, *Cancer Research* 19, 447 (1959).
9. G. M. Timmis, *in* "Cancer" (R. W. Raven, ed.), Vol. 6, p. 1, Butterworths, London, 1959.
10. R. B. Ross, *J. Chem. Educ.* 36, 368 (1959).
11. See R. Jones, Jr., *Natl. Cancer Inst. Monograph No.* 3, 127–149 (1960).
12. (a) W. C. J. Ross, "Biological Alkylating Agents." Butterworths, London, 1962; (b) J. A. Stock and R. Wade, Academic Press, New York, in preparation.
13. D. F. Gamble, H. W. Bond, and A. Burger, *in* "Medicinal Chemistry" (H. Burger, ed.), 2nd ed., p. 1077. Wiley (Interscience), New York, 1960.
14. J. L. Everett, J. J. Roberts, and W. C. J. Ross, *J. Chem. Soc.* pp. 2386–2392 (1953).
15. L. A. Elson, *Ann. N. Y. Acad. Sci.* 68, 826 (1958).
16. W. Davis, J. J. Roberts, and W. C. J. Ross, *J. Chem. Soc.* pp. 890–895 (1955).
17. F. Bergel and E. Reiner, *J. Chem. Soc.* pp. 2890–2893 (1959).
18. C. G. Raison and O. D. Stenden, *Trans. Roy. Soc. Trop. Med. Hyg.* 48, 446 (1954); *Brit. J. Pharmacol.* 10, 191 (1955).
19. R. F. Collins, M. Davis, and J. Hill, *Chem. & Ind. (London)*, p. 1072 (1954).
20. J. N. Ashley, R. F. Collins, M. Davis, and N. E. Sirett, *J. Chem. Soc.* p. 3298 (1958).
21. W. A. Skinner, H. F. Gram, and B. R. Baker, *J. Org. Chem.* 25, 777, 953 (1960).
22. W. A. Skinner, M. G. M. Schelstraete, and B. R. Baker, *J. Org. Chem.* 26, 1674 (1961).
23. F. Bergel, J. L. Everett, J. J. Roberts, and W. C. J. Ross, *J. Chem. Soc.* p. 3835 (1955).
24. F. Bergel and J. A. Stock, *J. Chem. Soc.* pp. 2409–2417 (1954).

25. A. S. Khokhlov, L. F. Larionov, M. A. Novikova, E. N. Shkodinskaja, V. I. Troosheikina, and O. S. Vasina, *Lancet* ii, 169 (1955); U.S.S.R. 104, 781 Feb. 25 (1957); *Chem. Abstr.* 51, 14811 (1957).
26. V. I. Troosheikina, *Byull. Eksptl. Biol. Med.* 46, 101–104 (1958).
27. P. C. Koller and U. Veronesi, *Brit. J. Cancer* 10, 703–714 (1956).
28. L. A. Elson, *Brit. Empire Cancer Campaign Repts.* 32, 453 (1954).
29. O. G. Fahmy and M. J. Fahmy, *J. Genet.* 54, 146–164 (1956).
30. A. R. Crathorn and D. G. Hunter, *Biochem. J.* 67, 37–41 (1957).
31. S. Zamenhof, G. Leidy, E. Hahn, and H. E. Alexander, *J. Bacteriol.* 72, 1–11 (1956).
32. H. E. Smith and J. M. Luck, *J. Org. Chem.* 23, 837–841 (1958).
33. O. Lutz and Br. Jirgensons, *Ber.* 63, 448 (1930).
34. F. Bergel, G. E. Lewis, S. F. D. Orr, and J. Butler, *J. Chem. Soc.* pp. 1431–1437 (1959).
35. H. F. Gram, C. W. Mosher, and B. R. Baker, *J. Am. Chem. Soc.* 81, 3103 (1959).
36. T. S. Osdene, D. N. Ward, W. H. Chapman, and H. Rakoff, *J. Am. Chem. Soc.* 81, 3100 (1959).
37. N. E. Golubeva, O. V. Kil'disheva, and I. L. Knunyants, *Doklady Akad. Nauk S.S.S.R.* 132, 836–838 (1960).
38. W. A. Skinner, K. A. Hyde, H. F. Gram, and B. R. Baker, *J. Org. Chem.* 25, 1756 (1960).
39. J. M. Luck, *Cancer Research*, 21, 262 (1961).
40. T. A. Connors, W. C. J. Ross, and J. G. Wilson, *J. Chem. Soc.* pp. 2994–3007 (1960).
41. T. A. Connors, Ph.D. Thesis, Univ. of London (1960).
42. T. A. Connors and W. C. J. Ross, *Chem. & Ind.* (*London*) pp. 492–493 (1960).
43. F. Bergel, J. M. Johnson, and J. A. Stock, *Chem. & Ind.* (*London*) p. 1487 (1959).
44. J. M. Johnson, *Chem. & Ind* (*London*) pp. 966–967 (1960).
45. N. A. Vodolazskaya, M. A. Novikova, E. N. Shkodinskaya, O. S. Vasina, A. Ya. Berlin, and L. F. Larionov, *Byull Eksptl. Biol. Med.* 44, 76–81 (1957); English translation *Bull. Exptl. Biol. Med.* 44, 1362–1367 (1957).
46. I. L. Knunyants, O. V. Kil'kisheva, and N. E. Golubeva, *Izvest. Akad. Nauk S.S.S.R., Otdel. Khim. Nauk* pp. 1418–1419 (1956).
47. F. Bergel and J. A. Stock, *J. Chem. Soc.* pp. 3658–3669 (1960).
48. Personal communication, Department of Surgery, Royal Marsden Hospital, London.
49. L. F. Larionov and Z. P. Sof'ina, *Doklady Akad. Nauk S.S.S.R.* 114, 1070–1072 (1957).
50. N. E. Golubeva, O. V. Kil'disheva, and I. L. Knunyants, *Doklady Akad. Nauk S.S.S.R.* 119, 83–86 (1958).
51. I. L. Knunyants, N. E. Golubeva, and O. V. Kil'disheva, *Doklady Akad. Nauk S.S.S.R.* 132, 836–838 (1960).
52. A. Lawrence Abel, *Brit. Med. J.* i, 952 (1960).
53. M. Ishidate, Y. Sakurai, and M. Izumi. *J. Am. Pharm. Assoc.* 44, 132 (1955).

54. M. Izumi, *Pharm. Bull. (Tokyo)* 2, 275–279 (1954).
55. W. L. Nyhan and H. Busch, *Federation Proc.* 17, 639 (1958).
56. M. Ishidate, Y. Sakurai, and I. Aiko, *Chem. and Pharm. Bull.* 8, 732 (1960).
57a. O. F. Ginzburg and M. I. Krylova, unpublished data.
57b. L. F. Larionov, *Vestnik Akad. Med. Nauk S.S.S.R.* 14, No. 6, 25–37 (1959).
58. W. C. J. Ross and G. P. Warwick, *Nature* 176, 298 (1955).
59. W. C. J. Ross and G. P. Warwick, *J. Chem. Soc.* pp. 1364, 1719, 1724 (1956)
60. F. Bergel and R. Wade, *J. Chem. Soc.* pp. 941–947 (1959).
61. A. F. Childs, L. J. Goldsworthy, G. F. Harding, F. E. King, A. W. Nineham, W. L. Norris, S. G. P. Plant, B. Selton, and A. L. L. Tompsett, *J. Chem. Soc.* p. 2174 (1948).
62. R. S. M. Bushby, personal communication; see *J. Chem. Soc.* p. 941 (1959) ; ref. 18.
63a. N. Brock, *Arzneimittel-Forsch.* 8, 1 (1958) ; H. Arnold and F. Bourseaux, *Angew. Chem.* 70, 539–544 (1958) ; H. Arnold, F. Bourseaux, and N. Brock, *Naturwissenschaften* 45, 64 (1958).
63b. O. M. Friedman and A. M. Seligman, *J. Am. Chem. Soc.* 76, 655 (1954).
64. L. F. Larionov, *Acta Unio Intern. contra Cancrum* 13, 393 (1957).
65. D. A. Lyttle and H. G. Petering, *J. Am. Chem. Soc.* 80, 6459 (1958).
66. R. M. Peck, R. K. Preston, and H. J. Creech, *J. Am. Chem. Soc.* 81, 3984 (1959).
67. H. J. Creech, R. F. Hankivitz, Jr., R. M. Peck, and R. K. Preston, *Proc. Am. Assoc. Cancer Research* 2, 195 (1957).
68. H. J. Creech, *Ann. N. Y. Acad. Sci.* 68, 868 (1958).
69. R. B. Ross and P. E. Swartzentruber, "Literature Survey of Nitrogen Mustards." Cancer Chemotherapy National Service Center, Bethesda, Maryland.
70. A. Haddow and G. M. Timmis, *Brit. Empire Canc. Camp. Repts.* 28, 58 (1950) ; *Lancet* 264, 207 (1953).
71. E. Miller, *Ann. N. Y. Acad. Sci.* 68, 1205 (1958).
72. G. M. Timmis and R. F. Hudson, *Ann. N. Y. Acad. Sci.* 68, 727 (1958).
73. H. R. Bierman, K. H. Kelly, A. G. Knudson, T. Maekawa, and G. M. Timmis, *Ann. N. Y. Acad. Sci.* 68, 1211 (1958).
74. L. Vargha, L. Toldy, Ö. Fehér, and S. Lendvai, *J. Chem. Soc.* p. 805 (1957).
75. A. Haddow, G. M. Timmis, and S. S. Brown, *Nature* 182, 1164–1165 (1958).
76. G. M. Timmis and S. S. Brown, *Biochem. Pharmacol.* 3, 247–248 (1960).
77. T. H. Goodridge, M. T. Flather, R. E. Harmon, and R. P. Bratzel, *Cancer Chemotherapy Repts.* 9, 78 (1960).
78. M. E. Baumann, C. Heidelberger, R. K. Maller, and F. A. McIver, *Cancer Research* 17, 277–301 (1957).
79. T. J. Bardos, Z. B. Papanastassiou, A. Segaloff, and J. L. Ambrus, *Nature* 183, 399–400 (1959).
80. A. Segaloff, T. J. Bardos, Z. B. Papanastassiou, J. L. Ambrus, and J. B. Weeth, *Proc. Am. Assoc. Cancer Research* 3, 62 (1959).

81. J. B. Weeth, A. Segaloff, and K. K. Meyer, *Proc. Am. Assoc. Cancer Research* **3**, 160 (1960).
82. S. McCracken and J. Wolf, *Cancer Chemotherapy Repts.* **6**, 52 (1960).
83. D. V. Razis, J. L. Ambrus, C. A. Ross, L. Stutzman, J. E. Sokal, and A. B. Rejali, *Proc. Am. Assoc. Cancer Research* **9**, 37 (1960).
84. S. Peterson, W. Gauss, and E. Urbschat, *Angew. Chem.* **67**, 217 (1955).
85. W. Gauss and S. Peterson, *Angew. Chem.* **69**, 252 (1957).
86. G. Domagk, *Ann. N. Y. Acad. Sci.* **68**, 1197 (1958).
87. W. Gauss, *Ber.* **91**, 2216 (1958).
88. A. Linke and B. Freudenberger, *in* "Über die Chemotherapie der Hämoblastosen und malignen Tumoren," Symposien-Aktueller therapeutischer Probleme, Heft 3. Enke, Stuttgart, 1960.
89. A. Linke, *Deut. med. Wochschr.* **85**, 1928 (1960).
90. J. A. Hendry, R. F. Homer, F. L. Rose, and A. L. Walpole, *Acta Unio Intern. contra Cancrum* **7**, 482–494 (1951).
91. A. L. Walpole, D. C. Roberts, F. L. Rose, J. A. Hendry, and R. F. Homer, *Brit. J. Pharmacol.* **9**, 306–323 (1954).
92. A. L. Walpole, *Ann. N. Y. Acad. Sci.* **68**, 750 (1958).
93. H. Jackson, B. W. Fox, and A. W. Craig, *Brit. J. Pharmacol.* **14**, 149–157 (1959).
94. H. Jackson, *Pharmacol. Revs.* **11**, 135–172 (1959).
95. K. Gerzon, J. E. Cochran, Jr., L. A. White, R. Monahan, E. V. Krumkalns, R. E. Scroggs, and J. Mills, *J. Med. Pharm. Chem.* **1**, 223 (1959).
96. P. N. Magee and J. M. Barnes, *Brit. J. Cancer* **10**, 114 (1956).
97. E. Farber and P. N. Magee, *Biochem. J.* **76**, 58P (1960).
98. A. Haddow, *Brit. Med. Bull.* **14**, 79 (1958).
99. C. D. Darlington, *Brit. J. Cancer* **2**, 118 (1948).
100. A. Todd, *Brit. Med. J.* **II**, 517 (1959).
101. E. J. Ambrose, A. M. James, and J. H. B. Lowick, *Nature* **177**, 576 (1956).
102. E. J. Ambrose, D. M. Easty, and P. C. T. Jones, *Brit. J. Cancer* **12**, 439 (1958).
103. K. A. Stacey, M. Cobb, S. F. Cousens, and P. Alexander, *Ann. N. Y. Acad. Sci.* **68**, 682–701 (1958).
104. G. P. Wheeler, J. S. Morrow, and H. E. Skipper, *Arch. Biochem. Biophys.* **57**, 133 (1955).
105. P. D. Lawley and C. A. Wallick, *Chem. & Ind. (London)* p. 633 (1957).
106. P. D. Lawley, *Biochim. et Biophys. Acta* **26**, 450 (1957).
107. P. D. Lawley, *Proc. Chem. Soc.* p. 290 (1957).
108. E. M. Press and J. A. V. Butler, *J. Chem. Soc.* p. 626 (1952).
109. J. J. Roberts and G. P. Warwick, *Nature* **179**, 1181–1182 (1957).
110. J. J. Roberts and G. P. Warwick, *Biochem. Pharmacol.* **1**, 60–75 (1958).
111. J. J. Roberts and G. P. Warwick, *Nature* **183**, 1509–1510 (1959).
112. J. J. Roberts and G. P. Warwick, *Nature* **184**, 1288–1289 (1959).
113. G. Hems, *Nature* **181**, 1721 (1958).
114. P. Brookes and P. D. Lawley, *J Chem. Soc.* p. 539 (1960).
115. P. Alexander, personal communication.
116. O. Creech, Jr., E. T. Krementz, R. F. Ryan, K. Reemtsma, and J. N. Winblad, *Ann. Surg.* **149**, 627 (1959).

117. E. T. Krementz, O. Creech, Jr., R. F. Ryan, and J. Wickstrom, *J. Bone and Joint Surg.* *41A*, No. 6, 977–987 (1959).
118. J. S. Stehlin, Jr., R. Lee Clark, Jr., J. L. Smith, Jr., and E. C. White, *Cancer* 13, 55–66 (1960).
119. B. J. Miller and J. C. Kistenmacher, *J. Am. Med. Assoc.* 173, 14–21. (1960).
120. O. C. Creech, Jr., E. T. Krementz, R. F. Ryan, K. Reemtsma, J. L. Elliot, and J. N. Winblad, *J. Am. Med. Assoc.* 171, 2069–2075 (1959).
121. B. R. Baker, *Cancer Chemotherapy Repts.* 4, 1 (1959).
122. S. Moore, W. H. Stein, and J. A. Fruton, *J. Org. Chem.* 11, 675 (1946).
123. O. M. Friedman and E. Boger, *J. Am. Chem. Soc.* 78, 4659 (1956).
124. L. Vargha, *Naturwissenschaften* 42, 582 (1955).
125. W. C. J. Ross and J. G. Wilson, *J. Chem. Soc.* p. 3616 (1959).
126. E. R. H. Jones and W. Wilson, *J. Chem Soc.* p. 547 (1949).
127. G. Drefahl and K. H. Konig, *Chem. Ber.* 87, 1628 (1945).
128. F. Bergel and R. Wade, *J. Chem. Soc.* p. 941 (1959).
129. A. Haddow and G. M. Timmis, *Acta Unio Intern. contra Cancrum* 7, 469 (1951).
130. A. Haddow, G. M. Timmis, and S. S. Brown, *Nature* 182, 1164 (1958).
131. S. M. Buckley, C. C. Stock, R. P. Parker, M. L. Crossley, E. Kuh, and D. R. Seeger, *Proc. Soc. Exptl. Biol. Med.* 78, 299 (1951).
132. G. Personeus, S. L. Halliday, D. McKenzie, and J. H. Williams, *Proc. Soc. Exptl. Biol. Med.* 81, 614 (1952).
133. F. L. Rose, J. A. Hendry, and A. L. Walpole, *Nature* 165, 993 (1950); J. A. Hendry, R. F. Homer, F. L. Rose, and A. L. Walpole, *Brit. J. Pharmacol.* 6, 235 (1951).
134. J. L. Everett and G. A. R. Kon, *J. Chem. Soc.* p. 3131 (1950).
135. A. Marxer, *Helv. Chim. Acta* 38, 1473 (1955).
136. W. Gauss and S. Peterson, *Angew. Chem.* 69, 252 (1957).
137. F. L. Rose, J. A. Hendry, and A. L. Walpole, *Nature* 165, 993 (1950).
138. M. R. Lewis and M. L. Crossley, *Arch. Biochem. Biophys.* 26, 319 (1950).
139. J. H. Burchenal, M. L. Crossley, C. C. Stock, and C. P. Rhoads, *Arch. Biochem. Biophys.* 26, 321 (1950).
140. A. Haddow, G. A. R. Kon, and W. C. J. Ross, *Nature* 162, 824 (1948).
141. G. A. R. Kon and J. J. Roberts, *J. Chem. Soc.* p. 978 (1950).
142. F. Bergel and J. A. Stock, *J. Chem. Soc.* p. 2409 (1954).
143. L. F. Larionov, E. N. Shkodinskaya, V. I. Troosheikina, A. S. Khoklov, O. S. Vasina, and M. A. Novikova, *Lancet* 269, 169 (1955).
144. W. Davis, J. J. Roberts, and W. C. J. Ross, *J. Chem. Soc.* p. 890 (1955).
145. J. L. Everett, J. J. Roberts, and W. C. J. Ross, *J. Chem. Soc.* p. 2386 (1953).
146. F. Bergel and G. E. Lewis, *J. Chem. Soc.* p. 1816 (1957).
147. F. Bergel and J. A. Stock, *J. Chem. Soc.* p. 3658 (1960); F. Bergel, J. M. Johnson, and R. Wade, *ibid.* p. 3802 (1962).
148. F. Bergel and J. A. Stock, *J. Chem. Soc.* p. 4563 (1957).
149. W. C. J. Ross, G. P. Warwick, and J. J. Roberts, *J. Chem. Soc.* p. 3110 (1955).
150. F. Bergel and J. A. Stock, *J. Chem. Soc.* p. 97 (1959).

151. C. C. Stock and S. M. Buckley, *Acta Unio Intern. contra Cancrum* **7**, 523 (1951).
152. L. F. Larionov, *Acta Unio Intern. contra Cancrum* **13**, 393 (1957).
153. H. J. Creech, R. F. Hankwitz, R. M. Peck, and R. K. Preston, *Proc. Am. Assoc. Cancer Research* **2**, 195 (1957).

CHAPTER 24

Inhibition of Acetylcholinesterase

Irwin B. Wilson

I. INTRODUCTION

There are many very potent inhibitors of acetylcholinesterase, and since acetylcholinesterase has a vital function in nervous activity, all are very toxic substances (1). Much information concerning two of the more interesting groups of inhibitors, organophosphates and carbamates, is given by R. D. O'Brien in this volume and in monographs by G. Schrader (2) and B. Holmstedt (3). This article is therefore limited to a brief presentation of the theoretical basis of the inhibition of acetylcholinesterase.

II. THEORY OF ENZYMIC HYDROLYSIS

We start with the formation of a reversible enzyme-substrate complex which occasionally undergoes further reaction to yield products and free enzyme. Observations with inhibitors and substrates suggest that the active site consists of two subsites, an anionic site, which binds and orients substituted ammonium ions, and an esteratic site, containing an acidic and a basic group (H—G) both of which are essential for hydrolytic activity. At the anionic site, ionic and "hydrophobic" forces contribute to the stability of complexes formed with inhibitors and substrates (4, 4a, 4b). The ionic bond contributes a factor of about thirty.

The contribution of hydrophobic bonds arises from the tendency of water to expel nonpolar groups and depends, of course, upon the nature and distribution of the hydrophobic substituent, being about **7** (relative to H) for a methyl group in tetramethylammonium ion or acetylcholine. In the case of tetrahedral quaternary ions one group must project into the solution and is without binding properties; but it may make a statistical contribution to binding; tetramethylammonium ion is bound **4** times better than trimethylamine, in accordance with the possibility of selecting the nonbinding methyl group in four ways. A binding contribution of four as against seven is not sufficiently different to confirm the physical picture, but it is consistent with it.

The esteratic site is the location where the hydrolytic process occurs, where the ester linkage is attacked, but it is also a binding site involving the formation of a covalent bond between the basic group and the carbonyl carbon atom. The strength of this contribution is small for acetylcholine, but it can be quite large for other compounds in which the carbonyl carbon atom is more acidic (Lewis acid) e.g., acetic anhydride (*4b*).

The binding of a molecule by a protein in aqueous solution depends upon the difference in the contact free energy of the molecule and the protein, and the molecule and water. In the case of a hydrocarbon group or other nonpolar group, the main driving force for binding is the tendency of the water to expel the group. The structure of the protein determines whether it can accommodate the molecule with respect to its size and shape and whether it can provide a nonpolar environment. Interestingly enough, it turns out that the energy change is small and that "hydrophobic bonds" are a consequence of a favorable entropy change, which is thought to arise by the release of an ordered mantle of water molecules from the hydrocarbons.

In the case of a polar group it would appear that the protein cannot play so passive a role but must wrest the group from the water if there is to be a binding contribution. Here, too, it is quite possible that the main driving force is the release of ordered water molecules.

In the case of ionic bonds in water it again turns out that the favorable entropy change attending the release of water molecules is the main driving force.

The nature of binding forces in solution has been reviewed by Kauzmann (*5*).

The hydrolytic process is thought to have the mechanism (*6*) shown in Eqs. (**1**) and (**2**).

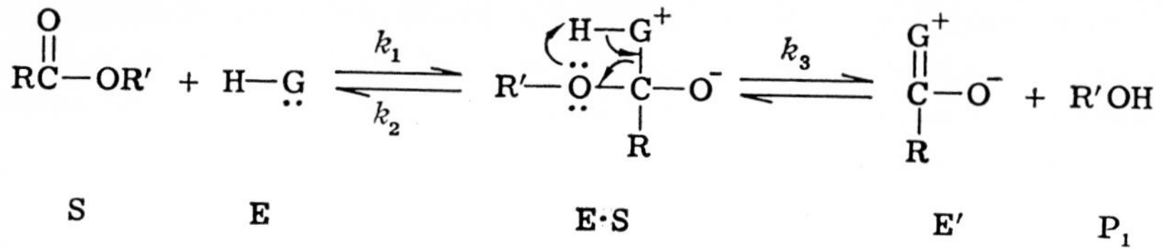

$$RC{-}OR' + H{-}G \underset{k_2}{\overset{k_1}{\rightleftharpoons}} R'{-}\ddot{O}{-}\overset{\displaystyle (H{-}G^+)}{\underset{R}{C}}{-}O^- \overset{k_3}{\rightleftharpoons} \overset{G^+}{\underset{R}{C}}{-}O^- + R'OH \qquad (1)$$

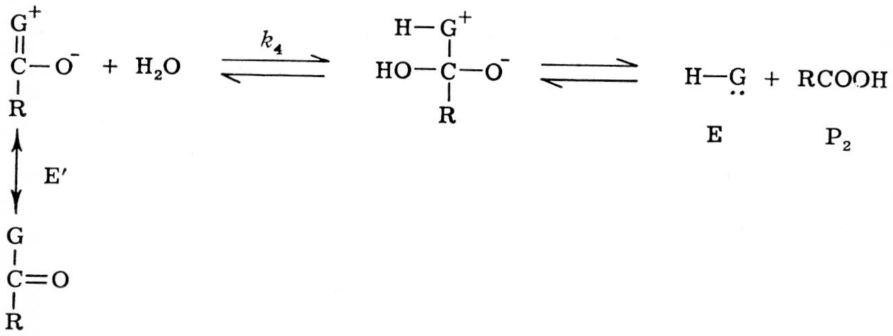

S   E   E·S   E'   P₁

$$\overset{G^+}{\underset{R}{C}}{-}O^- + H_2O \overset{k_4}{\rightleftharpoons} \overset{H{-}G^+}{\underset{R}{HO{-}C{-}O^-}} \rightleftharpoons H{-}G + RCOOH \qquad (2)$$

$$\overset{E'}{\updownarrow}$$

$$\overset{G}{\underset{R}{C{=}O}}$$

Here H—G̈ represents the esteratic site. The important feature is the formation of an acetyl-enzyme derivative as an intermediate and its subsequent hydrolysis. The rate equation for this formulation (7) is given in Eqs. (3)–(5).

$$\frac{1}{v} = \frac{1}{kE^0} + \frac{K_m}{kE^0}\cdot\frac{1}{(S)} \qquad (3)$$

$$K_m = \left(\frac{k_2 + k_3}{k_1}\right)\Big/\left(1 + \frac{k_3}{k_4}\right) \qquad (4)$$

$$k = \frac{k_3 k_4}{k_3 + k_4}; \qquad k_4 \text{ includes } (H_2O) \qquad (5)$$

It will be noted that all acetates must have the same value for k_4, and therefore the maximum value of k is k_4. A higher value of k implies a higher value of k_3. It is also interesting that a high value of k_3/k_4 tends to make K_m smaller, and if, as seems to be the case, k_3 is smaller than k_2, a high value of k will make K_m smaller. However, it appears that this effect is sizable only for substrates which are hydrolyzed with a speed comparable to acetylcholine.

The physical picture of the active site and the above mechanism reveal the possibility of two broad types of inhibitors. Members of one class simply form reversible addition complexes with the enzyme and might therefore be called prosthetic inhibitors. Members of the second class transfer an acid group to the esteratic site, yielding a product analogous to the acetyl enzyme but which hydrolyzes very much more slowly, possibly barely at all. These might be called oxydiaphoric inhibitors or acid-transferring inhibitors.

A. Prosthetic Inhibitors

The theory suggests that an inhibitor might not only compete with acetylcholine for the free enzyme, but might also combine with the acetyl enzyme. The kinetics of inhibition would, in general, therefore be expected to show competitive and noncompetitive components (8). A number of compounds do show noncompetitive components (9). The formal scheme is given in Eqs. (6)–(9).

$$E + S \rightleftharpoons E \cdot S \overset{k_3}{\rightleftharpoons} E' \overset{k_4}{\rightleftharpoons} E \tag{6}$$

$$E + I \rightleftharpoons E \cdot I; \quad K_I \tag{7}$$

$$E' + I \rightleftharpoons E' \cdot I; \quad K_I' \tag{8}$$

$$E^0 = E + E' + E \cdot S + E \cdot I + E' \cdot I \tag{9}$$

The steady-state solution is given in Eq. (10).

$$\frac{1}{v} = \frac{1}{kE^0}\left[1 + \frac{(I)}{K_I'[1 + (k_4/k_3)]}\right] + \frac{K_m}{kE^0}\left[1 + \frac{(I)}{K_I}\right]\frac{1}{(S)} \tag{10}$$

A noncompetitive component is indicated by a displacement of the v^{-1} intercept. The size of the displacement depends on the value of k_4/k_3 and, therefore, on the substrate. It is evident that if k_4/k_3 were large, the formation of the acetyl enzyme would be rate controlling, and a quite sizable inhibition of the deacylation would not significantly decrease the over-all velocity. This dependence upon the substrate has been observed. At present, it seems that the value of k_4/k_3 is considerably less than one for acetylcholine, perhaps $1/6$; and in this case we are therefore able to evaluate K_I'. It turns out that with rather small inhibitors, dimethyl-ammonium ion and trimethylammonium ion, the values of K_I', are about the same as K_I, i.e., the inhibitors are bound equally well by the acetyl enzyme and the free enzyme; a quite reasonable result. But with tetra-methylammonium ion and other tetrahedral quaternary ammonium ions, the binding with the acetyl enzyme is decidedly weaker than with the free enzyme. Acetylcholine, itself, fits into this latter category, and we are provided with a ready explanation of substrate inhibition. The binding of acetylcholine with the acetyl enzyme inhibits the deacylation step (7, 8).

We have already discussed three types of "bonds" which are formed between the enzyme and inhibitors and substrates: ionic bonds, hydrophobic bonds, and a covalent bond between a basic group of the enzyme and a carbonyl carbon atom. It appears that under suitable circumstances hydrogen bonds may also be involved. An example is found in the case of 3-hydroxyphenyltrimethylammonium ion (II) (10). Here the hydroxyl group makes a binding contribution of a factor of about 120, as judged from a comparison with phenyltrimethylammonium ion (I). A hydrogen bond seems to be the only source of such a large factor, and a number of observations are consistent with this possibility.

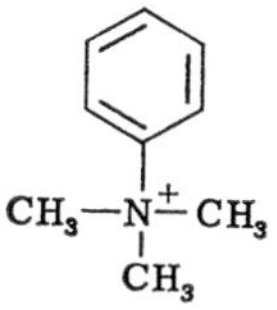

$$CH_3-\overset{+}{\underset{CH_3}{N}}-CH_3 \qquad\qquad CH_3-\overset{+}{\underset{CH_3}{N}}-CH_3$$

(I) 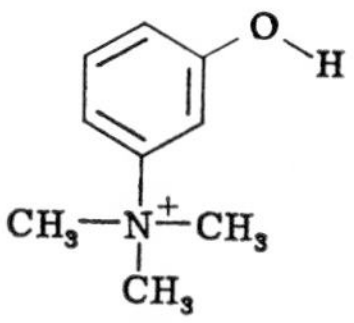   (II)

Except for the methyl groups, all atoms of this ion lie in a plane, and the position of the phenolic hydrogen has two possible positions: one as shown and the other obtained by rotation of 180° about the oxygen-ring axis. It is possible to show that the conformation shown is actually the one that is bound to the enzyme. This knowledge gives us the approximate position of the basic group with which it forms a hydrogen bond. This basic group may possibly be the basic group of the esteratic site to which we have already referred; but aside from the fact that the distance would fit, there is no supporting evidence for this possibility.

B. Oxydiaphoric Inhibitors

The two most widely studied groups of oxydiaphoric or acid-transferring inhibitors are derived from phosphoric acid and from carbamic acid. The former are often referred to as alkyl phosphates, and the latter as carbamates.

1. ALKYL PHOSPHATES

These compounds have the general structure shown in (III), where R_1 and R_2 may vary quite considerably. Typical substituents are hydrocarbon groups, alkoxy or phenoxy groups and their sulfur analogues, or amino or substituted amino groups. The group represented by X must

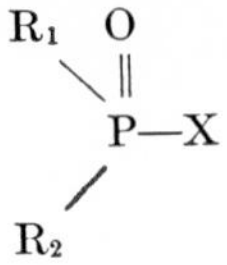

$$\begin{array}{c} R_1 \quad O \\ \diagdown \; \| \\ P-X \\ \diagup \\ R_2 \end{array}$$

(III)

be such that for the particular R's, it forms a labile bond with phosphorus, i.e., the compound must be a phosphorylating agent. Representative groups are F, CN, $O-C_6H_4-NO_2$, and $O-P(O)(OEt)_2$. Many more can be found in the article by Dr. O'Brien and in references (1) and (2).

Compounds containing thiono sulfur are, in general, poor anticholinesterases but may be quite toxic because of *in vivo* oxidation to the corresponding oxygen compound; e.g., parathion is converted to paraoxon (11).

Some well-known members of this group of inhibitors are shown in structures (IV)–(VIII).

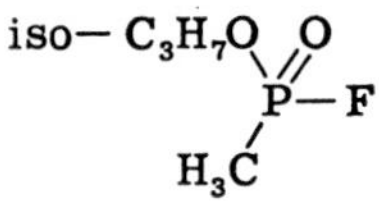

(IV)

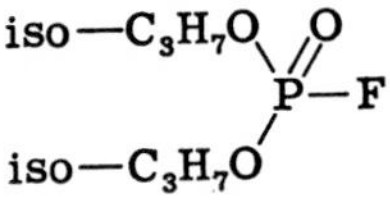

(V)

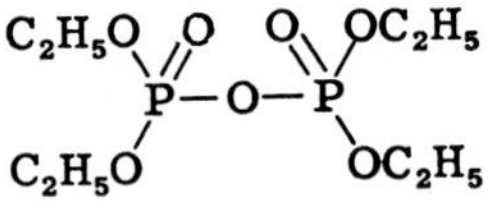

(VI)

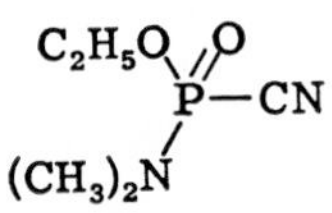

(VII)

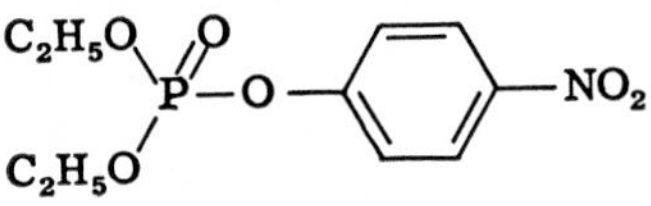

(VIII)

The mechanism of inhibition involves phosphorylation (4a, 12) and follows the scheme (13) shown in Eq. (11).

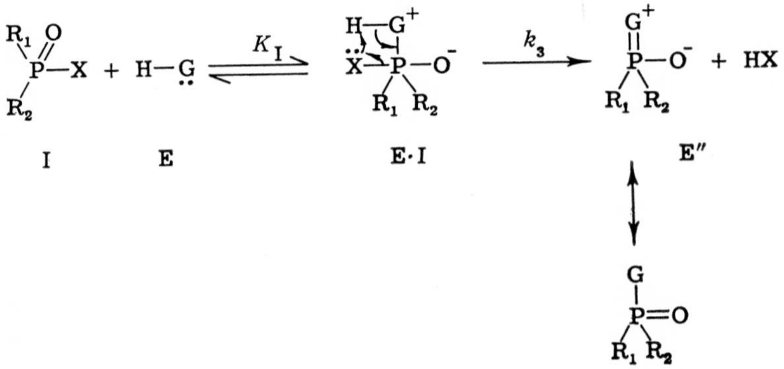

$$\begin{array}{cccccc} R_1 \; O & & & H\!-\!G^+ & & G^+ \\ \diagdown \| & & & \ddots\diagup & & \| \\ P-X \;+\; H\!-\!G & \underset{\longleftarrow}{\overset{K_I}{\longrightarrow}} & & X\!-\!P\!-\!O^- & \overset{k_3}{\longrightarrow} & P\!-\!O^- \;+\; HX \\ \diagup & & & \diagup \diagdown & & \diagup \diagdown \\ R_2 & & & R_1 \; R_2 & & R_1 \; R_2 \\[4pt] \quad I & \quad E & & E\cdot I & & E'' \end{array}$$

$$\begin{array}{c} \updownarrow \\ G \\ | \\ P\!=\!O \\ \diagup \diagdown \\ R_1 \; R_2 \end{array}$$

(11)

The symbol E″ is used to distinguish the inhibited enzyme (phosphoryl enzyme) from the acetyl enzyme for which we have already used the symbol E′.

The enzyme activity may recover, depending upon the R groups, by hydrolysis of the phosphoryl enzyme [Eq. (12)], but this is a very slow

$$
\begin{array}{ccccc}
\text{G} & & \text{H—G}^+ & & \text{R}_1 \;\; \text{O} \\
| & & | & & \diagdown \; \| \\
\text{P=O} + \text{H}_2\text{O} \rightleftharpoons \text{HO—P—O}^- \rightleftharpoons \text{H—\ddot{G}} + & & \text{P—OH} \\
\diagup \diagdown & & \diagup \diagdown & & \diagup \\
\text{R}_1 \quad \text{R}_2 & & \text{R}_2 \quad \text{R}_1 & & \text{R}_2
\end{array}
\tag{12}
$$

process at best. In principle, a steady state is reached in which the rate of inhibition equals the rate of recovery. The rate equation for the approach to this steady state is given by Eq. (13),

$$
\ln\left[\frac{\text{E}'}{\text{E}^0}\left(\frac{\mathcal{E}}{\text{E}'} - \left[\frac{\mathcal{E}}{\text{E}'}\right]_{ss}\right)\right] = -\frac{k_3}{1 + (K_I/\text{I})}\left(1 + \left[\frac{\mathcal{E}}{\text{E}'}\right]_{ss}\right)t
\tag{13}
$$

where $\mathcal{E} = \text{E·I} + \text{E}$ is the quantity measured if the concentration of inhibitor is diluted to a sufficiently low value during the measurement with substrate. In the steady state

$$
\left[\frac{\mathcal{E}}{\text{E}'}\right]_{ss} = \frac{k_4}{k_3}\left(1 + \frac{K_I}{\text{I}}\right)
\tag{14}
$$

Usually, the concentration of I required to produce a fairly rapid rate of inhibition, while small compared to K_I, is yet so high that $[\mathcal{E}/\text{E}']_{ss} = 0$.

This situation can arise because k_3 is usually very large compared to k_4. In such situations the rate equation reduces to Eq. (15).

$$
\ln\left(\frac{\mathcal{E}}{\text{E}^0}\right) = -\frac{k_3(\text{I})}{K_I}t = -k_3'(\text{I})t
\tag{15}
$$

This is the same equation as would be derived from a bimolecular reaction mechanism. Probably, in most cases the formation of a reversible complex is of little moment, but with special inhibitors, in particular those which are also substituted ammonium ions, such as (IX) and (X), the formation of an active reversible complex is probably the reason for their extreme potency (14). In the absence of such special features, the potency of inhibitors might be expected to follow their strength as phosphorylating agents, which in turn should parallel their anhydride character. Thus, k'_3 should bear some relation to the pK_a of HX. A plot of

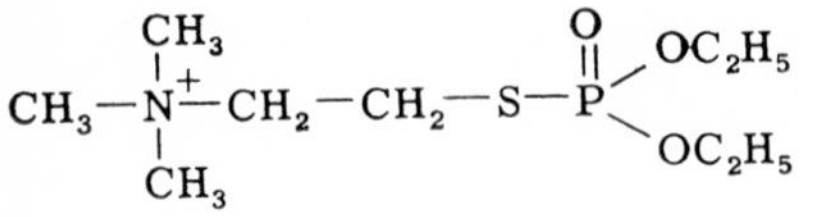

$$CH_3-\overset{\overset{\displaystyle CH_3}{|}}{\underset{\underset{\displaystyle CH_3}{|}}{N^+}}-CH_2-CH_2-S-\overset{\overset{\displaystyle O}{||}}{P}\overset{OC_2H_5}{\underset{OC_2H_5}{}}$$

(IX)

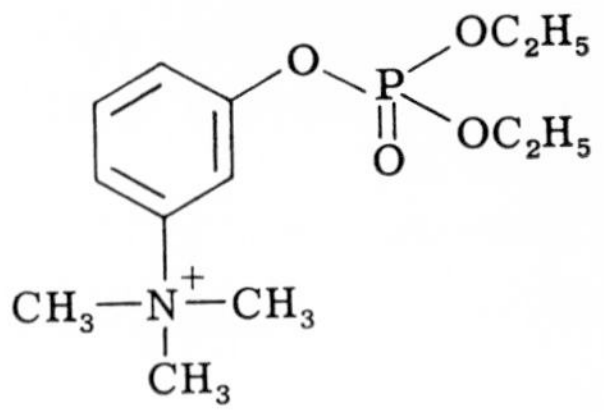

(X)

log k'_3 versus log k_{hyd} where k_{hyd} is the bimolecular rate constant for the alkaline hydrolysis of the phosphate ester, yielded a straight line for a group of diethyl phosphates (15).

The phosphoryl enzymes recover slowly in water (13). The inhibited enzymes derived from a series of inhibitors in which R_1 and R_2 are identical, but in which the group represented by X varies, should be identical and should recover with the same rate of speed, i.e., they should have the same value for k_4 (13). This has been clearly demonstrated by Aldrich (16).

The phosphoryl enzyme can also be reactivated by other nucleophilic agents (13), notably hydroxylamine and its derivatives. Choline is also a reactivator and here we must attribute its activity to the prior formation of an active reversible complex. Its nucleophilic activity is promoted by the formation of a suitable complex. With this promotion idea in mind, it was possible to prepare a compound, pyridine-2-aldoxime methiodide, with very remarkable reactivating power (17). This compound (XI),

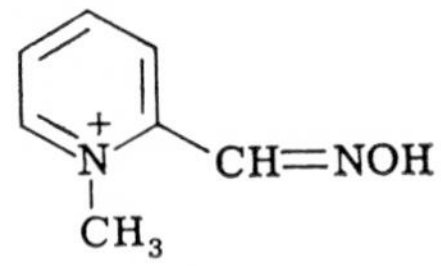

(XI)

especially in conjunction with atropine, is quite effective as an antidote for many of these poisons (18).

In this presentation it has been tacitly assumed that the group which is phosphorylated is the same as that which is considered to be acetylated during the normal activity of the enzyme. Evidence for this is that the phosphorylation is slowed in the presence of prosthetic inhibitors such as tetramethylammonium ion. It is also slowed in the presence of carbamates (19). Reactivation by choline is very strong evidence because choline is a poor nucleophile. The reactivation by hydroxylamine or choline is slowed by prosthetic inhibitors; the recovery in water (reactivation by water) presumably would also be slowed, but it has not been studied.

2. CARBAMATES

These compounds have the general structure (XII).

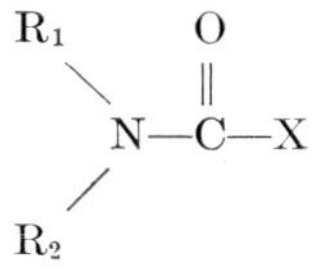

(XII)

It would appear that considerable variation in R_1 and R_2 would be possible, but the well-known carbamates are mostly methyl or dimethyl carbamates (XII–XV).

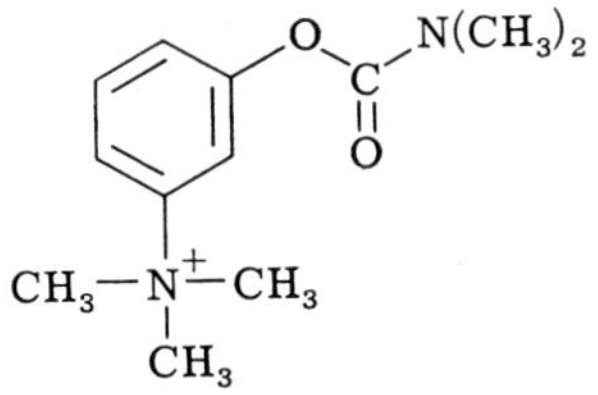

(XIII)

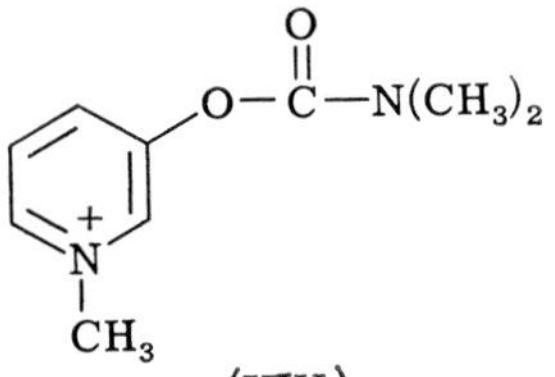

(XIV)

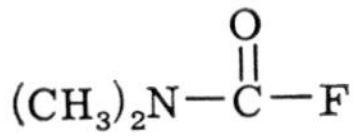

(XV)

In contrast to the alkyl phosphates, the potent inhibitors generally contain an X group which has some degree of molecular complementarity with acetylcholinesterase, as illustrated by neostigmine. These carbamates react with acetylcholinesterase in accordance with the scheme given for the alkyl phosphates, and the mathematical treatment is the same as for the alkyl phosphates (20). Here, however, k_4 is not so small; the carbamyl enzyme recovers with a half-time of about 2 minutes; the methylcarbamyl enzyme about 38 minutes; and the dimethylcarbamyl enzyme about 27 minutes. Steady states in accordance with Eq. (*14*) are readily obtained, but again it is often found that $I << K_I$, so that the equation of the steady state becomes [Eq. (16)]:

$$\left[\frac{\varepsilon}{E'}\right]_{ss} = \frac{k_4 K_I}{k_3 I} = \frac{k_4}{k_3' I} \tag{16}$$

and $I_{50} = k_4/k_3'$. In contrast to the usual alkyl phosphates, I_{50} now has a physical meaning for the particular inhibitor but one which is quite different from its meaning with prosthetic inhibitors. A measurement of I_{50}, since k_4 can also be measured, enables one to evaluate k_3'. These constants can be surprisingly high for the carbamyl and phosphoryl enzymes, but even the highest, 10^6–10^7 liter mole^{-1} min^{-1}, are a thousand times smaller than the corresponding value for the formation of the acetyl enzyme from acetylcholine.

The carbamyl enzymes are readily reactivated by hydroxylamine and choline but not by pyridine-2-aldoxime methiodide. Prosthetic inhibitors slow the recovery in water. Their effect on the carbamylation reaction has not been studied. Reactivation by choline again indicates that the group that is carbamylated is the same as the one that is phosphorylated and acetylated.

In our discussion of oxydiaphoric inhibitors, we have treated the cases in which the enzyme is inactivated by reacting with the inhibitor in the absence of substrate. Assay is made with diluted enzyme solution and during a short time interval. If substrate is present, the situation becomes much more complicated. Here the phosphorylation or carbamylation will be slowed because much of the enzyme is combined with the substrate. In addition, the inhibitor if it is not too potent, may act also as a prosthetic inhibitor by combining reversibly with the free enzyme or acetyl enzyme, as already discussed. By the time a steady state is reached, there may be considerable choline accumulated, and this compound can act as a prosthetic inhibitor; but even more important, it can reactivate the phosphoryl and especially the carbamyl enzymes.

In our discussion of prosthetic inhibitors, we indicated how competitive, noncompetitive, or mixed inhibition could arise by the reversible reaction of the inhibitor with the free enzyme or acetyl enzyme. This should not be interpreted as denying that noncompetitive or even competitive inhibition can also arise in some other way, perhaps involving some other sites.

In the case of the phosphoryl enzymes, the phosphorus atom has been recovered as a serine derivative after degradation (*21*). The acetyl and carbamyl enzymes cannot be recovered as amino acid derivatives (at least at present) because of their greater lability. It would appear that serine is part of the active site, but because serine itself is very far from being a reactive molecule, we don't quite know what to do with this information, although there have been numerous, similar suggestions.

Note added in proof: Since this paper was written, work has been published on methanesulfonic acid esters which have been shown to be another class of oxydiaphoric inhibitors. The methanesulfonyl-enzyme derivative obtained by reaction of the enzyme with these inhibitors does not hydrolyze in water, nor is the inhibited enzyme reactivated with hydroxylamine. Activity is restored, however, by reaction with quaternary pyridine oximes, particularly the 3-oximes, and by reaction with thiocholine. It is not appreciably reactivated by choline (*22, 23*). It has also been found that the reaction of certain oxydiaphoric inhibitors in which fluorine is the leaving group can be accelerated by substituted ammonium ions (*24, 25*).

ACKNOWLEDGMENTS

The author wishes to acknowledge support from the Division of Research Grants and Fellowships of the National Institute of Health, B-573C13 (U.S.P.H.S.) and GM-K3-15012.

REFERENCES

1. D. Nachmansohn and E. A. Feld, *J. Biol. Chem.* **171**, 715 (1947); H. W. Jones, B. J. Meyer, and L. Karel, *J. Pharmacol. Exptl. Therap.* **94**, 215 (1948).
2. G. Schrader, *Angew. Chem.* **62** (1952).
3. B. Holmstedt, *Acta Physiol. Scand.* **25**, Supp. 90 (1951).
4. D. H. Adams and V. P. Whittaker, *Biochim. et Biophys. Acta* **4**, 543 (1950); I. B. Wilson and F. Bergmann, *J. Biol. Chem.* **186**, 683 (1950); F. Bergmann, I. B. Wilson, and D. Nachmansohn, *ibid.* **186**, 693 (1950).
4a. I. B. Wilson and F. Bergmann, *J. Biol. Chem.* **185**, 479 (1950).
4b. I. B. Wilson, *J. Biol. Chem.* **197**, 215 (1952).
5. W. Kauzmann, *Advances in Protein Chem.* **14**, 1 (1959).
6. I. B. Wilson, F. Bergmann, and D. Nachmansohn, *J. Biol. Chem.* **186**, 781 (1950).
7. I. B. Wilson and E. Cabib, *J. Am. Chem. Soc.* **78**, 202 (1956).
8. R. M. Krupka and K. J. Laidler, *J. Am. Chem. Soc.* **83**, 1445 (1961); I. B. Wilson and J. Alexander, *J. Biol. Chem.* **237**, 1323 (1962).
9. S. L. Friess, *J. Am. Chem. Soc.* **79**, 3269 (1957).
10. I. B. Wilson and C. Quan, *Arch Biochem. Biophys.* **73**, 131 (1958).
11. R. Metcalf and R. March, *Ann. Entomol. Soc. Am.* **46**, 63 (1953); J. Gage, *Biochem. J.* **54**, 426 (1953).
12. E. F. Jansen, M. D. F. Nutting, and A. K. Balls, *J. Biol. Chem.* **179**, 201 (1949); E. F. Jansen, M. D. F. Nutting, R. Jang, and A. K. Balls, *ibid.* **185**, 209 (1950).
13. I. B. Wilson, *J. Biol. Chem.* **190**, 111 (1951); **199**, 113 (1952).
14. F. Hobbiger, *Brit. J. Pharmacol.* **9**, 159 (1954); L. E. Tammelin, *Acta Chem. Scand.* **11**, 859, 1340 (1957).

15. W. Aldrich, *Chem. & Ind. (London)* p. 473 (1954).
16. W. Aldrich and A. N. Davison, *Biochem. J.* **55**, 763 (1953).
17. I. B. Wilson and S. Ginsburg, *Biochim. et Biophys. Acta* **18**, 168 (1955) ; D. R. Davies and A. L. Green, *Discussions Faraday Soc.* **20** (1955).
18. H. Kewitz and I. B. Wilson, *Arch. Biochem. Biophys.* **60**, 261 (1956) ; H. Kewitz, I. B. Wilson, and D. Nachmansohn, *ibid.* **64**, 456 (1956) ; J. H. Wills, A. M. Kunkel, R. V. Brown, and G. E. Groblewski, *Science* **125**, 743 (1957).
19. G. B. Koelle, *J. Pharmacol. Exptl. Therap.* **88**, 232 (1946) ; K. B. Augustinsson and D. Nachmansohn, *J. Biol. Chem.* **179**, 543 (1949).
20. I. B. Wilson, M. A. Hatch, and S. Ginsburg, *J. Biol. Chem.* **235**, 2312 (1960) ; I. B. Wilson, M. A. Harrison, and S. Ginsburg, *ibid.* **236**, 1498 (1961).
21. N. K. Schaffer, S. C. May, and W. H. Summerson, *J. Biol. Chem.* **202**, 67 (1953) ; **206**, 201 (1954).
22. R. Kitz and I. B. Wilson, *J. Biol. Chem.* **237**, 3245 (1962).
23. J. Alexander, I. B. Wilson, and R. Kitz, *J. Biol. Chem.* **238**, 741-745 (1963).
24. R. Kitz and I. B. Wilson, *J. Biol. Chem.* **238**, 745-748 (1963).
25. H. P. Metzger, *Federation Proc.* **22**, 293 (1963).

CHAPTER 25

Organophosphates and Carbamates

R. D. O'Brien

I. INTRODUCTION

Organophosphates and carbamates are extremely potent inhibitors of cholinesterase and certain other esterases. They are commonly active in the range 10^{-6}–10^{-10} M and are therefore probably some of the most active enzyme inhibitors known. Most are effective *in vivo* as well as *in vitro* and are therefore highly toxic, lethal doses in the range of 0.1 to 10 mg/kg being common. Consequently the organophosphates have been developed extensively as chemical warfare agents (the well-known "nerve gases"). Other organophosphates and carbamates have found wide use as insecticides, and in some cases are highly toxic to insects but not to mammals. Another major claim of the organophosphates to distinction is their usefulness in elucidating the structure of the active centers of esterases, particularly cholinesterases and chymotrypsin, so that we now know more about the molecular structure of the centers in these esterases than in any other enzymes.

Some of the organophosphates and carbamates show marked selectivity toward particular esterases. This property has been used to distinguish between esterases, whose characteristic nonspecificity for substrate makes it impossible to do more than group them into rough classes, if substrate activity is the sole criterion. It has also been used in evaluating the role of such enzymes by studying the effect of their drastic inhibition in the whole animal and in various nervous tissue preparations.

Both groups of compounds have been used therapeutically for treatment of myasthenia gravis, in relief of intraocular pressure in glaucoma, and for relief of abdominal tension. The organophosphates are extremely important insecticides, whose estimated world use is $50,000,000 annually (1); the carbamates are used far less for this purpose but are increasing in importance. The organophosphates are probably the most important single class of chemical warfare agents.

The carbamoyl and alkyl phosphoryl groups occur in other compounds whose effects are not due to esterase inhibition, but from space considerations such compounds will not be considered here.

The terms we shall use to describe the various esterases follow.

(a) Acetylcholinesterase (erythrocyte cholinesterase, true cholinesterase): the acetylcholine-hydrolyzing enzyme which is inhibited by excess substrate, exhibits maximal activity against acetylcholine, and can hydrolyze acetyl-β-methylcholine (2). This enzyme is present mainly in erythrocytes and conductive tissue. It is vital for nerve transmission.

(b) Pseudocholinesterase (serum cholinesterase): the acetylcholine-hydrolyzing enzyme which is not inhibited by excess substrate, and hydrolyzes acetyl-β-methyl choline poorly. This enzyme is present in serum and numerous other tissues, such as pancreas. It has no known function and may be fully inhibited without ill consequences.

(c) Aliesterases: enzymes which cannot hydrolyze acetylcholine but can hydrolyze simple aliphatic esters (3). Many aliesterases can also hydrolyze triglycerides (and might then also be called lipases) and aromatic esters (and might then also be called aromatic esterases). Their normal functions are unknown.

Other enzymes mentioned (chymotrypsin, trypsin, thrombin, acetylesterase) are sufficiently well defined in standard texts (4).

The cholinesterases are considered to have two subsites in each active center; an anionic site, which binds the quaternary ammonium substituent of acetylcholine, and an esteratic site, which binds and then hydrolyzes the —C(O)O— group of acetylcholine. It was originally thought (5) that only acetylcholinesterase had an anionic site. Now it seems certain (6) that both have anionic sites, but probably acetylcholinesterase has two per esteratic site, pseudocholinesterase only one. Aliesterases and chymotrypsin have only an esteratic site. The esteratic sites of all the esterases are remarkably similar in their amino acid sequence (7).

The toxicity and antiesterase activity of these two great classes of compounds may be comparable, but their detailed mode of action, metabolism, and chemical properties are different. We shall therefore discuss them separately.

II. CARBAMATES

There is an excellent review of the medically useful carbamates (8), and there are two for the insecticidal carbamates (9, 9a). In the present article, a brief review of properties is given first; a more extensive and intensive discussion follows.

The general formula and some common compounds are given in Table I. The detailed structures are very diverse, but most of those commonly used as cholinesterase inhibitors have a quaternary nitrogen group, which presumably increases the affinity for cholinesterases by binding to the anionic site, while the —OC(O)— group binds to the esteratic site and is the major factor in preventing access of acetylcholine. Those, such as eserine, that lack a quaternary group, usually have a basic nitrogen group (pK_a of 8 or more), so that they are substantially ionized at pH 7. By contrast, the insecticidal carbamates are never basic, for ionization reduces toxicity to most insects.

Carbamates which are anticholinesterases *in vivo* are also anticholinesterases *in vitro* (in contrast to some organophosphates). Those which are anticholinesterases *in vitro* will inhibit mammalian cholinesterases *in vivo*, but will inhibit insect cholinesterase *in vivo* only if the carbamate is un-ionized.

A. Mechanism of Inhibition

The kinetics of cholinesterase inhibition by carbamates have been exhaustively investigated. Goldstein (10) has pointed out that the precise form of the kinetics depends upon the so-called "zone of behavior": in zone A, defined as the condition of inhibitor in great excess, the classic Michaelis-Menten treatment (11) is adequate. However, in zone C, defined as the condition of enzyme in excess, different equations are required. Zone B (intermediate) behavior requires a combination of the

TABLE I

$$\text{CARBAMATES: } XOC(O)NR_2$$

A. Mainly used as anticholinesterases *in vitro* (nontoxic to insects)	B. Insecticides[a]

1.[b]   Eserine (physostigmine)

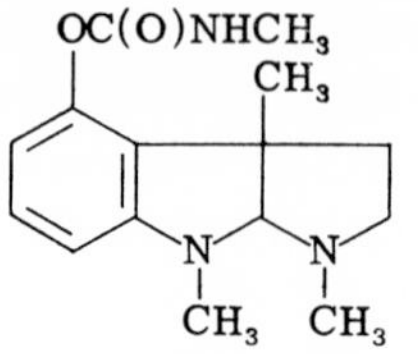

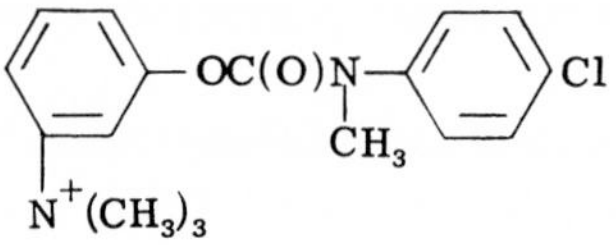

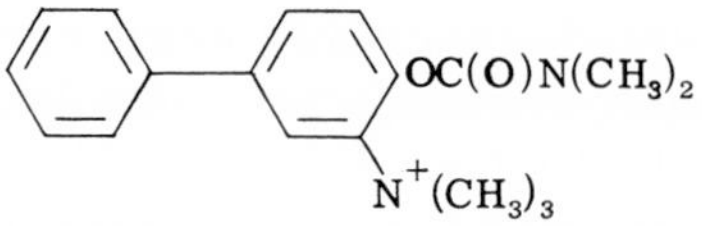

5.   Isolan

2.[b]   Nu[c] 1250

6.   Dimetan

3.[b]   Nu[c] 683

7.   Pyrolan

4.[b]   Prostigmine (neostigmine)

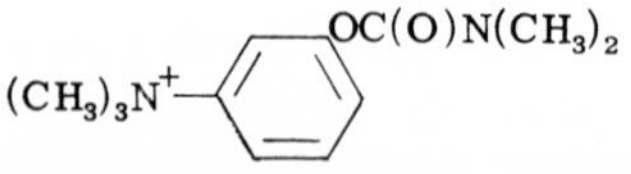

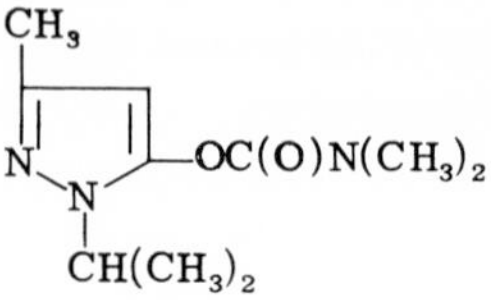

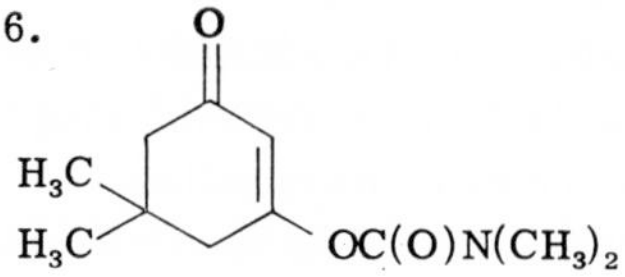

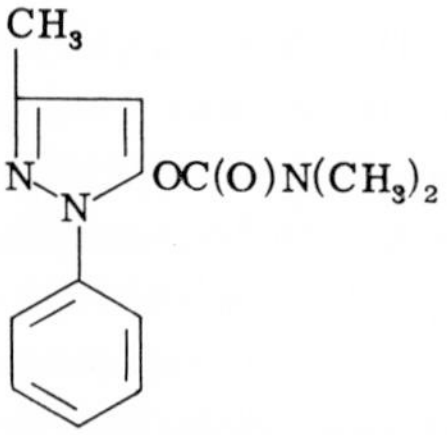

8.   Sevin

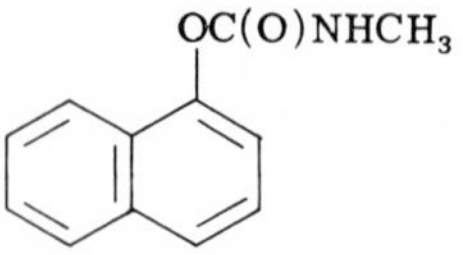

[a] The insecticidal carbamates are all potent anticholinesterases.

[b] Compounds 1, 3, and 4 are selective towards acetylcholinesterase as opposed to pseudocholinesterase. The reverse is true of compound 2.

[c] Nu is derived from "Nutley". These compounds are made by Hoffman La Roche Inc., Nutley, New Jersey.

A and C equations. Two important points that emerge from this and a preceding paper (*12*) are that in vitro results may depend upon enzyme concentration and that severe errors may be introduced by extrapolating from *in vitro* to *in vivo* conditions. Goldstein has extended his studies to numerous other carbamates (*13*). His results have been corrected to conform with more accurate steady-state kinetics by Myers (*14*).

Carbamates inhibit cholinesterase competitively and reversibly; the inhibition may therefore be reduced by washing (*15*), dialysis (*13, 16, 17*), or dilution (*10*), or addition of substrate (*10, 13*). Nevertheless, equilibrium with the enzyme is not immediate; the time depends on the nature and concentration of the inhibitor. Wilson (*18*) estimated a time of 63 seconds for electric eel cholinesterase with 9×10^{-7} M prostigmine at 25°. Goldstein (*13*) found that prostigmine was the slowest of three carbamates, Nu 1250 was faster, and Nu 585 (I), fastest, reaching equi-

$$(CH_3)_3\overset{+}{N}CH_2CH_2OC(O) \quad \diagup\!\!\!\diagdown \quad OC(O)N(CH_3)_2$$

(I)

librium after 1 hour at 0°. Myers (*14*) found that Nu 683 took 50–60 minutes to equilibrate at 37.5°; Matthes (*16*) found that eserine took more than 15 minutes to equilibrate at room temperature.

In the presence of substrate, much longer times are required for equilibrium, e.g., 50 minutes for 5×10^{-8} M eserine with red cell cholinesterase and 3×10^{-3} M acetylcholine at 37° (*19*).

The dissociation time for the enzyme-inhibitor complex is also slow, but in this case it is independent of the carbamate concentration used for inhibition. Wilson (*18*) reports a half-life of about 7 minutes at 25° for prostigmine and electric eel cholinesterase. Cohen *et al.* (*20*) have emphasized the slowness of reactivation by dialysis or substrate addition.

In many cases a true equilibrium is never observed; the inhibition increases first and decreases thereafter. This phenomenon is caused by enzymic degradation of the carbamate. This was particularly evident with dimethylcarbamoyl fluoride, whose maximum inhibition of brain cholinesterase *in vitro* was reached at 30 minutes (*21*). This finding is, however, not in accord with that of Augustinsson *et al.* (*22*), who found for this compound that inhibition of cholinesterase was the same with 6 or 180 minutes, incubation without substrate; it reacted progressively with butyrylcholinesterase. This topic is expanded below under the heading "metabolism."

It seems, therefore, that the carbamates act less as "true" inhibitors than as alternative substrates with very low turnover numbers (*13, 14, 21*). For Nu 683 with pseudocholinesterase, Myers (*14*) found that the rate of combination with the enzyme was about one-quarter of that for acetylcholine, and the rate of dissociation with hydrolysis was less than 10^{-6} times that for acetylcholine. There was negligible dissociation without hydrolysis.

However, the fact that the carbamates are alternative substrates still leaves two possibilities: (*a*) The inhibited enzyme might be a complex of enzyme with the whole carbamate molecule, whose subsequent hydrolysis constituted reversal of inhibiton. This hydrolysis could perhaps involve transient carbamoylation of the esteratic site. (*b*) The inhibited enzyme might be that with its esteratic site carbamoylated, and reversal of inhibition might involve hydrolysis of the carbamoylated enzyme. This case would be strictly analogous to that of the organophosphates, which give a relatively stable phosphorylated enzyme.

Although mechanism (*b*) has been favored in the past for the cases of a prostigmine analogue (*14*) and carbamoyl fluorides (*21*), recent workers have suggested that (*a*) is correct, principally because cholinesterase inhibition by *O*-phenyl carbamates is worsened by electrophilic phenyl substituents rather than improved, as is the case for organophosphates and as is to be expected if carbamoylation (which would involve an electrophilic attack on the enzyme) were the rate-controlling step (*23, 24*). This argument presupposes an identical mechanism for carbamoylation and phosphorylation. Very recent work of Wilson *et al.* (*24a*) strongly suggests that (*b*) is correct, for the reactivation rates of the inhibited enzymes are found to depend only upon the nature of the *N*-substituents; thus, dimethylcarbamoyl choline and dimethylcarbamoyl fluoride gave the same inhibited enzyme, presumably the dimethylcarbamoylated cholinesterase.

There is good evidence that the carbamates of type A in Table I are bound initially both to the esteratic and anionic sites of cholinesterase (*13, 25*), in contrast to most organophosphates, which attack only the esteratic site, and the noncarbamate alkaloids, such as methylene blue and atropine, which combine only with the anionic site (*13*). Presumably, the carbamoyl groups bind to the esteratic site, and the quaternary (or protonated tertiary) nitrogen to the anionic site. It would be most interesting to know if compounds of type B in Table I bind only to the esteratic site. The single piece of relevant evidence suggests that inhibition involves binding to both sites; for chymotrypsin, which has an esteratic site very like that of the cholinesterases [in its amino acid sequence and its susceptibility to organophosphates (*7*, *27*)] but lacks an anionic site, is not inhibited by type B carbamates (*26*).

If type B compounds do bind to the anionic site, it is presumably by van der Waals' forces [as has been discussed by Bergmann (*28*, *29*) for other compounds]. Since these forces depend upon a close fit of inhibitor with enzyme, it is possible that very precise structure-activity relations may exist in this group of carbamates.

B. Selective Enzyme Inhibition

Eserine and prostigmine have long been used as selective inhibitors of cholinesterases as against aliesterase (*3*, *30*, *31*). A discriminating concentration is 10^{-6} *M* in the case of eserine; this is stated (*32*) to inhibit almost completely both acetyl- and pseudocholinesterase, with little or no effect on aliesterase. Yet some cholinesterases, such as those of *Planaria* (a flatworm) and frog brain, are relatively insensitive to eserine (*33*), as Table II demonstrates. The *Planaria* enzyme is unusual in other ways: it hydrolyzes acetylcholine 16.5 times faster than acetyl-β-methylcholine, whereas the corresponding figure for dog brain is 3. It is also $\frac{1}{5}$ as sensitive to protigmine and $\frac{1}{1000}$ as sensitive to Nu 489 (II) as the dog brain enzyme.

TABLE II

SELECTIVITY OF ESERINE[a]

Concentration of eserine (*M*)	Inhibition of acetylcholine hydrolysis: *Planaria* (%)	Frog brain (%)	Dog brain (%)	Human erythrocytes (%)	Dog pancreas (%)	Human serum (%)
10^{-7}	0	0	88	94	95	92
10^{-6}	70	47	98	100	100	100
5×10^{-6}	89	—	100	100	100	100
10^{-5}	95	75	—	—	—	—

[a] Data of Hawkins and Mendel (*33*).

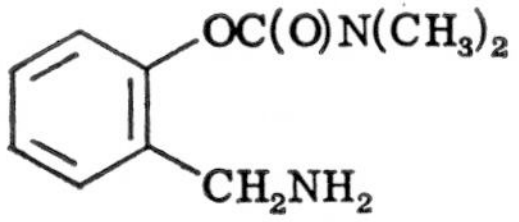

(II)

However, some carbamates are potent inhibitors of aliesterase. Stedman and Stedman in 1931 (*34*) showed that 12 compounds of the general type (III) inhibited liver aliesterase by up to 64% at 4×10^{-7} *M*.

$$(CH_3)_2NC\underset{R}{\overset{R}{|}}\bigg\langle\bigcirc\bigg\rangle OC(O)N(CH_3)_2$$

(III)

Nu 683 was used as a selective inhibitor of pseudocholinesterase by Hawkins and Gunter (*35*). For human tissues *in vitro*, 10^{-8} *M* Nu 683 inhibited serum pseudocholinesterase 92%, erythrocyte acetylcholinesterase not at all. Dog serum enzyme was less sensitive; 2.5×10^{-8} *M* Nu 683 inhibited it 55% and had no effect on the erythrocyte enzyme. Similar results were found *in vivo*; 0.06 mg/kg in a dog inhibited the serum enzyme 94% within 10 minutes when the erythrocyte enzyme was only 32% inhibited. No symptoms were observed.

The use of Nu 1250 as a selective inhibitor of true cholinesterase was proposed by Hawkins and Mendel (*36*). Its selectivity *in vitro* depended upon the species, the ratio of sensitivities of erythrocyte acetylcholinesterase to serum pseudocholinesterase being 1000 for man, 20 in the dog, and 5 in the horse. With human enzymes, 10^{-6} *M* Nu 1250 inhibited 96% of the erythrocyte cholinesterase and only 16% of serum cholinesterase. Similar effects were found *in vivo*, e.g., 0.4 mg/kg in rats inhibited 87% of the erythrocyte and 15% of the serum enzyme. The authors used this finding to show the unimportance of the serum enzyme, for signs of acetylcholine poisoning appeared only when the acetylcholinesterase was inhibited, and in spite of an almost unchanged pseudocholinesterase level. Casier and Vleeschouwer (*37*), working with the dog, claim precisely opposite results! A dose of 0.4 mg/kg gave total inhibition of the serum enzyme without affecting the erythrocyte enzyme; this was shown both with titrimetric and manometric techniques. Similar findings were made *in vitro*: 10^{-5} *M* Nu 1250 inhibited pseudocholinesterase 100%, yet had no effect on erythrocyte cholinesterase. Koelle (*38*) has reported briefly that Nu 1250 (and also Nu 683) "did not exhibit the marked selectivity against the enzymes of the cat which has been reported for certain other species." Thus, although the assumption seems general that Nu 1250 is a selective inhibitor of true cholinesterase, results may be highly dependent upon species.

Two other cases of striking selectivity were reported by Casida *et al.* (*26*): (IV) and (V) were respectively 300 times and more than 90,000 times more effective against acetylcholinesterase (from electric eel) than against pseudocholinesterase (human serum).

In spite of the traditional use of carbamates to inhibit cholinesterases rather than aliesterase, the results of Myers *et al.* (*39*) include 11 carbamates, all either *N*-phenyl or *O*-phenyl, which are little better against rat brain cholinesterase than rat brain aliesterase; and in every case they are much more potent against mycobacterial aliesterases than against brain cholinesterase, the maximal selectivity being over 800,000-fold.

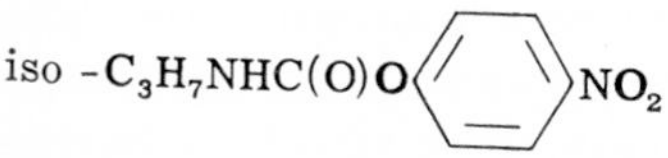
iso-C3H7NHC(O)O
NO2

(IV)

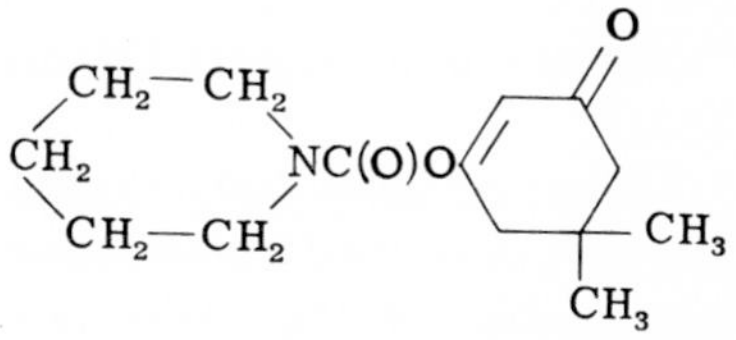
O
CH2—CH2
CH2
NC(O)O
CH2—CH2
CH3
CH3

(V)

Compounds of type B (Table I) have an extremely interesting selectivity that may be absent in type A compounds (*40*). As Table III

TABLE III

SELECTIVITY OF DIMETAN, PYROLAN, AND ESERINE[a,b]

Enzyme	Dimetan	Pyrolan	Eserine
Acetylcholinesterase	2.0×10^{-4}	1.2×10^{-5}	6.7×10^{-7}
Pseudocholinesterase	1.6×10^{-5}	6.1×10^{-7}	2.8×10^{-7}
Panparnit esterase	4.5×10^{-8}	3.6×10^{-9}	3×10^{-5}
Novocaine esterase	7.5×10^{-6}	2.0×10^{-7}	1.5×10^{-7}

[a] Figures are I_{50}'s (molar concentration for 50% inhibition).
[b] Data of Pulver and Domenjoz (*40*).

shows, their greatest activity is against esterases that hydrolyze the anti-Parkinsonianism agent panparnit (VI) and the local anesthetic Novocaine or procaine (VII).

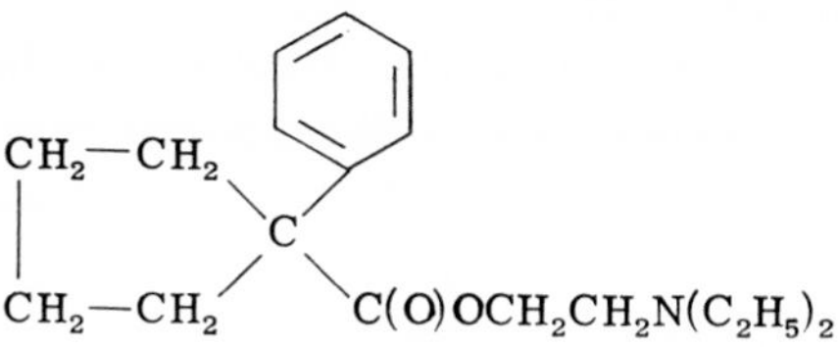
CH2—CH2
C
CH2—CH2
C(O)OCH2CH2N(C2H5)2

(VI)

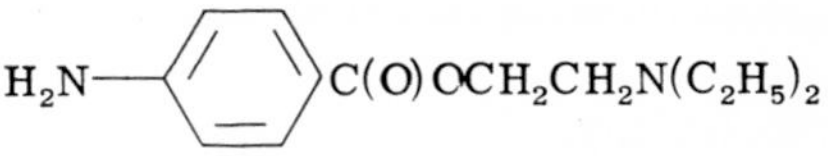
H2N
C(O)OCH2CH2N(C2H5)2

(VII)

C. Metabolism

Remarkably few studies have been concerned with the metabolism of carbamates. There is general agreement that cholinesterases degrade carbamates, as first reported in 1936 for prostigmine (17) and in 1943 for eserine (41). The reaction is often very slow; in the case of eserine and prostigmine the rate of hydrolysis by pseudocholinesterase preparations was about 10^{-7} times that of acetylcholine. There was good evidence that it was the cholinesterase itself that caused the hydrolysis (21). For Nu 683, Myers reported the rate constant of hydrolysis of the enzyme-inhibitor complex as 0.0115 min^{-1} at 38° for human serum cholinesterase (14).

However, these early studies must be treated with suspicion in the light of work described below, showing that other enzymes are in some cases responsible for the hydrolysis. Only in the case cited above as having "good evidence" was an attempt made to show that no other plasma constituent was responsible.

The hydrolysis of dimethylcarbamoyl fluoride by 16 rabbit tissues was studied by Augustinsson and Casida (42). Plasma was the most effective. Of 10 vertebrates studied, rabbit had the most effective plasma. Electrophoretic fractionation of rabbit plasma suggested that the enzyme involved (which was distinct from cholinesterase) was an aromatic esterase which also hydrolyzed diisopropyl phosphorofluoridate (DFP). However, the rabbit liver and kidney enzymes did not hydrolyze DFP. These findings make it unlikely that the reported rapid degradation of dimethylcarbamoyl fluoride by rat tissues (21) was due to cholinesterase, as the author had suggested.

The hydrolysis of Sevin was similarly examined (43) in 17 rabbit tissues and in plasmas from 15 species. Plasma was the most effective rabbit tissue, and the pig and rabbit had the most active plasma. In this case, however, electrophoresis revealed that the albumin fraction contained the activity, and the aromatic esterase and cholinesterase were inactive. The same was true for p-nitrophenyl N-alkylcarbamates (26). However, the N-methylated carbamoyl cholines were completely unaffected by plasma arylesterase, butyrylcholinesterase, cholinesterase, or albumin, even after 2 weeks' incubation (22)!

In insects, degradation has been reported only for Pyrolan by the cockroach. Bio-assay of the blood of treated cockroach indicated complete removal in 1 hour (44).

D. Toxicity

The carbamates with anticholinesterase activity appear to fall into two

TABLE IV

SELECTIVE TOXICITY OF CARBAMATES[a]

Carbamate	LD_{50} to mice or rats[b]	LD_{50} to houseflies
(A) Ionized or ionizable		
Eserine	0.8	200
Prostigmine	0.4	—
Nu 1250	0.3	590
Nu 683	1.0	560
(B) Not ionized or ionizable		
Isolan	54	0.4
Dimetilan	35	0.1
Pyrolan	62	2.3
Sevin	2000	2.6

[a] From Eldefrawi et al. (45), O'Brien and Fisher (46), and Spector (47).
[b] LD_{50} for (A) are to mice, intraperitoneal; for (B) to rats, oral.

well-defined groups, as shown in Table IV. Those which are ionic or strongly basic are very toxic to mammals but almost completely ineffective against insects. Those which are not ionic or ionizable may have good insect toxicity and are often less toxic to mammals than to insects.

Ionization has important effects upon several properties. Stevens and Beutel (48) examined the effect of quaternarization of bases of the prostigmine type in which the position of the dimethylamino group was either ortho or para, and the ring was alkylated in various ways. In all 12 cases, quaternarization greatly increased mouse toxicity, the range being 8–220-fold (but prostigmine itself, and the very different carbamate eserine, were only little better in the quarternarized than in the tertiary form). It seems very probable that this increased toxicity is due to improved anticholinesterase activity, due to better binding to the anionic site. This has been shown for the N-methyl analogue of prostigmine, whose quaternary form is a 500 times better anticholinesterase than its tertiary form (23).

However, insect toxicity is greatly decreased by quarternarization. For instance, although the N-methyl analogue of prostigmine is a better anticholinesterase than its tertiary form, it is 40 times less toxic to thrips (23). Brown et al. (49) found that five ionic prostigmine-like compounds, which had toxicities to mammals of the order of 0.2 mg/kg (50) had negligible toxicity to the four insect species tested. This dramatic influence of ionization is attributable to the insect's having all its cholinergic sites protected against ions; the central nervous system is protected (*51, 52*) as in mammals, and in the insect the neuromuscular junction (presumably the target for ionic anticholinesterases in mammals) is not cholinergic (*53, 54*).

Ionization is of importance in determining other properties of carbamates; for instance, eserine can block axonic transmission, prostigmine cannot (*55*). This may at first seem surprising in view of the fact that eserine, with its pK_a of 8.0, is 90% ionized at pH 7. However, even if one had a completely ion-excluding membrane protecting a system, and if the agent were 99.9% ionized, equal concentration would eventually be achieved on both sides of the membrane. But a quarternarized salt has no free base form with which to be in equilibrium. Structures such as R_4N—OH do not exist, contrary to the drawings in many textbooks, for nitrogen cannot form five covalent bonds (*56*). Consequently an ideal ion-excluding membrane would completely protect against quaternary salts.

The data on structure-activity relationships (including pharmacological and toxicological results) in medicinal-type carbamates is extensive, dating back to 1926. Fortunately, the data have been tabulated and fully reviewed (*8*), so in this article only a few comments about toxicity are required, with emphasis on the relationship to cholinesterase structure.

For mammalian toxicity, the work of Stevens and Beutel (*48*) on prostigmine analogues showed that in *p*-trimethylammoniumphenyl *N*-dimethylcarbamates almost any alkyl substituent in the ring greatly increased toxicity, the most effective being *m*-isopropyl (VIII).

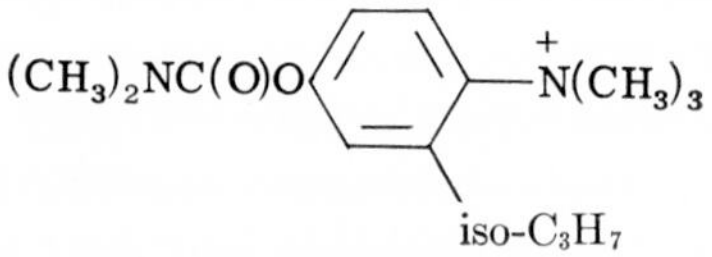

$$(CH_3)_2NC(O)O \underset{\underset{\text{iso-C}_3H_7}{\diagdown}}{\diagdown} \text{—} \overset{+}{N}(CH_3)_3$$

(VIII)

The LD_{50} of the nonalkylated compound was 120, and the LD_{50} of (VIII) was 0.075 mg/kg to mice, subcutaneous. Now a number of pieces of evidence suggest that if groups X and Y are *meta* substituted and X binds to the esteratic site, then Y is optimally located for the anionic site. Does the isopropyl group in (VIII) bind to the anionic site? If so, does one need the quaternary nitrogen at all? The answer to the second question is probably yes, for as mentioned above, quarternarization of the

tertiary derivatives of such compounds almost invariably increases toxicity profoundly. The possibility exists that the two substituents bind to
the two anionic sites which Bergmann considers acetylcholinesterase to
have (7, 28).

However, in a study by Haworth et al. (50) on a closely related group
of compounds, the position of the substituents was not critical; for instance, (IX) and (X) were equally toxic (0.16 and 0.17 mg/kg, mice,

$$\text{CH}_3\text{NHC(O)O} \quad \text{CH}_3 \qquad\qquad \text{CH}_3\text{NHC(O)O}$$

(IX)   (X)

subcutaneous). The only critical factor was that a large substituent
(e.g. isopropyl) should not be put in the *ortho* position. A smaller one
(e.g. ethyl) was permissible; presumably, the large substituent hinders
sterically the attachment of the carbamoyl group to the esteratic site.

Haworth et al. have also examined (57) analogues of carbamoyl
choline (Doryl), but none was more toxic than the Doryl itself.

The importance of the substitution on the carbamoyl nitrogen has been
briefly studied. In prostigmine derivatives, the monomethyl and dimethyl
substituents were equally good, and much better than the unsubstituted
form (50). These two substitution types are by far the commonest both
in the pharmacological and insecticidal carbamates.

Let us now consider the insecticidal action of carbamates.

Metcalf's group (23, 58) has made and studied 73 substituted phenyl
carbamates, including N-methyl, N-ethyl, N-benzyl, and N-phenyl derivatives (only the N-methyl compounds were effective). Their first series
of 49 compounds included no alkoxyphenyl compounds. For this series
they concluded that there was a direct relationship between toxicity to
thrips and anticholinesterase activity, with the exception that ionic compounds were inactive, as discussed above. However, examination of their
housefly-toxicity data reveals no such correlation; for instance, (XI) was
7 times more toxic to houseflies then (XII), yet it was 100 times less
effective than (XII) against housefly cholinesterase. A similar failure of
correlation was found by Casida (26) for 25 carbamates of varied par-
entage. Metcalf's second group (24 compounds) included only alkoxyphenyl carbamates (58). Once again a poor correlation was found, but
in this case a convincing reason was offered; those compounds which are

$$CH_3NHC(O)O \text{—} \langle \text{—} \rangle$$

(XI)

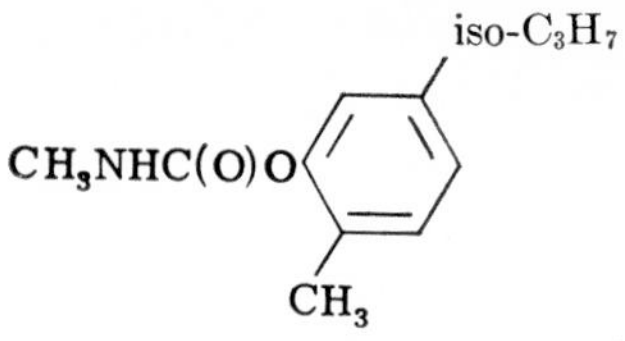

$$CH_3NHC(O)O \text{—} \langle \text{—} \rangle \text{—} iso\text{-}C_3H_7, CH_3$$

(XII)

nontoxic in spite of good anticholinesterase activity are rapidly degraded
in the insect. The evidence was that when 5 compounds of similar anticholinesterase activity, but widely varying (36-fold) in housefly toxicity,
were applied along with the synergist piperonyl butoxide (XIII) the
range of synergized toxicity was only fourfold. The assumption (which
has yet to be proved) was that the synergist acted by blocking degradation, which was important only in the compounds of low toxicity.

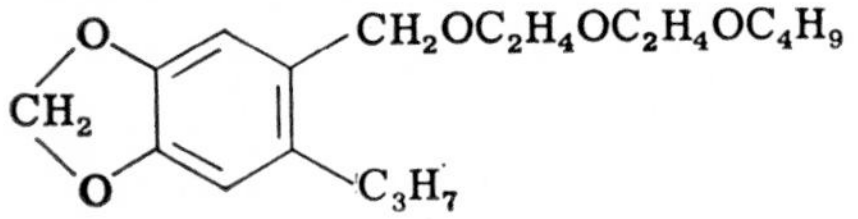

$$CH_2 \begin{array}{c} O \\ O \end{array} \text{—} \langle \text{—} \rangle \text{—} CH_2OC_2H_4OC_2H_4OC_4H_9, C_3H_7$$

(XIII)

With respect to thrips toxicity Kolbezen et al. (23) found N-methyl-
carbamates were most active. The m-tert-butylphenyl was the best compound, being toxic at 0.8 ppm, yet the p-tert-butylphenyl was ineffective
at 1000 ppm. The o-tert-butylphenyl was about half as good as the meta.
All the good compounds contained either alkyl or dimethylamino substituents either in the ortho or meta position, and apparently the alkyl
group had to be larger than ethyl. It is interesting that tert-butyl was
better than dimethylamino; perhaps this is because the methyl groups in
tert-butyl resemble sterically those in acetylcholine. If this is true there
must be van der Waals' binding of these alkyl groups to the enzyme,
possibly at or near the anionic site. It may be that some or all of the
affinity of cholinesterase for the tetrasubstituted nitrogen of acetylcholine
is due to van der Waals' binding of its substituents rather than coulombic
attraction for the N^+.

In general, the alkoxyphenyl compounds were better against houseflies
than the alkylphenyl, although nearly all were very poor. The best was
(XIV), with an LD_{50} of 6.5 mg/kg. Several of the alkoxyphenyl compounds were good against Culex mosquito larvae, giving 50% kill at less
than 1 ppm.

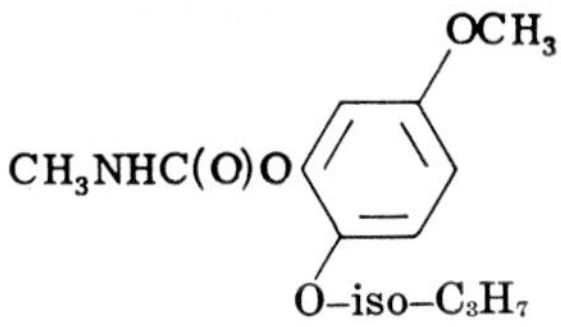

$$\text{CH}_3\text{NHC(O)O} - \overset{\displaystyle\text{OCH}_3}{\underset{\displaystyle\text{O--iso--C}_3\text{H}_7}{\bigcirc}}$$

(XIV)

For 9 substituted phenyl N-methylcarbamates, Kolbezen *et al.* (*23*) found that thrips toxicity was roughly proportional to hydrolytic stability. With houseflies, inspection of their data suggests this not to be the case, nor could Casida *et al.* (*26*) observe such a relationship for their compounds.

The data of Roan and Maeda (*59*) for five pyrazolyl carbamates against three fruit flies show little correlation (*a*) for any one species between anticholinesterase activity and toxicity or (*b*) for any one compound between selective toxicity and selective anticholinesterase activity. Nor could ionization account for the marked differences in toxicity. Differences in degradation may well be involved.

The toxicity to insects of carbamates is synergized by a variety of agents, many of which have no toxic action of their own. Examples are Lilly 18947 (2,4-dichloro-6-phenylphenoxyethyldiethylamine) (*60*) and various methylenedioxyphenyl compounds, such as piperonyl butoxide (XIII) (*58, 61, 62*). The mechanism is obscure, but is probably not due to improved penetration (*61*). Moorefield (*62*) points out that since such compounds can synergize so many diverse insecticides (pyrethrins, phosphates, carbamates, chlorinated hydrocarbons, etc.), an interference with detoxification is not an attractive hypothesis. However, Metcalf's observations, given above, rather suggest such an interference.

It has been reported that houseflies can develop resistance to the carbamate Sevin (*61*).

III. ORGANOPHOSPHATES

There have been numerous reviews of these compounds within recent years (*9a, 63–66*) and four books (*67–69a*).

Table V shows some representative structures. We shall use the term "organophosphates" to apply to all these compounds, and the terms "phosphate," "phosphorothionate," with the meanings shown in Table V, when more precise description is needed. The majority of organophosphates have the general formula (XV). Usually the side group X is rather

$$(RO_2)P(O \text{ or } S)X$$
$$(XV)$$

electrophilic, or else can bind to the anionic site. The term "latent inhibitors" means that the pure compounds are not effective inhibitors *in vitro*, but are converted to potent inhibitors ("activated") in the animal body.

TABLE V

ORGANOPHOSPHATES[a,b,c,d]

(A) Direct inhibitors of cholinesterase

AI. Phosphates $(RO)_2P(O)X$

1. $(C_2H_5O)_2P(O)SCH_2CH_2N(C_2H_5)_2$ 4. $(CH_3O)_2P(O)OC=CH—COOCH_3$
                                                                                                       |
                                                                                                     CH_3

       Amiton   Phosdrin

2. $(iso-C_3H_7O)_2P(O)F$ 5. $(C_2H_5O)_2P(O)OP(O)(OC_2H_5)_2$

       DFP   TEPP

3. $(C_2H_5O)_2P(O)C\langle\underline{\quad\quad}\rangle NO_2$

       Paraoxon

$$\begin{array}{c} RO \\ \diagdown \\ \quad P(O)X \\ \diagup \\ R \end{array}$$

AII. Phosphonates

---

6. $\begin{array}{c} iso-C_2H_5O \\ \diagdown \\ \quad P(O)F \\ \diagup \\ CH_3 \end{array}$ 7. $\begin{array}{c} (CH_3)_3N^+CH_2CH_2O \\ \diagdown \\ \quad P(O)F \\ \diagup \\ CH_3 \end{array}$

       Sarin (GB)   Cholinyl methylphosphono-
                                                                        fluoridate

---

(B) Latent inhibitors of cholinesterase

BI. Phosphorothionates $(RO)_2P(S)X$ and phosphonothionates $\begin{array}{c} RO \\ \diagdown \\ \quad P(S)X \\ \diagup \\ R \end{array}$

TABLE V (*Continued*)

8. $(C_2H_5O)_2P(S)OCH_2CH_2SC_2H_5$

   Demeton, thiono isomer

12. $(C_2H_5O)_2P(S)O$$NO_2$

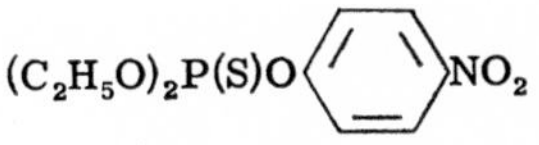

   Parathion

9. $(C_2H_5O)_2P(S)O$ $-iso-C_3H_7$

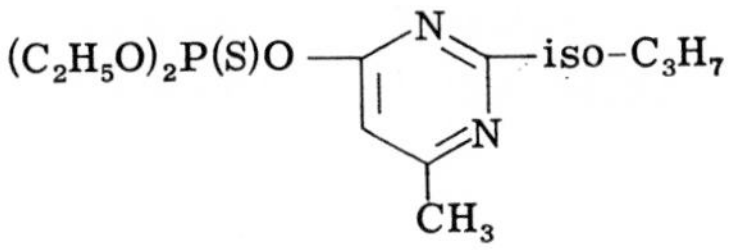

   Diazinon

13. $(CH_3O)_2P(S)O$

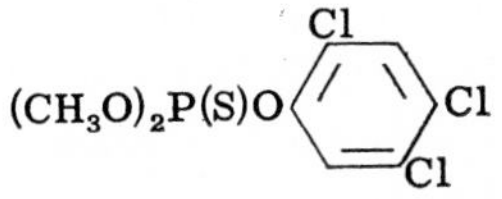

   Ronnel

10.

   $(CH_3O)_2P(S)SCH_2C(O)NHCH_3$

   Dimethoate

14. C_2H_5O $P(S)O$ NO_2

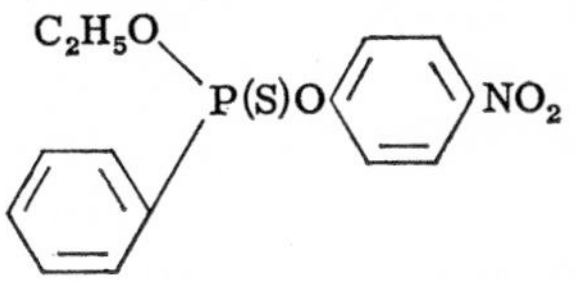

   EPN

11. $(CH_3O)_2P(S)SCHC(O)OC_2H_5$
         $\qquad\quad\ \ CH_2C(O)OC_2H_5$

   Malathion

BII. Phosphoramidates

15. $[(CH_3)_2N]_2P(O)F$

   Dimefox

17. $[(CH_3)_2N]_2P(O)OP(O)[N(CH_3)_2]_2$

   Schradan

16. C_2H_5O
            $\searrow P(O)CN$
       $(CH_3)_2N$

   Tabun

[a] Compounds 2, 6, 7, and 16 are potential warfare agents (they are too hazardous to use as insecticides).
[b] Compounds 3, 4, 5, 8, 12, 15, and 17 are insecticides which are also toxic to mammals.
[c] Compounds 9, 10, 11, and 13 are insecticides of low toxicity to mammals.
[d] Compound 1 is toxic to mites and mammals but to very few insects.

A. Mechanism of Inhibition

It is universally agreed that the organophosphates inhibit cholinesterases and several other esterases by phosphorylating their active (esteratic) site. The question of whether histidine or serine is phosphorylated will be discussed in Section III, E.

Some of the evidence for phosphorylation follows: (a) When chymotrypsin is inhibited by $(RO)_2P(O)X$, 1 mole of HX appears for every active site that is phosphorylated, suggesting the mechanism shown in Eq. (1).

$$ChE-H + (RO)_2P(O)X \rightarrow ChE-P(O)(RO)_2 + HX \tag{1}$$

This has been shown for DFP (70), TEPP (71), and paraoxon (72). (b) The characteristics of the inhibited cholinesterase depend only upon the nature of R and are independent of X (73). (c) The energy of activation of the inhibitory reaction is appropriate for a chemical reaction (74, 75). (d) The kinetics of inhibition are appropriate for a simple bimolecular reaction (76).

Some of the consequences of this mechanism are as follows. The inhibition is progressive; the longer the inhibitor is in contact, the greater the inhibition. If the inhibitor is in excess, the kinetics are simple first-order [Eq. (2)], where k is the first-order rate constant, t is the time of incuba-

$$k = \frac{2.303}{tI} \log \frac{100}{P} \tag{2}$$

tion, I the molar inhibitor concentration, and P the per cent activity at time t (76).

Although the potency of the organophosphates is most accurately described by the antiesterase rate constant k, it is commonly described by the I_{50}, which is the molar concentration of organophosphate to inhibit the enzyme 50%, or by the pI_{50}, which is the negative logarithm of the I_{50} (e.g., an I_{50} of 10^{-3} is the same as a pI_{50} of 3). For the I_{50} or pI_{50} to be meaningful, the time of incubation must be known, for the relation between k and I_{50}, as derived from the previous equation for $P = 50$, is given by Eq. (3).

$$k = \frac{0.695}{I_{50}} \tag{3}$$

These two equations are inapplicable at extremely low I_{50}'s where inhibitor and enzyme are at comparable concentrations. A more complicated second-order equation must then be used if a rate constant is required (67).

The inhibition is relatively irreversible; that is to say, in most cases little reversal occurs within a few hours at room temperature. Dialysis and washing are without effect. However, reactivation of the enzyme does occur slowly, due to hydrolysis of the phosphorylated enzyme, which restores the uninhibited enzyme. The rate of this spontaneous reactivation depends only on the alkyl substituents of the organophosphate and on the enzyme. For rabbit erythrocyte cholinesterase, Aldridge (77) found half-lives at 37° and pH 8 of 1.3 hours for dimethyl phosphates and 22 hours for diethyl phosphates. Diisopropyl phosphorylated cholinesterase recovered hardly at all. For other cholinesterases quite different results have been reported (75, 78, 79), except that all agree that the diisopropyl phosphorylated enzyme does not recover spontaneously.

The recovery can be greatly speeded up by the presence of various nucleophilic agents. Probably the best known reactivator is pyridine-2-aldoxime methiodide or 2-PAM [the iodide of (XVI)], whose excellence is reputed to be due to the fact that it has a nucleophilic oxime group, which attacks the phosphorylated esteratic site, at precisely the right distance from a quarternary ammonium group, which increases the affinity of the 2-PAM for the enzyme by binding to the anionic site (80).

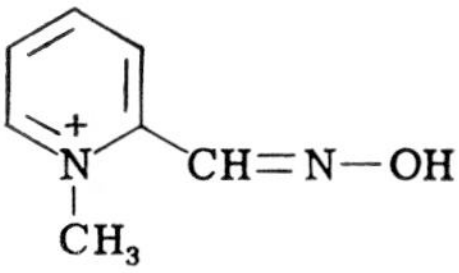

(XVI)

However, an even better reactivator is the more recently developed bispyridinium oxime (XVII), which is up to 22 times more potent than 2-PAM (81, 82). Numerous other oximes have been investigated, in-

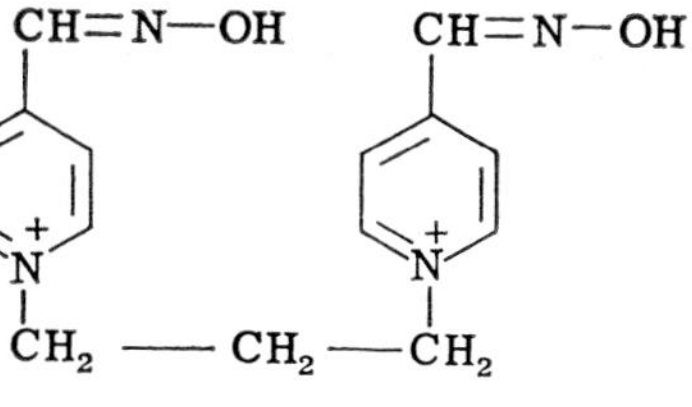

(XVII)

cluding those with such attractive names as MINA (monoisonitrosoacetone), DINA (diisonitrosoacetone), and DAM (diacetyl monoxime).

Although these compounds have proved valuable in studying the kinetics of reactivation (*83, 84*), their principle use has been as antagonists to organophosphate poisoning (*85, 86*), a topic which will not be dealt with here.

These reactivating agents are effective against most forms of phosphorylated cholinesterase, including the diisopropyl phosphorylated one, which is not reactivated spontaneously. However, there is evidence (*87*) that 2-PAM cannot reactivate cholinesterase inhibited by the activated form of schradan, hydroxymethylschradan (*88*), or that inhibited by cholinyl methylphosphonofluoridate (*89*) (Table V, 8). In this second case it seems probable that the phosphorylated enzyme has its anionic site blocked by the cholinyl moiety, so that 2-PAM loses what Wilson calls the "promoting" effect of its binding to that site (*90*).

The researches on induced reactivation by hydroxylamine and oximes led to the discovery of the phenomenon of "aging." It was first observed by Hobbiger (*91*) that freshly inhibited cholinesterase could be almost completely reactivated by appropriate agents, but that if the inhibited enzyme was allowed to stand, it became progressively less capable of reactivation. Aging is thus defined as the change of the enzyme from a re-activatable to an unreactivatable form. Hobbiger (*91*) and Jandorf *et al.* (*92*) attributed this aging to transphosphorylation; it fitted well into the then current view that histidine was the first amino acid in the esteratic site to be phosphorylated, and subsequently the dialkyl phosphoryl group was transferred to serine. However, recent studies (*27, 93, 94*) have convincingly shown for pseudocholinesterase that the serine is initially dialkyl phosphorylated, and that aging is caused by monodealkylation [Eq. (4)]. This has yet to be proved for acetylcholinesterase, but it is

$$\underset{\substack{\parallel \\ \text{ChE}-\text{P(OR)}_2}}{\text{O}} \rightarrow \underset{\substack{\parallel \diagup \\ \text{ChE}-\text{P} \diagdown \\ \text{OR}}}{\text{O} \quad \text{OH}} \tag{4}$$

significant to note that chymotrypsin, trypsin, and horse liver aliesterase do not show aging or monodealkylation, whereas pseudocholinesterase shows both. It therefore seems most probable that acetylcholinesterase, which shows aging, will also be shown to be monodealkylated.

B. Selective Enzyme Inhibition

Generally speaking, the organophosphates are effective against a wide range of esterases, including the cholinesterases, trypsin, chymotrypsin,

aliesterases, and thrombin. However, many organophosphates show sufficient variations in their efficiency against different esterases that they
may be used for selective inhibition, both *in vivo* and *in vitro*.

Table VI shows data for 10 compounds which distinguish between
pseudo- and acetylcholinesterase. It is noteworthy that the selectivity
depends a good deal upon enzyme source. This is dramatically illustrated
by Table VII, which gives extensive data for two particularly useful
selective inhibitors; for example, iso-OMPA (XVIII) has an 11,300-fold
selectivity between the two cholinesterases for the horse, but only 56-fold
for the human.

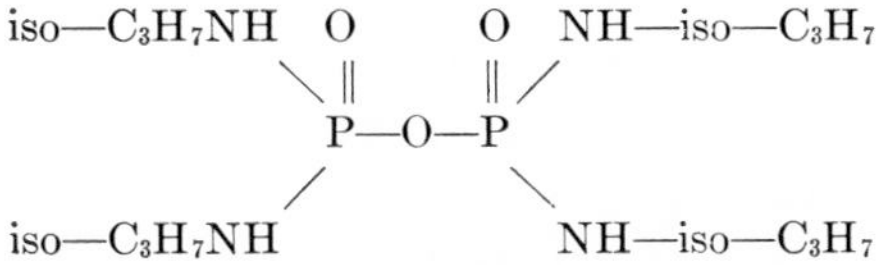

$$\text{iso—C}_3\text{H}_7\text{NH} \quad \underset{\underset{P}{\parallel}}{O} \qquad \underset{\underset{P}{\parallel}}{O} \quad \text{NH—iso—C}_3\text{H}_7$$

(XVIII)

In histochemical studies, Koelle (*38*) has successfully used DFP to
inhibit pseudocholinesterase while leaving the acetylcholinesterase intact.
However, it has been pointed out (*32*) that DFP is by no means specific
for pseudocholinesterase, and certain aliesterases, e.g., the ethyl chloro-
acetate-hydrolyzing enzyme of rat plasma, are very sensitive to it.

Myers *et al.* (*39*) studied 34 organophosphates in an attempt to find
one that would distinguish clearly between cholinesterase and aliesterase.
Of these, 5 showed a hundredfold selectivity or better, the best being
O-*p*-nitrophenyl *O*, *N*-diphenyl phosphoramidate (XIX) which was 1000

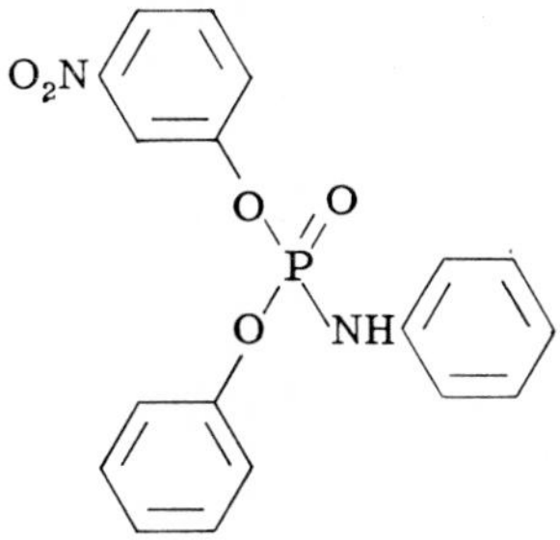

(XIX)

times more potent against the aliesterase (tributyrin as substrate) than
against the cholinesterase of rat brain. Of the well-known compounds,
TEPP showed distinct selectivity, being 200 times more potent against
the cholinesterase than the aliesterase. However, Stegwee (*95*) has re-

TABLE VI

SELECTIVE INHIBITION BETWEEN TRUE AND PSEUDOCHOLINESTERASE[a]

Inhibitor	Aldridge (94a)			Davison (75)		
	pI_{50} True	pI_{50} Pseudo	I_{50} True / I_{50} Pseudo	pI_{50} True	pI_{50} Pseudo	I_{50} True / I_{50} Pseudo
Dimethyl p-nitrophenyl phosphate	6.27	6.10	0.67	7.40	5.19	0.006
Diethyl p-nitrophenyl phosphate (paraoxon)	6.38	6.85	1.9	7.80	7.58	0 6
Diisopropyl p-nitrophenyl phosphate	5.50	6.50	10.0	6.49	7.15	4.5
Tetramethylphosphorodiamidic fluoride	1.96	3.31	22	—	—	—
N,N'-Diisopropylphosphorodiamidic fluoride (Mipafox)	3.82	7.42	3950	4.35	6.74	254
Diisopropyl phosphorofluoridate (DFP)	5.75	8.18	270	6.14	7.8	45
Di-n-propyl phosphorofluoridate	—	—	—	7.26	8.0	5.5
Diethyl phosphoric anhydride (TEPP)	6.52	8.39	73	7.85	7.92	1.2
N,N'-Diisopropylphosphorodiamidic anhydride (iso-OMPA)	2.51	6.48	9400	3.57	6.34	590
Diisopropyl phosphoric anhydride	5.96	8.68	520	—	—	—

[a] Results of Aldridge, horse erythrocyte (true cholinesterase) and serum (pseudocholinesterase); Davison, rat brain (true cholinesterase) or heart (pseudocholinesterase), 30 minutes, 37°.

TABLE VII

Variation of Selectivity of Two Organophosphates with Different Mammals[a]

Species	iso-OMPA			Mipafox		
	pI_{50} True cholinesterase	pI_{50} Pseudo cholinesterase	$\dfrac{I_{50}\ \text{True}}{I_{50}\ \text{Pseudo}}$	pI_{50} True cholinesterase	pI_{50} Pseudo cholinesterase	$\dfrac{I_{50}\ \text{True}}{I_{50}\ \text{Pseudo}}$
Horse	2.47	6.52	11,300	3.80	7.42	4200
Human	3.52	5.27	56	4.66	6.41	56
Guinea pig	2.34	5.89	3,600	4.21	6.51	200
Dog	2.42	6.54	3,200	4.06	7.29	1700
Rat	3.60	6.32	530	4.22	6.75	340
Sheep	3.20	—	—	4.41	—	—

[a] Results of Aldridge (94a).

ported that housefly aliesterase and cholinesterase are identically sensitive to TEPP.

Tris(o-cresyl) phosphate or TOCP (XX) has found use in distinguishing between aliesterases and cholinesterases. For housefly enzymes, Stegwee (95) found that *in vitro* 2.5×10^{-5} M TOCP inhibited 50% of the aliesterase, but none of the cholinesterase. Similar results were observed *in vivo*. However, Myers and Mendel (32) point out that some aliesterases (e.g., rat brain tributyrinase) are quite insensitive to TOCP. Table VIII shows that in human and rabbit it is strongly selective for pseudocholinesterase. Table VIII also shows the marked variation in

TABLE VIII

EFFECT OF TOCP *in vitro* ON ESTERASES[a]

	Inhibition caused by 1.8×10^{-4} M TOCP		
Species	Brain acetyl-cholinesterase (%)	Brain pseudo-cholinesterase (%)	Brain tributyrinase (%)
Human	9	91	21
Rabbit	18	49	24
Chicken	1	33	—
Rat	—	9	—

[a] Data of Earl and Thompson (95a).

sensitivity with species; the pseudocholinesterase of the rat is far less sensitive than that of the human. It should be borne in mind that the potency of TOCP *in vitro* is due to an impurity, for purified TOCP is an extremely weak inhibitor *in vitro*, but is converted to a potent one *in vivo* (96)—probably a hydroxylated and cyclized derivative (96a).

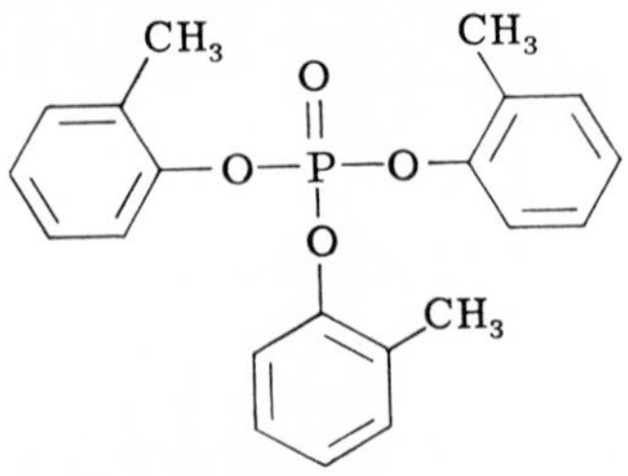

(XX)

A good example of the use of organophosphates to distinguish esterases other than cholinesterases has been the case of serum enzymes (*96b, 97, 98*). The following have been demonstrated:

A-esterase: not inhibited by paraoxon or DFP, hydrolyzes phenyl acetate and paraoxon.

B-esterase: inhibited by paraoxon and DFP, hydrolyzes phenyl acetate.

C-esterase: not inhibited by DFP, does not hydrolyze DFP, hydrolyzes *p*-nitrophenyl acetate and aliphatic esters (e.g., propyl acetate).

D-esterase: like C-esterase, but does not hydrolyze aliphatic esters and is more sensitive to *p*-chloromercuribenzoate.

Paraoxonase: hydrolyzes *p*-nitrophenyl acetate, paraoxon, DFP, but not phenyl acetate or TEPP.

DFPase: hydrolyzes DFP, tabun and possibly TEPP, but not paraoxon.

Myers (*99*) was able to distinguish the esterases of rat brain and pancreas, using paraoxon and diisopropyl *p*-nitrophenyl phosphate (DINP). In pancreas three aliesterases were found: (*a*) one responsible for all tributyrin hydrolysis, 17% of ethyl butyrate hydrolysis, and 1% of phenyl butyrate hydrolysis; insensitive to DINP, sensitive to paraoxon; (*b*) one responsible for 99% of the phenyl butyrate hydrolysis and 83% of the ethyl butyrate hydrolysis, sensitive to DINP and paraoxon; and (*c*) an esterase, probably cholesterolesterase, hydrolyzing amino acid esters, insensitive to DINP and paraoxon.

In brain, Myers (*99*), who had previously (*21*) found only one tributyrin-hydrolyzing enzyme when attempting discrimination with paraoxon, TEPP, or dimethylcarbamoyl fluoride, later found three: (*a*) a lipase, totally inhibited by 5×10^{-6} M DINP, which could hydrolyze both triacetin and tributyrin; (*b*) a DINP-resistant tributyrinase, sensitive to alkali (i.e., pH 10.5 for 30 minutes); and (*c*) a DINP-resistant triacetinase, insensitive to alkali.

Myers (*99*) and Aldridge (*100*) have very useful discussions on the problems associated with the use of organophosphates to distinguish between esterases.

C. Metabolism

This topic is so extensive that the present discussion must be abbreviated to a short summary of the reactions. An extensive discussion of *in vivo* and *in vitro* results has been given by O'Brien (*67*).

The reactions may be divided conveniently into activating reactions, restricted to compounds of class B in Table V, which increase antienzyme potency, and degrading reactions, which reduce potency. Usually the potency is increased or reduced by between 10^3 and 10^6 times by such reactions.

1. ACTIVATING REACTIONS

In order for the phosphorus of an organophosphate to attack the esteratic site, it must be somewhat electrophilic, i.e., attracted to a relatively negative site. Activating reactions are usually those which increase the positivity or "electrophilicity" of the phosphorus; for example, the P in P=O is more electrophilic than in P=S, due to the greater electron-withdrawing power of O than S.

a. Phosphorothionates. Virtually every phosphorothionate is oxidized to its phosphate *in vivo* by vertebrates and insects (*101–105*) and by appropriately fortified preparations of liver microsomes *in vitro* (*106–107*).

$$(RO)_2P(S)X \rightarrow (RO)_2P(O)X \tag{5}$$

The importance of this reaction was not evident until it was shown in 1951 (*108*) that the apparently high anticholinesterase activity of parathion was attributable to an impurity, the *S*-ethyl isomer, which is present in all but carefully purified samples. Isomerization is usual in all phosphorothionates; it occurs on storage and is accelerated by heat and ultraviolet light.

b. Phosphoramidates. For schradan it has been established that the activation, which has been shown *in vitro* (*109–111*) and is implied *in vivo* (because only thus can one explain the inhibited cholinesterase found in schradan poisoning) consists of oxidation to the hydroxymethyl derivative (XXI) (*88, 112*), not the *N*-oxide, as had been thought earlier (*113, 114*). Only one of the eight methyl groups is oxidized in this way. The same compound is produced by vertebrates, plants, and insects. The

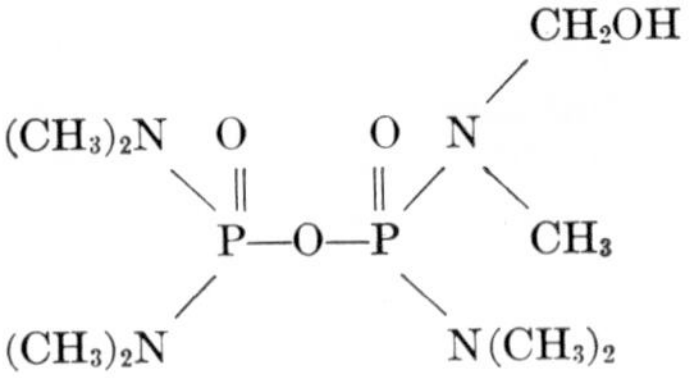

(XXI)

in vitro system which accomplishes this oxidation is apparently identical with the one mentioned above, which oxidizes phosphorothionates.

Dimefox is also activated (*115, 116*), and the product appears precisely analogous to that of schradan (*117*) and is therefore probably the corresponding hydroxymethyl derivative.

c. Thioethers. These compounds may be oxidized to their sulfoxides and sulfones. Thus, for the thiono isomer of Demeton one could have (XXII) (the sulfoxide) and (XXIII) (the sulfone). In view of the fact that

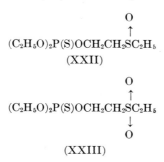

$$O$$
$$\uparrow$$
$$(C_2H_5O)_2P(S)OCH_2CH_2SC_2H_5$$

(XXII)

$$O$$
$$\uparrow$$
$$(C_2H_5O)_2P(S)OCH_2CH_2SC_2H_5$$
$$\downarrow$$
$$O$$

(XXIII)

Demeton normally contains both the above thiono isomer and thiolo isomer $(C_2H_{50})_2P(O)S$—, and that the thiono isomer can also be oxidized at its $P(S)$ group, it is clear that numerous metabolites can result, the maximum number of activation products being nine. Many such oxidations have been shown for Demeton in the mouse (*104*) and in plants (*118–120*), and for Thimet (XXIV) in plants (*121*).

$$(C_2H_{50})_2P(S)SCH_2SC_2H_5$$

(XXIV)

In plants the principle metabolite of Thimet appears to be the dithio-sulfoxide[1] (in cotton) or dithiosulfone (in alfalfa), although the most potent anticholinesterase is the fully oxidized thiolosulfone.

d. Tris(o-cresyl) Phosphate (TOCP). This compound (XX) was for years believed to be directly active as an anticholinesterase. However, in 1954 Aldridge (*122*) showed conclusively that it required activation and that pure TOCP was a poor anticholinesterase *in vitro*. The nature of the activation product has never been shown, although Myers *et al.* (*123*) have suggested, by analogy with the metabolism of *m*-dichlorobenzene and *o*-tolylurea, that it is the *p*-hydroxylated derivative or some metabolite of it. Recently Eto *et al.* (*96a*) have shown that it is a cyclized hydroxymethyl derivative.

2. Degrading Reactions

Just as metabolic reactions which enhance the positivity of the phosphorus increase its antiesterase activity, the opposite can occur. The commonest degradative reactions are hydrolytic, and in effect introduce an anion into the molecule which in turn renders the phosphorus less positive.

---

[1] The "dithio" prefix refers only to the sulfurs attached to phosphorus.

In another case the degradation is reductive; the electrophilic p-nitro-phenol group is converted to the nucleophilic p-aminophenol, with the same end effect.

a. Phosphatases. We shall use this term to cover enzymic hydrolysis of any phosphorus ester or anhydride when it occurs at P—O—C or P—S—C.

These phosphatases have usually been named after their substrates. There are DFPase, tabunase, sarinase, and paroxonase. However, there is ample overlap in activity of these various phosphatases. Purified DFPase hydrolyzed 10 other organophosphates of the 12 tested (*124*); purified paraoxonase hydrolyzed also DFP and tabun, but not TEPP (*125*); sarinase and tabunase may be identical (*126–127*). In other words "Xase" is an enzyme—or in some cases a group of enzymes—which has activity towards X, but usually to several other organophosphates as well. It is to be assumed that these enzymes also have less exotic substrates. Thus, Mounter (*128*) suggested that hog kidney DFPase was in fact an amino acid acylase, although later work (*124*) has tended to disprove his hypothesis.

In the case of DFPase, and probably of the other phosphatases, there are several enzymes in any one animal. The hog and rat had at least three, one in kidney and two in liver, which were distinguishable on the basis of their behavior toward Co^{++}, Mn^{++}, and histidine, and their relative activities toward DFP and its dibutyl analogue (*129*).

In general, the liver is the most active source of these phosphatases (*130, 131*), but not in the case of tabunase, for which spleen is most potent (*132*). Species variation is enormous; for instance, rabbit serum has 50 times more paraoxon-hydrolyzing activity then mouse serum (*131*). Liver and blood are likely to be particularly important because an organophosphate will usually have maximal exposure to these tissues. The importance of these degrading enzymes has been shown by experi-ments in which slow injection of phosphates greatly reduced their toxicity (*133*) and others in which levels of sarinase in the liver (but not the blood) of rabbits were directly related to susceptibility to sarin (*134*).

b. Carboxyesterases and Carboxyamidases. Most organophosphates which contain carboxyester or carboxyamide groups are hydrolyzed in mammals more readily at these groups than by phosphatases. An excep-tion is phosdrin (Table V, 4), according to *in vivo* and *in vitro* evidence in cows and humans (*135*). For malathion (Table V, 11) it has been clearly shown *in vitro* and *in vivo* that in mammals the principle degrada-tion is at the carboxy ester, although in insects phosphatase cleavage is more important [Eq. (6)] (*102, 136*).

$$(CH_3O)_2P(S)SCHCOOC_2H_5 \xrightarrow{\text{mammals}} (CH_3O)_2P(S)SCHCOOC_2H_5$$

$$\overset{|}{CH_2COOC_2H_5} \qquad\qquad\qquad \overset{|}{CH_2COOH}$$

$$\searrow \text{insects}$$

$$(CH_3O)_2P(S)OH$$

(6)

In fact the low toxicity of malathion to mammals has been attributed to this effective carboxy ester cleavage (*102, 137*). The carboxyesterase and carboxyamidase are inhibited *in vivo* and *in vitro* by EPN, TOCP, and other compounds, and as a result these compounds show marked synergism with malathion and other carboxy esters and carboxyamides, such as acethion and dimethoate (*138–142*).

All carboxy ester-containing phosphates are degraded by phosphatase action as well as carboxyesterase action (*102, 141, 143*). It is therefore undesirable to use terms such as "malathionase" for the mixed enzyme system (*138, 144*). Main and Braid (*144a*) have recently purified the liver enzyme which hydrolyzes one carboxy ester group of malathion; it is an aliesterase.

c. Oxidative Degradation. It has been shown in the case of Amiton (Table V) that it is degraded by substantially the same oxidative system of fortified liver microsomes which accomplishes the oxidation of phosphorothionates and phosphoramidates (*145*). The nature of this degradation is unknown.

d. Reductive Degradation. Parathion is very toxic to most vertebrates as well as insects, in spite of the widespread occurrence of enzymes in their bodies capable of destroying the activation product, paraoxon. However, the cow is remarkably insensitive to parathion (*146*). This has been shown to be due in part to the ability of microorganisms to reduce parathion and paraoxon to their amino derivatives [Eq. (7)], which are very poor anticholinesterases (*101, 147*). However, as the microorganisms were

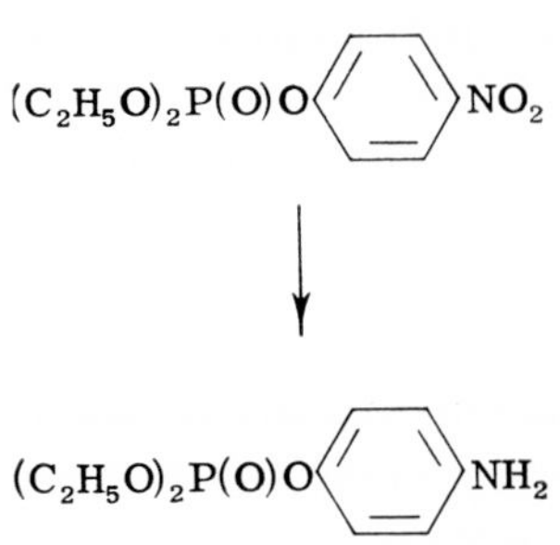

$$(C_2H_5O)_2P(O)O\!\!-\!\!\left\langle\begin{array}{c}\\\end{array}\right\rangle\!\!-\!\!NO_2$$

$$\downarrow$$

$$(C_2H_5O)_2P(O)O\!\!-\!\!\left\langle\begin{array}{c}\\\end{array}\right\rangle\!\!-\!\!NH_2$$

(7)

also vigorous in degrading parathion hydrolytically (*101*), it is not easy to affirm the importance of the reduction in reducing toxicity.

D. Toxicity

With a number of exceptions discussed later, the organophosphates tend to be toxic to vertebrates and insects. As far as the mammal is concerned, the toxic compounds fall roughly into two groups. First, there are those which attack only the esteratic site, such as TEPP, DFP, and paraoxon. Such compounds seldom have a toxicity below 0.5 mg/kg, and, in fact, those used as insecticides seldom have mammalian toxicity below 1–5 mg/kg, even by the intraperitoneal route (usually toxicities decrease with route according to the following order, to which there are, however, a number of exceptions: intravenous > intraperitoneal = inhalation > subcutaneous > oral = cutaneous). However, numerous compounds which contain strategically located quaternary or basic tertiary nitrogen groups can be expected to have their esteratic attack promoted by concurrent binding to the anionic site. Consequently, their mammalian toxicities are substantially higher, figures of 0.01–0.05 mg/kg being common.

For LD_{50} values of most organophosphates the reader is referred to Holmstedt (*65*) and Negherbon (*148*).

The organophosphates present numerous interesting cases of selective toxicity; for instance, malathion is a useful insecticide, but an adult human would have to consume some 150 gm of it if he wished to kill himself. DFP is a warfare agent with an LD_{50} to the mouse of 4 mg/kg, yet its LD_{50} to the toad is 1450 mg/kg (*149*). In many cases these selectivities may be satisfactorily explained on one or more of the following grounds.

1. METABOLISM

There is evidence that the low toxicity of malathion (*102*), Diazinon, dimethoate, and acethion (*103*) to mammals, as compared to insects, is due to rapid degradation in the mammal. The low toxicity of DFP to the toad has been tentatively attributed to rapid degradation in the blood (*149*).

2. PENETRATION

It has been pointed out in the section above on carbamate toxicity (Section II, D) that ionized anticholinesterases have negligible toxicity to most insects. This is equally true for the organophosphates; for instance, the toxicity ratio, mouse/housefly for Amiton oxalate (Table V, 1) was 2400 (*52*) and for Ro 30412 (XXV), 270 (*46*). Nevertheless, such

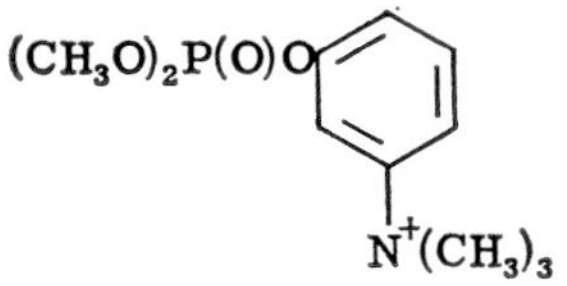

$$(CH_3O)_2P(O)O$$

$$N^+(CH_3)_3$$

(XXV)

ionized compounds may be effective towards certain insects, such as aphids and thrips, and also to mites (*150, 151*).

Schradan has a toxicity pattern quite like the ionized compounds, and its activation product also fails to penetrate the central nervous system of nonsusceptible insects (*152*). This effect may be connected with the failure of phosphoramidates in general to penetrate the central nervous system of mammals (*153*). Recent work by Saito (*154, 155*) has shown that activated schradan successfully penetrates the nervous system of schradan-susceptible insects, which have relatively flimsy nerve sheaths.

A difference in integument penetration has been shown to account for the eightfold difference in toxicity of malathion to the American and German cockroaches (*102*).

3. TARGET ENZYME

It is still generally believed that the primary target for organophosphate attack is cholinesterase, in both insects and mammals. Any differences in cholinesterase between species should be reflected in corresponding toxicity differences. So far such cases have been few. Diisopropyl *p*-nitrophenyl phosphorothionate was 250 times more toxic to the housefly than to the bee, and 1000 times more potent against housefly cholinesterase (*156*). DDVP (XXI) was 83 times more toxic to the housefly than the mouse, and 100 times more potent against housefly cholinesterase (*157*). DFP was 360 times more toxic to the mouse than the toad, and 100 times more potent against mouse cholinesterase (*149*).

E. Use in Elucidating Enzyme Structure

One of the most valuable contributions that the organophosphates have made to biochemistry has been in the elucidation of the structure of the active sites of esterases. A fine recent review by Cohen et al. (*27*) makes it unnecessary to do more here than sketch out the principles involved.

Use is made of the fact that organophosphates are highly specific phosphorylators of the esteratic site of numerous esterases. To increase this specificity, Cohen et al. (*159*) began by phosphorylating with unlabeled DFP in the presence of a large excess of butyrylcholine. By this means they phosphorylated available sites not in the active centers. Then, after dialytic removal of the DFP and substrate, DFP^{32} was used to label the esteratic sites. However, this phosphorylation of "surplus" sites appears not to have been used by others, nor in later work of this group (*27*). Other workers have used C^{14}-labeled DFP in some cases (*160*), and sarin-P^{32} has also been employed (*161*).

After reaction with the labeled organophosphate, the enzyme is degraded, the fragments are separated chromatographically, and further analysis is carried out on the fragments bearing the label. For the degradation, boiling HCl was first used (*159, 161*), but later workers have used crude mixed (*162*) or purified (*160*) proteolytic enzymes.

Such studies have now been carried out for chymotrypsin, trypsin, thrombin, liver aliesterase, and pseudocholinesterase. In the first three cases, the sequence asparagine-serine-glycine has been found. In the second two, glutamine-serine and perhaps glutamine-serine-alanine were found. In all 5 cases the serine was phosphorylated (*27*).

By such techniques one can of course only find the identity of the phosphorylated amino acid and those attached directly to it. Other amino acids, which by virtue of the secondary or tertiary structure of the native protein may be in proximity to the phosphorylated amino acid and may make a vital contribution to the properties of the active center, will not be detected.

REFERENCES

1. R. L. Metcalf, *Bull. Entomol. Soc. Am.* **5**, 3 (1959).
2. K. B. Augustinsson and D. Nachmansohn, *Science* **110**, 98 (1949).
3. D. Richter and P. G. Croft, *Biochem. J.* **36**, 746 (1942).
4. M. Dixon and E. C. Webb, "The Enzymes." Academic Press, New York, 1958.
5. D. H. Adams and V. P. Whittaker, *Biochim. et Biophys. Acta* **4**, 543 (1950).
6. F. Bergmann and M. Wurzel, *Biochim. et Biophys. Acta* **13**, 251 (1954).
7. F. Bergmann, *Discussions Faraday Soc.* **20**, 126 (1955).
8. A. Stempel and J. A. Aeschlimann, *in* "Medicinal Chemistry" (F. F. Blicke and R. H. Cox, eds.), Vol. III, p. 238. Wiley, New York, 1956.
9. H. Gysin, *Chimia (Switz.)* **8**, 205 and 221 (1954).
9a. R. L. Metcalf, "Organic insecticides." Wiley (Interscience), New York, 1955.
10. A. Goldstein, *J. Gen. Physiol.* **27**, 529 (1944).
11. L. Michaelis and M. L. Menten, *Biochem. Z.* **49**, 1333 (1913).

12. O. H. Straus and A. Goldstein, *J. Gen. Physiol.* **26,** 559 (1943).
13. A. Goldstein, *Arch. Biochem.* **34,** 169 (1951).
14. D. K. Myers, *Biochem. J.* **52,** 46 (1952).
15. W. N. Aldridge, *Biochem. J.* **54,** 442 (1953).
16. K. Matthes, *J. Physiol. (London)* **70,** 338 (1930).
17. L. H. Easson and E. Stedman, *Proc. Roy. Soc.* **121B,** 142 (1936).
18. I. B. Wilson, *Arch. intern. pharmacodynamie* **104,** 204 (1955).
19. A. S. V. Burgen, *Brit. J. Pharmacol.* **4,** 219 (1949).
20. J. A. Cohen, F. Kalsbeck, and M. B. P. J. Warringa, *Biochim. et Biophys. Acta* **2,** 549 (1948).
21. D. K. Myers, *Biochem. J.* **62,** 556 (1956).
22. K. B. Augustinsson, T. Fredriksson, A. Sundwall, and G. Jonsson, *Biochem. Pharmacol.* **3,** 68 (1959).
23. M. J. Kolbezen, R. L. Metcalf, and T. R. Fukuto, *J. Agr. Chem.* **2,** 864 (1954).
24. D. K. Myers, *Biochem. J.* **65,** 232 (1957).
24a. . B. Wilson, M. A. Hatch, and S. Ginsburg, *J. Biol. Chem.* **235,** 2312 (1960).
25. D. K. Myers, *Arch. Biochem.* **27,** 341 (1950).
26. J. E. Casida, K. B. Augustinsson, and G. Jonsson, *J. Econ. Entomol.* **53,** 205 (1960).
27. J. A. Cohen, R. A. Oosterbaan, H. S. Jansz, and F. Berends, *J. Cellular Comp. Physiol.* **54,** Suppl. 1, p. 231 (1959).
28. F. Bergmann, *Advances in Catalysis* **10,** 130 (1958).
29. F. Bergmann and R. Segal, *Biochem. J.* **58,** 692 (1954).
30. L. H. Easson and E. Stedman, *Biochem. J.* **31,** 1723 (1937).
31. B. Mendel and H. Rudney, *Biochem. J.* **37,** 59 (1943).
32. D. K. Myers and B. Mendel, *Proc. Soc. Exptl. Biol. Med.* **71,** 357 (1949).
33. R. D. Hawkins and B. Mendel, *J. Cellular Comp. Physiol* **27,** 69 (1946).
34. E. Stedman and E. Stedman, *Biochem. J.* **25,** 1149 (1931).
35. R. D. Hawkins and J. M. Gunter, *Biochem. J.* **40,** 192 (1956).
36. R. D. Hawkins and B. Mendel, *Biochem. J.* **44,** 260 (1949).
37. H. Casier and G. R. Vleeschhouwer, *Arch. intern. pharmacodynamie* **90,** 412 (1952).
38. G. B. Koelle, *J. Pharmacol. Exptl. Therap.* **100,** 158 (1950).
39. D. K. Myers, A. Kemp, J. W. Tol, and M. H. T. DeJonge, *Biochem. J.* **65,** 232 (1957).
40. R. Pulver and R. Domenjoz, *Experientia* **7,** 306 (1951).
41. S. Ellis, F. L. Plachte, and O. H. Strauss, *J. Pharmacol. Exptl. Therap.* **79,** 295 (1943).
42. K. B. Augustinsson and J. E. Casida, *Biochem. Pharmacol.* **3,** 60 (1959).
43. J. E. Casida and K. B. Augustinsson, *Biochim. et Biophys. Acta* **36,** 411 (1959).
44. R. Weissman and C. Kocher, *Z. angew. Entomol.* **33,** 297 (1951).
45. M. E. Eldefrawi, R. Miskus, and V. Sutcher, *J. Econ. Entomol.* **53,** 231 (1960).
46. R. D. O'Brien and R. W. Fisher, *J. Econ. Entomol.* **51,** 169 (1958).
47. W. B. Spector, ed., "Handbook of Toxicology," Vol. 1. Saunders, Philadelphia, 1956.

48. J. Stevens and R. Beutel, *J. Am. Chem. Soc.* **63**, 308 (1941).
49. A. W. A. Brown, D. W. B. Robinson, H. Hurtig, and B. J. Wenner, *Can. J. Research* **26D**, 177 (1948).
50. R. D. Haworth, A. H. Lamberton, and D. Woodcock, *J. Chem. Soc.* p. 182 (1947).
51. R. D. O'Brien, *Ann. Entomol. Soc. Am.* **50**, 223 (1957).
52. R. D. O'Brien, *J. Econ. Entomol.* **52**, 812 (1959).
53. P. A. Harlow, *Ann. Appl. Biol.* **46**, 55 (1958).
54. V. B. Wigglesworth, *Quart. J. Microscop. Sci.* **99**, 441 (1958).
55. I. B. Wilson and M. Cohen, *Biochim. et Biophys. Acta* **11**, 147 (1953).
56. J. R. Johnson, *in* "Organic chemistry," (H. Gilman, ed.), 2nd ed., Vol. 2, p. 1837. Wiley, New York, 1943.
57. R. D. Haworth, A. H. Lamberton, and D. Woodcock, *J. Chem. Soc.* p. 176 (1947).
58. R. L. Metcalf, T. R. Fukuto, and M. Y. Winton, *J. Econ. Entomol.* **53**, 828 (1960).
59. C. C. Roan and S. Maeda, *J. Econ. Entomol.* **47**, 507 (1954).
60. H. H. Moorefield and E. R. Tefft, *Contribs. Boyce Thompson Inst.* **20**, 295 (1959).
61. M. E. Eldefrawi, R. Miskus, and W. M. Hoskins, *Science* **129**, 898 (1959).
62. H. H. Moorefield, *Contribs. Boyce Thompson Inst.* **19**, 501 (1958).
63. J. E. Casida, *J. Agr. Food Chem.* **4**, 772 (1956).
64. T. R. Fukuto, *Advances in Pest Control Research* **1**, 147 (1957).
65. B. Holmstedt, *Pharmacol. Revs.* **11**, 567 (1959).
66. E. Y. Spencer and R. D. O'Brien, *Ann. Rev. Entomol.* **2**, 261 (1957).
67. R. D. O'Brien, "Toxic Phosphorus Esters." Academic Press, New York, 1960.
68. L. Rosival, L. Vrbovsky, and F. V. Selecky, "Toxikologia a farmakobiodynamika organofosforovych zlucenin." Vydavatelstvo Slovenskej Akademie Vied, Bratislava, Czechoslovakia, 1959.
69. B. C. Saunders, "Some Aspects of the Chemistry and Toxic Action of Organic Compounds Containing Phosphorus and Fluorine." Cambridge Univ. Press, London and New York, 1957.
69a. D. F. Heath, "Organophosphorus Poisons." Pergamon Press, New York, 1961.
70. E. F. Jansen, M.D. Fellowes-Nutting, R. Jang, and A. K. Balls, *J. Biol. Chem.* **185**, 209 (1950).
71. J. H. Fleischer, B. J. Jandorf, W. H. Summerson, and D. P. Norton, *Federation Proc.* **9**, 171 (1950).
72. B. S. Hartley and B. A. Kilby, *Biochem. J.* **50**, 672 (1952).
73. W. N. Aldridge and A. N. Davison, *Biochem. J.* **55**, 763 (1953).
74. W. N. Aldridge, *Biochem. J.* **54**, 442 (1953).
75. A. N. Davison, *Biochem. J.* **60**, 339 (1955).
76. W. N. Aldridge, *Biochem. J.* **46**, 451 (1950).
77. W. N. Aldridge, *Chem. & Ind.* (*London*) p. 473 (1954).
78. F. Hobbiger, *Brit. J. Pharmacol.* **6**, 21 (1951).
79. D. C. Mengle and R. D. O'Brien, *Biochem. J.* **75**, 201 (1960).
80. I. B. Wilson, S. Ginsburg, and C. Quan, *Arch. Biochem.* **77**, 286 (1958).
81. F. Hobbiger, D. G. O'Sullivan, and P. W. Sadler, *Nature* **182**, 1498 (1958).

82. F. Hobbiger, M. Pitman, and P. W. Sadler, *Biochem. J.* **75**, 363 (1960).
83. R. D. Davies and A. L. Green, *Biochem. J.* **63**, 529 (1956).
84. A. L. Green and H. J. Smith, *Biochem. J.* **68**, 28 and 32 (1958).
85. B. M. Askew, *Brit. J. Pharmacol.* **11**, 417 (1956).
86. I. P. Dultz, M. A. Epstein, G. A. Freeman, E. H. Gray, and W. B. Weil, *J. Pharmacol. Exptl. Therap.* **119**, 522 (1957).
87. H. Kewitz, *Arch. Biochem. Biophys.* **66**, 263 (1957).
88. E. Y. Spencer, R. D. O'Brien, and R. W. White, *J. Agr. Food Chem.* **5**, 123 (1957).
89. L. E. Tammelin and I. Enander, *Proc. 4th Intern. Congr. Biochem., Vienna, 1958, Abstr.* **4–10.**
90. I. B. Wilson, *Discussions Faraday Soc.* **20**, 119 (1955).
91. F. Hobbiger, *Brit. J. Pharmacol.* **10**, 356 (1955).
92. B. J. Jandorf, H. O. Michel, N. K. Schaffer, R. Egan, and W. H. Summerson, *Discussions Faraday Soc.* **20**, 134 (1955).
93. F. Berends, C. H. Posthumus, I. Van der Sluys, and F. A. Deierkauf, *Biochim. et Biophys. Acta* **34**, 576 (1959).
94. R. A. Oosterbaan, M. G. P. J. Warringa, F. B. Jansz, and J. A. Cohen, *Proc. 4th Intern. Congr. Biochem., Vienna, 1958, Abstr.* **4–12.**
94a. W. N. Aldridge, *Biochem. J.* **53**, 62 (1953).
95. D. Stegwee, *Nature* **184**, 1253 (1959).
95a. C. J. Earl and R. H. S. Thompson, *Brit. J. Pharmacol.* **7**, 264 (1952).
96. W. N. Aldridge, *Biochem. J.* **56**, 185 (1954).
96a. M. Eto, J. E. Casida, and T. Eto, *Biochem. Pharmacol.* **11**, 337 (1962).
96b. W. N. Aldridge, *Biochem. J.* **53**, 110 (1953).
97. F. Bergmann, R. Segal, and S. Rimon, *Biochem. J.* **67**, 481 (1957); **77**, 209 (1960).
98. A. R. Main, *Biochem. J.* **75**, 188 (1960).
99. D. K. Myers, *Biochem. J.* **64**, 740 (1956).
100. W. N. Aldridge, *Biochem. J.* **57**, 692 (1954).
101. M. K. Ahmed, J. E. Casida, and R. E. Nichols, *J. Agr. Food Chem.* **6**, 740 (1958).
102. H. R. Krueger and R. D. O'Brien, *J. Econ. Entomol.* **52**, 1063 (1959).
103. H. R. Krueger, W. C. Dauterman, and R. D. O'Brien, *J. Econ. Entomol.* **53**, 25 (1960).
104. R. B. March, R. L. Metcalf, T. R. Fukuto, and M. G. Maxon, *J. Econ. Entomol.* **48**, 355 (1955).
105. F. W. Plapp and J. E. Casida, *J. Econ. Entomol.* **51**, 800 (1958).
106. R. D. O'Brien, *Nature* **183**, 121 (1959).
107. A. N. Davison, *Biochem. J.* **61**, 203 (1955).
108. W. M. Diggle and J. C. Gage, *Biochem. J.* **49**, 491 (1951).
109. J. E. Casida and M. A. Stahmann, *J. Agr. Food Chem.* **1**, 883 (1953).
110. R. D. O'Brien and E. Y. Spencer, *J. Agr. Food Chem.* **1**, 946 (1953).
111. R. D. O'Brien and E. Y. Spencer, *J. Agr. Food Chem.* **3**, 56 (1955).
112. D. F. Heath, D. W. I. Lane, and P. O. Park, *Phil. Trans. Roy. Soc. London* **239B**, 191 (1955).
113. J. E. Casida, T. C. Allen, and M. A. Stahmann, *J. Biol. Chem.* **210**, 607 (1954).

114. H. Tsuyuki, M. A. Stahmann, and J. E. Casida, *J. Agr. Food Chem.* **3,** 922 (1955).

115. W. N. Aldridge and J. M. Barnes, *Nature* 169, 345 (1952).

116. M. L. Fenwick, J. R. Barron, and W. A. Watson, *Biochem. J.* **65,** 58 (1957).

117. B. W. Arthur and J. E. Casida, *J. Econ. Entomol.* 51, 49 (1958).

118. T. R. Fukuto, R. L. Metcalf, R. B. March and M. G. Maxon, *J. Econ. Entomol.* 48, 348 (1955).

119. T. R. Fukuto, J. P. Wolf, R. L. Metcalf, and R. B. March, *J. Econ. Entomol.* 49, 147 (1956).

120. T. R. Fukuto, J. P. Wolf, R. L. Metcalf, and R. B. March, *J. Econ. Entomol.* 50, 399 (1957).

121. J. S. Bowman and J. E. Casida, *J. Agr. Food Chem.* 5, 192 (1957).

122. W. N. Aldridge, *Biochem. J.* 56, 185 (1954).

123. D. K. Myers, J. B. J. Rebel, A. Kemp, and G. L. Simons, *Nature* 176, 259 (1955).

124. J. A. Cohen and M. G. P. J. Warringa, *Biochim. et Biophys. Acta* 26, 29 (1957).

125. A. R. Main, *Biochem. J.* 75, 188 (1960).

126. P. A. Adie, *Can. J. Biochem. Physiol.* 36, 21 (1958).

127. P. A. Adie and J. Tuba, *Can. J. Biochem. Physiol.* 36, 21 (1958).

128. L. A. Mounter, *Federation Proc.* 15, 317 (1956).

129. L. A. Mounter, *J. Biol. Chem.* 215, 705 (1955).

130. L. A. Mounter, L. L. H. Dien, and A. Chanutin, *J. Biol. Chem.* 204, 221 (1953).

131. W. N. Aldridge, *Biochem. J.* 53, 117 (1953).

132. K. B. Augustinsson and G. Heimburger, *Acta Chem. Scand.* 8, 753 (1954).

133. J. P. Saunders, *Federation Proc.* 12, 364 (1953).

134. P. A. Adie, *Can. J. Biochem. Physiol.* 34, 654 (1956).

135. J. E. Casida, P. E. Gatterdam, J. B. Knaak, R. D. Lance, and R. P. Niedermeier, *J. Agr. Food Chem.* 6, 658 (1958).

136. R. D. O'Brien, W. C. Dauterman, and R. P. Niedermeier, *J. Agr. Food Chem.* 9, 39 (1961).

137. R. D. O'Brien, *J. Econ. Entomol.* 50, 159 (1957).

138. J. W. Cook, J. R. Blake, G. Yip, and M. Williams, *J. Assoc. Offic. Agr. Chemists* 41, 399 (1958).

139. J. W. Cook and G. Yip, *J. Assoc. Offic. Agr. Chemists* 41, 407 (1958).

140. J. B. Knaak and R. D. O'Brien, *J. Agr. Food Chem.* 8, 198 (1960).

141. F. W. Seume and R. D. O'Brien, *J. Agr. Food Chem.* 8, 36 (1960).

142. F. W. Seume and R. D. O'Brien, *Toxicol. Appl. Pharmacol.* 2, 495 (1960).

143. R. D. O'Brien, G. D. Thorn, and R. W. Fisher, *J. Econ. Entomol.* 51, 714 (1958).

144. G. Yip and J. W. Cook, *J. Assoc. Offic. Agr. Chemists* 42, 405 (1959).

144a. A. R. Main and P. E. Braid. *Biochem. J.* 84, 255 (1962).

145. J. R. Scaife and D. H. Campbell, *Can. J. Biochem. Physiol.* 37, 279 (1959).

146. P. A. Dahm, F. C. Fountaine, J. E. Pankaskie, R. C. Smith, and F. W. Atkeson, *J. Dairy Sci.* 33, 747 (1950).

147. J. W. Cook, *J. Agr. Food Chem.* 5, 859 (1957).
148. W. O. Negherbon, "Handbook of Toxicology," Vol. III. Saunders, Philadelphia, 1959.
149. H. Edery and G. Schatzberg-Porath, *Arch. intern. Pharmacodynamie* 124, 212 (1960).
150. R. Ghosh and J. F. Newman, *Chem. & Ind. (London)* p. 118 (1955).
151. T. R. Fukuto, R. L. Metcalf, R. B. March, and M. G. Maxon, *J. Am. Chem. Soc.* 77, 3670 (1955).
152. R. D. O'Brien and E. Y. Spencer, *Nature* 179, 52 (1957).
153. K. P. DuBois, K. Doull, A. J. Okinaka, and J. M. Coon, *J. Pharmacol. Exptl. Therap.* 107, 464 (1953).
154. T. Saito, *Botyu-Kagaku* 25, 64 (1960).
155. T. Saito, *Botyu-Kagaku* 25, 71 (1960).
156. R. L. Metcalf and R. B. March, *J. Econ. Entomol.* 42, 721 (1949).
157. K. van Asperen, *Entomol. Exptl. Appl.* 1, 130 (1958).
159. J. A. Cohen, R. A. Oosterbaan, and M. G. P. J. Warringa, *Biochim. et Biophys. Acta* 18, 228 (1955).
160. G. H. Dixon, S. Go, and H. Neurath, *Biochim. et Biophys. Acta* 19, 193 (1956).
161. N. K. Schaffer, R. P. Lang, L. Simet, and R. W. Driski, *J. Biol. Chem.* 230, 185 (1958).
162. R. A. Oosterbaan, P. Kunst, and J. A. Cohen, *Biochim. et Biophys. Acta* 16, 299 (1955).

CHAPTER 26

Herbicides

W. A. Andreae

I. INTRODUCTION

The term *herbicide*, as used in agriculture, applies to a heterogeneous group of chemicals with the property of eradicating all vegetation or of selectively killing weeds without seriously injuring the cultivated crops. Since the turn of the century, the number of known herbicides has increased steadily, and at present about 80 are produced commercially. A comprehensive list can be found in the report of the Terminology Committee of the Weed Society of America (1). Almost all commercial herbicides were first developed empirically, and studies of their modes of action were undertaken only after their economic benefits were recognized. The results of these investigations are of considerable interest to biology and agriculture, since they furnish new insights into the physiological processes of plants and at the same time provide a rational approach to the development of new chemicals to satisfy specific needs.

This chapter deals with the metabolic relations between the applied chemical and the plant and is mainly concerned with those herbicides which specifically affect plant metabolism. A number of herbicides, such as metabolic inhibitors not specific for plants, inorganic salts, and petroleum oils, will not be discussed here beyond a brief mention. Metabolic poisons, such as sodium cyanide, sodium arsenite, calcium arsenate, or substituted phenols, when applied as herbicides may act through their established role of blocking or uncoupling specific enzyme systems, as discussed elsewhere in this volume, although other, as yet unknown toxic actions may be involved. In general, enzymes of plant or animal origin are sensitive to the same specific enzyme poisons. However, similar physiological processes in plants or animals may be mediated by different metabolic pathways, so that inhibitors may differ in their toxicity to plants or animals; for example, only a small part of the respiration of higher plants is cyanide sensitive (2), whereas the respiration of many animals is almost entirely inhibited by cyanide. General poisons, such as chloropicrin, methyl bromide, phenylmercuric acetate, and pentachlorophenol, are in use as soil sterilants where they are effective against weeds and weed seeds as well as insects. In practice, because of toxicity hazards, efforts are made to replace these general metabolic inhibitors by safer, plant-specific herbicides.

The first observation of selective weed killing was accidental and dates back to 1896, when a French vineyard was sprayed with copper sulfate as a preventive measure against fungal infection of the vines. When the spray drifted into the adjacent grain field, the selective kill of broadleaf weeds within the cereal crop was noted. Ammonium sulfate and iron sulfate are also selective weed killers, but their use as herbicides has been largely superseded by more effective organic compounds. At present, high concentrations of certain fertilizer salts, such as calcium cyanamide and kainite as well as dilute sulfuric acid, are used as selective weed killers in grain crops. Their herbicidal action may be ascribed to tissue corrosion on physical contact, although some as yet unrecognized metabolic action may also be involved. Ammonium sulfamate, borax, potassium cyanate, and sodium chlorate are herbicidal at relatively low concentrations, but in spite of long usage no satisfactory explanation of their action has been advanced.

Petroleum oils came into use as general plant eradicants about 40 years ago. More recently, it was noted that light oils are selective herbicides; for instance, Stoddard Solvent is relatively harmless to carrots and other umbelliferous plants but toxic to most other vegetation. The proportion of aromatic hydrocarbons in the oils seems to increase their toxicity. Oils per se are probably not metabolic inhibitors but act by physical plugging of the tissue vessels during transport. There is, however, good evidence that various oxidation products of aromatic hydrocarbons, when present in the atmosphere, are extremely phytotoxic (3).

The first part of this chapter deals with the physiological and bio-chemical effects of plant-specific herbicides on plant processes. The second part deals with the metabolic transformation of herbicides within the plant.

II. THE ACTION OF HERBICIDES ON THE PLANT

A. Auxin Herbicides

At present, three general types of naturally occurring plant growth regulators are recognized: the auxins, the gibberellins, and the kinins. Each possesses properties distinctly different from the others, and normal growth depends on their interactions. As yet, herbicidal activity has been found only among the synthetic auxin analogues. At low concentrations all auxins stimulate cell enlargement as measured by the pea stem or *Avena* coleoptile elongation test. A positive response in such isolated tissue segments is the only accepted criterion of auxin activity. With concentrations which are supraoptimal for growth, the stimulatory effect is progressively decreased. This has been referred to as the growth in-hibitory action, although even with relatively high concentrations growth still exceeds that of the control tissues. Auxins also regulate the meriste-matic activity of intact plants, so that the visible symptoms of auxin herbicide application are the result of their combined actions on cell elongation and cell division.

The first auxin was isolated by Kögel *et al.* (4) in 1934 and was identi-fied as 3-indoleacetic acid (IAA). IAA is still the only naturally occurring auxin whose structure is irrefutably established. Within a short time other indole acids and certain naphthalene acids were found to possess auxin activity, but not until 5 years later was there any hint, unpublished at the time, that growth regulators might possess selective herbicidal activity. In 1939 Slade, Templeman, and Sexton sprayed oat seedlings with naphthaleneacetic acid (NAA) and noted the selective phytotoxic action on broadleaf plants in a stand of oats. In 1942 substituted benzoic and phenoxyacetic acids were introduced as powerful auxins (5). In 1944 the first references to 2,4-D and 2,4,5-trichlorophenoxyacetic acid (2,4,5-T) as selective herbicides were published by Hamner and Tukey (6). The independent works on 2,4-D and 2-methyl-4-chlorophenoxy-

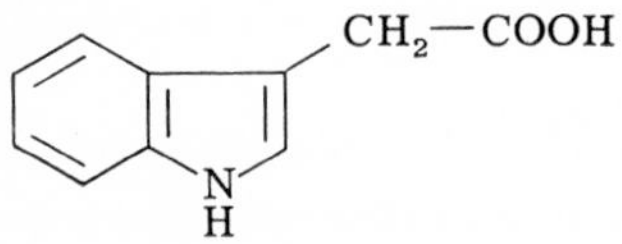

3-Indoleacetic acid
(IAA)

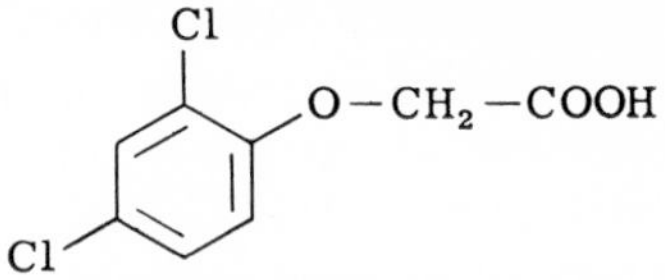

2,4-Dichlorophenoxyacetic acid
(2,4-D)

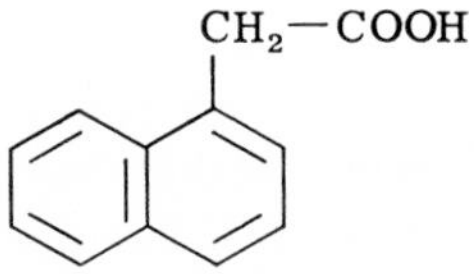

1-Naphthaleneacetic acid
(NAA)

acetic acid (MCPA) by Slade, Templeman, and Sexton (7), by Nutman, Thornton, and Quastel (8), carried out and reported in 1942 and later by Blackman (9) were not published until 1945 because of wartime restrictions but predated the work of Hamner and Tukey by several years.

Koepfli et al. (10), in 1938, on the basis of compounds then known, described certain requirements for auxin action: a ring system as a nucleus with at least one double bond in the ring; a side chain possessing a carboxyl group or a group easily converted into a carboxyl group; at least one carbon atom between the ring and the carboxyl group in the side chain; a particular spatial relationship between the ring system and the carboxyl group. With the introduction of substituted benzoic and phenoxyacetic acids it also seemed necessary to postulate that at least one *ortho* position in the ring must be free. However, a low activity of 2,6-dichlorophenoxyacetic acid in the pea test (11) makes the universality of this requirement questionable. Smith et al. (12) recognized that at least one hydrogen atom on the phenoxyacetic acid side chain is essential for activity. Thus, 2-(2,4-dichlorophenoxy)isobutyric acid is inactive, whereas 2-(2,4-dichlorophenoxy)propionic acid is active and is an effective herbicide with modified selectivity. The discovery by van der Kerk et al. (13) that S-(dimethylthiocarbamyl)thioacetic acid shows appreciable activity throws further doubt on many of these generalizations. Further details on various aspects of the structure-activity relations can be found in a recent review by Wain (14). At present, it would appear that

$$\underset{\text{S-(Dimethylthiocarbamyl)thioacetic acid}}{(CH_3)_2N-\overset{\overset{\text{S}}{\|}}{C}-S-CH_2COOH}$$

except for the substituted benzoic acids all active auxins possess an acetic acid moiety.

In recent years considerable attention has been paid to the cell wall as the primary site of auxin action, since auxin application stimulates cell wall synthesis (15) and increases cell wall plasticity (16). From electron microscope observations it appeared that during wall expansion the cellulose microfibrils did not change their orientation (17). Hence, cell wall expansion could not be caused by the stretching of the cellulose matrix. Attention was then focused on the quantitatively much smaller cell wall component, the pectic fraction, as the matrix-cementing substance. Bennet-Clark (18) first discussed the possible role of polygalacturonic acid chains on cell wall loosening. From physicochemical considerations it appears that the extensibility of the pectic acid component is controlled by the carboxyl group. As long as the carboxyl groups remain free, electrovalent bonds and to a lesser extent hydrogen bonds will provide considerable tensile strength and rigidity to the wall, but when the pectic acid is methylated to pectin there will be reduced tensile strength and greater plasticity. There are several experimental observations which support the pectin hypothesis of cell wall plasticity change. Calcium ions are known to inhibit growth and to cause electrovalent binding of adjacent pectic acid molecules (19). Chelators like ethylenediaminetetraacetic acid (EDTA) not only counteract the effect of added calcium but, for a limited time, resemble auxins as growth regulators (20). IAA has been reported to stimulate the incorporation of the methyl groups of applied methionine into the pectin molecule (21) and to inactivate the pectin methylesterase activity by binding this enzyme to a cell wall fraction (22). Thus, auxins would favor both plasticity, by stimulating the pectin synthesis, and decreased rigidity, by inhibiting the enzymic hydrolysis of pectin to pectic acid. Unfortunately there is no agreement on these hypotheses. The growth response to applied EDTA only superficially resembles a true auxin action (23); moreover, there is controversy about the effect of auxin on the pectin methylesterase activity; it has been reported to stimulate (24) rather than to inhibit this enzyme (22) and to be without effect on the binding of this enzyme to the cell wall (25).

Besides the action on cell wall metabolism, other metabolic effects of auxins have been investigated. The inhibitory effect of auxin on ascorbic acid oxidase activity (*26*) and the consequence of this inhibition on growth rates (*27*) have been the subject of over 20 papers by Marrè and co-workers in Milan. These papers have been critically reviewed (*28*).

2,4-D has recently been shown to have a direct effect on protein retention in detached leaves (*29*). Fully grown leaves, if inserted into water, lose most of their chlorophyll and more than half of their original protein content after a few days. Application of 2, 4-D, kinetin (6-furfurylaminopurine) (*30, 31*), or benzimidazole (*32*) preserves the protein content and the green color.

Auxins have been reported to alter the physical state of the cellular proteins in such a manner as to protect the tissues proteins from heat coagulation (*33*). The physiological significance of this observation must await further experimentation.

For many years it seemed plausible that auxins may form thio esters with coenzyme A (CoA), since nearly all active auxins possess an acetate side chain. Such auxin-CoA thio esters might be expected to affect plant metabolism at sites where acetyl CoA participates as the essential metabolite. There is, in fact, indirect evidence that auxins do form such thio esters in plants. The known β-oxidations of indolebutyric acid (*34*) and 2,4-dichlorophenoxybutyric acid (*35*) undoubtedly, by analogy with animal reactions, involve the intermediary formation of CoA thio ester, as would the observed formation of indoleacetylaspartic acid (*36*). Recently, the synthesis of the CoA thio esters of IAA, 2,4-D, and NAA has been accomplished by Zenk (*37*) using an enzyme preparation from liver mitochondria. While the CoA thio ester of IAA further reacted with glycine, it is of particular interest that the CoA thio ester of 2,4-D did not. There is, however, no evidence that the auxin thio esters participate in growth stimulatory processes, and, indeed, one could imagine that the reverse is the case. In the formation of the auxin thio ester as an intermediate in the continuous synthesis of indoleacetylaspartic acid, it is conceivable that IAA competes for CoA with synthetic processes of growth, and with high concentrations of IAA, growth would thus be inhibited.

Whether auxins stimulate or inhibit growth depends on their concentration and duration of their application. Bonner and Foster (*38*) proposed a scheme which assumes a two-point attachment between the auxin molecule and a specific receptor site within the tissues, giving a growth stimulatory auxin-receptor complex analogous to enzyme-substrate complexes. High concentrations would favor the condition where two auxin molecules become attached to the same receptor site, forming an inactive auxin-receptor-auxin complex. The kinetics of such a system lends itself to thermodynamic treatment, and a theoretical growth curve has been calculated for the *Avena* coleoptile-auxin system. The experimental results reported by Bonner and Foster (*38*) closely fitted the theoretical growth curve, but other workers, using slightly different experimental conditions, were unable to confirm these data (*39*). Even if one assumes that auxins react with a single, rate-limiting site the growth effect which can be measured experimentally requires so many diverse secondary reactions that the experimental conditions become very critical.

In contrast to the growth effects on isolated tissue sections where the action is immediate, the herbicidal effects in intact plants develop gradually and undoubtedly involve many other factors. While the effect of auxin herbicides can be ascribed, in part, to an intensification or prolongation of growth stimuli, death is probably due to the cumulative effects of a general metabolic derangement. Many differences in the chemical composition (carbohydrates, proteins, fats, etc.) of treated tissues have been reported, particularly in long-term experiments or with application of supraoptimal concentrations. These observations have been reviewed in detail (*40–42*). The reported changes are often minor or inconsistent and, taken by themselves, do little to clarify either growth stimulation or herbicidal activity. However, although individually these results are not impressive, combined they indicate a significant difference in the over-all metabolic balance. Since in the case of auxin herbicides, the effects of a single application extend over weeks, relatively small changes may, in time, bring about extreme metabolic derangements leading to the death of the plant. Indeed, a slow, generalized deterioration marks the final phases of 2,4-D treatment, and death cannot be ascribed to the modification of any one specific metabolic mechanism.

B. Inhibitors of Growth Regulator Action

Maleic hydrazide counteracts growth stimulation caused by applied IAA in the slit pea curvature test (*43*). This apparent antiauxin effect conceivably could be caused by lowering of the internal auxin level, since *in vitro* experiments have shown that maleic hydrazide accelerates the enzymic destruction of IAA (*44*). However, direct measurements of the internal auxin level in maleic hydrazide-treated tissues show no significant changes (*45*). It is more probable that maleic hydrazide, by accelerating the IAA loss from bio-assay solutions, curtails the availability of IAA to the tissues. The stimulatory action of maleic hydrazide on IAA oxidase activity is similar to that of certain monohydric phenols (*46*). Although the name maleic hydrazide implies a diketone structure (1,2-dihydropyridazine-3,6-dione), maleic hydrazide in solution exists only as the enol structure [6-hydroxy-3(2H)-pyridazinone] (47). The phenolic nature of maleic hydrazide, is further indicated by the fact that it is conjugated in the plant with sugars (48). Thus, maleic hydrazide resembles a monohydric phenol both in structure and biological activity.

Maleic hydrazide is an interesting growth retardant, since it acts without altering the over-all growth pattern. This type of inhibition stands in striking contrast to the action of the gibberellins, which specifically promote the internodal elongation of treated plants. Whereas maleic

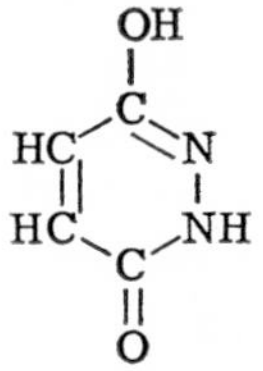

Maleic hydrazide 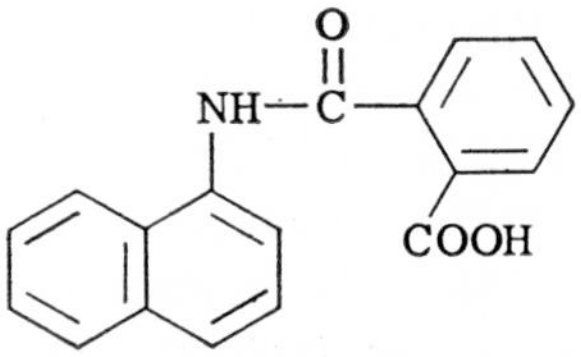   N-1-Naphthylphthalamic acid
                                           (NAP)

$$[(CH_3)_3N^+ - CH_2 - CH_2 - Cl]\ Cl^-$$

N-Trimethyl-2-chloroethylamine chloride

hydrazide overcomes the stimulatory effects of applied gibberellins, gibberellin does not overcome the inhibitory action of applied maleic hydrazide, which makes it difficult to accept maleic hydrazide as an antagonist of endogenous gibberellin (49).

Recently a new compound, N-trimethyl-2-chloroethylamine chloride, has been described as an antigibberellin, since not only does it decrease internodal elongation of intact plants but this inhibition is overcome by applied gibberellin (50).

Antiauxin activity has been ascribed to N-1-naphthylphthalamic acid (NAP), a herbicide which inhibits the geotropic response of roots, a response which is considered to be under auxin control (51).

C. Inhibitors of Cell Division

Since studies on cell elongation were of surprisingly practical benefit, other cellular functions, such as cell division, were investigated in the hope of developing new herbicides acting through other basic processes. Ethyl phenylcarbamate, a known inhibitor of cell division, was subsequently found to have a very desirable phytotoxic selectivity (52). In contrast to the auxin herbicides, grasses were more susceptible than broadleaf plants. Systematic studies of related carbamates led to the introduction of isopropyl *N*-phenylcarbamate (IPC) (*52*) and, later, isopropyl *N*-(3-chlorophenyl)carbamate (CIPC), and 4-chloro-2-butynyl *N*-(3-chlorophenyl)carbamate (barban) as selective herbicides.

Soon after the introduction of maleic hydrazide, this compound became known as an inhibitor of cell division (*53*), and some workers ascribed its action, not only on prolonging dormancy but also on growth retardation, to the inhibition of cell division (*54, 55*). While the phenylcarbamates and maleic hydrazide both interfere with normal mitosis, maleic hydrazide differs from other chromosome-breaking agents in not providing a sticky chromosome surface (*53*).

Isopropyl *N*-phenylcarbamate
(IPC)

4-Chloro-2-butynyl
N-(3-chlorophenyl) carbamate
(barban)

D. Inhibitors of Photosynthesis

Wessel and van der Veen (*56*), working with isolated chloroplasts, were the first to recognize that herbicidal phenylureas, such as 3-(*p*-chlorophenyl)-1,1-dimethylurea (monuron) and 3-(3,4-dichlorophenyl)-1,1-dimethylurea (diuron), are extremely powerful inhibitors of the Hill reaction and provided direct evidence that the phenylureas inhibit the mechanism of photosynthesis. The probable site of action of these herbicides on the Hill reaction has since been identified by two independent approaches. Bishop (*57*) showed that photoreduction by adapted algae, in contrast to photosynthesis, was not inhibited by diuron. Photoreduction differs from photosynthesis in that hydrogen replaces water as the ultimate electron donor; thus, photoreduction utilizes only part of the enzyme systems involved in photosynthesis, since the enzymes for splitting water are not required. Jagendorf (*58*), working with preparations of chloroplasts from higher plants, showed that the formation of ATP, a by-product of the Hill reaction, is not inhibited by monuron if *N*-methylphenazonium ions function as the electron carriers. Later, Krall *et al.* (*59*) found that if *N*-methylphenazonium ions serve as the electron carriers, there is no oxygen production during the Hill reaction; apparently, the reduced *N*-methylphenazonium ions are capable of entirely replacing water as the electron donor in the Hill reaction just as hydrogen replaces water in photoreduction of adapted algae. The results of these studies on the Hill reaction, therefore, fully confirm Bishop's original hypothesis that the mechanism of molecular oxygen production (i.e., the oxidation of water) is blocked by these phenylureas.

Phenylcarbamate herbicides, such as IPC and CIPC, also inhibit the Hill reaction but are much less potent than the phenylureas (*60*), whereas a new class of herbicides consisting of the anilides of aliphatic acids, such as *N*-(3,4-dichlorophenyl)-2-methyl pentanamide (karsil) cause inhibi-

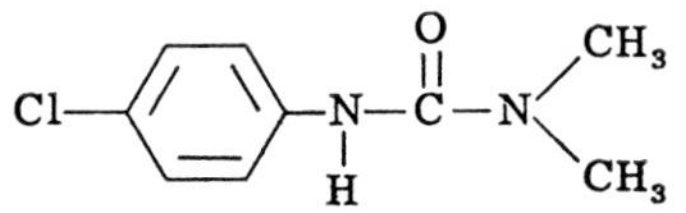

3-(*p*-Chlorophenyl)-1,
1-dimethylurea
(monuron)

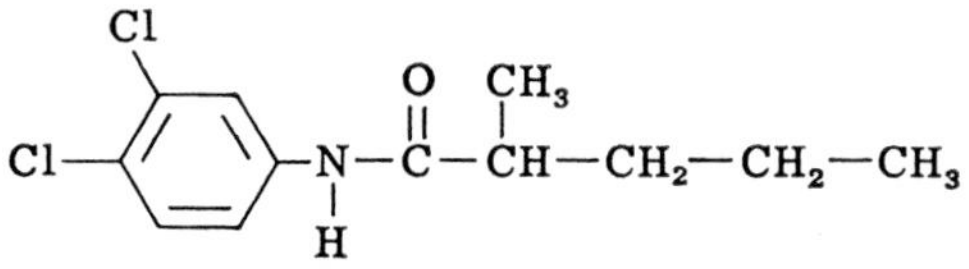

N-(3,4-Dichlorophenyl)-2-methyl
pentanamide
(karsil)

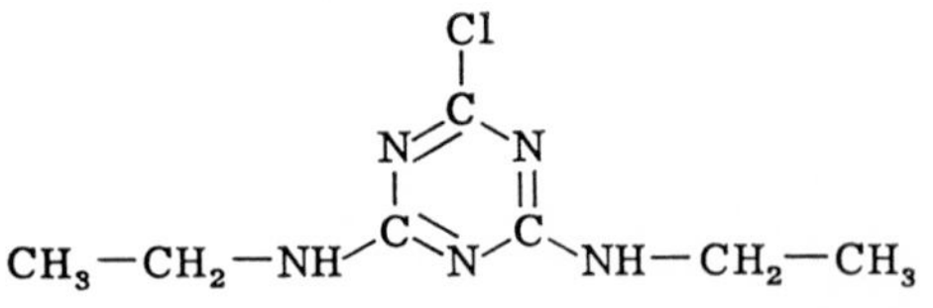

2-Chloro-4,6-bis(ethylamino)-*s*-triazine
(simazin)

tion of oxygen production at similarly low concentrations as diuron. The phenylureas, phenylcarbamates, and acylanilides are structurally related in that they are all anilides. Simazin [2-chloro-4,6-bis(ethylamino)-*s*-triazine] (*61*) and propazin [2-chloro-4,6-bis(isopropylamino)-*s*-triazine] also inhibit photosynthesis by inhibiting the oxygen production (*61a*).

E. Inhibitors of Normal Chloroplast Development

Herbicide application frequently destroys the green color of treated plants but with certain herbicides this is the major symptom. Amitrole (3-amino-1,2,4-triazole) at low concentrations induces chlorosis in young leaves, although the same low concentrations do not affect the chlorophyll content of the mature leaves. Apparently, leaves are highly susceptible at the stage of chloroplast development; if the plastids are not already formed at the time of treatment, the leaves remain permanently chlorotic

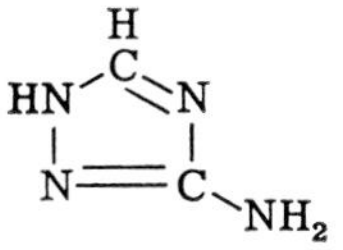

3-Amino-1,2,
4-triazole
(amitrole)

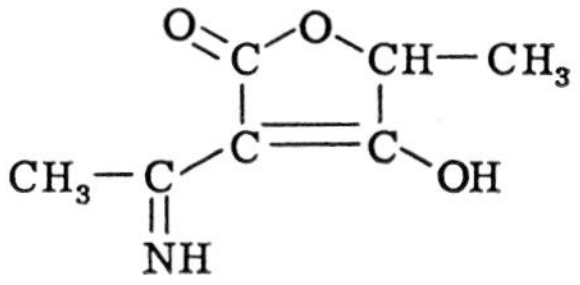

3-(α-Iminoethyl)-
5-methyltetronic acid

(62). The simultaneous application of riboflavin or other flavinoids reverses the amitrole effect, but purines such as adenine or guanine are ineffective (63). Derivatives of tetronic acids, such as 3-(α-iminoethyl)-5-methyltetronic acid also induce chlorosis in treated plants (64), but whether they act on chlorophyll synthesis, chlorophyll destruction, or plastid development is not known.

F. Inhibitors of Metabolic Synthesis

Recent work has shown 2,2-dichloropropionic acid (dalapon), a widely used herbicide, may act as an inhibitor of pantothenic acid synthesis (65), since growth inhibition by dalapon in yeast or in higher plants is reversed by β-alanine or pantothenate application. Pantothenate analogues, in which the hydroxyl group is replaced by chlorine, show the same effects as dalapon (65).

G. Herbicides as Inhibitors of More than a Single Process

It is reasonable to assume that the application of any herbicide would affect more than a single vital process; the most sensitive process, that is, the one which succumbs first or at the lowest inhibitor concentration, is considered the primary site of action. The classification of herbicides as inhibitors of growth, cell division, or photosynthesis is undoubtedly an oversimplification. Carbamates, for instance, were first classified as inhibitors of cell division (52), and only recently was it realized that certain carbamates may also inhibit photosynthesis (60). Amitrole, which is considered primarily an inhibitor of chloroplast synthesis (62), is an inhibitor of catalase activity in animal (66) and plant tissues (62) and an inhibitor of phosphorylase activity in plants (67). At present, opinions are still divided as to whether the primary site of action of maleic hydrazide is inhibition of auxin action (43), inhibition of gibberellin action (49), or inhibition of cell division (54); it has also been reported to inhibit dehydrogenase activity (68) and to interfere with carbohydrate metabolism (69).

The efficacy of a herbicide depends on more than the *in vitro* inhibition of a vital process; successful uptake by the roots or leaves, transport to the site of action, and metabolic stability within the tissue are also essential. Consequently, there is not always a good agreement between tests on isolated systems and tests on intact plants.

In determining what constitutes selective toxicity a better understanding of the uptake and transport mechanisms may be essential. Selectivity between susceptible and resistant species is usually one of degree only and largely depends on the age of the plant. In some cases morphological factors such as depth of root system or position of leaves may explain selectivity. The difference between grasses and broadleaf plants in their sensitivity to 2,4-D was explained, at one time, as a difference in the physical properties of the leaf surface; the spray solution runs off grasses more rapidly than from broadleaf plants, so that the latter remain wetted and in contact with the spray for a much longer period. However, under similar conditions dalapon is toxic to grasses and relatively inocuous to broadleaf plants, and consequently this interpretation of selectivity has become less tenable.

III. METABOLISM OF HERBICIDES BY PLANTS

Herbicides, besides affecting plant metabolism, are themselves metabolized within the plant. Metabolism may lead to the activation of otherwise inactive precursors or to the detoxication of active compounds. Plant species differ in their ability to react with certain herbicides, and in some cases, the observed difference in response of susceptible and resistant plant species coincides with the difference in their metabolic activities. The biochemical mechanisms involved are often quite similar to those already established in animal tissues: the hydrolysis of esters, amides, or nitriles to their corresponding acids; stepwise shortening of fatty acid side chains by β-oxidation; glycoside formation; and conjugation of organic acids with endogenous amino acids.

A. Conversion of Precursors to Active Herbicides

As long ago as 1935 naphthaleneacetonitrile (NAN) was recognized as possessing growth activity resembling that of NAA, and the activity of the nitrile was attributed to its conversion within the tissues to the active free acid (70). In recent years nitrile hydrolysis has been extensively studied. It was found that if oat tissues are incubated in indoleacetonitrile (IAN) solutions, IAA accumulates in amounts which can be detected chemically (71), whereas with pea tissues this is not possible (72). Since the growth of oat and wheat tissues is stimulated by IAN, while the growth of pea tissues is not (73), these results strongly suggest that IAN is not an auxin in its own right but must be converted to IAA for activation. Hydrolysis of IAN may not involve the intermediate formation of the amide, since peas respond to indoleacetamide while wheat does not show as good a growth response to the applied amide as to the nitrile (72). An enzyme, indoleacetonitrilase, has been found in the leaves and stem of barley plants (74). Unlike IAN the 2,4-dichlorophenoxyacetonitrile is hydrolyzed equally well by all plant species (75); the nitriles of 2,4-D and of 2,6-dichlorobenzoic acid (76) are active herbicides. Besides the hydrolyzing mechanism, plants contain a metabolic pathway by which IAN is oxidized to indolecarboxylic acid with the loss of one carbon (75).

The ester herbicides of the 2,4-D type are readily hydrolyzed within the plant to the free acids (77). In practice the esters are widely used, since the free acids form insoluble calcium salts which tend to precipitate from the spray solution. Moreover, the reduced polarity of the esters also increases their lipophilic properties and thus facilitates entry into the tissues. Not all esters are hydrolyzed by higher plants. The esters of chlorophenoxy alcohols, such as sesone (sodium 2,4-dichlorophenoxyethyl sulfate), are not active when applied directly (78). However, in the soil sesone is hydrolyzed by soil organisms to the corresponding alcohol, which is subsequently oxidized to 2,4-D and taken up by the plants through their roots (79).

In an attempt to impart greater selectivity to existing herbicides a number of amino acid derivatives were prepared (80, 81). In general, however, the L- or natural isomers of derivatives such as 2,4-dichlorophenoxy-acetylaspartic acid have activities similar to those of the parent compounds, whereas the D-isomers are not active. An interesting exception is the aspartic acid derivative of IAA, which is not active on pea tissues (*82*).

A successful contrivance by which greater specificity is imparted to auxin herbicides involves β-oxidation of their higher homologues. If a homologous series of dichlorophenoxy acids is examined for auxin or herbicidal activity, it becomes apparent that as the side chain is lengthened the activity alternates with each consecutive member (*83*). Compounds with an even number of carbons in the side chain possess an activity similar to that of 2,4-D, whereas compounds with an odd number of carbons have the same negligible activity as the parent dichlorophenol. While many plants are susceptible to all even-numbered homologues, there are exceptions, such as clover and celery, which are killed only by 2,4-D. These observations led to the development of 2,4-dichlorophenoxy-butyric acid [4-(2,4-DB)] and other phenoxybutyric acids as new herbicides with greater selectivity (*84*).

Some dipyridyl quaternary salts such as diquat (1,1'-ethylene-2,2'-dipyridylium dibromide) have herbicidal properties. All members in this series show a correlation between the redox potential and phytoxicity; apparently they are activated by a reduction process (*85*) in the green tissues. The simultaneous application of monuron, a specific inhibitor of reductions by chloroplasts, delays the onset of diquat symptoms in the light. It has been observed that dipyridyl compounds are reduced by illuminated chloroplasts (*86*). It seems probable, therefore, that photochemical processes are involved in the activation of diquat by reduction, but since diquat is also slightly active in the dark, metabolic reduction must play some part (*87*).

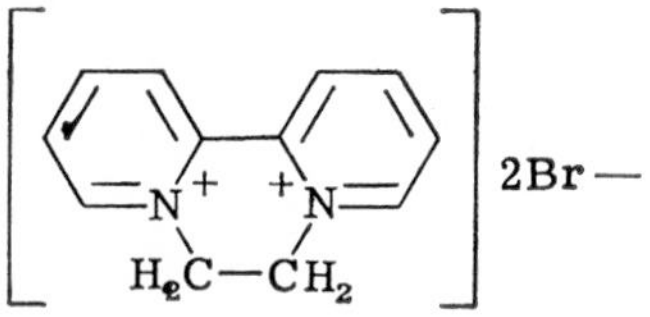

1,1'-Ethylene-2,
2'-dipyridylium dibromide
(diquat)

B. Metabolic Inactivation

The fact that the naturally occurring auxin IAA is not a herbicide, whereas the synthetic auxin analogue 2,4-D is a very effective one, may be due to their different metabolic fates in the plant. Applied IAA disappears very rapidly from the tissues, whereas 2,4-D persists long after its initial application. Two main processes have been found to be involved in IAA metabolism by tissues, namely, oxidative degradation and conjugation with aspartic acid or ammonia (88).[1]

Tissues extracts have long been known to oxidize IAA, and the system involved has been identified as a peroxidase-flavoprotein complex (89). Decarboxylation of the side chain or ring-opening have both been implicated as the initial step (90). In spite of many efforts, the primary products of IAA breakdown are still in doubt. Intact tissues incubated in an IAA solution degrade IAA after a lag period, which is inversely proportional to the concentration applied (91, 92). However, it is not clear as yet how much of this degradation can be attributed to oxidation within the tissues. Because of an inverse relationship between growth rate and IAA oxidase activity, some workers have considered that IAA oxidase plays an important part in regulating the level of endogenous IAA (92), while others consider that IAA oxidase plays little or no part in regulating the level of internal IAA (91, 93).

2,4-D is not attacked by IAA oxidase and is only slowly decarboxylated by tissue segments (94). It has been shown, however, that certain resistant plant tissues, such as the leaves of red currants, decarboxylate 2,4-D more rapidly than leaves of the susceptible black currant species (95), and resistance in the red currants has been ascribed to the ability of the plant to destroy 2,4-D. However, most 2,4-D-resistant plant species have a slow rate of 2,4-D decarboxylation, and another mechanism must account for the 2,4-D resistance of such plants.

Applied IAA accumulates in the tissues mainly as indoleacetylaspartic acid or indoleacetamide,[1] the former primarily in legumes, the latter in cereals (36, 88). It has been reported that IAA is biologically bound to tissue proteins and that it forms a stable complex (96), but this could not be confirmed by the author (91). IAA may accumulate in pea stem tissues if the acid is applied continuously at concentrations high enough to inhibit growth (82); such supraoptimal concentration for growth saturate the mechanism of indoleacetylaspartic acid formation. Removal of such IAA-treated tissues results in the almost quantitative conversion of the accumulated IAA to indoleacetylaspartic acid (82). Since applied indoleacetylaspartic acid does not stimulate or inhibit growth of pea epicotyls, conjugation has been regarded as a detoxication process (82).

2,4-D, unlike IAA, undergoes little conjugation with aspartic acid (34) and, in short term experiments, persists almost entirely as unaltered 2,4-D. In long term experiments, however, 2,4-D does give rise to certain unidentified substances (97–99), one of which could possibly be 2,4-

dichlorophenoxyacetylaspartic acid. Since, however, applied 2,4-dichloro-phenoxyacetylaspartic acid is as effective physiologically as 2,4-D (*80*), this substance could not be regarded as detoxication product.

Conjugation has not yet been demonstrated in plant extracts. However, Zenk (*37*) has synthesized indoleacetylglycine in enzyme preparations from liver mitochondria in the presence of the CoA thio ester of IAA and glycine; under the same conditions the thio ester of 2,4-D does not undergo conjugation.

Conjugation has been noted with a variety of substances, although the physiological significance is not clear. Amitrole is conjugated with alanine in dwarf bean plants (*100*) to a substance which still possesses physiological activity (*101*). Tryptophan application to various plant species results in its conjugation with endogenous malonic acid to malonyltryptophan (*102*). Glycosides of amitrole (*103*), of maleic hydrazide (*48*), and of cinnamic acid (*104*) have been found, but their physiological activity is unknown.

Other metabolic inactivations of herbicides have been observed, but the mechanism is as yet obscure. Corn, for instance, is remarkably resistant to simazin. This compound, although taken up by the plant, cannot be detected in the tissues. It is suggested that the resistance of corn is due to a detoxication mechanism (*42*); and indeed, extracts of corn decompose simazin, whereas extracts of wheat are ineffective. Heating of corn extracts destroys their ability to inactivate simazin (*105*), indicating that an enzymic process is involved.

At present, the main efforts to achieve better plant control are directed toward synthesis and large-scale screening tests of untried chemicals. Sometimes, unexpected compounds may possess surprisingly effective phytotoxic properties. For instance, Zytron [*O*-2,4-dichlorophenyl *O*-methyl isopropylphosphoramidothioate] was originally developed as an insecticide with anticholinesterase activity; as such it was of no practical value. However, for the selective control of crabgrass in lawns Zytron was found to be a valuable herbicide. While at present many effective compounds can still be discovered empirically, progress in the future will depend more and more on a better understanding of the biochemical functions of already known herbicides in plants.

---

[1] *Note added in proof:* The indoleacetamide reported to be found in indoleacetic acid-treated plants (*88*) has since been shown by M. H. Zenk, *Nature* **191**, 493 (1961), to be an artifact formed from indoleacetyl-β-D-glucose.

REFERENCES

1. Terminology Committee Weed Society of America, *Weeds* **8**, 487 (1960).
2. P. B. Marsh and D. R. Goddard, *Am. J. Botany* **26**, 724 (1939).

3. A. J. Haagen-Smit, *Ind. Eng. Chem.* **44**, 1342 (1952).
4. F. Kögl, A. J. Haagen-Smit, and H. Erxleben, *Z. physiol. Chem. Hoppe-Seyler's* **228**, 90 (1934).
5. P. W. Zimmerman and A. E. Hitchcock, *Contribs. Boyce Thompson Inst.* **12**, 321 (1942).
6. C. L. Hamner and H. B. Tukey, *Science* **100**, 154 (1944).
7. R. E. Slade, W. G. Templeman, and W. A. Sexton, *Nature* **155**, 497 (1945).
8. P. S. Nutman, H. G. Thornton, and J. H. Quastel, *Nature* **155**, 498 (1945).
9. G. E. Blackman, *Nature* **155**, 500 (1945).
10. J. B. Koepfli, K. V. Thimann, and F. W. Went, *J. Biol. Chem.* **122**, 763 (1938).
11. K. V. Thimann, *Plant Physiol.* **27**, 392 (1952).
12. M. S. Smith, R. L. Wain, and F. Wightman, *Ann. Appl. Biol.* **39**, 295 (1952).
13. G. J. M. van der Kerk, M. H. van Raalte, A. Kaars Sijpesteijn, and R. van der Veen, *Nature* **176**, 308 (1955).
14. R. L. Wain, *Advances in Pest Control Research* **2**, 263 (1958).
15. J. Bonner, *Proc. Natl. Acad. Sci. U.S.* **19**, 717 (1933).
16. A. N. J. Heyn, *Rec. trav. botan. néerl.* **28**, 113 (1931).
17. A. Frey-Wyssling. *Protoplasma* **25**, 261 (1936).
18. T. A. Bennet-Clark, *in* "The Chemistry and Mode of Action of Plant Growth Substances." (R. L. Wain and F. Wightman, eds.), p. 284. Academic Press, New York, 1956.
19. B. J. Cooil and J. Bonner, *Planta* **48**, 696 (1957).
20. O. V. S. Heath and J. E. Clark, *Nature* **177**, 1118 (1956); **178**, 600 (1956); *J. Exptl. Botany* **11**, 167 (1960).
21. L. Ordin, R. Cleland, and J. Bonner, *Plant Physiol.* **32**, 216 (1957).
22. K. T. Glasziou and S. D. Inglis, *Australian J. Biol. Sci.* **11**, 127 (1958).
23. C. H. Fawcett, R. L. Wain, and F. Wightman, *Nature* **178**, 972 (1956).
24. W. H. Bryan and E. H. Newcomb, *Physiol. Plantarum* **7**, 290 (1954).
25. E. F. Jansen, R. Jang, and J. Bonner, *Plant Physiol.* **35**, 567 (1960).
26. E. Marrè and O. Arrigoni, *Atti accad. nazl. Lincei, Rend., Classe sci. fis. mat. e nat.* **18**, 539 (1955).
27. S. Tonzig and E. Marrè, *Rend. ist. lombardo sci. Pt. I* **89**, 243 (1955).
28. A. W. Galston and W. K. Purvis, *Ann. Rev. Plant Physiol.* **11**, 239 (1960).
29. D. J. Osborne, *Nature* **188**, 240 (1960).
30. A. E. Richmond and A. Lang, *Science* **125**, 650 (1957).
31. K. Mothes, *Naturwissenschaften* **47**, 337 (1960).
32. C. Person, D. J. Samborski, and F. R. Forsyth, *Nature* **180**, 1294 (1957).
33. A. W. Galston and R. Kaur, *Proc. Natl. Acad. Sci. U.S.* **45**, 1587 (1959).
34. W. A. Andreae and N. E. Good, *Plant Physiol.* **32**, 566 (1957).
35. R. L. Wain and F. Wightman, *Proc. Roy. Soc.* **B142**, 525 (1955).
36. W. A. Andreae and N. E. Good, *Plant Physiol.* **30**, 380 (1955).
37. M. H. Zenk, *Z. Naturforsch.* **15b**, 436 (1960).
38. J. Bonner and R. F. Foster, *in* "The Chemistry and Mode of Action of Plant Growth Substances" (R. L. Wain and F. Wightman, eds.), p. 295. Academic Press, New York, 1956.
39. T. A. Bennet-Clark and N. P. Kefford, *J. Exptl. Botany* **5**, 293 (1954).

40. J. Bonner and R. S. Bandurski, *Ann. Rev. Plant Physiol.* 3, 59 (1952).
41. D. J. Wort, *Weeds* 3, 131 (1954).
42. E. K. Woodford, K. Holly, and C. C. McCready, *Ann. Rev. Plant Physiol.* 9, 311 (1958).
43. A. C. Leopold and W. H. Klein, *Physiol. Plantarum* 5, 91 (1952).
44. W. A. Andreae and S. A. Andreae, *Can. J. Botany* 31, 426 (1953).
45. L. J. Audus and R. Thresh, *Ann. Bontany* (*London*) 20, 439 (1956).
46. P. L. Goldacre, A. W. Galston, and R. L. Weintraub, *Arch. Biochem. Biophys.* 43, 358 (1953).
47. D. M. Miller and R. W. White, *Can. J. Chem.* 34, 1510 (1956).
48. G. H. N. Towers, A. Hutchinson, and W. A. Andreae, *Nature* 181, 1535 (1958).
49. P. W. Brian and H. G. Hemming, *Ann. Appl. Biol.* 45, 489 (1957).
50. N. E. Tolbert, *J. Biol. Chem.* 235, 475 (1960); *Plant Physiol.* 35, 380 (1960).
51. R. L. Jones, T. P. Metcalfe, and W. A. Sexton, *J. Sci. Food Agr.* 5, 32 (1954).
52. W. G. Templeman and W. A. Sexton, *Nature* 156, 630 (1945).
53. C. D. Darlington and J. McLeish, *Nature* 167, 407 (1951).
54. V. A. Greulach and J. G. Haesloop, *Am. J. Botany* 41, 44 (1954).
55. A. H. Haber and J. D. White, *Plant Physiol.* 35, 495 (1960).
56. J. S. C. Wessels and R. van der Veen, *Biochim. et Biophys. Acta* 19, 548 (1956).
57. N. I. Bishop, *Biochim. et Biophys. Acta* 27, 205 (1958).
58. A. T. Jagendorf, *Brookhaven Symposia in Biol.* 11, 236 (1958).
59. A. R. Krall, N. E. Good, and B. C. Mayne, *Plant Physiol.* 36, 44 (1961).
60. D. E. Moreland and K. L. Hill, *J. Agr. Food Chem.* 7, 832 (1959).
61. D. E. Moreland, W. A. Gentner, J. L. Hilton, and K. L. Hill, *Plant Physiol.* 34, 432 (1959).
61a. N. E. Good, *Plant Physiol.* 36, 788 (1961).
62. H. T. Pyfrom, D. Appleman, and W. G. Heim, *Plant Physiol.* 32, 674 (1957).
63. K. A. Sund, E. C. Putala, and H. N. Little, *J. Agr. Food Chem.* 8, 210 (1960).
64. J. Alamercery, C. L. Hamner, and M. Latus, *Nature* 168, 85 (1951).
65. J. L. Hilton, L. L. Jansen, and A. W. Gentner, *Plant Physiol.* 33, 43 (1958); *Weeds* 7, 381 (1959).
66. W. G. Heim, D. Appleman, and H. T. Pyfrom, *Am. J. Physiol.* 186, 19 (1956).
67. A. G. Gentile and J. E. Frederick, *Physiol. Plantarum* 12, 862 (1959).
68. F. M. R. Isenberg, C. O. Jensen, and M. L. Odland, *Science* 120, 464 (1954).
69. A. W. Naylor, *Arch. Biochem. Biophys.* 33, 340 (1951).
70. P. W. Zimmerman and F. Wilcoxon, *Contribs. Boyce Thompson Inst.* 7, 209 (1935).
71. B. B. Stowe and K. V. Thimann, *Arch. Biochem. Biophys.* 51, 499 (1954).
72. C. H. Fawcett, R. L. Wain, and F. Wightman, *Proc. Roy. Soc.* B152, 231 (1960).

73. E. R. H. Jones, H. B. Henbest, G. F. Smith, and J. A. Bentley, *Nature* **169**, 485 (1952).
74. K. V. Thimann and S. Mahadevan, *Nature* **181**, 1466 (1958).
75. C. H. Fawcett, R. C. Seeley, H. F. Taylor, R. L. Wain, and F. Wightman, *Nature* **167**, 1026 (1955).
76. H. Koopman and J. Daams, *Nature* **186**, 89 (1960).
77. A. S. Crafts, *Weeds* **8**, 19 (1960).
78. A. J. Vlitos, *Contribs. Boyce Thompson Inst.* **17**, 127 (1953).
79. L. J. Audus, *Nature* **171**, 523 (1953).
80. J. W. Wood and T. D. Fontaine, *J. Org. Chem.* **17**, 891 (1952).
81. C. F. Krewson, E. J. Saggese, and T. F. Drake. *Weeds* **8**, 107 (1960); *J. Agr. Food Chem.* **8**, 104 (1960).
82. W. A. Andreae and M. W. H. van Ysselstein, *Plant Physiol.* **31**, 235 (1956).
83. C. H. Fawcett, J. M. A. Ingram, and R. L. Wain, *Proc. Roy Soc.* **B142**, 60 (1954).
84. R. L. Wain, *Ann. Appl. Biol.* **42**, 151 (1955).
85. R. F. Homer, G. C. Mees, and T. E. Tomlinson, *J. Sci. Food Agr.* **11**, 309 (1960).
86. N. E. Good and R. Hill, *Arch Biochem. Biophys.* **57**, 355 (1955).
87. G. C. Mees, *Ann. Appl. Biol.* **48**, 601 (1960).
88. N. E. Good, W. A. Andreae, and M. W. H. van Ysselstein, *Plant Physiol.* **31**, 231 (1956).
89. A. W. Galston, J. Bonner, and R. S. Baker, *Arch. Biochem. Biophys.* **42**, 456 (1953).
90. P. M. Ray, *Ann. Rev. Plant Physiol.* **9**, 81 (1958).
91. W. A. Andreae and M. W. H. van Ysselstein, *Plant Physiol.* **35**, 225 (1960).
92. W. A. Galston and L. Y. Dalberg, *Am. J. Botany* **41**, 373 (1954).
93. W. R. Briggs, T. A. Steeves, I. M. Sussex, and R. H. Wetmore, *Plant Physiol.* **30**, 148 (1955).
94. R. L. Weintraub, J. N. Yeatman, J. A. Lockhard, J. H. Reinhart, and M. Fields, *Arch. Biochem. Biophys.* **40**, 277 (1952).
95. L. C. Luckwill and C. P. Lloyd-Jones, *Ann. Appl. Biol.* **48**, 613 (1960).
96. S. M. Siegel and A. W. Galston, *Proc. Natl. Acad. Sci. U.S.* **39**, 1111 (1953).
97. R. W. Holley, *Arch. Biochem.* **35**, 171 (1952).
98. E. G. Jaworski and J. J. Butts, *Arch. Biochem.* **38**, 207 (1952).
99. S. C. Fang and J. S. Butts, *Plant Physiol.* **29**, 56 (1954).
100. P. Massini, *Biochim. et Biophys. Acta* **36**, 548 (1959).
101. D. Racusen, *Arch. Biochem. Biophys.* **74**, 106 (1958).
102. N. E. Good and W. A. Andreae, *Plant Physiol.* **32**, 561 (1957).
103. A. C. Gentile and J. E. Frederick, *Physiol. Plantarum* **12**, 862 (1959).
104. P. N. Avadhani and G. H. N. Towers, *Can. J. Biochem. Physiol.* **39**, 1605 (1961).
105. W. Roth. *Compt. rend. acad. sci.* **245**, 942 (1957).

CHAPTER 27

Fungicides as Metabolic Inhibitors

Saul Rich and James G. Horsfall

I. INTRODUCTION

In common with most other toxicants, fungicides have come in for their share of research as metabolic inhibitors. And by the same token, most of the research has been done with working fungicides—those whose dramatic performance in disease control has attracted attention to their possible mode of action.

As far as we know, no working fungicide has been developed from a known antimetabolite. We might as well note, too, that despite a large array of data on metabolism, we have few or, perhaps, no cases where the whole of the activity of a working fungicide can be ascribed to a specific metabolic inhibition.

Metabolic inhibitors usually interact directly with metabolites or enzymes, or compete with metabolites. They may act also as physical toxicants by destroying the integrity of cellular structures, without which the orderly sequence of vital processes cannot proceed. The various pathways to metabolic inhibition are not mutually exclusive. We shall see that many individual fungicides inhibit metabolism in more than one way or at more than one stage in the metabolic sequence. The action of the successful fungicide, then, may be better compared to a shotgun blast than to a single shot from a sniping rifle. This is a major difference between most fungicides and other useful metabolic inhibitors, such as medical chemotherapeutants. The differences arise from the manner in which fungicides are sought. Medically useful compounds are screened for use on one species, man, and against a limited number of pathogens. Fungicides, however, must work on many kinds of plants or materials, against a wide range of fungi. This is a broad-spectrum action not common in medicine.

The discussion will be divided into sections devoted to the broad groups of fungicides, what they do to metabolism, and how they are presumed to do it.

Because of limited space, we will not attempt to give exhaustive reviews of the literature, but rather discuss pertinent research. Expanded literature reviews may be found in Horsfall (*1*), Rich (*2*), and Sisler and Cox (*3*).

II. INORGANIC FUNGICIDES

A. Metals

Copper in Bordeaux mixture is the best known metallic fungicide. It is not, however, the most toxic of metallic cations, being exceeded by both silver and mercury (*1*).

In spite of extensive research, argument still rages as to the properties of metallic cations that make them poisonous. Through most modern theories, however, runs the common theme that the toxicity of metallic cations is related to the stability of the bonding between the metals and reactive groups within the cell. Horsfall (*1*) correlated the toxicity of the various metals with the stability of their metal chelates, Shaw (*4*) with the insolubility of the metal sulfides, and Danielli and Davis (*5*) and Somers (*6*) with the electronegativity of the metal ion.

When metallic ions react with important cellular groups, the reaction may not be a simple substitution. Metals may break disulfide bonds, as in the reduction of cystine to cysteine, with the subsequent formation of mercaptides (*7, 8*). The opposite is also true. Metallic ions may aid formation of disulfide bonds; for example, cupric ions react with cystine to give cuprous cysteinate and cystine (*9*).

How do metallic ions affect enzyme systems *in vitro*? Owens (*10*) tested a series of metallic cations against four separate enzymes considered to be amino-dependent, sulfhydryl-dependent, iron-dependent, and copper-dependent. Mercury inhibits all four enzymes. This is expected, as mercury forms strong bonds with both sulfhydryl and amino groups and denatures proteins. Copper inhibits the amino- and sulfhydryl-dependent enzymes but has no effect on the metal-dependent enzymes. Copper should have replaced the iron in the iron-dependent enzyme, but did not appear to do so in Owens' studies. Zinc presumably has a particular affinity for the amino-dependent enzyme and inhibits it, but not the others. Iron has little effect on any of the four enzymes. Presumably, iron cannot form sufficiently strong bonds with amino or sulfhydryl groups to inhibit enzymes dependent upon them; nor would iron be expected to displace copper in the copper-dependent enzyme.

Byrde *et al.* (*11*) reported that cupric ion inhibits a number of sulfhydryl-dependent enzymes isolated from *Sclerotinia laxa*. Here again cupric ion showed little or no inhibition of iron-dependent enzymes.

Now for the effect of metals on the living fungus. McCallan *et al.* (*12*) found that in every species they tried spore germination is more sensitive to metal poisoning than is spore respiration. The differences, however, are small for silver, mercury, or copper. Greater differences in sensitivity of respiration and germination showed up in a number of fungi when their spores were treated with cadmium or zinc. The spore germination of some fungi is 10–500 times more sensitive to cadmium and zinc than is their respiration.

A surprising effect was the actual stimulation of *Neurospora* spore respiration by sublethal doses of silver. This effect is probably caused by the increased permeability of silver-treated spores, allowing easier entrance of metabolites.

McCallan and Miller (*13*) found that the mycelial respiration of some fungi is more sensitive to metal poisoning than is mycelial viability. In most cases the two functions are about equally sensitive. Respiration of mycelium is usually more sensitive to metal poisoning than is the respiration of spores. The opposite appears to be true for viability. Spore germination is usually more readily poisoned by metals than is mycelial growth.

It appears, then, that the more potent metallic ions—silver, mercury, and copper—usually inhibit both spore germination and spore respiration. The exception is copper sulfate, which is an effective poison for the germination of *Aspergillus* spores but has practically no effect on their respiration. The less potent metallic ions—cadmium, zinc, and cerium—often inhibit spore germination with little or no effect on spore respiration.

Some metallic ions, such as silver, destroy the integrity of semipermeable membranes, allowing metabolites to leak out (14).

Recently, Siegel and Crossan (15) studied the effect of sublethal doses of copper sulfate on the mycelial metabolism of the fungus Colletotrichum capsici. Copper cations inhibit both exogenous and endogenous respiration, and reduce both the reserve sugars and the free amino acids. Copper has very little effect on the bound amino acids of the fungus, except to increase the amount of valine and tyrosine.

Metallic ions can change fungus morphology without appreciably reducing growth. Nickerson and van Rij (16) converted a budding strain of bakers' yeast and changed a mycelial strain into a budding strain by feeding it cysteine. Nickerson and van Rij proposed that the cell wall of the yeast contains reducible disulfide bonds which control cell division. When the disulfide bonds are reduced, either enzymically or chemically, the yeast buds. When the sulfhydryl sites of the budding yeast are blocked by cobaltous ions or penicillin, the yeast becomes mycelial. Nickerson and Falcone (17) actually demonstrated the presence of reducible disulfide bonds in cell wall protein of bakers' yeast.

Surprisingly, copper does not give the cobalt effect (16); this in spite of the greater avidity of copper for sulfhydryl groups and the greater insolubility of the copper mercaptides. The answer may be that copper ion may not get into the cell fast enough to do its work. Cobaltous ion is very rapidly accumulated by yeast cells, even though it is not essential to their growth (18).

Metallic fungicides do act as metabolic inhibitors. They can inhibit respiration and growth. In some cases, e.g., cobalt on yeast, they can stop cellular division without stopping growth. Sulfhydryl-dependent enzymes are usually inhibited by metallic fungicides. But inhibition by metallic cations is not limited to sulfhydryl-dependent enzymes, e.g., mercuric ion inhibits catalase and polyphenol oxidase. Here, the effect may be protein denaturation, rather than the binding of active sulfhydryl groups. Other possible toxic mechanisms of metallic ions are: (a) ion antagonism; (b) displacement of a metal essential to the activity of an enzyme; and (c) the formation of a poisonous organometallic complex with free cellular or extracellular constituents.

B. Nonmetals

The only important inorganic, nonmetallic fungicide is sulfur. It is used either in its elemental form or as lime-sulfur, a mixture of calcium polysulfides.

Sulfur in the form of lime-sulfur inhibits fungal enzymes *in vitro*. Byrde *et al.* *(11)* tested the effect of lime-sulfur on enzymes from *S. laxa*. Lime-sulfur strongly inhibits the iron-dependent enzymes, but surprisingly, has no effect on the copper-enzyme polyphenol oxidase. Elemental sulfur slightly inhibits metal-dependent enzymes *in vitro* *(10)*.

How does sulfur affect fungal metabolism? According to McCallan and Miller *(19)*, sulfur added to spores in air with exogenous glucose depresses oxygen uptake for 3–6 hours. The inhibition of oxygen uptake is concomitant with H_2S production. After H_2S production diminishes, there is a great burst of oxygen uptake and a subsequent drop to the level of the untreated spores. We interpret this to mean that sulfur first knocks out the aerobic respiration, perhaps by inhibiting cytochrome c. Meanwhile the anaerobic cycle continues to produce pyruvate or a similar substrate, which piles up. Then, as the H_2S production drops, the aerobic system revives. The accumulated substrate from the anaerobic system fuels the revived aerobic system to produce the burst of oxygen uptake. As the accumulated substrate is used up, the oxygen uptake declines to that of the untreated spores.

Sulfur stimulates endogenous respiration. Total oxygen uptake of treated spores over a 12-hour period is about twice that of untreated spores *(19)*. Analogous to this is the effect of 2,4-dinitrophenol (DNP) on yeast *(20)*. In untreated yeast, under anaerobic conditions, endogenous CO_2 production is very low. DNP treatment apparently stimulates mobilization of reserves, stimulating evolution of CO_2, and causes additional ethanol production. Fungi treated with sulfur under anaerobic conditions and without glucose evolve additional CO_2 concomitant with H_2S production *(19)*.

In *Neurospora sitophila* conidia, colloidal sulfur, Na_2S and Na_2S_x prevent the production of citrate from exogenous acetate, and cause succinate to increase, indicating a "blockage of enzymes in the pathway between acetate and citrate and at least partial inhibition of the succinoxidase system" *(21)*.

The action of sulfur *in vivo* may well be different from its effect on enzymes *in vitro*. Sulfur prevents the darkening of the mycelial pellets of *Alternaria oleracea* *(19)*. This indicates inhibition of polyphenol oxidase and contrasts with the earlier statement that sulfur and lime-sulfur have little effect on polyphenol oxidase *in vitro* *(10, 11)*. It may be that the H_2S produced from sulfur by the living fungus is the actual inhibitor of polyphenol oxidase. H_2S would not be produced from sulfur mixed with purified polyphenol oxidase *in vitro*.

The role that H_2S production plays in the fungitoxicity of sulfur is one of the most intriguing problems in fungicide research. McCallan and Wilcoxon (*22*) concluded that H_2S production is definitely related to sulfur fungitoxicity. Their sulfur-sensitive fungi produced more than a self-poisoning amount of H_2S from sulfur. Their sulfur-resistant fungi did not.

Later, Miller *et al.* (*23*) took another look at the problem and decided "that the role of hydrogen sulfide in the toxic action of sulfur to fungus spores may have been previously exaggerated." This conclusion was based on the following: (*a*) colloidal sulfur is usually much more toxic than H_2S; (*b*) *Cephalosporium acremonium*, which is "especially resistant," produces 10 times as much H_2S as does the sulfur-sensitive *Monilinia fructicola*; (*c*) *M. fructicola* spores are killed after evolving 0.28 mg of H_2S from sulfur, while an equal weight of *Aspergillus niger* spores germinated 97% after giving off 0.23 mg of H_2S.

As an alternative to the "toxic H_2S" theory, Miller *et al.* proposed that "sulfur may exert its effect through its action as a hydrogen acceptor and therefore its interference in the normal dehydrogenation and hydrogenation reactions."

It appears to us, however, that the data used to unseat the H_2S theory also unseats the substitute theory. If the amount of H_2S produced is a measure of the activity of sulfur as a hydrogen acceptor, then those spores which produce the most H_2S should be the most severely damaged. This, of course, is not so.

Owens (*21*) suggested that free radicals of sulfur are formed in sulfur-polysulfide-H_2S conversions and that it is these highly reactive, free radicals which are the toxicant. But again, the same contradiction arises. Those species that most actively produce H_2S should most actively produce free radicals and be most readily poisoned by sulfur. As before, this is not so.

Perhaps the best way to resolve this question is to look at sulfur toxicity from the point of view of the fungus. Whether or not a fungus spore will be poisoned by a unit dose of sulfur depends on two things: first, the total number of vulnerable, vital sites within the fungus and, second, the amount of the dose which penetrates to these sites. For example, a spore which is inhibited when only 10 vital, vulnerable sites are attacked is much more susceptible to poisoning than a spore that requires the blocking of 1000 sites before it is inhibited. In other words, the more cellular sites competing for a toxicant, the less toxicant is available at each site. If some sites bind the toxicant without injury to the cell, an even smaller amount is available for toxic action. Further, given two species both requiring 1000 sites to be blocked, one may be much less permeable to the poison and may, therefore, be considered more resistant.

Let us now go back to the data of Miller *et al.* (*23*). Sulfur-resistant *C. acremonium* spores produce 10 times as much H_2S from sulfur as does the same weight of sulfur-sensitive spores of *M. fructicola*. However, a unit weight of *C. acremonium* spores contains 150 times as many spores as the same weight of *M. fructicola* spores. Therefore, each *M. fructicola* spore is attacked by 15 times as much H_2S as is each *C. acremonium* spore. As toxicity is measured by the response of individual spores, the production of H_2S from sulfur may well be correlated with the fungitoxicity of sulfur.

Now, how about the amount of sulfur entering the spore? Miller *et al.* emphasized that sulfur-resistant spores such as those of *Stemphylium sarcinaeforme* absorb sulfur poorly and thus produce much less H_2S than do the more susceptible species.

Again, correlating sulfur sensitivity with H_2S production does not help us decide which of the three theories of sulfur action is correct. Perhaps all three are equally important to the fungitoxicity of sulfur.

The production of H_2S from sulfur by fungus spores is, then, the most prominent interaction between sulfur and spores, but it may or may not be directly related to sulfur toxicity. One point seems to be evident. The production of H_2S appears to be closely geared to spore germination. Miller *et al.* reported that ground up spores produce no H_2S from sulfur and that only viable spores can reduce sulfur to H_2S. Spores treated with toxic amounts of sulfur or other fungicides lose their ability to evolve H_2S from sulfur as they lose their germinability. Still, McCallan and Miller (*19*) found that spores may produce H_2S from sulfur anaerobically, and fungus spores do not germinate without oxygen.

III. ORGANIC FUNGICIDES

A. Dithiocarbamates

Derivatives of dithiocarbamic acid are the most widely used of the organic fungicides, and thus their ability to inhibit metabolism has been intensively studied.

There are two groups: the dialkyldithiocarbamate, or DDC group, and the ethylenebisdithiocarbamates, based on the disodium salt. As disodium ethylenebis(dithiocarbamate) is called nabam, we shall refer to the ethylenebisdithiocarbamates as the nabam group.

1. DDC GROUP

The DDC fungicides are made by allowing dialkylamines to react with CS_2. The most successful of the DDC fungicides are those derived from the dimethylamine. These are sodium dimethyldithiocarbamate or NaDDC (I) and its ferric and zinc salts, ferbam and ziram. Also in this group is tetramethylthiuram disulfide, or thiram (II), the oxidation product of NaDDC.

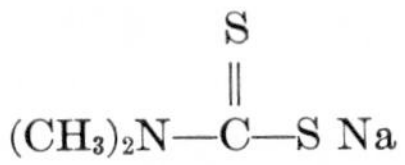

$$(CH_3)_2N—\overset{\overset{\textstyle S}{\|}}{C}—S\ Na \qquad\qquad (CH_3)_2N—\overset{\overset{\textstyle S}{\|}}{C}—S—S—\overset{\overset{\textstyle S}{\|}}{C}—N(CH_3)_2$$

(I) 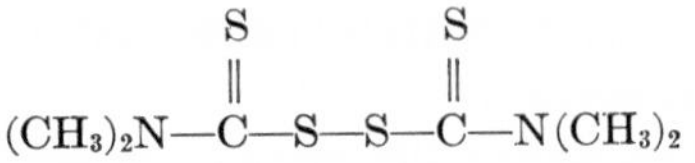   (II)

According to Klöpping (24), growth of A. niger and Penicillium italicum is affected by $\frac{1}{25}$ to $\frac{1}{100}$ of the dosage of NaDDC that will affect respiration. He concluded that the DDC types as well as the nabam types "most probably act by interfering with certain assimilatory processes."

Klöpping attributed the toxicity of the DDC group to the dithiocarbamate ions because depressing ionization depresses fungitoxicity and enhancing it increases fungitoxicity.

DDC fungicides can inhibit enzymes dependent for activity on amino groups, on sulfhydryl groups, or on iron and copper (10). Chefurka (25) demonstrated that DDC fungicides strongly inhibit the sulfhydryl-dependent enzymes glucose-6-phosphate dehydrogenase and 6-phosphogluconate dehydrogenase, isolated from houseflies, and that the inhibition could be partly alleviated by the addition of cysteine. From this he concluded that DDC fungicides act on sulfhydryl-dependent enzymes of the aerobic hexose monophosphate oxidation pathway of carbohydrate metabolism.

Sisler and Cox (26) also thought that DDC compounds inactivate sulfhydryl enzymes, because (a) thiram inhibits fermentation by yeast of glucose, fructose-1,6-diphosphate, and glyceraldehyde-3-phosphate, and (b) the inhibition is alleviated by cysteine, glutathione, and diphosphopyridine nucleotide (DPN). They concluded that thiram inhibits triosephosphate dehydrogenase. They presumed that the sulfhydryl compounds change thiram to a less active form and that DPN protects from oxidation the sulfhydryl groups necessary for the activity of triosephosphate dehydrogenase.

In Fusarium roseum, ziram inhibits synthetic processes that use up a-ketoglutarate, without inhibiting the glucose oxidation cycle that manufactures keto acids (27).

Owens (28) noted a correlation between the ability of DDC fungicides to inhibit polyphenol oxidase *in vitro* and their toxicity to *A. niger*. He could demonstrate no correlation using *Botrytis cinerea*, *P. italicum*, and *Rhizopus nigricans*. As DDC compounds are powerful chelators, Owens suggested that metal inactivation may be a principal toxic mechanism of DDC fungicides against some fungi but not others. Metal inactivation as a toxic mechanism for DDC fungicides had been proposed earlier by Horsfall (29).

One of the most interesting peculiarities of the DDC group is the bimodal dosage response curves first reported by Dimond *et al.* (30). They found that toxicity of thiram to spores of *S. sarcinaeforme* increases as expected with increasing dosage up to a certain concentration. Then, surprisingly, more and more thiram becomes *less and less* toxic. Further increases in thiram dosage beyond this inversion point are again increasingly toxic. The bimodal dosage response to DDC fungicides was later found for *Venturia inaequalis* (31), *A. niger* (32), and yeast (33).

The currently accepted theory for the bimodal response is that of Goksøyr (33), who worked with yeast. He theorized that NaDDC forms two types of chelates with the cupric ions in the growth medium. At the lower concentrations of NaDDC there is insufficient DDC ion to fully satisfy the bivalent cupric ions in the medium; hence, a copper-DDC half-chelate is formed: $Cu(DDC)^+$. This, Goksøyr concluded, is extremely toxic. With the addition of more NaDDC, the $Cu(DDC)^+$ becomes saturated to form the extremely stable full chelate $Cu(DDC)_2$. The full chelate is relatively nontoxic, and its formation at the expense of the half-chelate accounts for the dip in toxicity. More NaDDC after the complete chelation of the cupric ions allows the formation of the zinc, manganese, and iron dithiocarbamates. It is the build-up of the latter metal-DDC complexes that produces the second rise in toxicity. Goksøyr detected the presence of the various DDC-metal complexes spectrophotometrically.

From his enzyme inhibition studies (34), Goksøyr concluded that DDC compounds do not inhibit respiration by blocking ATP. Instead, he felt that the main injury to respiration is due to inhibition of succinic dehydrogenase.

The mechanism of action of the DDC fungicides has also been investigated at van der Kerk's laboratory in Utrecht. The results of this work are summarized by Kaars Sijpesteijn and Janssen (35).

They classified their test fungi into three groups, according to their sensitivity to NaDDC. The growth of the first, or "sensitive," group is inhibited by about 0.2 ppm of NaDDC. This group of organisms, which includes *Glomerella cingulata,* does not show a bimodal response to NaDDC, but remains inhibited by any larger dose of NaDDC.

The second group of fungi shows a "first zone of inhibition" at 0.5–2 ppm of NaDDC; then a "zone of inversion growth" as growth resumes at 5, 10, or 20 ppm of NaDDC; and a "second zone of inhibition" as the concentration of the fungicide exceeds 50 ppm. This group includes *A. niger.*

The third, or "insensitive," group is inhibited only when the concentration exceeds about 50 ppm of NaDDC. *Fusarium oxysporum* is an example of this group.

NaDDC fungitoxicity can be alleviated by histidine and other imidazole derivatives only when the concentration of NaDDC did not exceed 50 ppm. From this the authors suggested that the toxic mechanism of low concentrations of NaDDC differs from that of higher concentrations of NaDDC.

Kaars Sijpesteijn and Janssen explained their results as follows. The first, or "sensitive," group is sensitive to both $Cu(DDC)^+$ and to $Cu(DDC)_2$. Hence, no inversion growth with *G. cingulata.* The second group of fungi is sensitive to $Cu(DDC)^+$ but not to $Cu(DDC)_2$. *A. niger,* therefore, is not poisoned by the higher concentrations of NaDDC which combine with $Cu(DDC)^+$ to give $Cu(DDC)_2$. This produces the zone of inversion growth. The third or "insensitive" group of fungi is not poisoned by either form of copper-DDC chelate. The "insensitive" fungi are poisoned only when all the metals in the growth medium are chelated, and free DDC^- ions appear. Free DDC^- ions are toxic to all three groups of fungi, as they are all poisoned by concentrations of NaDDC exceeding 50 ppm. These authors emphasized the importance of free DDC^- ions in the second zone of inhibition. In this respect, they differ from Gøksøyr *(33),* who believed that the zinc-, manganese-, and iron-DDC chelates are the poisons in the second zone of inhibition. Kaars Sijpesteijn and Janssen supported their own view with the evidence that other metal-binding compounds, such as histidine, reverse toxicity in the first zone of inhibition but not in the second zone of inhibition. They take this to mean that metal chelates are involved in the first zone but *not* in the second zone.

Kaars Sijpesteijn and Janssen concluded from their own work and that of others that DDC fungicides inhibit enzymes having essential dithiol groups. They proposed that the enzymes inhibited are those that require dihydrolipoic acid as a coenzyme.

Owens *(21)* analyzed organic acids in the conidia of *N. sitophila* treated with various fungicides. He found that thiram and ferbam, like elemental sulfur, appears to inhibit at least one enzyme needed to form citrate from acetate. Ziram, however, does not have this effect. Instead, it inhibits metabolism of pyruvate and a-ketoglutarate. Owens concluded that the toxicity of elemental sulfur, thiram, and ferbam are related to the ability of these compounds to produce free radicals. The ziram effect is different, he argued, because ziram cannot produce free radicals. Owens also suggested that the ziram effect may result from the inactivation of aconitase. The essential iron of aconitase could be removed by ziram. The more stable iron-DDC chelate would form by taking the iron from aconitase and replacing it with zinc.

The DDC fungicides, then, may inhibit metabolism in at least two ways. They may inactivate sulfhydryl-dependent enzymes, such as dehydrogenases; or they may bind metals essential to such enzymes as polyphenol oxidase or aconitase.

2. NABAM GROUP

Dimond et al. (36) first reported the fungitoxicity of nabam (III). They noted particularly that when a thin film of the water-soluble nabam dries, the resulting fungitoxic residue has "tenacity." In other words the water-soluble nabam leaves a water-insoluble toxic residue when dried.

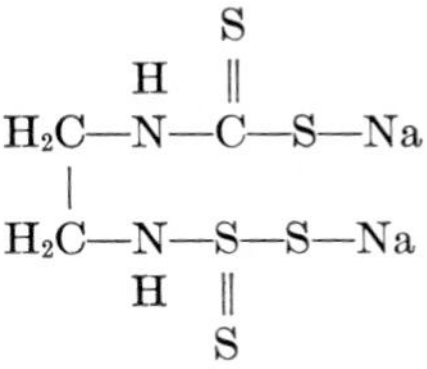

$$
\begin{array}{c}
\text{S} \\
\text{H} \quad \| \\
\text{H}_2\text{C--N--C--S--Na} \\
| \\
\text{H}_2\text{C--N--S--S--Na} \\
\text{H} \quad \| \\
\text{S}
\end{array}
$$

(III)

Barratt and Horsfall (37), speculating about the toxic mechanism of nabam, suggested that it might act as a metal binder or possibly by releasing toxic H_2S. Barratt and Horsfall mentioned the possibility of nabam breaking down to diisothiocyanate but concluded that the latter is too unstable to be a likely possibility. Significantly, they also reported that dry spray deposits of zineb, the zinc ethylenebis(dithiocarbamate), becomes more fungitoxic with age. They presumed that this increased potency "is due to the gradual formation in the spray deposit of a more toxic derivative."

That nabam fungicides act by releasing toxic H_2S was shown to be untenable by Rich and Horsfall (38).

Meanwhile, Klöpping (24) proposed that nabam fungicides actually are toxic because they oxidize to diisothiocyanate. His argument is based on three observations. First, the comparative sensitivity of the four fungi he used is approximately the same for nabam fungicides and for diisothiocyanates. This comparative sensitivity he called the "biological spectrum." Second, the four fungi are much more sensitive to diisothiocyanates than they are to the parent nabam fungicides. Third, nabam fungicides can be oxidized to give corresponding diisothiocyanates.

The biological spectrum for the nabam fungicides is distinct from that of the DDC fungicides. Klöpping therefore concluded that the toxic mechanisms of the two groups of fungicides are also distinct. .

Ludwig and Thorn (39) aerated large batches of commercial nabam and found that this treatment increased fungitoxicity. As the aerated solution became more toxic, nabam disappeared and was replaced by a new fungitoxic material which was identified as ethylenethiuram monosulfide, so-called ETM. Ludwig and Thorn concluded that the fungitoxicity as well as tenacity of nabam fungicides is caused by their oxidation to ETM. Later, Ludwig et al. (40) demonstrated that metallic ions catalyze the formation of isothiocyanates from ETM. This they could detect only in a nonaqueous medium (chloroform). Ludwig and Thorn (41) also found that trace amounts of managanese catalyze the oxidation of nabam to ETM.

What do the metabolic studies tell us about the relation between nabam fungicides and isothiocyanates? As Klöpping (24) also tested metabolic effects of these fungicides, we should begin with his work. He studied their effect on the O_2 uptake of A. niger. For our purpose, his two most significant experiments were those testing nabam and tetramethylenediisothiocyanate (TDI). He could not use ethylenediisothiocyanate because it is too unstable. Klöpping's experiments show that, although TDI is more potent than nabam as a growth inhibitor, nabam is by far the more potent inhibitor of O_2 uptake. Thus, Klöpping's own data show that they act differently.

Before we present other pertinent studies, we should discuss the special status of sodium N-methyldithiocarbamatae (IV). Klöpping was the first to point out that this compound, although structurally reminiscent of the DDC types, actually is quite different. It is more like a half-molecule of nabam sliced between the ethylene carbons. He noted that sodium N-methyldithiocarbamate, because of the mobile hydrogen on the nitrogen atom, can break down to methyl isothiocyanate. In addition this compound gives a biological spectrum of the nabam class.

If nabam fungicides act by producing isothiocyanates, we suggest that

$$\overset{\displaystyle S}{\underset{\displaystyle (CH_3)N—C—S—Na}{\overset{\displaystyle H \ \ \|}{}}}$$

(IV)

sodium N-methyldithiocarbamate or its breakdown product, sodium methylisothiocyanate, should give metabolic effects similar to those of nabam. Let us see if they do.

In vitro, nabam completely inhibits polyphenol oxidase activity whereas sodium N-methyldithiocarbamate has very little effect on this enzyme (*28*).

Owens included nabam fungicides and methyl isothiocyanate in his studies of the effect of fungicides on the organic acid metabolism of *N. sitophila* (*21*). Here again the nabam fungicides differ drastically from methyl isothiocyanate. Nabam fungicides inhibit citrate metabolism. Methyl isothiocyanate does not. Nabam fungicides do not affect the metabolism of malate, succinate, or a-keto acids. Methyl isothiocyanate strongly inhibits the metabolism of these acids. Owens suggested that nabam fungicides inhibit aconitase, whereas methyl isothiocyanate inhibits essential dehydrogenases.

Wedding and Kendrick (*42*) used *Rhizoctonia solani* to compare the toxicity of sodium N-methyldithiocarbamate with that of its breakdown product methyl isothiocyanate. They measured the production of $C^{14}O_2$ from uniformly labeled glucose-C^{14} by the mycelium of *R. solani* and found that both fungicides inhibit glucose metabolism, "but in a manner indicating different modes of action for the two toxicants."

Wedding and Kendrick also measured loss of dry weight and leakage of P^{32}-labeled cell constituents from the treated mycelium. The highest doses of sodium N-methyldithiocarbamate caused the mycelium to lose 30% of its weight and 50% of its leachable P^{32}. In both cases, the losses increased with increasing concentrations of fungicide. In contrast, methyl isothiocyanate had practically no effect on cellular permeability. Wedding and Kendrick concluded that "N-methyl dithiocarbamate and methyl isothiocyanate do not have a completely common mode of action."

Ludwig and Thorn (*43*) compared isothiocyanate formation by DDC and nabam fungicides and the ability of these fungicides to inhibit enzymes *in vitro*. For this study, they used Chefurka's (*25*) data on the inhibition of glucose-6-phosphate dehydrogenase and 6-phosphogluconate dehydrogenase from the housefly. ETM, which produces isothiocyanate, and thiram, which does not, are equally strong inhibitors of both enzymes. Conversely, disodium tetramethylenebisdithiocarbamate, which produces isothiocyanate, and *N,N'*-dimethylethylenethiuram monosulfide, which does not, are only very weak inhibitors of the housefly enzymes. The ability of these fungicides to produce isothiocyanates, then, has no relationship to their action as inhibitors of Chefurka's enzymes. After studying the 20 years of research on the dithiocarbamate fungicides, Ludwig and Thorn concluded that "the two types of dithiocarbamate cannot be readily divorced"; and "much more research is obviously needed before any basic mode or modes of action can be firmly established."

Our own studies suggest that the nabam fungicides produce most of the reactions of the DDC types and others besides. This greater reactivity is probably caused by the mobile hydrogen on the nitrogen atom that occurs in the nabam types, but not in the DDC types.

B. Quinones

Two of the most potent of fungicides are tetrachloro-1,4-benzoquinone or chloranil (V), and 2,3-dichloro-1,4-naphthoquinone or dichlone (VI). McNew and Burchfield (*44*) reviewed the literature on the biological and biochemical activity of quinones. They proposed that quinone fungicides may act by "binding of enzymes to the quinone nucleus by substitution or addition at the double bond, an oxidative effect on sulfhydryl enzymes, or a change in redox potential in some subjects such as gram-positive bacteria."

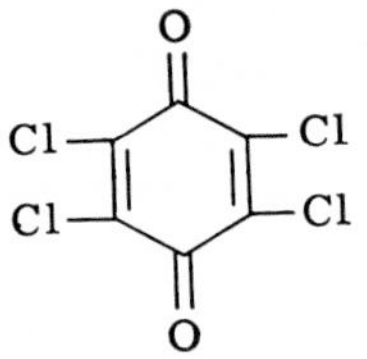

(V) 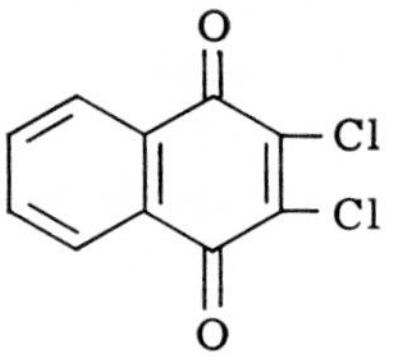   (VI)

Owens (*45*) found that quinone fungicides inhibit both amino-dependent and sulfhydryl-dependent enzymes. Those compounds that strongly inhibit the enzymes are very fungitoxic. The reverse is not true, however; for example, 3,4-dichlorotoluene, which does not inhibit the enzymes, is also quite fungitoxic. Perhaps, living fungi convert 3,4-dichlorotoluene to a quinone and so poison themselves. Another anomaly is 2-methyl-1,4-naphthoquinone which is very fungitoxic but does not inhibit Owens' enzymes. Owens ascribed the discrepancy to the water-insolubility of this compound. Earlier, Colwell and McCall (*46*) had shown that

2-methyl-1,4-naphthoquinone does, indeed, form addition products with sufhydryl compounds and that the fungitoxicity of this compound is alleviated by adding sulfhydryl compounds to the testing system. Colwell and McCall, however, raised another problem. They found that 2-methyl-3-methoxy-1,4-naphthoquinone is a good fungicide in spite of its inability to form reaction products with sulfhydryl compounds. They concluded that the toxic mechanism of 2-methyl-3-methoxy-1,4-naphthoquinone must differ from that of other naphthoquinones.

Owens and Miller (47) treated fungus spores with radioactive fungicides and then disintegrated the treated spores ultrasonically. Most of the absorbed dichlone appears in the water-soluble fraction. Only 15% of the dichlone in the water-soluble fraction is bound to water-soluble protein. That portion of the absorbed dichlone not in the water-soluble fraction is firmly bound to particulate fractions believed to be mitochondria and microsomes. Owens and Miller also observed that substances from *N. sitophila* spores react aerobically with dichlone to give at least five separate but unidentified brown and yellow products.

Dichlone acts as an uncoupler of respiration and phosphorylation in a manner similar to the action of 2,4-dinitrophenol (48). Mahler et al. (49) earlier had found a similar burst of molecular oxygen when metalloflavoprotein enzyme systems are treated with quinones. They suggested that quinones uncouple phosphorylations by diverting electrons from the enzymes to molecular oxygen.

Owens and Novotny (48) believed that the "toxicity of dichlone is due to concomitant inhibition of phosphorylation, certain dehydrogenases and carboxylases and inactivation of coenzyme A. This involves many loci distributed throughout practically all major metabolic pathways, precluding effective metabolic by-passes and growth."

Dichlone inhibits coenzyme A, but not cell-free aceto-Co A-kinase or citrogenase. It reacts with coenzyme A or glutathione to give a mixture of mono- and disubstituted products (50).

Presumably, the principal fungitoxic mechanisms of quinones are inhibition of sulfhydryl- and amino-dependent enzymes, inactivation of coenzyme A, and uncoupling of phosphorylation.

Quinones not only disrupt fungi, but fungi also modify quinones. The modification of quinones by fungi may make a derivative either more or less toxic to the fungus.

Byrde and Woodcock (51) converted the weakly fungitoxic 1,4-diacetoxy-2,3-dichloronaphthalene to a potent fungicide by adding a fungal acetylesterase. They postulated that the acetylated dichloronaphthalene is de-esterified to the fungitoxic 2,3-dichloro-1,4-naphthohydroquinone. Horsfall (1) suggested that a fungal phenol oxidase changes the hydroquinone to the still more toxic dichlone.

Rich and Horsfall (52) demonstrated that polyphenol oxidases from dark colored fungi may oxidize phenols to quinones and polymerize the quinonoid pigments. They proposed that this process would act as a detoxifying mechanism to protect dark-colored fungi against fungitoxic phenols and quinones.

C. Heterocyclic Nitrogen Compounds

Heterocyclic nitrogen compounds include a large number of fungicides (53). Their similarity in chemical structure, however, is not paralleled by a similarity in fungitoxic mechanism. The ethylenethioureas (54, 55), nitrosopyrazoles (56), and tetrahydropyrimidines (57) may well act as physical toxicants. Physical toxicants injure by disrupting the physical integrity of the cell, rather than by direct chemical reaction with a vital constituent.

The three heterocyclic nitrogen fungicides we will discuss are 2-heptadecyl-2-imidazoline (glyodin), 8-quinolinol (oxine), and N-(trichloromethylthio)-4-cyclohexene-1,2-dicarboximide (captan).

1. GLYODIN

Glyodin (VII) is perhaps the only commercial fungicide so far proposed to act as a competitive inhibitor. West and Wolf (58) reported that guanine, xanthine, and xanthosine competitively reverse the toxicity of glyodin to the growth of M. fructicola. None of the other purine or purine derivatives they tested are effective. West and Wolf concluded that glyodin is a competitive inhibitor of guanine or xanthine synthesis. They were unable to detect the accumulation of the purine precursor, 5-amino-4-imidazolecarboximide, in the culture filtrates of cultures partially inhibited with glyodin. Therefore, they could not suggest just what enzyme or enzymes are inhibited by glyodin.

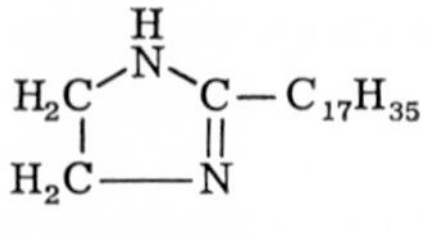

$$\begin{matrix} & H & \\ & \overset{|}{N} & \\ H_2C\diagdown & & \diagdown \\ & & C - C_{17}H_{35} \\ H_2C\diagup & & \diagup \\ & & \| \\ H_2C\!\!-\!\!-\!\!-\!\!N & \end{matrix}$$

(VII)

Other experiments with glyodin are also enlightening. Glyodin, an excellent surfactant, is rapidly sorbed by fungus spores (59). In addition it is a potent inhibitor of respiration. McCallan *et al.* (*12*) found that the extremely low ambient dose of glyodin that inhibits respiration concomitantly inhibits spore germination. The characteristics of rapid sorption by spores, and potent inhibition of respiration and germination are also shared by silver ions (*12, 59*). Silver disrupts the semipermeability of the spore, allowing the escape of cell contents (*14*). Without confirming data, we would predict that glyodin also disrupts the permeability of conidia as other surfactants do.

Glyodin, then, may well be a competitive inhibitor of purine synthesis. In addition, however, glyodin is a potent inhibitor of respiration and could have a profound effect on the permeability of spores. As a protein reactant, glyodin may be a nonspecific inhibitor of many enzymes, e.g., polyphenol oxidase (*28*).

2. Oxine

The toxic mechanism of oxine (VIII) has probably been investigated by a greater number of laboratories than that of any other fungicide. Zentmyer (*60*) stimulated this burst of activity by proposing that the fungitoxicity of oxine is due to its ability to chelate essential minor elements. Research on the toxic mechanism of oxine has been reviewed by Horsfall (*1*) and more recently by Rich (*2*).

(VIII)

In many respects oxine is similar to the DDC fungicides, which are also chelators. Both can produce a bimodal dosage response. Both show the differences in toxicity among the unchelated compound, the half-chelate, and the full chelate.

Oxine analogues must have two properties to be highly fungitoxic: they must be able to chelate, and they must be lipoid-soluble (*61*).

Rich (*2*) proposed that the highly toxic copper oxinate acts at vital sites which can only be attacked by compounds with high lipoid solubility. Once within these sites, e.g. microsomes, the half-chelate may block functional groups by being bound to cellular constituents through the unsatisfied metallic atom. The less toxic, and more water-soluble, unchelated oxine may poison by taking essential metals from water-soluble constituents of the cell.

Block (*61*) reported that oxine is a powerful inhibitor of cresolase, a copper-dependent enzyme. Surprisingly, the polyphenoloxidase from *Agaricus campestris*, also copper-dependent, is only very slightly inhibited by oxine (*28*).

Owens (*21*) found that the effect of oxine on the organic acid metabolism of *N. sitophila* conidia is similar to that of the nabam fungicides and not like the DDC fungicides. He suggested that oxine inhibits aconitase *in vivo* by removing the Fe^{++} atom essential to the activity of this enzyme.

Esposito and Beckman (*62*) have recently reported that pterins, pterinoids, and their precursors alleviate the toxicity of copper oxinate to microspores of *Fusarium oxysporum*. They proposed a mechanism of copper-oxine action based on interference with pterin biosynthesis and the metabolism of compounds with the group

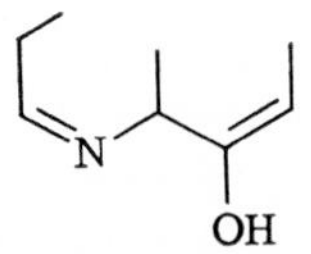

Oxine, then, may inhibit fungal metabolism by sequestering essential metals or, as a metal chelate, may block functional sites.

3. CAPTAN

Theories about the fungitoxicity of captan (IX) feature either the carboximide or the S—CCl$_3$ moieties of the molecule as the poisonous portion. Horsfall and Rich (*63*) proposed that the S—CCl$_3$ group acts to get captan into the cell, where the carboximide does the poisoning. Lukens and Sisler (*64*) demonstrated the rapid reaction *in vitro* between captan and sulfhydryl groups to release thiophosgene. They suggested that "the trichloromethylthio group attaching to vital cellular components through sulfur or acting through a thiophosgene intermediate can account for the fungitoxicity of captan to *Saccharomyces pastorianus*."

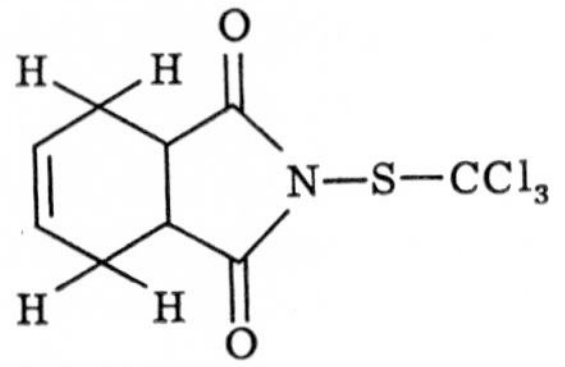

(IX)

Captan is eighty-fold more effective as an inhibitor of *M. fructicola* respiration than it is as a spore germination inhibitor (*12*). In *F. roseum* and *S. pastorianus*, captan appears to interfere with decarboxylation reactions that require thiamine pyrophosphate (*65*). Dugger *et al.* (*66*) studied captan inhibition of enzymes from higher plants. They concluded that "this inhibition probably is caused by the reaction of the intercellular breakdown product of captan, thiophosgene, through C-bridge(s) to the apoenzyme of carboxylase interfering with the coenzyme-enzyme linkage necessary for decarboxylation."

Owens and Novotny (*67*) proposed that captan acts as an intact molecule, forming substitution products with essential thiol groups of the cell, as in Eq. (1).

$$R\text{—}S\text{—}CCl_3 + HS\text{—}R \rightarrow R\text{—}S\overset{\displaystyle Cl_2}{\overset{\displaystyle |}{\text{—}C\text{—}}}S\text{—}R + HCl \qquad (1)$$

To them the breakdown of captan is secondary, and captan appears to inhibit "a number of enzymes in phosphorous metabolism, certain oxidases and dehydrogenases, carboxylases and coenzyme A." Later, Owens and Blaak (*50*) found that captan does indeed interact with coenzyme A.

According to Byrde and Woodcock (*68*), the toxicity of captan is due primarily to its ability to accumulate within the fungus spore, and that the S—CCl$_3$ group acts both as a "lipophile and toxophore."

Presumably, then, captan interacts with sulfhydryl compounds of the cell. The interaction may be as the intact captan molecule; or captan may be destroyed in the interaction by rupture of the N—S bond to give tetrahydrophthalimide and thiophosgene. The highly reactive thiophosgene in turn may injure the cell at many sites. It is also possible that tetrahydrophthalimide may inhibit dehydrogenases as does glutarimide and succinimide (*69*). Although captan can poison in so many possible ways, its toxicity to some fungi can be alleviated simply by the addition of *l*-histidine (*70*).

IV. CONCLUSIONS

This discussion is by no means a complete report of fungicides as metabolic inhibitors. It is meant to illustrate that fungicides do inhibit metabolism.

In common with other kinds of metabolic inhibitors, fungicides attack sulfhydryl groups, amino groups, and essential metals; act as protein denaturants, alkylating agents, and competitive inhibitors; and disrupt the physical integrity of cells.

If fungicides have a group distinction, it is their individual ability to poison in many different ways. Rarely is a fungicide limited to a single toxic mechanism. In this respect they may be considered nonspecific. To a particular fungus, under particular conditions, however, a fungicide may be highly specific. For example, glyodin, which is known to have other modes of toxic action, inhibits the mycelial growth of *M. fructicola* in culture by competitively inhibiting the synthesis of guanine *(58)*.

It is often questionable whether the metabolic inhibitions reported are in every case responsible for fungitoxicity. Therefore, past studies of fungicides as metabolic inhibitors have not been too useful in predicting fungitoxicity. Where do we go from here? Two questions desperately need answers. What specific metabolic systems are vital to spore germination and mycelial growth? What fractions of a poisonous dose within the cell cause specific metabolic inhibitions? The answers to these two questions would pinpoint the metabolic lesions most important to fungitoxic action.

REFERENCES

1. J. G. Horsfall, "Principles of Fungicidal Action." Chronica Botanica, Waltham, Massachusetts, 1956.
2. S. Rich, *in* "Plant Pathology" (J. G. Horsfall and A. E. Dimond, eds.), Vol. II, p. 553. Academic Press, New York, 1960.
3. H. D. Sisler and C. E. Cox, *in* "Plant Pathology" (J. G. Horsfall and A. E. Dimond, eds.), Vol. II, p. 507. Academic Press, New York, 1960.
4. W. H. R. Shaw, *Science* **120**, 361 (1954).
5. J. F. Danielli and J. T. Davis, *Advances in Enzyomol.* **2**, 35 (1947).
6. E. Somers, *Nature* **184**, 475 (1959).
7. H. B. Vickery and C. S. Leavenworth, *J. Biol. Chem.* **86**, 129 (1930).
8. P. W. Preisler and D. B. Priesler, *J. Am. Chem. Soc.* **54**, 2984 (1932).
9. L. Harris, *Biochem. J.* **16**, 743 (1922).
10. R. G. Owens, *Contribs. Boyce Thompson Inst.* **17**, 221 (1953).
11. R. J. W. Byrde, J. T. Martin, and D. J. D. Nicholas, *Nature* **178**, 638 (1956).
12. S. E. A. McCallan, L. P. Miller, and R. M. Weed, *Contribs. Boyce Thompson Inst.* **18**, 39 (1954).
13. S. E. A. McCallan and L. P. Miller, *Contribs. Boyce Thompson Inst.* **18**, 483 (1957).
14. L. P. Miller and S. E. A. McCallan, *Rept. 14th Intern. Hort. Congr., The Netherlands, 1955* **1**, p. 546 (1955).
15. M. R. Siegel and D. F. Crossan, *Phytopathology* **50**, 680 (1960).
16. W. J. Nickerson and N. J. W. van Rij, *Biochim. et Biophys. Acta* **3**, 461 (1949).
17. W. J. Nickerson and G. Falcone, *Science* **124**, 318 (1956).
18. W. J. Nickerson and K. Zerahn, *Biochim. et Biophys. Acta* **3**, 476 (1949).

19. S. E. A. McCallan and L. P. Miller, *Contribs. Boyce Thompson Inst.* 18, 497 (1957).
20. A. Rothstein and H. Berke, *Arch. Biochem. Biophys.* 36, 195 (1952).
21. R. G. Owens, *in* "Developments in Industrial Microbiology" (B. Miller, ed.), Vol. 1, p. 187. Plenum Press, New York, 1960.
22. S. E. A. McCallan and F. Wilcoxon, *Contribs. Boyce Thompson Inst.* 3, 13 (1931).
23. L. P. Miller, S. E. A. McCallan, and R. M. Weed, *Contribs. Boyce Thompson Inst.* 17, 151 (1953).
24. H. L. Klöpping, "Chemical Constitution and Antifungal Action of Sulfur Compounds." Schotanus and Jens, Utrecht, 1951.
25. W. Chefurka, *Enzymologia*, 18, 209 (1956).
26. H. D. Sisler and C. E. Cox, *Am. J. Botany* 42, 351 (1955).
27. H. D. Sisler and N. L. Marshall, *J. Wash. Acad. Sci.* 47, 321 (1957).
28. R. G. Owens, *Contribs. Boyce Thompson Inst.* 17, 473 (1954).
29. J. G. Horsfall, "Fungicides and their Action." Chronica Botanica, Waltham, Massachusetts, 1945.
30. A. E. Dimond, J. G. Horsfall, J. W. Heuberger, and E. M. Stoddard. *Conn. Agr. Expt. Sta. (New Haven) Bull.* 451, 635 (1941).
31. H. B. S. Montgomery and H. Shaw, *Nature* 151, 333 (1943).
32. A. M. Kaars Sijpesteijn, M. J. Janssen, and G. J. M. van der Kerk, *Biochim. et Biophys. Acta* 23, 550 (1957).
33. J. Goksøyr, *Physiol. Plantarum* 8, 719 (1955).
34. J. Goksøyr, *Univ. Bergen Årbok, Naturvitenskap. Rekke No.* 3, 1 (1958).
35. A. Kaars Sijpesteijn and M. J. Janssen. *Antonie van Leeuwenhoek J. Microbiol. Serol.* 25, 422 (1959).
36. A. E. Dimond, J. W. Heuberger, and J. G. Horsfall, *Phytopathology* 33, 1095 (1943).
37. R. W. Barratt and J. G. Horsfall, *Conn. Agr. Expt. Sta. (New Haven) Bull.* 508, 1 (1946).
38. S. Rich and J. G. Horsfall, *Am. J. Botany* 37, 643 (1952).
39. R. A. Ludwig and G. D. Thorn, *Plant Disease Reptr.* 37, 127 (1953).
40. R. A. Ludwig, G. D. Thorn, and C. H. Unwin, *Can. J. Botany* 33, 42 (1955).
41. R. A. Ludwig and G. D. Thorn, *Can. J. Botany* 36, 473 (1958).
42. R. T. Wedding and J. B. Kendrick, Jr., *Phytopathology* 49, 557 (1959).
43. R. A. Ludwig and G. D. Thorn, *Advances in Pest Control Research* 3, 219 (1960).
44. G. L. McNew and H. P. Burchfield, *Contribs. Boyce Thompson Inst.* 16, 357 (1951).
45. R. G. Owens, *Contribs. Boyce Thompson Inst.* 17, 273 (1953).
46. C. A. Colwell and M. McCall, *J. Bacteriol.* 51, 659 (1946).
47. R. G. Owens and L. P. Miller, *Contribs. Boyce Thompson Inst.* 19, 177 (1957).
48. R. G. Owens and H. M. Novotny, *Contribs. Boyce Thompson Inst.* 19, 463 (1958).
49. H. R. Mahler, A. S. Fairhurst, and B. Mackler, *J. Am. Chem. Soc.* 77, 1514 (1955).
50. R. G. Owens and G. Blaak, *Phytopathology* 50, 649 (1960).

51. R. J. W. Byrde and D. Woodcock, *Ann. Appl. Biol.* **40**, 675 (1953).
52. S. Rich and J. G. Horsfall, *Proc. Natl. Acad. Sci U.S.* **40**, 139 (1954).
53. J. G. Horsfall and S. Rich, *Contribs. Boyce Thompson Inst.* **16**, 313 (1951).
54. S. Rich and J. G. Horsfall, *Science* **120**, 122 (1954).
55. R. G. Ross and R. A. Ludwig, *Can. J. Botany* **35**, 65 (1957).
56. S. Rich and J. G. Horsfall, *Phytopathology* **42**, 457 (1952).
57. W. E. Rader, C. M. Monroe; and R. R. Whetstone, *Science* **115**, 124 (1952).
58. W. West and F. T. Wolf, *J. Gen. Microbiol.* **12**, 396 (1955).
59. L. P. Miller, S. E. A. McCallan, and R. M. Weed, *Contribs. Boyce Thompson Inst.* **17**, 173 (1953).
60. G. A. Zentmyer, *Phytopathology* **33**, 1121 (1943).
61. S. S. Block, *J. Agr. Food Chem.* **3**, 229 (1955).
62. R. G. Esposito and C. H. Beckman, *Phytopathology* **51**, 576 (1961).
63. J. G. Horsfall and S. Rich, *Yale Sci. Mag.* **27**, 12 (1953).
64. R. J. Lukens and H. Sisler, *Phytopathology* **48**, 235 (1958).
65. P. E. Hochstein and C. E. Cox, *Am. J. Botany* **43**, 437 (1956).
66. W. M. Dugger, Jr., T. E. Humphreys, and B. Calhoun, *Am. J. Botany* **46**, 151 (1959).
67. R. G. Owens and H. M. Novotny, *Contribs. Boyce Thompson Inst.* **20**, 171 (1959).
68. R. J. W. Byrde and D. Woodcock, *Ann. Appl. Biol.* **47**, 332 (1959).
69. H. E. Latuasan and W. Berends, *Rec. trav. chim.* **77**, 416 (1958).
70. S. Rich. *Phytopathology* **49**, 321 (1959).

CHAPTER 28

Trypanocidal Agents

Bruce A. Newton

I. INTRODUCTION

Chemotherapy of trypanosomiasis enjoys the distinction of being one of the oldest branches of chemotherapy: Ehrlich's earliest experiments in this field were directed towards the development of a cure for sleeping sickness. During the 60 years which have elapsed since these first investigations, an astronomical number of trypanocidal compounds have been described in the literature, but of these only a few have withstood the test of time and are in current use for the treatment of trypanosomiasis of man or of domestic animals. It is with these "survivors" that the present chapter will be mainly concerned. A more complete survey will be found in references (1–4a).

Without exception, the compounds now used for prophylaxis or treatment of trypanosomiasis represent the products of an empirical approach to the problem of selective toxicity. As a result of painstaking screening of large numbers of compounds a mass of data has been accumulated which relates chemical structure to trypanocidal activity; yet, in most cases, little or nothing is known about the mechanism of this activity. This lack of knowledge is a reflection of our general ignorance of the biochemistry of trypanosomes.

It is the aim of this chapter to present a brief account of the structure and properties of trypanocidal agents in current use and to discuss the results of biochemical investigations which may throw some light on their mechanism of action. By so emphasizing the gaps in our knowledge it is hoped that more workers will be encouraged to examine the inhibitory actions of these compounds.

II. SUMMARY OF TRYPANOCIDAL AGENTS IN CURRENT USE

A. African Trypanosomiasis

1. HUMAN (SLEEPING SICKNESS)

Causative organisms: *Trypanosoma gambiense* (West African), *Trypanosoma rhodesiense* (East African).

Drugs for prophylaxis: suramin, pentamidine, and melaminyl antimony compounds.

Drugs for treatment: tryparsamide and melaminyl arsenicals.

2. BOVINE

Causative organisms: *Trypanosoma brucei, Trypanosoma congolense, Trypanosoma vivax.*

Drugs in use: phenanthridines (ethidium and prothidium), Antrycide, berenil, and suramin complexes of the preceding compounds.

B. South American Trypanosomiasis

HUMAN (CHAGAS DISEASE)

Causative organism: *Trypanosoma cruzi*. No effective chemotherapeutic agent available.

III. ARSENICALS

The history of arsenic as a chemotherapeutic agent dates back to 1863 when Bechamp (5), a French apothecary, synthesized a water-soluble compound by heating arsenic with aniline. This compound, subsequently named Atoxyl (I), was found to be 30 times less toxic than Fowler's solu-

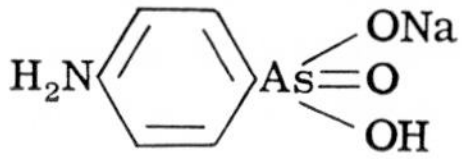

$$H_2N-\underset{\text{(I)}}{\bigcirc}-As\overset{ONa}{\underset{OH}{=}}O$$

tion (a mixture of potassium arsenite and arsenious oxide, which was in use as a therapeutic agent at that time). Some 40 years later Thomas and Breinl (6) showed that Atoxyl cured experimental trypanosomiasis at one-tenth of the tolerated dose. Ehrlich's investigation (7) of this compound provided an explanation for the different toxicities of Fowler's solution and Atoxyl; he showed that Atoxyl is arsanilic acid, a compound in which arsenic is undissociable, whereas in Fowler's solution the arsenic is present as arsenite ions, which can readily penetrate into tissues and cells to combine with any available positively charged group. These findings mark the beginning of a search for selectively toxic organic arsenicals, which has continued until the present day. Friedheim (8) estimated that by 1932 some 12,500 compounds had been synthesized and tested.

The biological activity of organic arsenicals in relation to their structure has been reviewed in detail by Eagle and Doak (9), and recent advances have been discussed by Friedheim (10). The more general aspects of arsenicals as metabolic inhibitors form the subject of Chapter 20 in this volume; the present section will, therefore, be restricted to a brief discussion of the trypanocidal activity of organic arsenicals.

A. Organic Arsenicals in General Use as Trypanocides

Arsenicals are of prime importance for the treatment of advanced cases of trypanosomiasis, as they are the only drugs available which are active against trypanosomes in the cerebrospinal fluid. Two types of compound are in general use.

1. TRYPARSAMIDE (II)

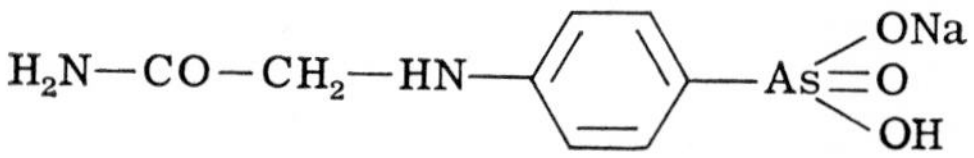

$$H_2N-CO-CH_2-HN-\underset{\text{(II)}}{\bigcirc}-As\overset{ONa}{\underset{OH}{=}}O$$

This compound is frequently administered in combination with suramin or pentamidine.

2. MELAMINYL ARSENICALS

Friedheim (11) first synthesized organic arsenicals containing the melamine nucleus. The trivalent Melarsen oxide (III) and the pentavalent Melarsen (IV) are effective in the treatment of advanced cases, but are more toxic than tryparsamide. It was later found (8) that the di-

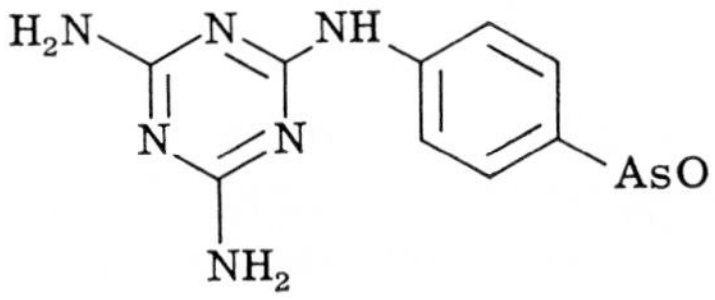

(III)

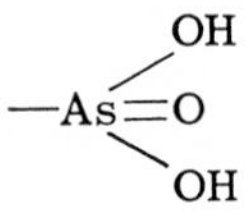

(IV) 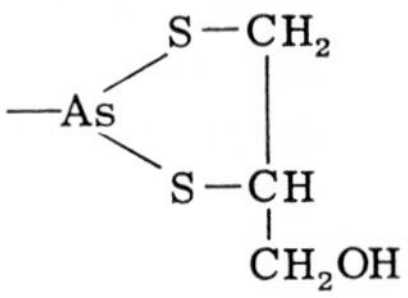   (V)

mercaprol (BAL) derivative of Melarsen named Mel B (V) has a reduced toxicity for the host, and this compound is proving to be of particular value in the treatment of advanced infections which show resistance to tryparsamide. The antimony analogue of Melarsen has shown promise as a long-acting prophylactic (12).

B. Mechanism of Trypanocidal Action

1. REACTION WITH THIOL GROUPS

Ehrlich (13) showed that trivalent organic arsenicals are trypanocidal in vitro and in vivo, whereas pentavalent derivatives are relatively nontoxic in vitro but exert a powerful trypanocidal action in vivo. To explain these findings Ehrlich suggested that pentavalent compounds are converted to the trivalent form in vivo. This view has since received sound experimental support (14–16a).

The most striking property of trivalent arsenic compounds is their avidity for thiol groups, the reaction [Eq. (1)] resulting in mercaptide formation. Voegtlin *et al.* (*14*) demonstrated the presence of thiol groups

$$2\ \text{R—SH} + \text{O=As—R'} \rightarrow \begin{array}{c} \text{R—S} \\ \diagdown \\ \text{As—R'} + \text{H}_2\text{O} \\ \diagup \\ \text{R—S} \end{array} \tag{1}$$

in trypanosomes and showed that compounds such as glutathione inhibited the trypanocidal activity of trivalent arsenicals *in vitro*. These findings led to the suggestion that the "primary chemoreceptor" for arsenicals in trypanosomes is glutathione. This view was subsequently modified as the importance of free thiol groups for enzyme activity was recognized.

Peters and Wakelin (*17*) found that pyruvate oxidase of animal cells is particularly sensitive to arsenicals, and their work led, first, to the suggestion that trivalent arsenicals form stable ring compounds with dithiols, and second, to the prediction that a dithiol may be involved in pyruvate oxidation (*18*), a prediction to be substantiated later by the discovery of lipoic acid. The combination of an organic arsenical with a

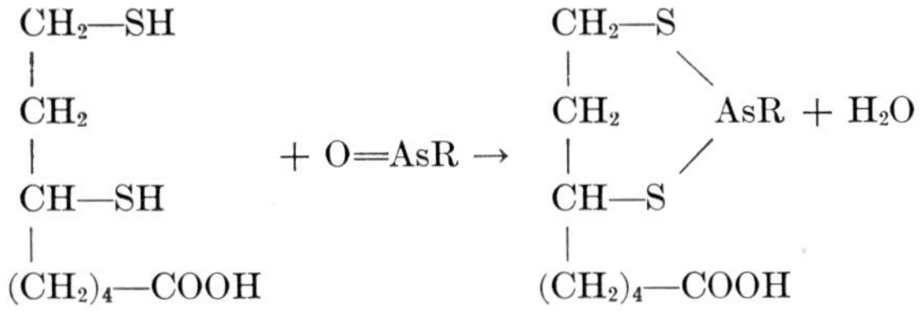

$$\begin{array}{c} \text{CH}_2\text{—SH} \\ | \\ \text{CH}_2 \\ | \\ \text{CH—SH} \\ | \\ (\text{CH}_2)_4\text{—COOH} \end{array} + \text{O=AsR} \rightarrow \begin{array}{c} \text{CH}_2\text{—S} \\ | \quad \diagdown \\ \text{CH}_2 \quad \text{AsR} + \text{H}_2\text{O} \\ | \quad \diagup \\ \text{CH—S} \\ | \\ (\text{CH}_2)_4\text{—COOH} \end{array} \tag{2}$$

dithiol [Eq. (2)] is not reversed by an excess of a monothiol compound, but can be reversed by dithiols.

2. SELECTIVE ACTIVITY

The toxicity and trypanocidal activity of organic arsenicals having closely related chemical structures may vary as much as one hundredfold, and there may also be marked differences in the activity of a given compound against different trypanosomes. Two possible explanations for this selective activity have been discussed by Eagle and Doak (*9*). First, there is a variation in either the number or reactivity of cellular thiol groups; second, there is a variation in cell permeability. Most of the data available favor the latter hypothesis. Barron and Singer (*19, 20*) studied the action of a number of arsenicals on isolated enzymes and found that the susceptibility of different enzymes to the same arsenical, or the same enzyme to a number of different arsenicals, was generally of the same order. However, some exceptions were recorded by these workers and by Banks and Controulis (*21*), and it was suggested that differences in susceptibility may arise from different spatial arrangements of thiol groups on enzyme proteins. Eagle and Doak (*9*) found no correlation between the toxicity or activity of a number of arsenicals and the hydrolysis constants of their thioarsenite derivatives, suggesting that variations in antimicrobial activity or toxicity are not due to differences in the rate or equilibrium constants of the reaction of these compounds with thiol groups. There is, however, a report of one arsenical which appears to be active against protozoan enzymes but inactive against similar enzymes from mammalian tissues. Seaman (*22*) found that arsonoacetic acid (VI)

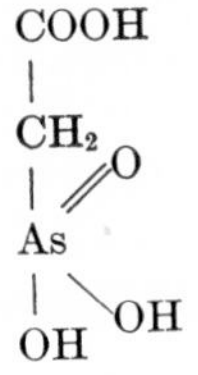

$$
\begin{array}{c}
\text{COOH} \\
| \\
\text{CH}_2 \\
| \quad \diagup\!\!\diagup \text{O} \\
\text{As} \\
| \quad \diagdown \text{OH} \\
\text{OH}
\end{array}
$$

(VI)

acts as a competitive inhibitor of succinic dehydrogenase isolated from a number of protozoa, but this compound does not inhibit succinic dehydrogenase prepared from mouse or rat tissues (*23*). Evidence was presented to show that compound (VI) is active in the pentavalent form and not the trivalent form and that it acts by combining with the carboxyl affinity points of the enzyme, thiol groups being unaffected.

Evidence in favor of a variation in cell permeability to organic arsenicals first came from the qualitative studies of York and associates (*24*), who showed that trypanocidal arsenicals are bound by organisms and that inactive compounds are not. These findings were extended by Eagle and Magnuson (*25*), who found a correlation between the trypanocidal activity of 10 different arsenicals and the amount of these compounds bound by trypanosomes. From these studies it was concluded that arsenobenzene is highly toxic to all cells, and it was suggested that the addition of substituent groups may depress activity against one type of cell more than another, probably by changing the ability of the compound to penetrate cell permeability barriers; this, however, remains to be proved.

3. ANTAGONISM OF ARSENICALS

A number of compounds others than thiols are known to protect cells against the cytotoxic action of arsenicals; these include quinoid dyes (26), ascorbic acid (27), aminobenzoic acid (28), benzoic esters (29), and Surfen C (30). There is little similarity in chemical structure between these compounds and arsenobenzene, and it seems unlikely that they will compete with arsenicals for thiol groups. Williamson and Lourie (30) have suggested that these antagonists may modify the cell surface and prevent drug uptake, but experimental support for this idea is still lacking. It has also been noted that inhibition of trypanocidal activity by a number of these compounds is not paralleled by decreased toxicity (29).

While it is generally accepted that the cytotoxic action of organic arsenicals depends on their ability to combine with thiol groups of essential enzyme systems, the mode of action of these compounds cannot be fully described until the mechanism of these antagonisms has been elucidated (9). Further study of this problem should yield valuable information about permeability barriers of parasite and host cells.

IV. SURAMIN

A. Development and Structure

In 1904 Ehrlich and Shiga (31) made the fundamental discovery that trypan red, a member of the Congo red series of dyes, can cure experimental trypanosomiasis in mice. Following this, Nicolle and Mesnil (32) examined a range of cotton dyes for curative action against *Trypanosoma gambiense* in monkeys and rats; the most active compound found was afridol violet. The search for active colorless derivatives of these dyes led, some 16 years later, to the synthesis of suramin (synonyms: Bayer 205, Antrypol) (VII). The steps in the evolution of this substance from the azo dyes have been described by Balaban and King (33). The structure of suramin was elucidated by Fourneau et al. (34). It is now apparent, from the results of numerous workers, that minor modifications in this complex structure result in the loss of trypanocidal activity. One of the earliest characteristics of suramin to be recognized was the long duration of its prophylactic action and its persistence in the blood stream. The work of Spinks (35) suggests that different structural features in the molecule are responsible for this persistence and for trypanocidal activity, since demethylation results in a loss of the latter without affecting reten-

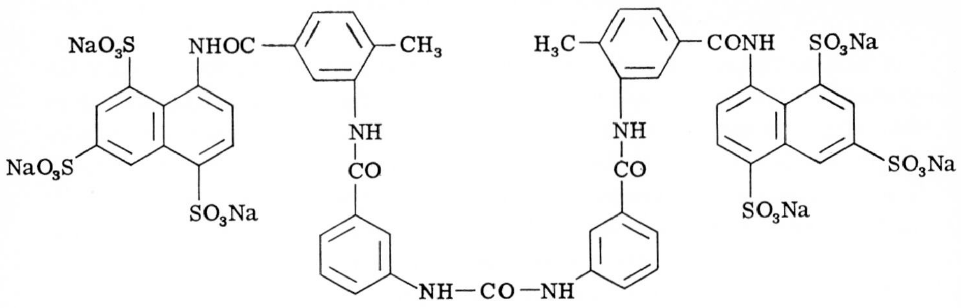

(VII)

tion of the drug. There is no evidence that suramin is modified or degraded *in vivo*.

B. Mechanism of Action

1. Effects on Growth and General Metabolism

There is still little information which throws light on the nature of the trypanocidal activity of suramin. Early work suggested that the drug was active only *in vivo*, but von Jancso and von Jancso (*36*) showed that *in vitro* activity could be demonstrated, provided that contact between drug and trypanosomes was maintained for at least 24 hours. This slow action, which has recently been described in greater detail by Hawking and Sen (*37*), differs from the action of arsenosobenzenes, which show immediate trypanocidal activity *in vivo* and *in vitro*.

A number of workers have found that, *in vitro*, respiration and glucose metabolism of trypanosomes is initially unaffected by suramin (*38, 39*); however, after 6 hours' contact with the drug, oxygen consumption by *Trypanosoma brucei* is reduced, and glycerol is found to accumulate (*40*). More recently, Town *et al.* (*41*) found that suramin is a potent inhibitor of glucose fermentation by yeast juice, but is without effect on intact yeast cells (*42*). Suramin does not appear to have any immediate effect on the motility of trypanosomes, but Hoffmann-Berling (*43*) has observed that it is an extremely potent inhibitor of the adenosine triphosphate-induced movement of flagella and undulating membranes of glycerinated trypanosomes.

2. Cytological Changes

Von Jancso and von Jancso (*44*) observed that suramin treatment of certain strains of trypanosomes results in the appearance of giant multi-nuclear forms, suggesting that cytoplasmic division is affected before nuclear division. Similar observations have been made recently by Ormerod (45), who found also that after 5–6 hours' contact with suramin basophilic granules appear in the cytoplasm of trypanosomes. Similar changes are induced by a number of quaternary ammonium trypanocides; the possible significance of these findings will be discussed in Section VI of this chapter. Sen and co-workers (46) have studied the cytochemical changes in *Trypanosoma evansi* resulting from suramin treatment and report a marked increase in cytoplasmic mucopolysaccharide.

TABLE I

ENZYMES INHIBITED BY SURAMIN

Enzyme	References
Trypsin	(48)
Fumarase	(49)
Hyaluronidase	(50)
Urease	(51)
Hexokinase	(51)
Succinic dehydrogenase	(51, 52)
Choline dehydrogenase	(51)
Ribonuclease	(53)
β-Galactosidase	(54)
Lysozyme	(55)

3. ENZYME INHIBITION BY SURAMIN

There have been numerous reports of enzymes which are inhibited by suramin (Table I) but these have been of little help in pinpointing the site of trypanocidal action of this compound. Wills (47) found that the inhibition of a number of enzymes by suramin was particularly sensitive to changes in pH value; for example, 3×10^{-4} M suramin gives 100% inhibition of urease at pH 5 but is without effect at pH 5.3. This sharp pH response led to the development of a rapid method for determining the isoelectric point of suramin-sensitive enzymes which has proved to be particularly suitable for use in the early stages of enzyme purification.

Stoppani and Brignone (52) studied the action of suramin on purified succinic dehydrogenase and found that the drug behaves as a competitive inhibitor; however, the 1-naphthylamine-4,6,8-sulfonate portion of the molecule was found to behave similarly, and this compound is known to be without trypanocidal activity.

Ten years ago von Brand (2), discussing the mode of action of suramin wrote, "it is evident that further physiological studies are urgently needed." This summing up is still applicable.

V. AROMATIC DIAMIDINES

A. Structure and Development

The introduction of aromatic diamidines as trypanocidal agents resulted from a search for chemicals capable of reducing the blood sugar level. It had been observed that the survival time of trypanosomes in blood is prolonged if glucose is added (56, 57), and Poindexter (58) found that insulin decreased the rate of trypanosome multiplication *in vivo* and prolonged the life of the host. Synthalin (VIII) had at one time been

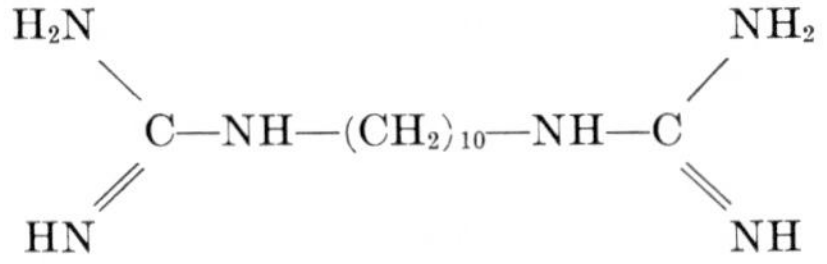

$$
\begin{array}{cc}
H_2N & NH_2 \\
\diagdown & \diagup \\
C\!-\!NH\!-\!(CH_2)_{10}\!-\!NH\!-\!C & \\
\diagup\diagup & \diagdown\diagdown \\
HN & NH
\end{array}
$$

(VIII)

used for the treatment of diabetes mellitus; this prompted von Jancso and von Jancso (59) and Schern and Artagaveytia-Allende (60) to test this compound for trypanocidal activity; it was found to be remarkably active. These workers suggested that hypoglycemia, caused by Synthalin, interfered with trypanosome metabolism, but later Lourie and York (61) demonstrated that the compound is trypanocidal at concentrations which have no effect on the blood sugar level. These observations led to the synthesis of a series of diguanides, amidines, and isothioureas (62, 63). The trypanocidal activity of these compounds was found to be markedly affected by alterations in chain length or in the guanyl group. From several hundred compounds screened for trypanocidal activity, stilbamidine (IX), pentamidine (X), and propamidine (XI) have been the most successful in the treatment of trypanosomiasis and leishmaniasis. The phar-

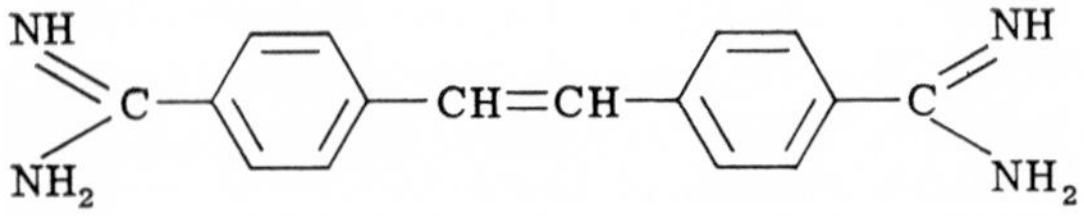

$$
\begin{array}{c}
NH \\
\diagdown\!\!\diagdown \\
C\!-\!\!\bigcirc\!\!-\!CH\!=\!CH\!-\!\bigcirc\!\!-\!C \\
NH_2 \\
\end{array}
\quad
\begin{array}{c}
NH \\
\diagup\!\!\diagup \\
\\
NH_2
\end{array}
$$

(IX)

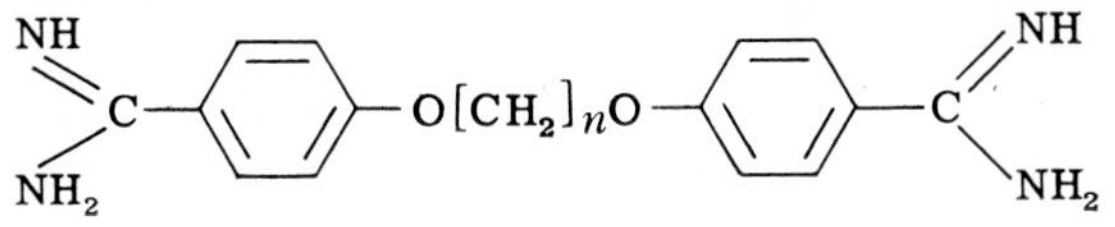

NH
‖
C—⬡—O[CH$_2$]$_n$O—⬡—C
NH$_2$ NH
      NH$_2$

$n = 5$ (X); $n = 3$ (XI)

macology and action of these compounds have been reviewed in detail by Schoenbach and Greenspan (64). A more recent addition to this group of compounds is berenil (XII), which is active against *Trypanosoma congolense* infections in cattle (65).

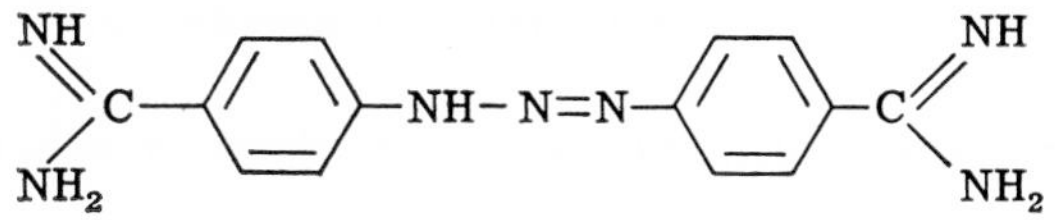

NH
‖
C—⬡—NH—N=N—⬡—C
NH$_2$ NH
      NH$_2$

(XII)

B. Selective Activity

The aromatic diamidines inhibit the growth of protozoa, bacteria, fungi, and neoplastic cells, generally at concentrations well below those found to be toxic to host tissues. However, within the genus *Trypanosoma*, a wide variation in sensitivity to these drugs has been observed; this is as yet unexplained. At first it appeared that there might be some correlation between diamidine sensitivity and resistance to cyanide. Trypanosomes of the brucei group, which are sensitive to these drugs (62), do not contain a normal cytochrome-cytochrome oxidase system as judged by their resistance to cyanide (66, 67), whereas *Trypanosoma lewisi* and *Trypanosoma cruzi*, which have a cyanide-sensitive respiration (68, 69), are diamidine resistant (70, 71). However, the work of Adler and his collaborators (72) has shown that various species of *Leishmania* are sensitive to diamidines and also to cyanide.

As antibacterial agents, the diamidines are generally more effective against gram-positive than gram-negative organisms (73).

C. Mechanism of Action

There have been few studies of the action of aromatic diamidines on trypanosomes which help to elucidate their mechanism of action. More information has been gained from studies with bacterial and tumor cells.

1. EFFECTS ON METABOLISM

Marshall (74) has shown that stilbamidine does not interfere with glucose or oxygen consumption by *T. evansi*; however, an accumulation of pyruvate and a change in the amounts of various phosphorylated intermediates were observed. These findings led to the suggestion that the drug inhibits the decarboxylation of pyruvic acid. Bernheim (75) however, found that the oxidation of amino acids by *Escherischia coli* and *Staphylococcus aureus* is more sensitive to propamidine than the oxidation of glucose, pyruvate, or succinate by these organisms. Further work (76) showed that the oxidation of L-proline and L-alanine is inhibited by propamidine at concentrations which stimulate the oxidation of L-serine and asparagine. Both propamidine and pentamidine inhibit mono- and diamine oxidases (77, 78).

More recently, Amos and Vollmayer (79) have reported that transamination between glutamic acid and a-ketoisovaleric acid by dried preparations of *E. coli* is inhibited by pentamidine. Hicks (80) confirmed this finding, but pointed out that 10^{-3} M pentamidine is required to produce a 40% inhibition of transaminase activity, whereas growth is inhibited by 5×10^{-5} M pentamidine. Hicks also studied the effect of pentamidine on enzyme synthesis in *E. coli*; growth in the presence of a sublethal concentration does not inhibit the synthesis of transaminase or β-galactosidase, but the cells have a lower enzyme content than control cells grown to the same density. β-Galactosidase activity of cell-free extracts is 99% inhibited by 3×10^{-3} M pentamidine; this inhibition can be reversed by excess substrate. Discussing these results, Hicks suggests that pentamidine may reduce the rate of enzyme synthesis by limiting, in some way, the availability of free amino acids for protein synthesis. The competitive inhibition of β-galactosidase by pentamidine, she points out, is comparable to the inhibition of glucosidase and maltase by histidine or other monoamines which has been observed by Halvorson and Ellias (81) and by Larner and Gillespie (82). The latter authors have suggested that amines, as free bases, combine with the imidazole ring of enzyme-bound histidine. It is possible that diamidines may act in a similar manner.

2. ANTAGONISM AND REVERSAL OF DIAMIDINE ACTION

Many nitrogen compounds interfere with the activity of diamidines (83). Bichowsky (84, 85) made a detailed study of this problem; peptones and meat extracts were found to antagonize pentamidine, but 10% serum does not; substances with polar groups similar to diamidines (creatine and arginine) lack antidiamidine activity; ribonucleic acid (RNA) and deoxyribonucleic acid (DNA) were found to reverse pentamidine bacteriostasis if added to cultures up to 24 hours after the addition of drug. These findings led Bichowsky to suggest that the growth inhibitory action of diamidines may be due to a direct interaction with nucleic acid. Snapper *et al.* (*86*) were led to a similar conclusion after observing the appearance of basophilic granules in myeloma cells from patients treated with stilbamidine. These granules can be removed by treatment with ribonuclease and are thought to be composed of RNA and bound stilbamidine.

Snell (*87*) has shown that a number of polyamines protect bacteria from diamidine action, and Elson (*88*) has reported that phospholipids exert a similar effect.

3. INTERACTION OF DIAMIDINES AND RELATED COMPOUNDS WITH ISOLATED NUCLEIC ACIDS AND NUCLEOPROTEINS

Kopac (*89*) examined the effect of a number of diamidines on nucleoproteins isolated from mammalian tissues and viruses. He found that stilbamidine enhances interfacial denaturation of these substances when they are placed at oil-water interfaces, and proposed that the drug acts by "weakening critical side-chain linkages with the production of a two-dimensional instead of a three-dimensional protein pattern." In a similar system pentamidine decreases denaturation.

Recently there have been a number of reports (*90, 91*) of interactions between polyamines and isolated nucleic acids. In particular, diamines with the general structure

$$H_2N(CH_2)_nNH_2$$

have been found to protect infective nucleic acid prepared from T2 bacteriophage against heat denaturation (*92*). These diamines are structurally similar to diamidines, and it is interesting that their ability to protect bacteriophage nucleic acid was found to be a function of their chain length; cadaverine, a compound with a five-carbon chain was the most active. Mahler *et al.* (*93*) have recently found that diamines in combination with DNA raise its denaturation temperature; again cadaverine was found to be the most active of a series of compounds with chains containing from two to eight carbon atoms.

Thus, it is clear that both diamines and diamidines are capable of interacting with, and modifying the physicochemical properties of, isolated nucleic acids and nucleoproteins. While such an interaction could well account for both the trypanocidal and bactericidal action of aromatic diamidines, it seems unlikely that the wide variation in the action of these drugs on closely related species of trypanosomes is due to variations in drug-nucleic acid affinities. Schoenbach and Greenspan (64), discussing this problem, point out that the effectiveness of both stilbamidine and pentamidine in protozoal infections, despite the inability of the latter to denature nucleoproteins in Kopac's system (89), suggests that two mechanisms should be considered: enzyme inhibition and modification of nucleoproteins.

A factor which may prove to be of considerable importance in determining the sensitivity of trypanosomes to diamidines is the chemical structure of the cell surface of these organisms. It has been suggested by a number of workers that the sensitivity of bacteria to cationic compounds may be affected by the phospholipid content of the bacterial cell walls (94–96). Mitchell and Moyle (97) found that gram-negative bacteria contain twice as much phospholipid as gram-positive bacteria; in view of the observed antagonism of diamidine action by phospholipids (88) it seems possible that the greater sensitivity of gram-positive bacteria to these drugs may be related to this fact. It would be of the greatest interest to learn something of the chemical composition of the surface structures of diamidine-sensitive and diamidine-resistant trypanosomes.

VI. QUATERNARY AMMONIUM TRYPANOCIDES

Ehrlich (98) found that acriflavine (trypaflavine) (XIII) is an active trypanocide with a low toxicity for mice. Some years later, Schnitzer and Silberstein (99) showed that 6-nitro-9-aminoacridines enhanced trypano-

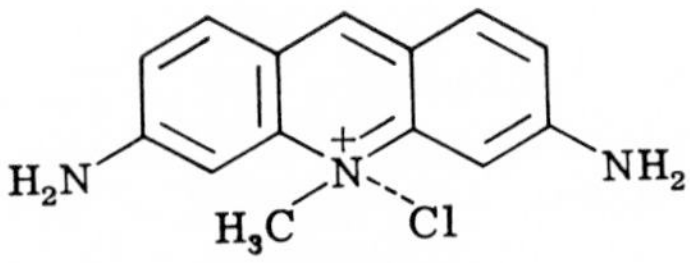

(XIII)

cidal activity and that a further increase in activity resulted from the addition of a doubly alkylated amino group in position 5. More recently, the relationship between chemical structure and biological activity of acridine derivatives has been studied in detail by Albert and his collaborators (100). As a result of these and other studies, it has become clear that quaternization is generally a prerequisite for trypanocidal activity in both acridine and quinoline derivatives, although unquaternized derivatives of both classes of compounds may have considerable antimalarial or antibacterial activity (e.g., mepacrine and proflavine). The quaternary ammonium compounds most widely used at the present time fall into two groups: phenanthridine derivatives and Antrycide.

A. Phenanthridines

A number of phenanthridinium compounds, originally synthesized by Morgan *et al.* (*101*), have been used with varying success against *T. congolense* and *Trypanosoma vivax* infections in cattle. Walls (*102*) demonstrated that high trypanocidal activity in this series of compounds is a property of quaternary salts containing a primary amino group in the 7- and a phenyl group in the 9-position; the activity is much increased by the presence of a second amino group; thus, 2,7-diamino-9-phenyl-10-methylphenanthridinium bromide [dimidium bromide (XIV)] and the 10-ethyl analogue (ethidium [bromide (XV)] are particularly effective (*103*).

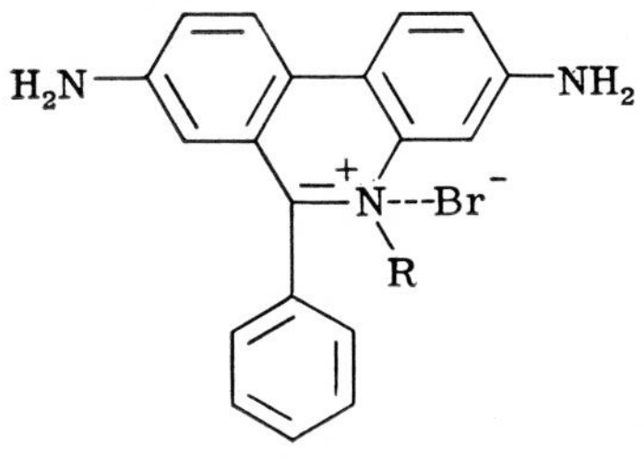

$$R = CH_3 \ (XIV); \ R = C_2H_5 \ (XV)$$

More recently, the demand for drugs with increased prophylactic action has resulted in the synthesis of compounds (XVI) (prothidium) and (XVII) (metamidium) (*104*, *105*) and in the preparation of complexes of various quaternary ammonium compounds with suramin (*106*).

1. MECHANISM OF TRYPANOCIDAL ACTION

a. Effects on Growth in vivo and in vitro. Lock (*107*), examining the action of dimidium bromide on *T. congolense* and *T. brucei* maintained *in vitro,* found that prolonged exposure to the drug does not kill the trypanosomes, although some loss of infectivity was detected when the drug-treated organisms were injected into animals. Hawking (*108*) has compared the action of phenanthridines with that of trivalent arsenicals, stilbamidine and acriflavine, and has pointed out that there are fundamental differences. The phenanthridines are typified by a slow action

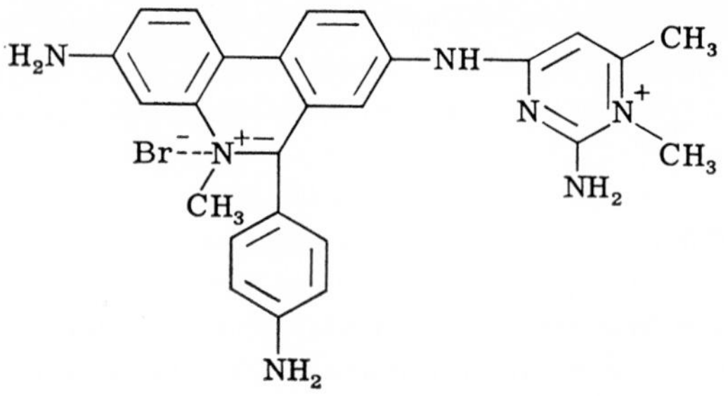

(XVI)

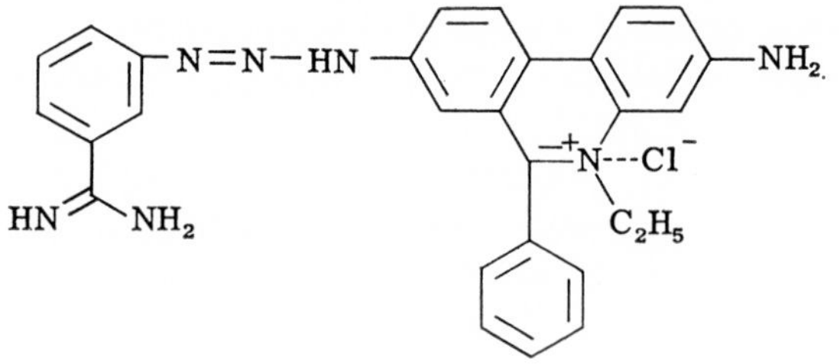

(XVII)

in vivo, and a latent period of 24 hours or more is commonly observed before any decrease in the number of blood stream trypanosomes results (cf. suramin), whereas arsenicals, stilbamidine, and acriflavine act without a lag period.

In vitro studies using the trypanosomid flagellate *Strigomonas oncopelti* as test organism have also shown that growth and cell division are not immediately inhibited by phenanthridines *(109)*; at least a doubling in the number of organisms occurs before growth is inhibited. For *S. oncopelti* these drugs are irreversibly active only against growing organisms.

b. Effects on Catabolic Processes. There have been no detailed studies of the effect of phenanthridines on the respiration or carbohydrate metabolism of trypanosomes. However, it has been observed that the motility of flagellates remains unimpaired for many hours after cell division has been inhibited by phenanthridines *(109, 110)*, so that a direct action of these drugs on metabolic systems involved in energy production or utilization is unlikely.

c. Effects on Nucleic Acid and Protein Synthesis. Evidence that phe-nanthridines may act primarily on nucleic acid synthesis is accumulating. Ormerod (*110*) showed by histochemical techniques that after 8 hours' contact with dimidium bromide basophilic granules appear in the cyto-plasm of trypanosomes. These granules were shown to contain bound drug and ribonucleoprotein. Ormerod proposed, as a working hypothesis, that these drugs may act by combining with and splitting cytoplasmic ribonucleoprotein into its constituent RNA and protein.

Newton (*109*) studied the action of ethidium and dimidium bromides on nucleic acid and protein synthesis by *S. oncopelti* and found that during the course of growth in the presence of these drugs the DNA content of organisms falls to half the control value, whereas the RNA content is little affected. Experiments with washed cell suspensions of the same organism showed that both drugs rapidly inhibit DNA synthesis but permit protein and RNA synthesis to continue for a limited period of 2–3 hours with a net increase in both components of 40–50%.

d. Uptake of Phenanthridines by Trypanosomes. Acriflavine is rapidly bound by trypanosomes, and the internal concentration may rise to 8000 times the external concentration (*108*). The phenanthridines, on the other hand, seem to be bound in relatively small amounts. Using C^{14}-labeled ethidium bromide, Newton (*109*) found that 0.05 μg drug was bound per 10^6 cells of *S. oncopelti*; more recently, Taylor (*111*) obtained a simi-lar value for the uptake of prothidium by *Trypanosoma rhodesiense.* A study of the kinetics of ethidium bromide uptake (*109*) revealed two types: (1) an initial rapid uptake, which occurs in the absence of nucleic acid synthesis and which does not affect the subsequent growth of organ-isms; and (2) an additional uptake by growing organisms, which appears to follow the course of RNA synthesis and which results, eventually, in an inhibition of growth. Discussing these results, Newton suggested that inactivation of RNA at the time of its synthesis might explain the ob-served decrease in growth rate of drug-treated organisms, since a correla-tion between the growth rate and RNA content of cells has now been established for a number of microorganisms (*112–115*). However, this would not explain the rapid inhibition of DNA synthesis which occurs before the inhibition of either RNA or protein synthesis, unless an active RNA or ribonucleoprotein is in some way involved in DNA synthesis. Further investigation of the mechanism of action of these compounds may give some information about the interrelationships existing between DNA, RNA, and protein synthesis.

e. Production of Akinetoplastic Strains. The kinetoplast is a character-istic feature of trypanosomide flagellates, and there is now good evidence that it contains DNA (*116, 117*). Werbitzki (*118*) observed in 1910 that a number of organic dyes with an orthoquinoid structure cause the disappearance of the kinetoplast; akinetoplastic strains may also arise spontaneously. Both induced and spontaneous akinetoplastic strains breed true for an indefinite period, and the organisms appear to be normal in every other respect. Hoare (*119*), discussing the genetic aspects of this phenomenon, suggests that it may be regarded as a mutation determined by plastogenes, the loss of the kinetoplast being comparable to the loss of plastids in phytoflagellates. In this respect it is interesting that prothidium has recently been reported to produce akinetoplastic strains of *T. evansi* (*120*).

2. Effects of Phenanthridines on Other Cellular Systems

a. Bacteria. Seaman and Woodbine (*121*) have studied the antibacterial action of 120 phenanthridines. Their results indicate that changes in chemical constitution affect antibacterial and trypanocidal activity in a similar manner. McIlwain (*122*) found that the antibacterial activity of amino acridines is annulled by nucleic acids, and Seaman and Woodbine have reported a similar effect for dimidium bromide. Nucleic acid will protect bacteria if added within 12 minutes of inoculating into drug-containing medium (*123*).

Gale and Folkes (*124*) found that 10^{-5} M ethidium bromide inhibits the incorporation of adenine-C^{14} and glycine-C^{14} by preparations of disrupted staphylococci, and Richmond (*125*), studying the synthesis of a lytic enzyme by *Bacillus subtilis*, reported an immediate inhibition of enzyme synthesis by 5×10^{-5} M ethidium bromide.

More recently Elliott (*125a*) has shown ethidium bromide to be a potent inhibitor of a partially purified DNA-polymerase system prepared from *Escherichia coli*, and has suggested that the drug may inhibit this system by forming a complex with DNA.

b. Viruses. Dickinson and Codd (*126*) found that a number of phenanthridines inhibit the development of a bacteriophage of *Pseudomonas aeruginosa* at a much lower concentration than that having any effect on the growth of the host. This activity was not due to an inactivation of free bacteriophage. Several compounds which are active against bacteriophage also inhibit the development of influenza virus in eggs, but were found to be inactive when tested against the same virus growing in mice (*127*).

c. Tissue Cultures. Pelc and Micou (*128*) have recently observed that the morphology of HeLa cells changes markedly following ethidium bromide treatment; the size of the nucleoli decreases to 10% of the control value in 25 hours; nuclear material becomes granular, and the cytoplasm shrinks; the mitotic index declines to 50% after 7 hours and to 2.5% after 25 hours. These workers also studied the effect of ethidium bromide on the incorporation of amino acids and nucleic acid precursors into HeLa cells, using autoradiographic techniques to study the localization of radioactivity within the cells. Their results show that the incorporation of tritiated cytidine into the RNA of nucleoli is more severely affected than the incorporation of tritiated thymidine into DNA; cytidine or adenine into nuclear RNA; or amino acids into protein. However, the incorporation of precursors into the total RNA of cells is less affected than their incorporation into DNA. Discussing these results, Pelc and Micou assume that RNA is first synthesized in association with nuclear DNA, then moves to the nucleolus, and finally into the cytoplasm; this hypothesis is based on the findings of Goldstein and Micou (*129*). If this is the case, the inhibition of incorporation of precursors into cytoplasmic RNA can be regarded as secondary to the effect on nucleoli. The authors also suggest that ethidium bromide may inhibit an early stage in the incorporation of nucleic acid and protein precursors, such as phosphorylation or attachment to soluble RNA, since they found no inhibition of incorporation of precursors which had entered cells before addition of drug to the system.

More recently Kandaswamy and Henderson (*129a*) found that ethidium bromide inhibited the incorporation of adenine, guanine, and hypoxanthine into nucleic acid by Ehrlich ascites tumor cells *in vitro* at concentrations which had little effect on the incorporation of glycine or orotic acid.

3. Interaction with Isolated Nucleic Acids

Albert (*130, 131*) has shown that the antimicrobial action of phenanthridines and the closely related acridines and benzquinolines is dependent upon the compounds existing as cations. He suggests that the simplest interpretation of the mode of action of these compounds is a competition with hydrogen ions for vitally important anionic groups in the organism. These anionic groups probably have a pK_a of 9 or higher; thus, they could be hydroxyl groups in tyrosine residues of protein or in purine or pyrimidine residues of nucleic acid. Albert has also pointed out that there is a correlation between the antimicrobial activity of this series of compounds and the "area of flatness" in the molecules. Phenanthridine and acridine molecules are fully conjugated and hence are flat molecules; they have an area of approximately 38 A². Hydrogenation of one ring of 5-aminoacridine to yield 5-aminotetrahydroacridine reduces the flat area of the molecule to 28 A^2 and also reduces its bacteriostatic activity by a factor of 30 to a level comparable to that of 4-aminoquinoline, which also has a flat area of 28 A^2.

The mutagenic properties of acridines and the carcinogenic activity of benzacridines are well established, and it is interesting that a planar polycyclic structure is also a requirement for these activities (133). The recent work of Lerman (132) on the interaction of acridine derivatives with isolated DNA has thrown some light on this requirement for planarity. He has shown that the interaction results in a marked increase in the viscosity and a decrease in the sedimentation coefficient of DNA. A study of X-ray diffraction patterns of fibers of the DNA-drug complex has shown that the combination has caused a considerable modification of the usual helical structure. Lerman states that these changes are contrary to those expected to result from simple electrostatic effects or aggregation; they are, however, consistant with an interaction of acridine molecules between adjacent nucleotide-pair layers by extension and unwinding of the deoxyribose phosphate backbone of the DNA molecule. A study of models revealed acridine to be geometrically suitable for accommodation in the internucleotide spaces of DNA. Other cations were found to diminish the viscosity of DNA. Recent observations (Newton, 1961, unpublished) have shown that ethidium bromide also increases the viscosity of DNA preparations. These findings may explain the mutagenic and antimicrobial activities of this series of compounds.

B. Antrycide

1. STRUCTURE AND ACTIVITY

Antrycide (XVIII) has proved to be effective in the treatment of *T. congolense* and *T. vivax* infections in cattle (134). The molecule contains a 4-aminoquinaldine residue linked by an —NH group in the 6-position to a pyrimidine ring; both halves of the molecule contain a quaternary nitrogen atom.

(XVIII)

2. MECHANISM OF ACTION

Antrycide is typified by a relatively slow trypanocidal action *in vivo* and *in vitro* (*37*, *135*); trypanosomes remain motile and continue to divide for periods up to 24 hours after the administration of drug. In this respect Antrycide resembles the phenanthridines and suramin (*108*).

Sen *et al.* (*136*), studying the action of Antrycide on *T. evansi*, found that growth in the presence of drug results in a reduced alkaline phosphatase activity and an accumulation of intracellular mucopolysaccharide,[1] similar changes had been observed following growth of this organism in suramin (*46*). In addition, these workers found that the lethal action of antrycide is annulled if large amounts of methionine, cysteine, or glutathione are administered at the same time as the drug. Ormerod also reported similarities between suramin, phenanthridines, and Antrycide (*137*); all these compounds induce the formation of basophilic granules in the cytoplasm of trypanosomes. These findings led Hawking to suggest that the mechanism of action of these drugs may be similar (*108*). However, Town *et al.* (*138*) found that Antrycide has no effect on a number of yeast enzymes, all of which are inhibited by suramin, and Newton (*139*), comparing the action of ethidium bromide and Antrycide on *S. oncopelti*, found that these two compounds exert very different effects on growth and nucleic acid synthesis. Antrycide does not completely inhibit the growth of this organism in either a peptone glucose medium or a synthetic medium (*140*) but changes the pattern of growth from a logarithmic form to a linear form. Analysis of organisms grown in the presence of Antrycide showed that the synthesis of RNA, DNA, and protein all follow linear courses. However, in synthetic media, in which *p*-aminobenzoic acid is present in limiting amounts and the organisms are dependent upon exogenously supplied purines, Antrycide inhibits RNA synthesis before affecting DNA synthesis. These findings led to a study of the effect of Antrycide on purine-C^{14} incorporation (*141*). It was found that this drug is a potent inhibitor of purine incorporation; the net synthesis of nucleic acids, or the incorporaton of glycine-C^{14}, uracil-C^{14}, or P^{32} are, on the other hand, less affected. The inhibition of adenine incorporation is unaffected by the ratio of purine to drug. Antrycide does not affect the permeability of *S. oncopelti* to adenine-C^{14}, nor does it inhibit the conversion of this purine to nucleoside or nucleotide; these results suggest that the drug inhibits at some point in the polymerization of acid-soluble nucleotides to nucleic acids. The drug does not affect the activity of polynucleotide phosphorylase isolated from *S. oncopelti*. The sensitivity

---

[1] Ormerod (*136a*) recently queried the validity of this finding on the grounds that the histochemical technique used was inadequate.

of purine incorporation to Antrycide is interesting in view of the fact that a number of trypanosomide flagellates are known to have an absolute growth requirement for purine (*142, 143*). In the case of these organisms this action of antrycide could account for its trypanocidal activity.

VII. SUMMING UP

From the data presented in this chapter it will be clear that there is an urgent need for detailed biochemical studies on the mechanism of action of trypanocidal agents; at the present time it is impossible to state the precise mode of action of any chemotherapeutic agent. Such studies offer two rewards. First, the compounds may prove to be valuable biochemical tools, the use of which will aid in the mapping of biochemical pathways involved in growth and cell division. From this point of view it seems that the quaternary ammonium compounds may prove to be particularly interesting, as they appear to exert selective effects on RNA and DNA synthesis. Second, information about the specificity of drug action which will be gained should speed the development of a more rational approach to chemotherapy. While it is true that the drugs in use at the present time are capable of controlling both the human and bovine forms of African trypanosomiasis, the development of new compounds is still a necessity, as recently pointed out by Goodwin (*144*), in order to combat drug-resistant variants (*145, 146*). In addition, there is a need for compounds which can be more easily administered to large populations and which will exert prolonged prophylactic action. Finally, there remains what is perhaps the most challenging problem in the field of chemotherapy of trypanosomiasis; the development of a compound active against *T. cruzi*. So far this organism has defied all chemotherapeutic treatment. Many compounds have shown *in vitro* activity against this organism or activity against infections in laboratory animals, but all have proved useless when tested clinically. The explanation of this may lie in the difference in the life history of this parasite compared with that of African species; *T. cruzi* divides in the tissues of the host and not in the blood stream. Nothing is known of the biochemistry of the intracellular forms.

REFERENCES

1. G. M. Findlay, "Recent Advances in Chemotherapy" 3rd ed., Vol. II. Churchill, London, 1951.
2. T. von Brand, *in* "Biochemistry and Physiology of Protozoa" (A. Lwoff, ed.), Vol. I, p. 177. Academic Press, New York, 1951.

3. L. G. Goodwin and I. M. Rollo *in* "Biochemistry and Physiology of Protozoa" (S. H. Hutner and A. Lwoff, eds.), Vol. II, p. 225. Academic Press, New York, 1955.
4. W. A. Sexton, "Chemical Constitution and Biological Activity," 2nd ed. Spon, London, 1953.
4a. J. Williamson, *Exptl. Parasitol.* 12, 274 (1962).
5. M. A. Bechamp, *Compt. rend. acad. sci.* 56, 1172 (1863).
6. H. W. Thomas and A. Breinl, *Liverpool School Trop. Med. Mem.* 16 (1905).
7. P. Ehrlich, *Lancet* ii, 445 (1913).
8. E. A. H. Friedheim, *Am. J. Trop. Med.* 29, 173 (1949).
9. H. Eagle and G. O. Doak, *Pharmacol. Revs.* 3, 107 (1951).
10. E. A. H. Friedheim, *Ann. Trop. Med. Parasitol.* 53, 1 (1959).
11. E. A. H. Friedheim, *Proc. 3rd Intern. Congr. Microbiol., New York* p. 428 (1939).
12. J. Le Rouzic, *Bull. Med. A. O. F. Spec. No.* pp. 53, 63 (1949).
13. P. Ehrlich, *Ber.* 42, 17 (1909).
14. C. Voegtlin, H. A. Dyer, and C. S. Leonard, *U.S. Public Health Service Rept.* 38, 1882 (1923).
15. C. Voegtlin, H. A. Dyer, and D. W. Miller, *J. Pharmacol. Exptl. Therap.* 23, 55 (1924).
16. C. Voegtlin, *Physiol. Revs.* 5, 63 (1925).
16a. F. Hawking, T. J. Hennelly, and J. H. Quastel, *J. Pharmacol. Exptl. Therap.* 59, 157 (1937).
17. R. A. Peters and R. W. Wakelin, *Biochem. J.* 40, 513 (1946).
18. L. A. Stocken and R. H. S. Thompson, *Physiol. Revs.* 29, 168 (1949).
19. E. S. G. Barron and T. P. Singer, *Science* 97, 356 (1943).
20. E. S. G. Barron and T. P. Singer, *J. Biol. Chem.* 157, 221 (1945).
21. C. K. Banks and J. Controulis, *J. Am. Chem Soc.* 68, 944 (1946).
22. G. R. Seaman, *Arch. Biochem. Biophys.* 35, 132 (1952).
23. F. Tietze and I. M. Klotz, *Arch. Biochem. Biophys.* 35, 355 (1952).
24. W. York, F. Murgatroyd, and F. Hawking, *Ann. Trop. Med.* 25, 351 (1931).
25. H. Eagle and H. J. Magnuson, *J. Pharmacol. Exptl. Therap.* 82, 137 (1944).
26. N. von Jancso and H. von Jancso, *Z. Immunitätsforsch.* 88, 275 (1936).
27. V. Fischl and L. Fischl, *Z. Immunitätsforsch.* 83, 324 (1934).
28. J. Williamson and E. M. Lourie, *Ann. Trop. Med,* 40, 255 (1946).
29. W. I. Schleyer and R. J. Schnitzer, *J. Immunol.* 60, 265 (1948).
30. J. Williamson and E. M. Lourie, *Nature* 161, 103 (1948).
31. P. Ehrlich and K. Shiga, *Berlin klin. Wochschr.* pp. 329, 362 (1904).
32. M. Nicolle and F. Mesnil, *Ann. inst. Pasteur* 20, 417 (1906).
33. I. E. Balaban and H. King, *J. Chem. Soc.* p. 3068 (1927).
34. E. Fourneau, J. Trefouel, and J. Vallee, *Ann. inst. Pasteur* 38, 81 (1924).
35. A. Spinks, *Biochem. J.* 42, 109 (1948).
36. H. von Jancso and N. von Jancso, *Zentr. Bakteriol., Parasitenk. Abt. 1 Orig.* 132, 257 (1934).
37. F. Hawking and A. B. Sen, *Brit. J. Pharmacol.* 15, 567 (1960).
38. B. von Fenyvessy and L. Reiner, *Biochem. Z.* 202, 75 (1928).

39. B. von Issekutz, *Arch. exptl. Pathol. Pharmakol. Naunyn-Schmiedeberg's* 137, 479, 499 (1933).
40. F. Glowazky, *Z. Hyg. Infektionskrankh.* 119, 741 (1937).
41. B. W. Town, E. D. Wills, and A. Wormall, *Nature* 163, 735 (1949).
42. E. D. Wills and A. Wormall, *Biochem. J.* 44, xxxix (1949).
43. H. Hoffmann-Berling, *Biochim. et Biophys. Acta* 16, 146 (1955).
44. N. von Jancso and H. von Jancso, *Zentr. Bakteriol. Parasitenk. Abt. 1 Orig.* 132, 257 (1934).
45. W. E. Ormerod, *Brit. J. Pharmacol.* 6, 334 (1951).
46. H. G. Sen, B. N. Dutta, and H. N. Ray, *Bull. Calcutta School Trop. Med.* 3, 122 (1955).
47. E. D. Wills, *Biochem. J.* 50, 421 (1952).
48. A. Beilinsohn, *Zhur. Eksp. Biol. i Med.* 11, 52 (1929).
49. J. H. Quastel, *Biochem. J.* 25, 1121 (1931).
50. J. M. Beiler and G. J. Martin, *J. Biol. Chem.* 174, 31 (1948).
51. E. D. Wills, *Biochem. J.* 57, 109 (1954).
52. A. O. M. Stoppani and J. A. Brignone, *Arch. Biochem. Biophys.* 68, 432 (1957).
53. N. Grubhofer, *Z. physiol. Chem. Hoppe-Seyler's* 302, 217 (1955).
54. E. E. B. Smith and G. T. Mills, *Biochem. J.* 52, i (1952).
55. L. Bergamini and W. Ferrari, *Boll. ist. sieroterap. milan.* 27, 89 (1948).
56. C. Biot, R. Biot, and C. Richard, *Compt. rend. soc. biol.* 71, 368 (1911).
57. A. Laveran and F. Mesnil, "Trypanosomes et Trypanosomiasis," 2nd ed. Masson, Paris, 1912.
58. H. A. Poindexter, *J. Parasitol.* 21, 292 (1935).
59. N. von Jancso and H. von Jancso, *Z. Immunitätsforsch.* 86, 1 (1935).
60. K. Schern and R. Artagaveytia-Allende, *Z. Immunitätsforsch.* 89, 21 (1936).
61. E. M. Lourie and W. York, *Ann. Trop. Med. Parasitol.* 31, 435 (1937).
62. H. King, E. M. Lourie, and W. York, *Ann. Trop. Med. Parasitol.* 32, 177 (1938).
63. J. N. Ashley, H. J. Barber, A. J. Ewins, and A. D. H. Self, *J. Chem. Soc.* p. 103 (1942).
64. E. B. Schoenbach and E. M. Greenspan, *Medicine* 27, 327 (1948).
65. H. Jensch, *Arzneimittel-Forsch.* 5, 634 (1955).
66. S. R. Christophers and J. D. Fulton, *Ann. Trop. Med. Parasitol.* 32, 43 (1938).
67. B. von Fenyvessy and L. Reiner, *Biochem. Z.* 202, 75 (1928).
68. A. Gieger, I. J. Kliger, and R. Comaroff, *Ann. Trop. Med. Parasit.* 24, 319 (1930).
69. T. von Brand, E. M. Johnson, and C. W. Rees, *J. Gen. Physiol.* 30, 163 (1946).
70. E. M. Lourie and W. York, *Ann. Trop. Med. Parasitol.* 33, 289 (1939).
71. S. Adler, I. Tchernomoretz, and M. Ber, *Ann. Trop. Med. Parasitol.* 39, 14 (1945); 42, 1 (1948).
72. S. Adler and I. Tchernomoretz, *Ann. Trop. Med. Parasitol.* 35, 9 (1941).
73. W. O. Elson, *J. Infectious Diseases* 76, 193 (1945).
74. P. B. Marshall, *Brit. J. Pharmacol.* 3, 1 (1948).
75. F. Bernheim, *Science* 98, 223 (1943).

76. F. Bernheim, *J. Pharmacol. Exptl. Therap.* **80**, 199 (1944).
77. H. Blaschko and R. Duthie, *Biochem. J.* **39**, 347 (1945).
78. A. N. Davison, *Bull. soc. chim. biol.* **40**, 1737 (1959).
79. A. Amos and E. Vollmayer, *J. Bacteriol.* **73**, 172 (1957).
80. R. M. Hicks, *Biochim. et Biophys. Acta* **46**, 143 and 152 (1961).
81. H. Halvorson and L. Ellias, *Biochim. et Biophys. Acta* **30**, 28 (1958).
82. J. Larner and R. E. Gillespie, *J. Biol. Chem.* **223**, 709 (1956).
83. H. I. Kohn, *Science* **98**, 224 (1943).
84. L. Bichowsky, *Proc. Soc. Exptl. Biol. Med.* **57**, 163 (1944).
85. L. Bichowsky-Slomnitzki, *J. Bacteriol.* **55**, 27 and 33 (1948).
86. I. Snapper, A. E. Mirsky, H. Ris, B. Schneid, and M. Rosenthal, *Blood* **2**, 311 (1947).
87. E. E. Snell, *J. Biol. Chem.* **152**, 475 (1944).
88. W. O. Elson, *J. Biol. Chem.* **154**, 717 (1944).
89. M. J. Kopac, *Cancer Research* **7**, 44 (1947).
90. D. L. Keister, *Federation Proc.* **17**, 84 (1958).
91. S. Razin and R. Rozansky, *Arch. Biochem. Biophys.* **81**, 36 (1959).
92. A. Fraser and H. R. Mahler, *J. Am. Chem. Soc.* **80**, 6456 (1958).
93. H. R. Mahler, B. D. Mehrotra and C. W. Sharp, *Biochem. Biophys. Research Communs.* **4**, 79 (1961).
94. C. E. Chaplin, *J. Bacteriol.* **64**, 805 (1952).
95. R. Fishcher and P. Larose, *Nature* **170**, 715 (1952).
96. B. A. Newton, *Symposium Soc. Gen. Microbiol.* **8**, 62 (1958).
97. P. Mitchell and J. Moyle, *J. Gen. Microbiol.* **10**, 533 (1954).
98. P. Ehrlich and L. Benda, *Ber.* **46**, 1931 (1913).
99. R. Schnitzer and W. Silberstein, *Z. Hyg. Infektionskrankh.* **109**, 519 (1929).
100. A. Albert, "The Acridines, Their Preparation, Properties and Uses." Arnold, London, 1951.
101. G. Morgan, L. P. Walls, C. H. Browning, R. Gulbranson, and J. M. V. Robb, *J. Chem. Soc.* p. 389 (1938).
102. L. P. Walls, *J. Chem. Soc.* p. 294 (1945).
103. T. I. Watkins and G. Woolfe, *Nature* **169**, 506 (1952).
104. T. I. Watkins and G. Woolfe, *Nature* **178**, 368 (1956).
105. W. R. Wragg, K. Washbourn, K. N. Brown, and J. Hill, *Nature* **182**, 1005 (1958).
106. J. Williamson and R. S. Desowitz, *Nature* **177**, 1074 (1956).
107. J. A. Lock, *Brit. J. Pharmacol.* **5**, 398 (1950).
108. F. Hawking, Symposium on Growth Inhibition and Chemotherapy, p. 88. 6th Intern. Congr. Microbiol., Rome (1953).
109. B. A. Newton, *J. Gen. Microbiol.* **17**, 718 (1957).
110. W. E. Ormerod, *Brit. J. Pharmacol.* **6**, 334 (1951).
111. A. E. R. Taylor, *Brit. J. Pharmacol.* **15**, 230 (1960).
112. T. Casperson and K. Brand, *Protoplasma* **35**, 507 (1941).
113. R. Jeener and J. Brachet, *Enzymologia* **11**, 222 (1944).
114. P. C. Caldwell, E. L. Mackor, and C. Hinshelwood, *J. Chem. Soc.* p. 3151 (1950).
115. E. F. Gale and J. P. Folkes, *Biochem. J.* **53**, 483 (1953).
116. J. H. Barrow, *Trans. Am. Microscop. Soc.* **73**, 242 (1954).

117. R. W. Horne and B. A. Newton, *Exptl. Cell. Research* 15, 103 (1958).
118. F. W. Werbitzki, *Zentr. Bakteriol., Parasitenk. Orig.* 53, 303 (1910).
119. C. A. Hoare, *J. Protozool.* 1, 28 (1954).
120. H. N. Ray and M. N. Malhotra, *Nature* 188, 870 (1960).
121. A. Seaman and M. Woodbine, *Brit. J. Pharmacol.* 9, 265 (1954).
122. H. McIlwain, *Biochem. J.* 35, 1311 (1941).
123. A. Seaman and M. Woodbine, *Proc. 6th Intern. Congr. Microbiol., Rome* 1, 636 (1953).
124. E. F. Gale and J. P. Folkes, *Biochem. J.* 69, 620 (1958).
125. M. H. Richmond, *Biochim. et Biophys. Acta* 34, 325 (1959).
125a. W. H. Elliott, *Biochem. J.* 86, 562 (1963).
126. L. Dickinson and S. Codd, *J. Gen. Microbiol.* 6, 1 (1952).
127. L. Dickinson, B. H. Chantrell, G. W. Inkley, and M. J. Thompson, *Brit. J. Pharmacol.* 8, 139 (1953).
128. S. R. Pelc and J. Micou, unpublished observations.
129. L. Goldstein and J. Micou, *J. Biophys. Biochem. Cytol.* 6, 301 (1959).
129a. T. S. Kandaswamy and J. F. Henderson, *Nature* 195, 85 (1962).
130. A. Albert, S. D. Rubbo, R. Goldacre, M. Davey, and J. Stone, *Brit. J. Exptl. Pathol.* 26, 60 (1945).
131. A. Albert, "Selective Toxicity." Metheun, London, 1960.
132. L. S. Lerman, *J. Mol. Biol.* 3, 18 (1961).
133. J. P. Greenstein, "Biochemistry of Cancer." Academic Press, New York, 1954.
134. F. H. S. Curd and D. G. Davey, *Brit. J. Pharmacol.* 5, 25 (1950).
135. B. A. Newton, *J. Gen. Microbiol.* 19, ii (1958).
136. H. G. Sen, H. N. Ray, and D. N. Dutta, *Bull. Calcutta School Trop. Med.* 2, 18 and 56 (1954).
136a. W. E. Ormerod, *Trans. Roy. Soc. Trop. Med. Hyg.* 55, 313 (1961).
137. W. E. Ormerod, *Brit. J. Pharmacol.* 6, 325 (1951).
138. B. W. Town, E. D. Wills, and A. Wormall, *Nature* 164, 233 (1949).
139. B. A. Newton, *in* "Drugs, Parasites and Hosts" (L. G. Goodwin and R. H. Nimmo-Smith, eds.), p. 142. Churchill, London, 1962.
140. B. A. Newton, *Nature* 177, 279 (1956).
141. B. A. Newton, *Biochem. J.* 77, 17P (1960).
142. G. J. Bone and M. Steinert, *Nature* 178, 308 (1956).
143. J. Williamson and I. M. Rollo, *Nature* 170, 376 (1952).
144. L. G. Goodwin, *in* "Strategy of Chemotherapy" (S. T. Cowan and E. Rowatt, eds.), Symposium Soc. Gen. Microbiol. No. 8, p. 336. Cambridge Univ. Press, London and New York, 1958.
145. A. Bishop, *Biol. Revs.* 34, 445 (1959).
146. R. J. Schnitzer and E. Grunberg, "Drug Resistance of Microorganisms." Academic Press, New York, 1957.

CHAPTER 29

Cations and Anions: Inhibitions and Interactions in Metabolism and in Enzyme Activity

E. J. Hewitt and D. J. D. Nicholas

I. INTRODUCTION

Cations and anions derived mainly from rock materials in the earth's crust are found in soluble form in the environment of microorganisms, plants, and animals. They play a profound part in maintaining osmotic pressures within cells and are required for growth processes and metabolism of living things. Thus, a number of mineral nutrients are specifically required for the growth of plants and animals, and by definition a shortage of an essential element cannot be remedied by supplying another. Not only are absolute amounts of these elements important, since below certain levels deficiency effects result in upset metabolism and diminished growth, but the ratios in which they occur in the environment influence cell metabolism. Thus, toxicity effects can be produced by too high a concentration of one nutrient relative to others.

311

In this chapter, some of the salient points in regard to cationic and anionic interactions will be considered in microorganisms, plants, and animals, but no attempt will be made to catalogue the very exhaustive list of inhibitions and competitions that are recorded in the literature.

II. PHYSIOLOGICAL INTERACTIONS

A. Essential Elements

An adequate supply of cations and anions in the correct proportions is indispensable for the normal growth of plants and animals. Thus, in the plant kingdom (in bacteria, fungi, and green plants), the following mineral nutrients have been shown to be essential for growth: N, P, K, Mg, Ca, Na, S, Fe, Cu, Zn, Mn, Mo, B, Cl, Co, and V. Not all of these have been shown to be essential for all plants, but all of them have been shown to be required for some species. An essential element is one that cannot be replaced by another (1). Cobalt has been shown to be required by some bacteria, e.g., *Rhizobia* (2–5), and vitamin B$_{12}$ by bacteria, e.g., *Lactobacillus leichmanii* (6), and by algae (7) but not by higher forms. Vanadium is known thus far to be essential for the alga, *Scenedesmus obliquus*, only (8), although it is a well-known constituent of the blood of tunicates (9). Another factor that has a bearing on interaction of the nutrients is the different amounts required for optimum growth. Thus, N, P, K, and Mg are usually required in larger amounts by plants, whereas trace quantities of the other nutrients suffice. Although Ca is required in macro amounts by higher plants, traces only are necessary for algae, fungi, and bacteria (10). Boron, although essential for higher plants, has not been shown, unequivocally, to be required by fungi and bacteria. The animal requirements for nutrients differ from those of plants in that inorganic nitrogen is not utilized; boron is not essential, but iodine is indispensable for higher forms.

B. Nutrient Interactions in Microorganisms

1. REPLACEMENT IONS

It is well established that microorganisms require markedly different amounts of inorganic salts for maximum yields. A few examples of these different requirements, shown in Table I, probably reflect differences in their metabolism. Instances are known where one metal ion can replace

TABLE I
VARIATIONS IN METAL ION REQUIREMENTS OF DIFFERENT BACTERIA GROWN
IN SIMILAR MEDIA

Metal ion	Organism	Requirement for maximum growth (ppm)
Mg^{+2}	Pseudomonas aeruginosa	2
	Aerobacter aerogenes	3
	Azotobacter chroococcum	32
Mn^{+2}	Lactobacillus arabinosus	0.1
	Lactobacillus casei	0.03
	Streptococcus faecalis	<0.03
K^+	Lactobacillus casei	30
	Streptococcus faecalis	15

another completely. Thus, a K^+ requirement for growth of *Streptococcus faecalis* can be replaced by Rb^+ (11–14). It has not been established, however, whether there is a small minimal requirement for K^+ even in the presence of Rb^+. A similar effect has been observed in algae, e.g. *Chlorella* (15). Although calcium is required for growth of green algae (15) and some fungi (16), there is evidence that strontium can substitute for it. Again, critical experiments, in which the medium is rigorously freed from the nutrient to be replaced, have not been done. Thus, more work is required to establish whether or not there is a complete replacement of one element by another for growth in these bacteria.

A much more common phenomenon, however, is the partial replacement or sparing action of one mineral nutrient for another. The manganese requirement of *Lactobacillus arabinosus* was decreased when magnesium was present in the medium, and calcium and strontium have a smaller sparing action, as shown in Fig. 1 (12). In *Leuconostoc mesenteroides*, although rubidium reduced the requirement for potassium, it did not substitute for it completely (12). Presumably, in these instances the "sparing" nutrient cannot take over all the functions of the element it replaces. Vanadium can partially replace molybdenum in nitrogen fixation in some *Azotobacter* species (17–19).

There are instances where a requirement for a mineral nutrient is much reduced when the nitrogen source in the medium is changed. Thus, Steinberg (20, 21) showed that when *Aspergillus niger* was grown in media containing ammonium salts instead of nitrate the molybdenum requirement was markedly reduced. The reason for this has now been clarified, since the enzyme nitrate reductase contains molybdenum

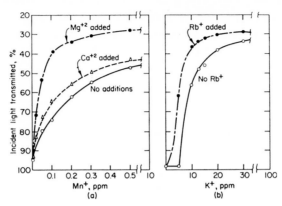

FIG. 1. *a*, The effect of Ca^{2+} and Mg^{2+} on the Mn^{+2} requirement of *Lactobacillus arabinosus*. *b*, The effect of Rb^+ on the K^+ requirement of *Streptococcus equinus* (*Leuconostoc mesenteroides* P-60). Redrawn by permission of the *Journal of Bacteriology*. From MacLeod and Snell (*12*).

(*22–26*). Molybdenum is essential for nitrogen fixation in bacteria, and this requirement is also reduced when the organisms are grown on ammonium salts when atmospheric nitrogen is not utilized (*27*). Holland and Meinke (*28*) reported that more iron was required by *S. faecalis* when serine was omitted from the medium.

2. ION ANTAGONISMS

Perhaps the first report of the antagonistic effect of trace metals on growth of a microorganism was that of Pfeffer in 1895. He was impressed by the fact that only minute amounts of trace metals resulted in relatively large increases in yields of *A. niger* and concluded wrongly that these substances stimulated abnormal growth. He based his argument on the old Arndt-Schultze concept of the stimulatory effect of poisons on animal cells. He did not realize that the good growth of the fungus obtained in unpurified culture medium was due to trace metals present as contaminants. Thus, he assumed that trace metals added to the cultures stimulated growth above the expected normal level.

It was left to Bertrand and Javillier (*29*) and Steinberg (*30*) to show that trace metals were in fact essential for the growth of *A. niger*. The results of their pioneer experiments with pure culture techniques have been confirmed by others, so that the concept of an essential nutrient for growth is now firmly established.

The counteraction of the effects on growth and metabolism of one ion by another is often referred to as *ion antagonism*. MacLeod and Snell

(11, 31) suggest that ions that suppress growth do so by interfering with one or more of the essential metabolic functions in which the nutrient is involved. They showed that in *S. faecalis* when potassium or rubidium was the essential nutrient it was antagonized by sodium or cesium. They suggest that this be explained by assuming that the enzyme protein can combine with potassium or rubidium to form an active metal-enzyme complex, but that sodium or cesium forms an inactive complex with the same protein. Thus, sodium and cesium would be inhibitory metal ions as follows:

$$\begin{array}{l} \text{Enzyme} + \text{K}^+ \rightarrow \text{K-enzyme} \\ \text{Enzyme} + \text{Rb}^+ \rightarrow \text{Rb-enzyme} \end{array} \quad \text{Active metal-enzyme}$$

$$\begin{array}{l} \text{Enzyme} + \text{Na}^+ \rightarrow \text{Na-enzyme} \\ \text{Enzyme} + \text{Cs}^+ \rightarrow \text{Cs-enzyme} \end{array} \quad \text{Inactive metal-enzyme}$$

which depicts the possible mode of action of activation and inhibition of enzymes in *Streptococcus faecalis* by alkali metals *(14)*.

Depending on the reversibility of the association of the ions with the enzyme, the inhibition could be noncompetitive, should the ions be tightly bound, or competitive, if the inhibitory elements are readily released from the protein by the active ions. Examples are discussed later with regard to cationic inhibition of dual metal-activated enzymes.

In *Lactobacillus casei*, the antagonistic sodium ion increases the potassium requirement, as shown in Fig. 2, and the ammonium ion is even more

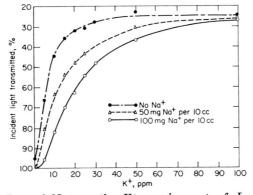

FIG. 2.   The effect of Na$^+$ on the K$^+$ requirement of *Lactobacillus casei*. Redrawn by permission of the *Journal of Biological Chemistry*. From MacLeod and Snell *(11)*.

inhibitory in this and in other organisms *(11)*. These effects are often complex, since one ion may replace the related ion for some metabolic function but inhibit it for others, and these effects may occur at the same or at different concentrations. Thus, MacLeod and Snell (11, 12) found that rubidium substantially decreased the requirement of L. mesenteroides for potassium, but at higher concentrations it inhibited growth by competing with potassium for sites that specifically require the latter element. Similar phenomena occur between essential cations and related non-essential ones in many microorganisms and in higher plants described later.

Lavollay and Laborey (32–34) have studied the relation between the concentration of an essential element and the yield of A. niger. They derived an equation [Eq. (1)] for the effect of increasing magnesium concentration in the medium from deficiency to sufficiency levels on the

$$P = A(1 - C^{-2.53x}) \tag{1}$$

yield curve, where P is the weight of felt corresponding to the concentration x of the limiting nutrient in the medium. When a value of 100% was used for A, the activity coefficient C was calculated to be 2.53. The value of C for a given element in the medium gives a measure of its importance as a factor in the development of the organism. Where $x = 1/C$, the basic equation becomes

$$P = A(1 - e^{-1}) \tag{2}$$

or

$$P = A \frac{63}{100} \tag{3}$$

It is thus possible to determine C graphically by determining the abscissa x_C of the point corresponding to $P = A$ (63/100) on the yield curve. The activity coefficient is inversely proportional to the concentration which gives 63% of the maximum yield.

Lavollay and Laborey showed that concentrations of a nutrient that result in fractions of maximum yield are all proportional to x_C. They (32) showed that yield curves, as a fraction of the concentration of an essential element in the medium, are considerably modified with changes in the composition of the media. The interaction is illustrated in Figs. 3a, b, and c from Lavollay (34a), where a family of yield curves as a fraction of Mn or Zn can be considerably modified when the over-all composition of the basal medium is changed. In the top figure the amounts of Mg in milligrams that give 50% of maximum yields (abscissas) are plotted for each of the media dilutions on the ordinate axis. Steinberg's basal medium was

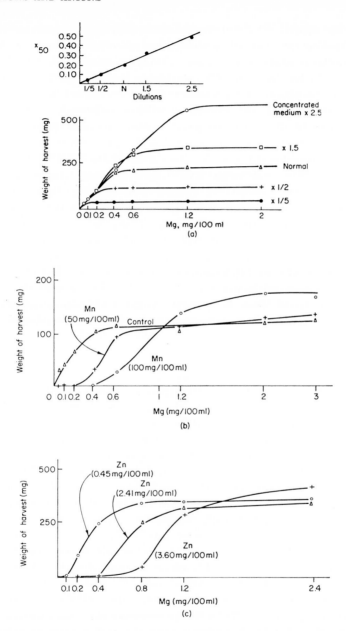

FIG. 3. a, Action of Mg in media of different over-all concentrations. Concentrated or diluted Steinberg medium. b, Interaction of Mn and Mg. Excess of Mn. Steinberg medium. c, Interaction of Zn and Mg. Steinberg medium. From Lavollay (34a).

used as the normal (N). It is clear that the Mg requirements are directly proportional to the over-all concentration of other nutrients in the medium. Similar results were found for other micronutrients; thus, the amount of Zn resulting in 50% maximum yield in each of a series of dilutions of Steinberg's basal medium, from 1 to 0.2, are similarly proportional to the over-all constitution of other constituents of the medium. The intersections of the yield curves reveal that toxic concentrations of Zn or Mn at low Mg levels are beneficial at higher levels. Similar experiments have been described by Abelson and Aldous ($34b$, $34c$), Sivarama Sastry et al. ($34c$), and Adiga et al. ($34d$) for several fungi and yeasts. Magnesium or iron was able to antagonize to varying degrees the effects of excesses of cobalt, nickel, or manganese on such activities as growth, acid formation, and glucose utilization. Thus, in A. niger ($34d$) magnesium reversed the effects of zinc and nickel on acid production but not those of cobalt. Magnesium, however, reversed the effects of all three metals, as glucose utilization and growth had no effect on inhibition of acid production in the presence of any of the three metals but reversed the effects of all of them on growth. Adiga et al. ($34d$) suggested that cobalt excess induced iron deficiency, while zinc excess induced magnesium deficiency.

3. CHELATION OF METALS

The absorption of ions by microorganisms varies greatly and is often dependent on the composition of the culture medium (15). Thus, with some Lactobacilli (e.g., L. casei and L. arabinosus) the addition of citrate to the medium inhibits growth, since it complexes with manganese and magnesium so that uptake is reduced as shown in Fig. 4a (13). The effect can be reversed, however, by adding more of the cations. The uptake of magnesium and manganese by S. faecalis was not, however, affected by citrate (15). Hutner et al. (6) consider that the absorption of metal ions involves chelate formation with constantly renewed chelating groups on the cell surface. Absorption of metal ions involves a competition between ligands on the cell membrane and those in the culture medium. It may be that chelates of manganese and magnesium formed with S. faecalis have a higher stability than those formed with L. casei. Hutner et al. have exploited the use of chelating agents including EDTA to demonstrate requirements of trace metals by some organisms (6). The effects of citrate on the uptake of magnesium by S. faecalis and uptake of calcium by Chlorella in the presence and absence of EDTA are illustrated in Fig. 4b (35). In both instances the growth is reduced when either chelate is present. Not all metals behave in this way, since in Chlorella the uptake

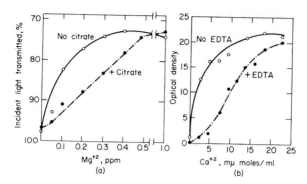

FIG. 4. (*a*), The comparative response of *Streptococcus faecalis* to Mg²⁺ in the presence and absence of citrate (20 mg citrate ion/ml). Redrawn by permission of the author and publisher. From MacLeod (*13*). (*b*), The comparative requirement of *Chlorella* for Ca²⁺ in a glucose-urea-salts medium versus a glucose–urea–ethylenediaminetetraacetate (2.5 mg/5 ml)-salts medium. Redrawn by permission of the author and publisher. From Walker (*35*).

of iron from iron combined with EDTA or ferricyanide in the culture medium was better than when ferrous sulfate was used (*36*).

Albert (*37*) has considered in some detail the chemistry of metal-binding agents, including oxine (I) and pteridines, in relation to their selective toxicity on microorganisms. He suggests that the antibacterial action of oxine is due to metal binding. Albert *et al.* (*38*) prepared six isomers of oxine which have no way of chelating since they cannot form

8-Hydroxyquinoline (oxine)

(I)

5- or 6-membered rings to include the metal, for obvious spatial reasons. These had no antibacterial action. Oxine, however, chelates readily and at 10^{-5} *M* inhibited the growth of *Staphylococci* and *Streptococci*. Thus, the connection between chelation and antibacterial action was established. The mechanism could be due to the removal of essential metals resulting in deficiency effects, as had been suggested by Zentmyer (*39*), or else caused by the toxic action of metal-oxine complexes formed in the medium. The results of Albert *et al.* (*40, 41*) with *Staphylococcus aureus*

suggest that the latter theory is probably correct. An unusual phenomenon was observed by them, namely, that toxicity effects decreased as the
concentration of oxine increased. Their results (Table II) show that

TABLE II

THE EFFECT OF INCREASED CONCENTRATIONS OF OXINE IN CULTURE BROTH ON
GROWTH OF *Staphylococcus aureus*[a]

Concentration of oxine 1/M	Growth after exposure[b]			
	0 (hours)	1 (hour)	3 (hours)	24 (hours)
800	+++	+++	+++	+
1600	+++	+++	+++	+
3200	+++	+++	+	+
6400	+++	+++	+	−
12,800	+++	+	+	−
25,000	+++	+	−	−
50,000	+++	+	−	−
100,000	+++	−	−	−
200,000	+++	+++	+++	+++

[a] *S. aureus* in meat broth at pH 7.0–7.3 (20°).
[b] The bactericidal test in this and the following tables is based on that of
A. Miles and S. Misra. At the end of the given time, samples were withdrawn,
diluted, and inoculated on a dried blood agar plate. The plates were read after
48 hours at 37°. Symbols: −, no growth; +, up to 50 colonies; ++, 50–150
colonies; +++, uncountable. [*J. Hyg.* 38, 732 (1938).]

Staphylococci, killed in an hour by $10^{-5}\,M$ oxine, were unaffected by
$10^{-3}\,M$ oxine even after 3 hours, and even a saturated solution failed to
inhibit them. This effect is known as *"concentration quenching."* Since
this phenomenon occurred in culture medium only and not in distilled
water, it was suggested that the oxine might act by chelating with metals
in the broth. Thus, the bacteria suspended in distilled water were not
affected by $10^{-5}\,M$ oxine; but when a similar amount of iron was added,
it was bactericidal, although iron alone was without effect. The toxic agent
appears to be the oxine-iron complex. When complex media were used,
there was sufficient iron present as a contaminant to form the oxine complex. Albert *et al.* claim that the toxic action is due to formation of either
a 1:1 complex (II) or the 2:1 complex, both of which are "unsaturated,"
but not to the formation of a 3:1 complex (III) which is obtained when
oxine is in excess, since it has no residual combining power, a necessary
feature for reactivity.

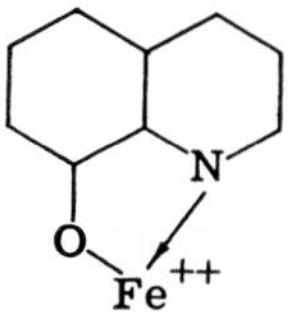

1:1 Ferric complex of oxine

(II)

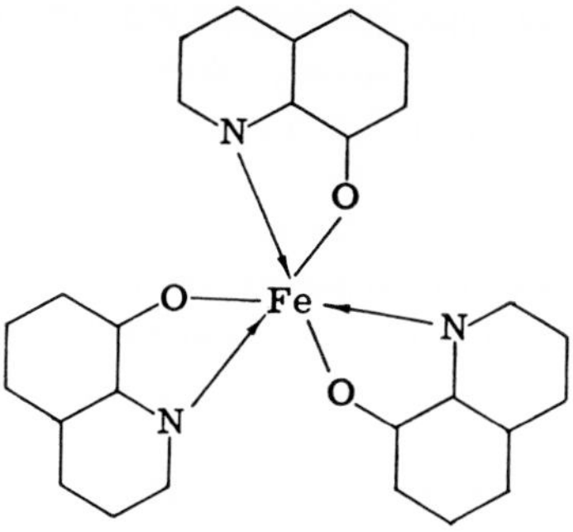

3:1 Ferric complex of oxine

(III)

It has been shown (by the use of C^{14}-labeled oxine prepared from aniline-C^{14} and glycerol-C^{14}) that oxine enters the bacterial cell without causing harm. This is also true in the fungus *A. niger* and in yeasts where toxicity occurs only when cupric ions are present in the medium in association with oxine (*42*).* The data of Albert (*37*) given in Table III show

TABLE III

PROTECTIVE ACTION OF COBALT AGAINST THE BACTERICIDAL ACTION OF IRON-OXINE AND COPPER-OXINE[a,b]

Tube	Conc. of metal added (1/M)			Growth after exposure (hours)[c]			
	$FeSO_4$	$CuSO_4$	$CoSO_4$	0	2	4	24
1	Nil	Nil	Nil	+++	+++	+++	+++
2	50,000	Nil	Nil	+++	—	—	—
3	50,000	Nil	50,000	+++	++	++	+++
4	Nil	50,000	Nil	+++	—	—	—
5	Nil	50,000	50,000	+++	—	—	—
6	Nil	50,000	10,000	+++	+++	+++	+++

[a] From Albert (*37*).

[b] *S. aureus* in metal-depleted broth at pH 7.3 (20°); $M/25,000$ oxine present in every tube.

[c] Symbols are the same as those used in Table II.

* O. T. G. Jones showed that copper was specifically required for the inhibitory effect of oxine on the synthesis of bacteriochlorophyll by *Rhodopseudomonas spheroides*. The production of a copper-pheophorbide complex was suggested as a possible mechanism of action for the copper-oxine chelate. [*Biochem. J.* 88, 335 (1963).]

that ferrous, ferric, and cupric ions are equally toxic in association with oxine in *S. aureus*, where as nickel, zinc, cobalt, cadmium, manganese, and calcium have no cotoxicant action with oxine-iron, provided the stability constant of the new complex is greater than or similar to that of oxine iron. Experiments have shown that cobalt is unique in that it protects the bacteria from iron-oxine inhibition even at low concentrations. The results of Rubbo *et al.* (*40*) show that as little as $4 \times 10^{-5} M$ cobaltous sulfate prevents the bacteriostatic effect of either oxine or iron-oxine, each at $10^{-5} M$. Nordbring-Hertz showed that cobalt protected yeasts against copper-oxine (*43*). Molybdenum can partially reverse the toxic action of copper-oxine in some fungi (*44*). It is unlikely that the protective action of cobalt is due to its combining the oxine in preference to iron, since the amount of cobalt that is effective is much less than the iron present. It is known that the stability constant of nickel-oxine is higher than for the cobalt-oxine, yet nickel has no protective action at low concentrations. Albert suggests that mercapto compounds and ascorbic acid in cells are readily oxidized by atmospheric oxygen, especially when traces of iron or copper are present, to yield hydrogen peroxide, which in turn oxidizes more substrate (*37*). Thus, small amounts of these metals set up a chain reaction within the cell that oxidizes substrates. Albert suggests that cobalt acts as a chain breaker in this reaction, thus reducing substrate oxidation in the bacterial cells. Further biochemical work is, however, necessary to decide whether this is the mechanism by which cobalt reverses the iron-oxine inhibition in bacterial cells.

Many derivatives and analogues of oxine have been tested against the tubercle bacillus (*121*). Provided that the 2-position of the molecule is kept intact, all are inhibitory. The copper complexes of the analogues are also more inhibitory than the iron complexes, and cobalt reverses the toxic effect. The substituted azoxines with short side chains (*N*) and the *N*-oxides of pyridine, quinoline, and benzoquinoline are antibacterial provided a hydroxy group is in the 2-position (IV) to make chelation possible, and a mercapto group in this position, e.g., 2-mercaptopyridine-*N*-oxide, (V) has been found to be as intensely antibacterial as oxine (I).

(IV)   (V)   (VI)

Although the chelated complex (VI) has a different structure than that of oxine (I), the mode of action is probably similar, since both materials are bactericidal only when iron is added, and this effect is reversed either by cobalt or by an excess of the substance itself (*37*).

The fungicide copper-dimethyldithiocarbamic acid (VII), also used as the sodium (NaDCC), iron, or zinc salt, has a triphasic effect on the growth of *A. niger* (*45*). The first zone of inhibition is at 1 ppm but only when cobalt, or preferably copper, is present, whereas iron is ineffective. Increasing the concentration of NaDDC to 10 ppm reverses the inhibition, due to the conversion of the 1:1 complex (VII) to a saturated 2:1

$$
\begin{array}{c}
\text{S} \\
\| \\
(CH_3)_2N \cdot CS\!-\!Cu^+
\end{array}
$$

Cupric dimethyldithiocarbamate (1:1)

(VII)

complex. At 50 ppm a third toxic phase is apparent, and this is believed to be the inhibitory action inherent in the material, independent of the metals. It is of interest that Goksøyr (*46*) and Sijpesteijn and associates (*47*) showed that copper but not iron is a cotoxicant of oxine in *A. niger* and that cobalt did not offset this effect. The inactivity of cobalt may be related to oxidation-reduction potentials of the complexes. Weinberg (*48*) reported that antibacterial and antifungal action of kojic acid is increased by metallic ions, but the mechanism involved is not known.

Isoniazid [the hydrazide of isonicotinic acid (VIII), R = H] is effective against the tubercle bacillus, and, because it chelates metals, it was thought that this might be its mode of action [Eq. (4)].

R = H, R = CH$_3$

(VIII)   (IX)

Albert (*49*) showed that the affinity of isoniazid for heavy metals is similar to that of glycine. A number of workers (*50*) have suggested that because isoniazid must first form the anion (IX) to chelate metals and because 1-isonicotinoyl-1-methylhydrazine (VIII, R = CH$_3$) is inactive and cannot form an anion, the inhibitory mechanism involves metal chelation. Albert points out that this theory is unlikely to be correct, since neither of the two isomers of isoniazid has any marked action on *M. tuberculosis* although they have a very high affinity for metals (*51*).

It is now known that the mode of action of isoniazid is due to its combining with pyridoxal and replacing nicotinamide in DPN, thus inhibiting vital metabolic processes in the cell.

The tetracycline antibiotics (X) terramycin and aureomycin also chelate divalent metals with the same avidity as glycine. (Substituent groups, Cl and OH, occur at X and Y in different members of this group.)

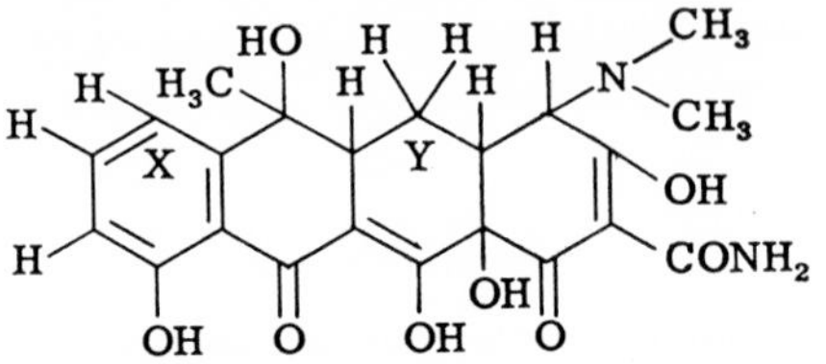

(X)

They form stable complexes with Fe^{3+} and Al^{3+} (52). The action of tetracyclines on bacteria is much slower than that of oxine, and they are active even in the absence of iron. Saz and Marmur (53) and Saz and Slie (54) found that aureomycin could effectively remove manganese by chelation from enzyme proteins, as will be discussed in the next section. Thus, there is some evidence that this antibiotic inhibits enzymes by chelation with the metals required to activate them.

4. Toxicity Effects of Metals

a. Physicochemical Character. Interest in the toxic effects of metal ions on microorganisms has stemmed from attempts to control pathogens, whether they be bacteria, fungi, or algae. Early investigators tried to assign the toxicity effect to some special chemical or physical property of the cation or anion. Thus, Matthews in 1904 (55) thought that the electrode potential of a metal was an important feature, and Jones (56) considered that the logarithm of the toxic concentration for 18 or so metals that he used to inhibit a planarian, *Polycelis nigra*, was a linear function of their standard electrode potentials. Danielli and Davies (57) have suggested that the intensity of the covalent binding of a particular ion with ionogenic groups, e.g., imidazole, carboxyl, phosphate, or sulfhydryl, on the cell surface is primarily responsible for metal toxicity effects. They discount the oxidation-reduction theory proposed by earlier workers and claim that the electronegativity value of the metal is a measure of its chemical reaction. By determining the energy of covalent bond formation between metal ion and oxygen-containing groups on the cell surface, they derived an exponential relation between the logarithm of toxic concentration of the metal ion and its electronegativity value. Somers (*58–60*) has examined *in vitro* the fungistatic activity of some 24 metal cations against spores of *Altenaria tenuis* and *Botrytis fabae*. The metal salts, mainly nitrates, were tested in aqueous solution without an added stimulant for spore germination. The logarithm of the metal ion concentration at the ED_{50} value (50% spore inhibition) was found to conform to the exponential relation with electronegativity of the metals, as proposed by Danielli and Davies. The data of Somers, illustrated in Fig. 5, have been viewed differently by Miller (*61*), who considers the

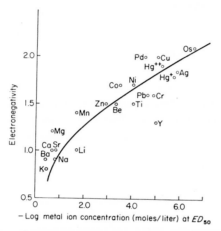

FIG. 5.   Graph of toxicity of metal cations to *Botrytis fabae* against electronegativity of the metal. From Somers (*58*).

interpretation that the site of inhibitory action is associated primarily with the surface of fungal cells to be incorrect. Miller and his co-workers (*62, 63*) have shown that conidia of pathogenic fungi readily take up labeled ions in a matter of minutes after exposure to the tracer solution and that there is free movement into the spores. They found no evidence for toxic elements accumulating at cell surfaces. They consider that the metal toxicant acts on receptor sites within the spores and that the inhibitory mechanism is more complex than can be explained by a simple difference in the electronegativity of the elements. Further work is required to resolve the two viewpoints, and it may well be that toxic metals inhibit active sites at membrane surfaces as well as within the cells.

b. *Fungitoxicity*. Several books and reviews have covered various aspects of the toxic action of metals on fungi, since this topic is of great economic importance (*16, 64–66*). After an extensive study of existing data, Horsfall (*65*) concluded that the following order of toxicity applies to a range of fungal species: $Ag > Hg > Cu > Cr > Ni > Pb > Co > Zn > Ca$, but the position of nickel is variable. The tests are usually carried out with germinating spores in the absence of culture media because of the complications of metal chelation discussed in the previous section. Silver, mercury, and copper are probably the most toxic metals for microorganisms at equivalent concentrations. Inorganic salts of the same metal may vary in their toxicity effects on microflora. Thus, copper as cupric ammonium sulfate is bound more firmly to fungal spores than is copper sulfate (67), and silver iodide is usually less inhibitory than are other silver halides (68).

Amino acids and hydroxy acids are secreted by fungal spores, and these readily complex metals, which then penetrate rapidly into the cells (64–66). Results of radioactive tracer techniques using S^{35}, Ag^{110}, Hg^{203}, Cd^{115}, Zn^{65}, and Ce^{144} show that these ions are taken up rapidly by fungal spores from dilute solutions (1–10 μg/ml). Usually, over 50% of the total uptake occurred within a few minutes and reached a maximum of 10,000 times the external concentration. The dose required to inhibit the germination of 50% of the spores (ED_{50}) ranged from 85 to 11,500 μg/gm spore weight, as shown in Table IV (64). Silver is the most toxic metal at equivalent concentrations.

TABLE IV

ED_{50} VALUES IN MICROGRAMS PER GRAM (PPM) OF SPORE WEIGHT OF VARIOUS FUNGITOXICANTS FOR SPORES OF SOME REPRESENTATIVE FUNGI[a]

Fungitoxicant	Alternaria oleracea	Monilinia fructicola	Neurospora sitophila	Venturia pyrina
Sulfur (based on H_2S evolution)	6800[b]		11,500	
Cerium	>7100[c]	4600	>970[c]	
Cadmium			1200	
Mercury		2830	5030	
Silver	360	250	165	85
2-Heptadecyl-2-imidazoline			5800	9300
2,3-Dichloro-1,4-naphthoquinone	400	385	560	

[a] McCallan, S. E. A. (1957) in "Crop Protection Conference 1956," p. 90. Butterworths, London.

[b] ED_{95}.

[c] No effect on germination at these doses.

Silver and cerium do not interfere with the uptake of one another by fungal spores and are likely, therefore, to have different receptor sites, whereas the closely related rare earths, e.g., cerium and neodymium,

inhibit one another, indicating common adsorption centers. When silver
and mercury are applied together, more mercury is absorbed, presumably
because silver increases the permeability of the cell membrane. Radioactive phosphorus and sulfur leach out readily from fungal spores
immersed in water.

The response of fungal spores to a metal toxicant depends on the concentration of metal, on the ratio of toxicant to spores, on interactions with
other metals present, and on complex formation with spore exudates
(64, 65).

There are instances where organometal complexes are more toxic than
individual cations, as discussed earlier for oxine complexes. Thus, organic
mercurials are more toxic than inorganic mercury to bacteria and fungi.
(65, 69), and stannous or stannic ions are nontoxic, whereas tri-n-butyltin
acetate inhibits fungal growth at 0.1–0.5 ppm (70).

The uptake of copper and mercury by *Tilletia tritici* was found to be
nonlinear with respect to external concentration of the metals and thus
follows the Freundlich adsorption isotherm (68, 71). Copper supplied as
a salt was readily removed in acid from the spores, but the metal of
cupric ammonium sulfate, a coordination complex, was retained despite
acid treatment. There is evidence that uptake of ionic copper by the
fungus spores is quantitatively compensated by release of hydrogen ions,
ferrous iron, and magnesium. Divalent cations reduce the uptake and
toxicity effects of heavy metals in fungal spores (68). Thus, the uptake
of silver is reduced by adding copper and, more effectively by mercury.
The effect of hydrogen ions in counteracting copper toxicity in spores of
A. tenuis by removing the metal is shown in Fig. 6 (72).

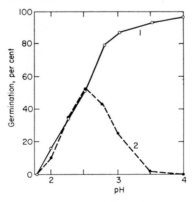

FIG. 6.   The effect of pH on the toxicity of copper chloride to spores of
Alternaria tenuis. Curve 1 (solid line), control; curve 2 (broken line), 0.0001
M CuCl₂. Drawn from data of Biedermann and Müller (72).

Inorganic sulfur and its organic derivatives have been used as fungicides from early times. It was suggested that the toxic action of sulfur was due to the formation of hydrogen sulfide in the fungus spore (65, 73, 74), since the reduced compound is known to be fungistatic (75) and fungicidal (76). The results of Miller *et al.* (77) show that toxicity of elementary sulfur on a weight basis is greater than an equivalent amount of hydrogen sulfide for a range of fungi, as shown in Table V. Thus, it is

TABLE V

THE RELATIVE TOXICITIES OF SULFUR AND HYDROGEN SULFIDE[a,b]

Species	Wettable sulfur	Colloidal sulfur	Hydrogen sulfide
Monilinia fructicola	54	0.5	2.8[c]
Cephalosporium acremonium	>1000	0.3	12[c]
Aspergillus niger	>1000	0.3	15[c]
Glomerella cingulata	>1000	0.4	20[c]
Neurospora sitophila	>1000	1.0	38[c]
Rhizopus nigricans	>1000	2.7	5.9
Alternaria oleracea	>1000	18	15
Stemphylium sarcinaeforme	>1000	31	8.8

[a] From Miller, McCallan, and Weed (77), by permission of the Boyce Thompson Institute for Plant Research, Inc.

[b] Toxicity is expressed as the dose, in parts per million, required to kill 50% of spores in an exposure of 24 hours; concentrations are of the external solution or suspension.

[c] Highly significant difference between colloidal sulfur and hydrogen sulfide.

unlikely that the toxic effect is caused by hydrogen sulfide only, and it is now agreed that sulfur vapor is the active principle in inhibiting the spores. Selenium and tellurium are much less toxic to fungi than is sulfur, although selenium accumulated in the mycelia of *A. niger* in competition with sulfur. Reduced sulfur compounds counteracted selenium toxicity effects (78). Similar data obtained for *Chlorella vulgaris* can be explained as competitive inhibition of metabolite analogues of selenium and sulfur (79).

C. Higher Plants

Inhibitory effects of cations and anions on the growth and metabolism of plants are revealed as deficiency conditions induced by excesses of other elements, and as toxicity symptoms apparently not related to this type of mechanism. Some examples of the more outstanding physiological effects are considered here.

1. INHIBITION OF CHLOROPHYLL SYNTHESIS BY INDUCED IRON DEFICIENCY

a. *Metal-Induced Deficiency.* The early work on this problem was stimulated by the observations of effects of manganiferous soils on the growth of pineapple (*Ananas comosus*) by Kelley (*80*), McGeorge (*81*), and Johnson (*82, 83*) in Hawaii and on the growth of beans (*Phaseolus vulgaris*) in Puerto Rico by Hopkins, Pagàn, and Ramirez-Silva (*84*), who found that excessive concentrations of manganese induced typical iron deficiency in these plants. Several other metals, including copper, cobalt, nickel, chromium, zinc, and cadmium, may also induce iron deficiency in various plants, as shown by the rapid response in terms of renewed chlorophyll production on spraying or painting the foliage with ferrous sulfate or an iron chelate compound. The effects of these metals have been reviewed or described by Wallace and Hewitt (*85*), Hewitt (*86–88*), Millikan (*89, 90*), Twyman (*91, 92*), Nicholas (*93–95*), Forster (*96*), Nicholas and Thomas (*97, 98*), De Kock (*99*), and Vergnano and Hunter (*100*).

One of the first attempts to provide a physiological basis for the interaction between iron, which is directly involved in chlorophyll synthesis, and other metals, particularly manganese and cobalt, was made by Somers and Shive (*101*), Somers *et al.* (*102*) in work with soybean (*Glycine max*). They concluded from the visible appearance of the plants and the respiratory carbon dioxide output that manganese excess and iron deficiency were practically synonymous for the same physiological disorder, caused by a too high manganese/iron ratio in the plant. Manganese deficiency was also suggested less emphatically to correspond with iron excess. The mechanism suggested to be responsible for the effects of the ratio was that excess manganese was present in the trivalent state, and on account of the high redox potential produced the manganese was able

$$Mn^{2+} \rightarrow Mn^{3+} + e^-; \qquad (E_0 = 1.51 \text{ volts}) \qquad (5)$$

to oxidize ferrous to ferric iron, which was immobilized by some means. As ferrous iron was commonly assumed at that time to represent the "active" or functional state in the cell, the mechanism of induced deficiency was thereby explained. The immobilization of ferric iron was thought to occur by precipitation with phosphate or by formation of unavailable ferric phosphoprotein complexes, a reaction regarded as likely by Noack and Liebeck (*103*). Phosphoprotein compounds such as ferritin may contain up to 23% of iron according to Granick (*104*). According to Shive and his associates cobalt, which has a correspondingly higher redox potential value, should be more effective than manganese, and this was experimentally confirmed.

This simple hypothesis raises several points which have been the subject of further work. The first requirement for the idea to be acceptable would be a biochemical mechanism for the oxidation of manganese from Mn^{2+} to Mn^{3+} *in vivo*. At the time the hypothesis was presented, none was known. The later work of Kenten and Mann (*105–107*) has, however, provided evidence that such a mechanism is feasible. These workers have shown that peroxidase systems can cause the enzymic oxidation of manganese from $^{2+}$ to $^{3+}$ or $^{4+}$ states. Numerous simple and complex monophenols and resorcinol can serve as essential cofactors for this system. The mechanism may be represented by the following reactions, in which the notation of George (*108*) is used for peroxidase action:

$$\text{Peroxidase (Per)} + H_2O_2 \rightarrow \text{Per I}$$
$$\text{Per I} + \text{ROH (monophenol)} \rightarrow \text{Per II} + RO^\bullet \text{ (free radical)} + H_2O$$
$$\text{Per II} + \text{ROH} \rightarrow \text{Per} + RO^\bullet + H_2O$$
$$2RO^\bullet + 2Mn^{2+} + 2H^+ \rightarrow 2ROH + 2Mn^{3+}$$
$$\text{Sum:} \quad H_2O_2 + 2H^+ + 2Mn^{2+} \rightarrow 2Mn^{3+} + 2H_2O \qquad (6)$$

Free Mn^{3+} ions cannot exist long and are rapidly reduced by *o*-diphenols, such as catechol, pyrogallol, guiacol, and caffeic acid. The oxidation is also brought to a standstill by polymerization of the free radicals: $nRO^\bullet \rightarrow (RO)_n$. Trivalent manganese may, however, be stabilized as a chelate by pyrophosphate, which is produced in reversible pyrophosphorylase reactions, or possibly by naturally occurring organic compounds, such as citrate. The oxidation of manganese has been observed to occur in the presence of illuminated chloroplasts (*109*) and has been identified as an *in vivo* reaction in peas (*110*).

The hypothesis of Shive and others discussed above was criticized by Leeper (*110a*) and independently by Hewitt (*86–88, 111*) at the time, partly on account of the need to invoke a mechanism not then known for the prior oxidation of manganese or cobalt to higher valence states, and partly for another reason, namely, that manganese and cobalt are not unique in their capacity to induce iron deficiency, which occurs also in the presence of an excess of copper, chromium, zinc, cadmium, and other metals. It was pointed out that the order of relative effectiveness of several metals given at equivalent concentrations was not consistent with the relative values of the redox potentials produced by couples involving the simple ionic states. Thus, whereas copper was found to be especially effective as an inhibitor of chlorophyll, the couple involving ionic copper has a low potential (*112*). For the reaction $Cu^+ \rightarrow Cu^{2+} + e^-$, $E_0 = 0.17$ volts, while the value for manganese, already given, is much greater; but manganese is far less effective than copper for inducing chlorosis. Moreover, the value $E_0 = 0.77$ volts for the reaction $Fe^{2+} \rightarrow Fe^{3+} + e^-$ is intermediate between the other two. Hypotheses based on electrode potentials of simple ionic systems are therefore not compatible with the facts.

A more serious difficulty is that metals such as zinc and cadmium, which do not undergo valence changes of the type under consideration, are nevertheless, respectively, moderately or highly active as inhibitors of chlorophyll synthesis in beet (*86–88, 111*) and in other plants where zinc has been more widely tested.

An alternative hypothesis was first suggested by Hewitt (*86–88*), namely, that the action of the metals which inhibit chlorophyll synthesis may be explained by the relative stability of their combination as chelate compounds. The stability constants K_S for organometal complexes are represented in the simplest form by the expression

$$K_s = \frac{[MC]}{[M^+]\ [C]} \tag{7}$$

where C is the chelating compound. The relative values of K_S are often independent of the nature of the chelating ligand and are principally a function of the metal. This relationship has been studied for several chelating compounds by Pfeiffer *et al.* (*113*), Mellor and Maley (*114, 115*), Irving and Williams (*116*), Ackerman *et al.* (*117*), Yamasaki and Sone (*118*), Albert (*119*), and Maley and Mellor (*120*) and has been termed the "avidity series" by Albert (*37, 121*). There are exceptions to this relationship, which is discussed again later in connection with competitive effects of metals, but the general order of increasing avidity (K_S) for many ligands may be given (*116–119*) as:

$$Mg^{2+} < Mn^{2+} < Fe^{2+} < Cd^{2+} < Zn^{2+}\quad < Fe^{3+} < Ni^{2+}\quad < Co^{3+} < Co^{2+} < Co^{2+}$$

K_S for Fe^{3+} may exceed that for Cu^{2+} where porphyrins, 8-hydroxyquinoline, or ethylenediaminetetraacetic acid are concerned, and the values for Fe^{2+} and Fe^{3+} may be reversed, as for a,a'-dipyridyl and o-phenanthroline. Stabilities for cobalt complexes may be relatively low or high (*117, 121*). Steric factors or ease of oxidation or reduction may cause abnormal orders of relative stabilities (*116–118*).

The order of effectiveness of metals as inhibitors of chlorophyll synthesis by sugar beet (*Beta vulgaris*) [(*86–88*) and data for chlorophyll in Table VI] is in increasing order:

$$Mn^{2+} < Cr^{3+} < Zn^{2+} < CrO_4^{2-} < Cu^{2+} < Co^{2+} < Cd^{2+}$$

Ni^{2+} was rated between Zn^{2+} and Cr^{3+}. This metal is extremely toxic in other respects, and it is likely that its effects on inhibiting chlorophyll

TABLE VI

Effects of Heavy Metals as Cations and Anions for Different Periods on Chlorophyll Production (mg/100 gm Fresh Weight) by Sugar Beet Plants Grown with Nitrate or Urea as Sources of Nitrogen[a]

Metal treatments and Mo level[b]	Period of metal treatments:							
	4 Weeks				9 Weeks			
	Nitrate		Urea		Nitrate		Urea	
	Mo_1	Mo_2	Mo_1	Mo_2	Mo_1	Mo_2	Mo_1	Mo_2
Basal	158	151	110	100	132	87	113	99
$+Cr^{3+}$	146	95	84	32	110	26	86	14
$+Cr^{6+}$	71	137	18	14	31	45	17	3
$+Mn^{2+}$	139	53	78	20	119	31	71	13
$+Co^{2+}$	8	10	10	9	18	11	14	14
$+Cu^{2+}$	28	10	11	14	7	4	8	8
$+Zn^{2+}$	104	47	94	34	113	46	85	23
$+Cd^{2+}$	6	14	4	4	11	16	7	7
LSD (5%)	15				12			

[a] From Hewitt (*128*).
[b] Mo given as Mo^{6+} (MoO_4^{-2}) at 5×10^{-7} M (Mo_1) or 5×10^{-5} M (Mo_2). Metals in basal level: Mn^{2+}, 10^{-5} M; Cu^{2+}, Zn^{2+}, 10^{-6} M. Metals given at 3×10^{-4} eq/liter when in excess, namely, Mn^{2+}, Co^{2+}, Cu^{2+}, Zn^{2+}, Cd^{2+} at 1.5×10^{-4} M; Cr^{3+} at 10^{-4} M, and Cr^{6+} (CrO_4^{-2}) at 5×10^{-5} M; and Fe given as Fe^{3+} (citrate) at 2.5×10^{-5} M.

synthesis were tested at too high a concentration to permit a reliable estimate of the effectiveness. Later work on the effects of metals on chlorophyll production by oat plants (*Avena sativa*) by Hunter and Vergnano (*122*) indicated the following increasing order of effectiveness:

$$Mn^{2+} < Zn^{2+} < CrO_4^{2-} < Co^{2+} < Cu^{2+} < Ni^{2+}$$

In other experiments with oats, Hewitt (*88*) found cobalt to be by far the most active of all the metals listed, but with sugar beet the differences between cobalt and copper are probably not significant. The position of cadmium is at present anomalous in terms of a stability complex hypothesis, since the avidity orders of Ackerman *et al.* (*117*) and Albert (*121*) place cadmium much lower in the series. The activity of cobalt in chlorophyll inhibition has been reported to be high or moderate for the same species (*88, 122*). At present, in spite of some exceptions, the hypothesis that metal inhibition of chlorophyll synthesis is related in general to the relative stability constants (K_s) of organometal ligands appears the most satisfactory, but other factors or mechanism may be concerned with effects of certain metals. Shaw (*122a*) has recently drawn attention to the general application of the relationship already pointed out in connection with the work on plants. The general order of toxicity of heavy metals in metabolism of several animal microorganisms was shown to be $Cu > Ni > Co > Fe > Mn$. The position of Zn was variable but usually between Co and Ni, or Ni and Cu.

The effect of valence or of whether the metal is present as a cation or as an anion is apparently of importance, as shown by the different responses to chromium (Table VI); lower concentrations as Cr^{6+} (CrO_4^{2-}) are more effective than higher concentrations as Cr^{3+}, a feature early observed by Koenig (*123*).

The extent of inhibition induced by a given metal is also altered by the nitrogen nutrition and by the level of interacting metals, as shown by work of Millikan (*89, 124*), Warington (*125–127*), and Hewitt (*128, 129*), and by Table VI. The data given here show that inhibition of chlorophyll production by Mn^{2+}, Cr^{3+}, and Zn^{2+} is greatly increased by an interaction with the Mo^{6+} present, which exceeds additive effects and is independent of the method of nitrogen nutrition. Mo^{6+} alone had little effect in the younger plants but was inhibiting later. Effects of Co^{2+}, Cu^{2+}, and Cd^{2+} were so severe that no interaction with Mo can be inferred from the data, but the condition of the plants and their yields indicated that some interaction did in fact occur. There was also a significant interaction between Mo^{6+} and Cr^{6+}, but whereas Mo^{6+} accentuated effects with the other metals regardless of nitrogen source, the reverse effect clearly occurred with Cr^{6+} and nitrate; this has been confirmed in separate experiments. No explanation is available at present to account for these results. It is not clear how far species, climatic, or other effects may enter into these interactions, since results obtained from Millikan (*89, 124*) with flax (*Linum usitatissimum*) showed an opposite effect of Mo^{6+} to that reported here for Mn^{2+} and Zn^{2+} on beet, while results described by Warington (*125*) with soybean and flax are in agreement with the work described above. A further complication is that in Millikan's (*89, 124*) work ammonium molybdate was used, while Warington (*125–127*) and Hewitt (*128, 129*) used sodium molybdate. Hewitt (*128, 129*) found that urea or ammonium nitrogen increased the inhibitory effects of Mn^{2+}, Zn^{2+}, and Cu^{2+} with sugar beet or spinach beet, respectively, but in the presence of Mo^{6+} and ammonium nitrogen the interaction, which was independent of nitrogen source and large with sugar beet (*128*), was small for Zn^{2+} and nil with Mn^{2+} for spinach beet (*129*). Millikan (*124*) concluded that ammonium nitrogen decreased the toxic effects of Mn^{2+}, Zn^{2+}, etc. in the presence of Mo^{6+}, as compared with the large effects observed with urea or nitrate. Differences between the results reported by Millikan on one hand and Warington on the other are best explained at present in terms of the amount of NH_4^+ nitrogen introduced by the use of ammonium as opposed to sodium molybdate, but some irreconcilable points still remain to be resolved in further work. It must also be remembered, as already pointed out by Hewitt (*87, 88, 129*), that the mechanism of chlorophyll inhibition by different metals, although showing a suggestive relationship with stability constant values, may be different for different metals, but no evidence on this point is available.

The idea that stability constants explain the relative effectiveness of different metals implies that the mechanism of the inhibition is that of competition between metals at an active site. There is some evidence from the work of Somers *et al.* (*101, 102*), Twyman (*91, 92*), Crooke, Hunter, and Vergnano (*130*), and Crooke (*131*) that the ratio of iron to the inhibiting metal, when measured as total content in the plant, determines in part, and sometimes very considerably, the extent to which the inhibitory effect is produced. This would be consistent with a mechanism of competitive inhibition. The differences which are apparent in Table VI with respect to duration of treatments are also explicable on the same basis, since Crooke and Knight (*132*) have shown similar effects for nickel in oats and have related these to the relative changes in iron and nickel content during the course of growth and the progress of inhibition as revealed by chlorophyll production.

The site or sites at which inhibition or competition may occur are unknown. Specific absorption sites may be involved, and ion antagonism effects will occur. Thus, Crooke *et al.* (*130*), Crooke (*131*), and De Kock (*99*) showed that heavy metals in the ionic state depress iron uptake into roots and leaves. De Kock further observed that the order of toxicity to growth of mustard plants of several metals presented in ionic form namely, $Cu^{2+} < Ni^{2+} > Co^{2+} > Zn^{2+} > Cr^{3+} > Mn^{2+}$, closely followed the order of chelate stability constants. When these metals were present in a chelated form with ethylenediaminetetraacetic acid they were much less toxic, induced little chlorosis, and had no depressing effect on iron uptake.

Twyman (92) originally put forward a hypothesis that iron must be combined at certain active sites in the cell before being introduced into the states (enzymes, etc.) which are functional in metabolism. He considered that inadequate concentration of iron, or competition by another metal, viz. manganese, led to an irreversible change in the iron-receptor site, which was unable to function as required. This view has never been proved or disproved but still has merit. De Kock (99) concluded that in the roots, where injury was most marked, the metals in the ionic form competed with the iron for sites possibly of a protein nature. Competition with ribonucleic acid (RNA) or ribonucleoprotein complexes would be likely, as RNA is often heavily contaminated with metals when isolated. De Kock (99) has postulated a role for phosphorus as a chemical site in phosphoprotein binding of metals. This would possibly resemble the physiological function of the ferric phosphoprotein ferritin described by Granick (132a).

The possibility that inhibition of chlorophyll formation involves competition between heavy metals and some molecule related to chlorophyll has been put forward, especially by Sideris and Young (133). Following the finding by Granick (134) that protoporphyrin IX accumulated in a chlorophyll-deficient mutant of Chlorella, they (133) suggested that manganese competes with iron in a porphyrin precursor of chlorophyll for which the natural ferrous iron compound was supposed to be a requisite for the insertion of magnesium. Magnesium protoporphyrin is also found in chlorophyll-deficient mutants of Chlorella (135). This idea is attractive but as yet without evidence to support it. Recently, however, Labbe and Hubbard (136) have found that the insertion of iron into protoporphyrin to produce hem in rat liver is an enzymically controlled process. Since iron must presumably be combined with the enzyme before insertion into the protoporphyrin, an analogous reaction might occur with insertion of magnesium into ether-soluble magnesium-containing precursors of chlorophyll obtained by Smith (137). It is conceivable that heavy metals might compete at the enzyme surface, especially if hematin, which is quite abundant in plant cells and is closely related to chlorophyll content (138) is an enzymically formed prerequisite for magnesium protoporphyrin production. Eyster (139) found a close correlation between catalase activity and chlorophyll content of genetic strains of albino and green corn. It appears that while catalase activities are similar in both types when grown in darkness, where high values occur, transfer to light causes a marked depression of catalase in the albino strains, due to destruction or inactivation by light. De Kock, Commissiong, Farmer and Inkson (140) found a similar result for mustard. Recent work by Agarwala, Kumar, and Sharma (141) suggests however that hematin formation may not be the limiting step at which heavy metals inhibit chlorophyll production. This conclusion is reached because, whereas Co^{2+}, Ni^{2+}, and Cr^{3+} are known to inhibit chlorophyll production, their presence resulted in greatly increased catalase production in the embryo of germinating barley but in depressed peroxidase production. Thus, the synthesis of different compounds which contain porphyrin structures and of two which are iron porphyrin compounds is affected differently by the heavy metals. In contrast to the results with barley (141), De Kock et al. (140) found that a nickel excess slightly depressed catalase activity in mustard and markedly decreased hem and chlorophyll but markedly increased peroxidase activity. They suggested that peroxidase is synthesized preferentially. Healy, Cheng, and McElroy (141a) reported similar experiments with metal toxicities, especially of cobalt, on changes in enzyme patterns in *Neurospora crassa*, which contains no chlorophyll. Excess cobalt depressed catalase, peroxidase, indophenol oxidase (cytochrome oxidase), succinic dehydrogenase, and also isocitric dehydrogenase, but increased nitrate reductase, DPNase, and glucose-6-phosphate dehydrogenase. They suggested that cobalt competed with iron and that additional iron partially but not wholly reversed the effects of cobalt. Simple competition was not, therefore, the only mechanism involved. The differences in the effects of cobalt on the activity of two hematin enzymes, catalase and peroxidase, in two plant and one fungal species are noteworthy. The situation is further complicated by the observations of Wang and Waygood (142), who concluded that nickel not only inhibits formation of chlorophyll by etiolated wheat tissues but also inhibits chlorophyll breakdown in excised leaves in light or darkness and increases the chlorophyll a/b ratio. The idea of competition at the surface of an enzyme which either inserts magnesium in place of iron into a protochlorophyll precursor or which is involved in synthesis of precursor of protochlorophyll seems, nevertheless, to fit the facts best at present.

A second paper by Labbe and Hubbard (143) has now shown that manganese at $5 \times 10^{-5} M$ inhibits to the extent of 50% the incorporation of iron into protoporphyrin by the enzyme and that the effect is noncompetitive. Cobalt, however, is incorporated into protoporphyrin by the enzyme; but as the cobalt complex would be more stable than that of magnesium, inhibition could also be by this mechanism. The search for a metal-inserting enzyme for porphyrin metabolism in plants would be a worthwhile pursuit, and a study of its properties might explain the known facts of metal-induced chlorosis.

b. Bicarbonate-Induced Deficiency. The presence of bicarbonate ions in nutrient media often leads to typical iron deficiency. It is not clear at present whether or not this effect comprises an inhibition of the type relevant to this chapter. The subject has been reviewed, and recent work has been presented in a symposium edited by Bear (*144*). Miller (*145*) reported that cytochrome oxidase activity was decreased in preparations obtained from soybean plants grown with bicarbonate. When split-root methods were used, so that bicarbonate and phosphate were separated from iron, bicarbonate did not affect cytochrome oxidase activity directly; but when phosphorus supply was increased, cytochrome oxidase activity was decreased. The role of bicarbonate when presented to the intact plant appears to be indirect and may differ from the *in vitro* inhibition. The general conclusion seems to be that bicarbonate increases the uptake of phosphate. Hale and Wallace (*145a*) obtained evidence of competitive inhibition of bicarbonate on iron uptake when iron was given as an anionic chelate.

Miller and Evans (*146, 147*) found that 0.1 mM bicarbonate was inhibitory to cytochrome oxidase of plant roots *in vitro*. Whether these observations bear any direct relation to the role of iron in chlorophyll synthesis is unknown. The presence of bicarbonate may influence the valence state of iron in cells, since ferrous bicarbonate is both weakly dissociated and readily autoxidizable. Bayer (*148*) has proposed this mechanism as the means of iron assimilation into the ferric combination with ferritin in animals. Warner and Weber (*149*) have pointed out the extreme stability of the transferrin complex in animal iron metabolism. This ferric iron protein involves a bicarbonate group in the chelating center and is very stable.

Rhoads and Wallace (*150*) put forward an interesting idea which depends on the role of bicarbonate in CO_2 fixation. It is suggested that fixation of CO_2 by phosphoenolpyruvic acid, which results in the liberation of an equivalent of inorganic phosphate, may provide the mechanism for bicarbonate-induced chlorosis, which acts indirectly on iron availability by the increased liberation of inorganic phosphate. This idea is consistent with the views of De Kock (*99*) regarding the role of phosphorus in iron availability and with the occurrence of high citric acid concentrations under conditions of lime-induced or bicarbonate-induced chlorosis (*151–154*). Bicarbonate may therefore inhibit iron metabolism in plants, as revealed by effects on cytochrome oxidase activity or by chlorophyll production, in two separate ways. Bicarbonate inhibition is discussed again in the section on enzymic effects in relation to anion inhibition and cytochrome systems.

2. Metabolic Activity of Chlorate and Other Halogen Compounds

a. *Compounds of Chlorine, Bromine, and Iodine.* Åberg (*155*) has contributed a most informative discussion on the affects of chlorate, perchlorate, hypochlorite, fluoride, bromide, and iodide, and of other halogen oxyacid salts, on plants in particular, with numerous references also to macroorganisms and animal subjects. His main conclusion regarding the inhibitory effects of chlorate, well known as a herbicide, is that chlorate is reduced especially in light by nitrate reductase, the enzyme responsible for nitrate reduction, since characterized by Nason and Evans (*156*), Evans and Nason (*157*), Nicholas *et al.* (*22*), Nicholas and Nason (*23*), and Nicholas and Stevens (*25*) as pyridine nucleotide-dependent molybdoflavoprotein systems.

Evidence for this view was based on the antagonistic effect (*155, 157a*) of nitrate on chlorate toxicity and the accentuation by light. The statement (*155*, p. 98) that the nitrate-reducing system of the highly resistant Aspergillaceae (*155*, p. 89) is different from that of higher plants is no longer valid, as both groups require molybdenum for a similar enzyme system. It is more likely either that chlorate is not metabolized in non-photochemically dependent systems of these fungi or that, if reduction occurs, the specific toxic intermediate is not produced. Quastel, Stephenson, and Whetham (*158*) found that nitratase of several bacteria reduced chlorate. The product was thought to be chlorite. It must, however, be noted that injury also occurs to roots and in darkness to very young leaves, so that either other methods of reduction may exist in these tissues or rapid translocation of these products can occur. A point of interest is that chlorate toxicity is greatly accentuated by the inclusion of vanadium.[1] This element antagonizes the action of molybdenum in certain systems dependent on molybdenum. Spencer (*159*) found that 10^{-3} M vanadate caused total inhibition *in vitro* of wheat (*Triticum oestivum*) embryo nitrate reductase, and Hewitt and Bond (unpublished work) found that vanadium inhibits nitrogen fixation in root nodules of *Alnus* grown with a low level of molybdenum. Åberg (*155*) concluded that chlorate as such is not toxic but that intermediate reduction products, possibly chlorite or hypochlorite, are the active compounds. From data

[1] This reference cannot be traced but was read by one of us in *Nature* several years ago (Hewitt).

on growth inhibition of roots and fresh weights of wheat plants, Åberg concluded that relative toxicity was in the order:

$$ClO^- > ClO_2^- >> ClO_3^- > ClO_4^-$$

Lees and Simpson (*159a*) distinguished between reversible inhibition of growth by chlorate in *Nitrobacter* (*157a*) and a noncompetitive and irreversible reaction between chlorate and the enzyme responsible for oxidation of nitrite to nitrate.

Bromate toxicity is similar to that produced by chlorate, but iodate is far less active, possibly because it tends to produce iodide as the direct product of reduction. Iodide, however, is toxic to wheat and corn (*Zea mays*), while chloride and bromide are relatively inert (*155, 160*). Cotton (*161*) reported that iodide was toxic to buckwheat (*Fagopyrum esculentum*), Lewis and Powers (*160*) concluded that iodide toxicity in corn resembled iron deficiency. Hageman, Hodge, and McHargue (*162*) found that iodide above 4 ppm reduced the dry weight and ascorbic acid content of tomato (*Lycopersicon esculentum*) plants. Åberg (*155*) found that iodide was 50–100 times more toxic than iodate to wheat and resulted in suppression of chlorophyll production and of root hair development and that leaf blades grew in a horizontal plane. Perchlorate is also much less toxic than chlorate and produces different symptoms (*155*). The mechanism is unknown.

b. Possible Mechanism of Chlorate Toxicity. It is possible that the observation by George (*163*) concerning the reaction between horse-radish peroxidase and certain oxidizing agents may explain both the toxicity of chlorate and the sensitivity of plants as compared with animals and certain fungi. George (*163*) found that horse-radish peroxidase reacts to form specific complexes with KIO_4, $KBrO_3$, ClO_2, $NaClO_2$, HOCl, HOBr, and $K_2S_2O_8$ (with Ag^+) but not with $KClO_3$ or KIO_3.

The complexes formed were spectrographically similar to the peroxidase-H_2O_2 complexes. These compounds were tested in a peroxidase-guaiacol system at pH 7.0 and pH 5.4. The activity of HOCl exceeded, and that of ClO_2 equaled, the activity produced with H_2O_2 at pH 5.4, while at pH 7.0 the enzyme was destroyed or an abnormal oxidation occurred. HOBr was also highly active (one-fifth the activity of H_2O_2 at pH 5.4), while $NaClO_2$ gave 1% of the activity produced with H_2O_2. Activity was decreased by increasing the pH to 7.0, and this effect of pH also occurs with the toxic action of chlorate (*155*). Although $KClO_3$ (unlike $KBrO_3$) was unable to form complexes with peroxidase, its reduction by light (possibly by nitrate reductase?) to HOCl or $NaClO_2$ would yield compounds able to react with peroxidase where effective concentrations are of the order of 1–10 μM. Animal tissues are devoid of nitrate reductase mechanisms except for liver aldehyde and xanthine oxidases, and here excretion may prevent contact between enzyme and substrate, or specificity may preclude reduction. In fungi, e.g., *A. niger*, which has an active peroxidase system, the failure of chlorate to become toxic is not explained. However, the complexes formed by horse-radish peroxidase (a plant enzyme) and cytochrome c peroxidase are different with respect to the state of oxidation of the enzyme, as shown by the production of peroxidase I and II, and cytochrome c peroxidase II complexes (*163*), respectively. The two enzymes differ also in that cytochrome c peroxidase does not react with HOCl or HOBr. Other examples of different specificity of peroxidases, e.g., in coupled peroxidations are also known. Specificity of *Aspergillus* peroxidase or of its nitrate reductase may therefore protect the organism from chlorate toxicity.

c. *Fluoride*. Åberg (*155*) found that fluoride did not have a markedly inhibitory effect on wheat, in agreement with the earlier and more comprehensive work of Bartholemew (*164*). Recently, the problem of fluoride injury to plants has been studied by McNulty and Newman (*165*) in relation to chloroplast pigment concentration, and effects of fluoride or fluorine on plant growth have also been reviewed.

Fluoride injury may appear suddenly. Disintegration of chloroplasts was reported by Adams and Solberg (*166*), and by McNulty and Newman (*165*) to be the primary lesion before later cell collapse. These workers studied particularly the effects of fluoride on the concentration and synthesis of chlorophyll and carotenoids in leaves of beans. Fluoride depressed the concentrations of chlorophylls a and b, of ether-soluble magnesium compounds, and of carotene about equally in terms of relative differences. Treatment with fluoride did not inhibit photochemical conversion of protochlorophyll to chlorophyll. Fluoride also inhibited the production of protochlorophyll and chlorophyll in etiolated leaf discs, but did not apparently affect the metabolism of magnesium-porphyrin compounds once these were formed.

The activity of fluoride as an enzyme inhibitor is discussed later. It is relevant here, however, to note the effects of fluoride on respiration as an over-all physiological process in plants. This subject has been critically reviewed by James (*167, 168*) and Hackett (*169*). The general conclusion is that the effect may be complex. Concentrations of the order of 10^{-2} M may be required to effect 50% inhibition of respiration, while 10^{-3} M may be without influence, e.g., *Avena coleoptile* used by Bonner and Thimann (*170*). Fluoride complexes with magnesium and iron and may therefore inhibit a great many enzymes and possibly to different extents. Enzymes reported to be affected include enolase, phosphoglucomutase, succinic dehydrogenase, cytochromes, phosphatases and pyrophosphatase. The extent of fluoride inhibition will also probably depend on the internal magnesium and phosphate concentrations, where magnesium fluorophosphate formation is involved, and possibly on that of manganese also, since manganese may reactivate fluoride-inhibited enzymes, which can function in the presence of either magnesium or manganese, according to Nillson, Alm, and Burström (*171*). Lethal synthesis of fluoro organic acids is noted later.

3. INTERACTIONS AND TOXICITIES OF OTHER MINERAL ELEMENTS

a. Aluminum. Phosphorus metabolism in plants may be inhibited by aluminum. The effect of aluminum on plants varies very greatly with different species, and the literature is too copious to review here. Comparative experiments (*172–174*, and unpublished) showed that some species of cultivated plants, e.g., many brassicas, oat (*A. sativa*), tolerate aluminum concentrations in nutrient media that severely injure or are lethal to others, e.g., beet (*B. vulgaris*), barley (*Hordeum vulgare*) and celery. In one species *P. vulgaris* (dwarf French beans) the variety determined the tolerance to aluminum. One (Masterpiece) was relatively tolerant to aluminum at concentrations greater, as well as less, than the equivalent supplies of phosphate, while another (Prince) was severely injured soon after germination even when the phosphate level was in excess of the equivalent aluminum concentration which was relatively harmless to the first variety. In this example the symptoms of injury were not those of phosphorus deficiency; but in beet and barley, aluminum induces phosphorus deficiency symptoms and also specific root injury in the form of apical hypertrophy and cell necrosis, leading to root distortion. The failure of lateral roots to emerge has been shown by Rees and Sidrak (*175*) for barley. In contrast to the phosphorus-antagonizing effect seen in barley, swedes (*Brassica rapa*) may be adequately supplied with phosphorus wholly as aluminum phosphate (*172, 173*). The mechanisms by which aluminum interferes in phosphorus metabolism in some plants but not in others and the reasons for the great differences in tolerance among species or varieties are unknown. Wright (*176, 177*) concluded that reaction between aluminum and phosphate occurred within the plant, especially in roots, and showed that when barley plants were grown with aluminum in the nutrient solution the amounts of phosphate extracted by dilute sulfuric acid (pH 3.0) were one-quarter or one-half those obtained from roots grown without phosphorus. When a sulfuric acid solution of pH 1 was used, there was little difference between the two treatments, and the amounts extracted were nearly equal to the total phosphorus content of the plants. Wright and Donahue (*178*), by using radioactive phosphorus and by applying the property of aluminum as a hematoxylin mordant, showed that aluminum and phosphorus both accumulated in similar regions of roots, namely, on the surface and in cells between the epidermis and the endodermis. Wallihan (*179*) concluded that induced phosphorus deficiency did not account for the effects of aluminum toxicity. The wide differences in species tolerance to aluminum implied above is more clearly revealed when the aluminum accumulator plants are considered. The reasons for the differences between these plants described by Chenery (*180*) and the nonaccumulatory types of low or high tolerance are unknown. An excellent review of early work on aluminum in plants was made by Hutchinson (*181*). Randall and Vose (*181a*) have now distinguished two effects of aluminum on phosphate absorption by roots of rye grass. One is already well known as inhibitory. The other is interpreted to be a metabolically dependent stimulation of phosphate uptake which occurs at low aluminum concentrations around 0.18 mM. They suggest that aluminum stimulates the activity of a cytochrome system which is involved in phosphate uptake by formation of high-energy phosphate bonds. However, it is feasible that the action of aluminum is in promoting the hydrolysis of such compounds at the inner surfaces of cell or vacuole membranes, and that the inhibition by cyanide of aluminum-dependent phosphate uptake means only that the high-energy phosphate bonds are not produced in the first place.

    b. Alkali Metals. In higher plants, potassium is the only metal of this group for which universal evidence of essential requirement is available. It is possible that species adapted to saline habitats, e.g., *Atriplex vesicaria* and *Halogeton glomeratus*, also have an absolute requirement for sodium, as shown by Brownell and Wood (*182*) and Williams (*183*), respectively, and many species may benefit from sodium at low or normal levels of potassium (*184*). In a number of instances, however, lithium, sodium, and rubidium have been shown to affect growth and metabolism of plants in either beneficial or inhibitory ways.

    One of the simplest effects is presumably that of sodium at high concentrations as an apparent antagonist of calcium, an effect which may occur in celery (*Apium graveolens*) at the stem apex, in sugar beet in young leaves, in cauliflower (*Brassica oleracea* var. *Botrytis*) in the flower stems, and in tomato in the fruit. The magnitude of this effect is dependent upon the associated anion and is greater with sulfate than with chloride. Hydration of the sodium ion may be a factor in inducing physiological water deficit independently of unfavorable effects of high osmotic pressure produced by high salt concentrations. Effects of salinity as an inhibitor of growth are well reviewed by Eaton (*185*) and Magistad (*186*), and effects of sodium on water content were studied by Richards and Shih (*187, 188*).

More specific effects of alkali metals on growth have been described by Haas (*189*) and Aldrich, Vanselow, and Bradford (*190*) for lithium on Citrus, where marginal mottling of mature leaves is produced, and by Richards (*191, 192*) for rubidium. Excess rubidium given to barley caused production of abnormally broad leaves, which were twisted, brittle, and had prominent midribs. Later and quite abruptly, leaf shape changed to a short narrow form, and color faded from deep-green to gray-green, while excessive tillering, representing the formation of up to 100 additional stem meristems, occurred. Thus, rubidium could both partially replace potassium and produce toxic effects. There also appeared to be an interrelationship with phosphorus metabolism. The role of potassium in many phosphorylating systems in plants where rubidium is an alternative metal, e.g., in pyruvate kinase (*193, 194*), in acetic thiokinase (*195*), and in photosynthetic phosphorylation (*196*), provides a clue to this effect, since rubidium fully replaces potassium in the two enzyme systems and partially substitutes in photosynthetic phosphorylation but is inhibitory to the synthesis of protein by pea (*Pisum sativum*) ribosomes *in vitro*, where potassium is essential (*197*). The alkali metals also modify amino acid and amide patterns in a complex manner, as shown by Richards and Berner (*198*) and Coleman and Richards (*199*). Excessive concentrations of sodium or rubidium tended to reproduce the patterns produced by potassium deficiency, particularly with respect to amide accumulation, while at lower concentrations these metals partially or substantially restored the amino acid pattern to a normal state representative of an adequate potassium supply. In many respects lithium was unable to restore the abnormal pattern, particularly with respect to the accumulation of putrescine in barley and in the production of asparagine. These examples illustrate the complexity to be expected in studying inhibitory effects of alkali metals, which also possess beneficial functions when given at lower concentrations under potassium deficiency conditions.

c. *Boron.* Boron is toxic to plants, probably as borate, when concentrations appreciably exceed those required for normal growth. The range of tolerance is very wide, as shown by the work of Eaton (*200*). Thus, Citrus was injured at 1 ppm of boron in culture solution, while turnip (*B. rapa*) and beet tolerated over 10 ppm. Other examples are given by Hewitt (*184*). Sunflower (*Helianthus annuus*) may show injury to older leaves at levels producing optimum growth of young leaves (*200*). In many species, including walnut (*Juglans regia*), tomato, and potato (*Solanum tuberosum*), a pronounced blackening or dark rim occurs in margins of older leaves (*184*). The question of tolerance concerns internal physiological factors rather than accumulative capacity, since both musk melon (*Cucumis* sp.) and *Zinnia* show high accumulation but differ greatly in tolerance (*200*).

The significance of boron toxicity in plants and whether this is related to its normal role are not yet clear. Borate ions materially affect the activity of the phenolase group of enzymes. This effect has been obtained consistently in experiments by Reed (*201*), MacVicar and Burris (*202*), Klein (*203*), Nason, Oldewurtel, and Propst (*204*), and Yasunobu and Norris (*205*). The effective concentrations which cause 50% or greater inhibition range from 10^{-2} M for tomato polyphenol oxidase (*202*) to 4×10^{-3} M for dopa oxidation by tyrosinase (*205*). Yasunobu and Norris concluded that inhibition was competitive. The mechanism was considered to be due to the complex formation between borate ion and polyphenols (*206*) and was increased under high pH conditions. The interpretation of these results is complicated by the fact that enzyme production appears to be limited by the presence of increasing amounts of boron in the culture medium (*203*). Possibly, borate-phenol complexing *in vivo* suppresses enzyme induction, for it has been shown that under conditions of boron deficiency (*207, 208*), there is a marked accumulation of phenols, including caffeic and chlorogenic acids, which are polyphenolase substrates. Boron toxicity may therefore be related to suppression of enzyme synthesis as well as of activity.

Borate ions also inhibit potato phoryphorylase, (*209*) and inhibition attains 50% at 5×10^{-2} M BO_3^-. The complex formation between borate and polyhydryl compounds, including sugars, (*206*) is well known. A significant point, however, is the difference shown by the sugar phosphate esters. Where the C-5 or C-6 alcoholic groups are esterified, e.g., ribose-5- or glucose-6-phosphates, borate complexes are formed, as judged by the retarding influence in chromatographic separations, while in the C-1 position, e.g., glucose-1-phosphate, no such effect is observed. It might be anticipated, therefore, that borate ions may influence phosphate ester metabolism, though Dugger and Humphries (*210*) recorded no effect of borate on phosphoglucomutase, which catalyzes the interconversion of glucose-6- and glucose-1-phosphates. Cohen (*210a*) found that borate modifies the equilibrium in the pentose isomerase system of *E. coli;* the proportion of D-ribulose produced from D-arabinose at equilibrium is increased from 15% to 70–90% by the presence of 0.1 M

concentration of borate. Pubols, Zahnley, and Axelrod (*210b*) observed a similar effect in the xylose isomerase system from higher plants, the equilibrium being shifted to the keto form from 20% without to 70% with 0.067 *M* borate. The over-all activity of the corresponding ribose isomerase system was, however, inhibited 85% by 0.03 *M* borate. It might be expected, therefore, that under certain circumstances the natural ratio of xylulose to ribulose would be greatly altered by changes in cell boron content with indirect effects on the production of xylulose phosphate for which a kinase has been reported in plants *210b*).

d. Manganese, Cobalt, and Nickel. The relationships between the metals listed here and iron deficiency or chlorophyll synthesis have been discussed separately. In addition to this specific effect, other toxic effects are observed; there is at present insufficient chemical or histological evidence to explain the precise nature of the interactions observed for most of the metals mentioned. The visible effects upon growth probably reflect secondary and complex effects which will not be considered here in detail. A few points, however, merit note.

Manganese toxicity in plants (*172–175, 211*) often results in the appearance of numerous dark-brown necrotic areas, small or large, in leaves, petioles, and stems. Two possibilities may be involved. Cell death, which is commonly associated with this condition, might result in the liberation of phenols which are the substrates for browning reactions in the presence of the polyphenolase-tyrosinase enzyme systems. Alternatively, as cell death approaches, the latent phenolases might become active. In either case localized browning reactions would occur. It has also been shown by the work of Kenten and Mann (*109, 110*) that manganese in contact with illuminated chloroplasts or absorbed *in vivo* by pea plants can be oxidized to higher valence states. It is not possible at present to state the precise nature of the products formed. In the presence of pyrophosphate, trivalent manganipyrophosphate accumulates, but MnO_2 might be formed and would yield Mn^{3+} in the dismutation [Eq. (8)].

$$MnO_2 + Mn^{2+} + 4H^+ \rightleftharpoons 2Mn^{3+} + 2H_2O \qquad (8)$$

The chemical autoxidation of photoreduced riboflavin also provides a mechanism for the formation of Mn^{3+} in the presence of pyrophosphate and a monophenol cofactor (*212*). It is significant that higher valence states of manganese could not be detected in other species [barley, tomato, Brussel sprouts (*B. oleracea* var. *gemmifera*)] tested by Kenten and Mann (*110*) which also produce dark brown lesions with excess manganese (*172, 173, 211*). It is possible that both accumulation of higher valence states of manganese and browning reactions account separately for the observed symptoms of manganese toxicity.

The histological effects of cobalt and nickel excesses in oat were described by Vergnano and Hunter (*213*). Nickel caused agglutination of chloroplasts, followed by lysis of cell contents. Mesophyll cells collapsed and shrank to irregular masses or enlarged and burst, with colorless contents. Epidermal collapse followed these changes. Xylem development was weak, and phloem contained heavily staining inclusions. Cobalt caused somewhat similar changes, but cell rupture was infrequent, and xylem and phloem remained normal. Excess nickel may induce symptoms closely resembling manganese deficiency in potato and tomato but not in other plants (*88, 128*). Cobalt caused suppression of leaf lamina expansion in young leaves of tomato plants and induced lesions somewhat resembling manganese deficiency in older leaves. Ahmed and Twyman (*214*) observed a marked antagonism between cobalt and manganese in tomato and found that small additions of cobalt partially suppressed the effects of manganese excess.

Further references to earlier literature on miscellaneous toxic effects of several elements, including aluminum, lithium, chromium, vanadium, cobalt, nickel, and titanium, are given by Koenig (*123*), Pfeiffer *et al.* (*215*), Brenchley (*216–218*), Haselhof *et al.* (*219*), Scharrer (*220*), Millikan (*89, 90*), Nicholas (*95*), and Forster (*96*).

e. Vanadium and Molybdenum. Vanadium was found by Spencer (*159*) to be a specific and effective inhibitor at 10^{-3} M of nitrate reductase from wheat embryo. Vanadium toxicity might therefore be manifested as nitrate accumulation in some circumstances. Unpublished work by one of us (Hewitt) with G. Bond shows that vanadium and tungsten both inhibit growth of *Alnus glutinosa* when dependent on atmospheric nitrogen fixation as a source of nitrogen under limiting conditions of molybdenum supply. Vanadium toxicity in flax, soybean, and pea was observed by Warington (*125, 126*). The toxic concentration was between 1 and 10 ppm as $VOCl_2$. Primary roots of soybean plants were dwarfed, swollen, and gelatinous. Lateral root growth was suppressed, and excessive cork formation occurred where splits developed in the surface. Foliage was initially abnormally dark-green and later chlorotic, as in iron deficiency and as was also found in sugar beet (*86*). The shoot color of flax was especially dark blue-green in those plants where chlorosis due to iron deficiency did not develop later, and leaves were erect against the stem axis (*125, 126*). Peas also showed slight chlorosis and abnormal thickening of the roots. Histological studies were not reported.

Molybdenum toxicity is not commonly seen in plants, in contrast to the effects described elsewhere for animals. Where high concentrations of molybdate have been given (*89, 90, 125–127, 221–223*), two types of response have been observed. One is the production of globules of golden-yellow pigment in epidermal cells, as in flax, potato tubers, tomato leaves, and stems. Pigment was concluded by Warington (*221*) and Millikan (*89*) to be a molybdenum-tannin complex. It appears in root meristematic cells of flax (*89, 125, 126*) and lettuce (*Lactuca sativa*) (*222*) at 0.5 ppm molybdenum and in leaves at higher concentrations. The other common effect is the appearance of a deep-blue granular pigment. Warington (*221*) concluded that this was molybdenum-anthocyanin complex. It appears in tomato petioles, cauliflower leaves and stems (*223*) and leaf palisade cells of *Solanum nodiflorum* and is often located in cortex, epidermis, and parenchymatous cells. Warington (*221*) also observed a reduction of leaf lamina of tomato to almost only the midrib. Concentrations of 0.5–5.0 ppm are usually involved, according to species and region, and the reactions may be detoxication mechanisms rather than evidence of an inhibitory relationship.

Molybdate also interacts with the metals that induce iron deficiency, as already described, and, as noted above, the nature of the interaction may be complex or variable. It is clear from Warington's work (*125, 126*) that vanadium is more toxic than molybdenum on a weight basis and most probably also on a molecular weight basis.

The effects of molybdate as an inhibitor of acid phosphatase are described later.

f. Mercury, Lead, and Thallium. The cytological effects of mercury are most acutely shown in processes of cell division and growth. A study of inhibitory effect of phenylmercury compounds on cell division in onion (*Allium cepa*) root was described by Macfarlane (*224*), and by Macfarlane, Schmock, and Miessing (*225*). The effective range was between 10^{-6} and 10^{-4} M for phenylmercury hydroxide when roots were immersed in the solution for 1 hour and then washed in tap water. Two concentrations were established for reference purposes, namely the "minimum lethal dose" for elongating (nondividing) cells, estimated to be 3.4×10^{-6} M by Macfarlane, Schmock, and Miessing (*225*), and the "effective mitotic concentration" at which clumping of chromosomes occurred in meristematic cells, estimated to be 3.4×10^{-5} M (*224*). The internal concentration at this level was estimated to be 8×10^{-7} M.

At external concentrations below 2×10^{-5} M the growth rate was accelerated, prophase and telophase stages were increased in frequency, and some chromosomal fragments and bridges appeared 24 hours later. At $2–5 \times 10^{-5}$ M concentrations subapical swelling occurred. Polynucleate cells appeared, and tetraploid nucleic were also present. Chromatids were sticky, and nuclei contained extra nucleoli, or nucleoli remained attached to the mitotic spindle. Concentrations of $3\text{--}8 \times 10^{-5}$ M inhibited spindle formation, and effects resembled colchicine-type mitosis with a blocked metaphase state followed by amitosis and tetraploid nuclei. Above 8×10^{-5} M cell death occurred, chromosomes were clumped, and nucleoli were destroyed. Pycnosis occurred in the resting nucleus stage.

The effects of these treatments were partially reversed (80%) by a 23-fold excess of cysteine. Twofold excess of glutathione temporarily antagonized the effects on spindle formation, but radiomimetic effects of chromosome breakage still appeared after 24 hours. A hundredfold excess of glutathione reversed all effects of mercury, but there was a short lag period during which amitosis still occurred before the recovery of normal mitosis occurred, and occasional chromosome fractures still appeared after 24 hours. Macfarlane (226) concluded that mercury acted as an —SH poison, possibly on the succinoxidase system. Phenylmercury acetate (10^{-6} M) caused 50% inhibition of onion root succinoxidase and led to reversible spindle inhibition and also irreversible polyploidy and radiomimetic effects.

Elemental mercury in vapor form was shown by Zimmerman and Crocker and others [see Crocker (227)] to be highly toxic to young peach seedlings and rose blooms; Crocker states that this response had been known for many years, since 1797.

A recent and quite distinct observation of effects of mercury on coffee plants was reported by Bock, Robinson, and Chamberlain (228), who found that phenylmercury acetate sprays reduced the zinc content of the affected leaves of *Caffea arabica* from 14–30 ppm to 3.6–13 ppm and induced symptoms of zinc deficiency. Arsenic also has this effect. The mechanism is obscure and possibly complex. It is possible that zinc uptake depends upon temporary combination with —SH sites on root surfaces.

Lead, which also forms sulfides readily, is relatively nontoxic to plant growth, but may nevertheless cause growth inhibitions. The subject has been reviewed by Keaton (229), and useful early work was described by Hammett (230–233) and Hammett and Justice (234, 235).

The experiments reported by both these investigators and by several others show that lead accumulates in roots, where the toxic effects are most noticeable. Hammett (232) found that lead accumulated in nuclei of *Zea*, *Allium*, and *Vicia* root tips as well as along cell walls. Nucleoli also showed an affinity for lead. Hammett (233) found that lead at 0.125 ppm, i.e., 6×10^{-7} M, in the nutrient medium caused an appreciable decrease in mitosis in *Zea* root tips and caused a 75% decrease in *Allium* root tips. At $5 \times 10^{-6} M$ the decrease was 98% in *Zea*, and at $2.5 \times 10^{-5} M$ it was 95% in *Allium*. Cell expansion was apparently not affected at these concentrations. Hammett and Justice (*234*) observed that lead was fixed by nuclei particularly during the process of mitosis, when affinity was greatly increased. Hammett and Justice (*235*) concluded from histochemical tests that lead combined with free sulfhydryl groupings which appear during mitosis. Lead sodium thiosulfate, which is relatively unionized, was far less toxic than lead nitrate.

Copper, which also forms compounds with sulfhydryl radicals, was found to accumulate in meristematic regions of mustard roots by De Kock (*99*) and of Citrus roots by Smith (*236*). Copper also accumulated in the phloem regions (*99*), where sulfhydryl concentrations tend to be high.

Thallium is toxic to plants (*237*), and tolerance differs among species. In comparative tests McCool (*238*) found that maize (corn) was killed by 8 ppm in sandy loam, while waxbean (*Vicia* sp.) was unaffected; 70–100 ppm appeared to be the lethal concentration. Corn showed interveinal chlorosis, and soybean, waxbean, and buckwheat showed vascular injury. Wheat and rye (*Secale cereale*) showed general chlorosis, and alfalfa (*Medicago sativa*) showed yellowing at leaf bases. McMurtrey (*239*) observed frenching of tobacco (*Nicotiana tabacum*) affected by thallium toxicity. Crafts (*240, 241*) observed thallium toxicity to oat. The growth of the coleoptile was less sensitive than that of the first leaf which was unable to grow. Chlorosis of mature leaves was considered to be a general though possibly secondary feature of thallium poisoning.

Pratt, Babicka, and Polivkova (*242*) found that 27 ppm thallium was the threshold concentration in a culture solution for toxicity to oat and broad bean (*Vicia faba*). They concluded that cell division was the sensitive stage for thallium inhibition and that cell expansion was less affected. Premature maturity and differentiation of cells was observed. Primary roots developed necrotic areas, and secondary roots were suppressed.

D. Animal Metabolism

The principal disorders in animal metabolism ascribed to toxic or inhibitory effects of anions or cations are caused by selenium and molybdenum. The effect of fluoride and some effects of excesses of manganese, zinc, copper, and cobalt are sometimes important and are noted here. Cyanogenic glycosides may also be poisonous.

1. SELENIUM

a. Origin and Nature of Selenosis. Selenium toxicity in animals is well known in certain areas, especially in the cattle areas of North America (*243, 244*) and extremely locally in Eire (*245*), and is frequently related to soils derived from Cretaceous shales, e.g., in South Dakota, where Moxon (*243, 246*) has carried out classic investigations. The problems of uptake from seleniferous soils and from feeding on seleniferous plants, such as species of *Astragalus*, are outside the scope of this article. One point of some importance, however, is that selenium toxicity is approximately the same regardless of whether the selenium is administered in an "assimilated" organic form, i.e., as seleniferous wheat grain, as selenate, as selenite, or as selenomethionine or selnocysteine (*244, 247, 248*). On the other hand, elemental selenium and selenopropionic acid are much less injurious.

These observations indicate that the toxic action of selenium is related to chemical reactivity on one hand, e.g., selenate or selenite rather than as elemental selenium which is less readily absorbed and is relatively insoluble, and, on the other, to a specific type of combination of which the selenium analogues of thiol compounds seem to be the most likely examples since selenopropionic acid is not so effective.

The symptoms of selenium poisoning in animals are complex and presumably the result of a syndrome originating in biochemical lesions which may be widespread in the animal. The principal effects have been described by Underwood (*244*), Moxon (*243, 246*), Moxon and Rhian (*249*), Trelease and Beath (*250*), Franke (*251*), Franke and Potter (*252*), and Franke and Tully (*253*). They comprise chronic and acute stages depending mainly on dosage but traditionally described as "alkali disease" and "blind staggers," respectively.

One of the characteristic symptoms of chronic selenium toxicity in horses, cattle, and pigs is the abnormality in epidermal tissues, particularly abnormality related to keratin development, as shown by loss of hair, especially long hair of mane and tail, soreness of pads, roughening of the coat, and corrugation and sloughing of hoofs. Erosion of joints in long bones is revealed in stiffness and lameness. Atrophy of the liver, with cirrhosis, and atrophy of heart muscles also occur. In acute cases, blindness, paralysis, and respiratory failure are the characteristic manifestations of metabolic disturbance. In chick embryos, Franke *et al.* (*254*) have found that injection of selenium salts into eggs or feeding highly seleniferous grain causes the production of monstrosities, indicating a biochemical effect at very early stages of development. Here again, however, the visible effects included abnormal feathers, deformed beaks, and lack of eyes, indicative of disturbance in keratin and epidermal metabolism.

b. Possible Mechanisms of Toxicity. The mechanism of selenium toxicity is not understood. The formation of selenium analogues of thiol compounds, e.g., selenomethionine, selenocysteine, and others, indicates a possible means of inhibition similar to the mechanism whereby azaguanine, or *p*-fluorophenylalanine, or methyltryptophan interferes in the synthesis of nucleic acids or proteins. Selenium-containing proteins have been inferred as being present in seleniferous wheat by Painter and Franke (*255*) and in tissues of rats and dogs fed selenium by McConnell, Roth, and Dallam (*256*); but, whereas animals are readily affected, plants are much less susceptible, and a general explanation on these lines is not entirely satisfactory unless it is assumed that partial substitution in plant proteins, especially of accumulator species, is not inhibitory to normal metabolism.

An alternative or additional possibility concerns the action of several selenoamino acids, including especially selenomethionine as antioxidants, as shown by Zalkin, Tappel and Jordan (*256a*) and by Olcott, Brown, and Van der Veen (*257*). Zalkin *et al.* (*256a*) were able to reproduce antioxidant effects related to selenium ingestion *in vivo* as well as *in vitro* in chicks. Peroxide formation in relation to hemoglobin-catalyzed oxidation of linoleic acid was completely suppressed by selenomethionine plus phenylselenoglycine and *a*-tocopherol, while each alone was much less effective. The mechanism was suggested to involve free radical formation where the selenium atom is more stable than the smaller sulfur atom. Olcott *et al.* (*257*) concluded that selenomethionine was first oxidized to an unknown derivative (which could be the free radical) before exerting its antioxidant function.

It would not be surprising if the presence of excess selenium resulted in a serious disturbance of oxidation-reduction systems normally dependent on thiols or possibly on other reactions where antioxidant action might alter the redox potential or lead to respiratory failure, apparent anaerobiosis, or other pathological conditions. The abnormally low levels of ascorbic acid observed in instances of selenium toxicity might reflect increased oxidation through other channels, which are not inhibited by selenium.

The function of organic arsenicals, arsenate, or arsenite as inhibitors of thiol metabolism, discussed in Chapter 26, may be relevant to the problem of selenium toxicity. Arsenic in all these forms has been found to act as a partial antidote to selenium poisoning (*243*). Although the idea of arsenic-selenium combination was not considered a likely explanation of the effect, the combination of arsenicals with thiol groups could well be parallelled by combination with HSe— groups which would in consequence be inactivated equally well if active either as —SH analogues or as free radical-forming antioxidants.

2. MOLYBDENUM

a. Nature of Disorder. Molybdenosis or molybdenum toxicity in animals was first identified by Ferguson, Lewis, and Watson (*258, 258a*) as the cause of the scouring disorder of cattle known as "teart" in England and since identified elsewhere (*259*). Cunningham (*260*) identified a similar condition under the name of "peat scours," where a low copper status is also involved. Excess of dietary molybdenum uptake from herbage, especially when containing legumes, is the primary cause, but the disorder has complex aspects.

The symptoms of molybdenum toxicity vary with the animal concerned, and tolerance also differs greatly. Horses and pigs are relatively tolerant and do not normally show effects of molybdenum excess. Cattle are the most sensitive; sheep, rabbits, and rats are also relatively susceptible. Symptoms in cattle include scouring, harshness and discoloration of the coat, and finally anemia. The scouring may occur within 24 hours of animals grazing severely "teart" pastures. Young rabbits suffer from anemia, alopecia, and deformity of the front legs but do not show loss of hair color which is associated with the other symptoms described under conditions of copper deficiency.

b. Interrelationships with Copper and Sulfur. The mechanism of molybdenum toxicity is not understood. It has been shown quite clearly from the work of Ferguson *et al.* (*258*), Marston (*261*), Cunningham (*262*), Comar, Singer, and Davis (*263*), Davis (*264*), Dick (*259*), Gray and Ellis (*265*), Gray and Daniel (*266*), and Arrington and Davis (*267*) that copper administered orally or subcutaneously counteracts molybdenum excess and that the two elements are mutually antagonistic in effects on metabolism and physiology. The interaction between molybdenum and copper is apparent over a wide range of concentrations, and this is reflected under field conditions in two ways. In "teart" disorders, excess molybdenum is the causal agent, and the condition is counteracted by giving high doses of copper. In peat scours, incipient copper deficiency is the principal condition; it is accentuated or induced beyond the threshold by only moderate increases in molybdenum intake and is counteracted by normal copper fertilizing of the pastures.

The molybdate antagonism of copper metabolism is complicated by the presence of sulfate; this relationship was discovered by Dick (*268,*

269), working on sheep, and has been fully described by him (*259*) in the following manner. Sulfate intake determines the distribution of molybdenum between blood plasma and red cells. Sulfate depresses molybdenum uptake into red cells but not into the plasma, and sulfate uptake causes the depletion of molybdenum from red cells but not from plasma. Sulfate intake also causes the increased excretion of molybdenum and its depletion from all tissues and organs except the excretory organ, i.e. kidney. Selenate, tungstate, silicate, and phosphate do not have this effect.

At very low sulfate levels, no effect of molybdate could be detected over a wide range on blood copper in sheep. As sulfate levels were raised, there was a pronounced and rapid increase in blood copper concentrations with increased molybdate intake; these changes were due to increasing levels in the plasma copper. After prolonged periods the content of copper in the blood falls again to levels associated with copper deficiency. During the period of a few days when there is an initial rise in blood copper and during the intermediate period when equilibrium values are attained, there is a marked fall in the content of copper stored in the liver, as the result of high molybdate and high sulfate intakes. Prolonged periods of this combined treatment lead eventually after several months to symptoms of copper deficiency.

The appearance of the wool provides a sensitive and almost immediate indication of changes in sulfate/molybdenum/copper balance. Thus, sudden addition of high sulfate (5–10 gm/day) and high molybdate (100 mg/day) lead to the immediate appearance of a band of "steely wool" in the fleece and an associated high blood copper level. When sheep were maintained with 6 mg/day of molybdenum and 4 gm/day of sulfate and a similar copper intake of 6 mg/day, copper deficiency and steely wool appeared only after 11 months and were associated with low blood copper content and depletion of copper reserves of the liver.

Dick (*259*) concluded that the effect of sulfate is to antagonize the transport of molybdenum across membranes, thus preventing intestinal absorption, transfer from plasma to red cells, and reabsorption through the kidney tubules after excretion by the ultrafiltration mechanism of the glomerulus. He also postulated that, by impeding molybdenum movement through membranes, the movement of copper was also restricted. Although the evidence from the complex interaction among the three factors is compatible with this view, it is not supported by direct experimental observations. In fact, the rapid development of the lesion in the fleece, with simultaneous rise of blood copper, might be more compatible with a more direct biochemical mechanism, e.g., some aspect of a copper-thiol reaction involved in disulfide bonding of keratin in the wool.

There is now evidence that molybdenosis involves sulfide or thiol metabolism. Gray and Daniel (*266*) found that methionine counteracts molybdenum toxicity in the rat, and Daniel and Gray (*270*) observed a similar interaction between molybdenum and growth of *L. leichmanii*. This work led Van Reen and Williams (*271*) to suggest that the effects of methionine and other sulfur compounds might be due to effects of sulfate produced after their oxidation in the tissues. Ramaiah and Shanmugasundrum (*271a*) likewise found in *N. crassa* that cysteine, methionine, homocysteine, thiosulfate, or sulfate reversed molybdenum toxicity, but concluded that the effect of molybdenum was to inhibit the assimilation of sulfate to the thiol compounds. In this connection, molybdenum may inhibit sulfate activation by ATP (*526a*) (see Section III,C,2,h).

Mills and associates (*272*) suggested on the basis of such results, the work of Dick (*259*), and the abnormally high activity of liver alkaline phosphatase described by Van Reen (*273*), which they also confirmed, that two distinct aspects of molybdenum-sulfur interactions are concerned. One is the antagonism between sulfate and molybdenum in transport or permeability postulated by Dick (*259*), and the other is a more direct enzymic effect. Mills *et al.* (*272*) discovered that molybdenum produced a drastic decrease in sulfide oxidase activity in rat liver preparations. Halverson, Phifer, and Monty (*274*) suggested that this discovery might provide a biochemical basis for explaining molybdenum toxicity. Mills *et al.* (*272*) pointed out that sulfide is a normal product of sulfate metabolism in ruminants and that a failure to detoxicate sulfide might result from molybdenum excess. Sulfide toxicity might be revealed in several ways but has not been identified in a clinical sense as a result of molybdenosis. Halverson *et al.* (*274*) considered that the molybdenum-sulfate-copper effect might be due to immobilization of copper as sulfide as envisaged by Monty (*272, 274*). In this connection Mills [private communication and (*275*)] has shown that sulfide toxicity to rats is accentuated by molybdenum. Work by Ichihara (see *272*) shows that sulfide oxidase requires copper as a cofactor and is also dependent in some way on hypoxanthine.

This interesting observation naturally led Mills *et al.* (*272*) to test the effects of molybdenum on the hypoxanthine content of rat liver, since molybdenum activates xanthine oxidase of liver, as noted later. No appreciable differences were found, however, and there was no difference in uricase activity. This is also a copper-containing metalloenzyme, and its substrate is the product of xanthine oxidase activity. These associations are, however, still suggestive of a basis for molybdenum-copper-sulfide interactions at a biochemical level. Mills (private communication) has summarized the relationships in the following way for the rat. High dietary copper maintains high sulfide oxidase activity and also minimizes copper immobilization as sulfide. High sulfide oxidase results in high endogenous sulfate, which antagonizes molybdenum accumulation in the liver. This balance (namely, high sulfide-sulfate transformation) therefore maintains a normal Cu/Mo status. If the molybdenum uptake is increased, sulfide oxidase is depressed, copper may possibly be immobilized, sulfate production is decreased, and molybdenum accumulation progresses. The situation therefore deteriorates in a self-induced manner as sulfide accumulates.

The accentuated copper deficiency induced by dietary sulfate in ruminants (*259*) and the apparently opposite effect of methionine in rats (*266*) and bacteria (*270*), the increased sulfide sensitivity of rats given molybdate (*275*), and the prevention by sulfate of molybdenum accumulation in ruminants (*259*) and in liver, particularly in rats (Mills, private communication), collectively pose some apparent anomalies. A clue to the problem may lie in the observations of Halverson *et al.* (*274*). They found that although "cysteine" (? oxidized or reduced) promoted initially increased growth of molybdenum-poisoned rats when fed a low copper diet, "cystine" finally resulted in decreased hemoglobin, increased diarrhea, and greater mortality. By comparison, sulfate resulted in a greater growth stimulation, less anemia, and no diarrhea or mortality. In the presence of a higher copper intake cystine completely counteracted molybdenum excess. The role of cystine was considered to be that of producing dietary sulfide. Siegal and Monty (*275a*) found that the addition of sulfate to diets containing excess molybdate resulted in a restoration of liver sulfide oxidase of rats within 15 days of the change. Cystine caused a rapid further decrease in 2 days, followed by a stabilization of the value which was eventually equalled in livers of rats maintained on the original high molybdate diet. They attributed the effect of molybdate on sulfide oxidase to that of decreased food intake.

It seems possible that the effects of sulfate, cystine, and thiol compounds on the molybdenum-copper balance will depend on the extent to which sulfates are converted either to thiol compounds or to free sulfide in different species, and on the dietary copper level. In rats the first reaction may be more important, and in ruminants the second may predominate. If sulfide oxidase is very active, the sulfate effect may be mainly the antagonizing of molybdenum uptake or accumulation, but if sulfate reduction exceeds sulfide oxidation, copper deficiency may occur.

It is possible to envisage other interactions between molybdenum and copper on an enzymic basis. Work with *N. crassa* by Nicholas and Commissiong (276) showed that copper is able to reverse the competitive inhibition of molybdate on acid phosphatase, which is probably of general significance (277–279), and also has an opposite effect to molybdenum on cytochrome oxidase. There was no inhibition of alkaline phosphatase (276). This difference was considered to be due to the instability of molybdenum-phosphate complexes at high pH values. The marked increase in alkaline phosphatase activity in rat liver produced by molybdenum excess (273) could be a response to inhibited acid phosphatase activity.

Finally, the significance of molybdenum in xanthine oxidase activity may be reconsidered. The presence of molybdenum in liver xanthine and aldehyde oxidases is well known. So far, the activity of these enzymes has not been implicated in explanations of molybdenum toxicity. It is possibly relevant that the activity of xanthine oxidase of milk increases in activity over a wide range of molybdenum concentration up to a rate of about 500 atoms Mo/enzyme molecule (280), and molybdate is known as the liver "xanthine oxidase factor," which is required for normal activity. The enzyme, which is versatile and somewhat nonspecific in its functions, leads to the production of hydrogen peroxide in reactions where oxygen is the terminal electron acceptor. Aldehyde oxidase also yields hydrogen peroxide. Excessive xanthine and aldehyde oxidase activities might not be particularly injurious for this reason, owing to the very high catalase activity of liver. However, xanthine oxidase also rapidly oxidizes sulfite to sulfate in the presence of catalytic amounts of hypoxanthine by a coupled oxidation elucidated by Fridovich and Handler (281). It is of speculative interest whether this reaction is related to the interactions between copper and molybdenum. Kun and Fanshier (282) discovered that the β-mercaptopyruvate-cleaving enzyme is a copper protein from which the copper is relatively easily dissociated. This enzyme catalyzes the transfer of sulfur from β-mercaptopyruvate (HS—CH=C(OH)COOH), but not from cysteine, to a sulfur acceptor for which sulfite serves effectively to produce thiosulfate. In the absence of the acceptor (sulfite) a "half-reaction" occurs with the formation of H_2S. Other mercapto derivatives might be metabolized in vivo. As xanthine oxidase oxidizes sulfite and its activity is proportional to molybdenum supply, molybdenum excess might cause a depression of available sulfite and a resulting accumulation of H_2S. This could immobilize both copper in the enzyme and copper required elsewhere, and also inhibit sulfide oxidase by this means. Hydrogen sulfide is directly inhibitory to the cleaving enzyme. The system would therefore develop into a self-inhibiting system additive and similar to that already proposed for the depression of sulfide oxidase, which incidentally was measured as thiosulfate formation (*272*). Ichihara's observation (*272*) that hypoxanthine is required for sulfide oxidase activity may be related to the work of Kun and Fanshier (*282*) and Fridovich and Handler (*281*). There is a third mechanism directly related to the previous one just described which may also contribute to the effects of molybdenum toxicity in certain circumstances. The enzyme rhodanese, which is widely distributed in animal tissues, was shown by Sörbo (*283*) to catalyze the conversion of cyanide to thiocyanate, probably as a natural detoxicating mechanism. This reaction depends upon the presence of thiosulfate.

$$CN^- + S_2O_3^{2-} \rightarrow CNS^- + SO_3^{2-} \tag{9}$$

Now thiosulfate is formed during sulfide oxidation and during β-mercaptopyruvate cleavage, and both reactions would be (or are known to be) depressed by molybdenum activation of xanthine oxidase. Under these conditions cyanide liberated from glycosides and nitriles might attain toxic concentrations. It is possibly significant that cyanide toxicity is treated by sulfur or cysteine therapy with rapid production of thiocyanate in liver, according to Blackley and Coop (*284*), and that Coop (*285*) has noted that clovers which carry much of the excess molybdenum are also rich in cyanogenic glycosides.

3. OTHER ELEMENTS

a. Cobalt. Cobalt excess is relatively unusual in animals; and by comparison with the drastic effects described for plants, relatively high levels of intake are required to produce toxic effects. Cobalt toxicity, when it occurs, results initially in polycythemia or excess red blood cell production, first recognized as a response to high cobalt intake by Waltner and Waltner (*286*), and is a widely observed effect in many species (*287*). This might reflect merely an accentuation or extension of the process by which cobalt therapy reverses anemia. Higher levels of cobalt of about 4–10 mg/kg body weight may induce an anemia. The possible mechanisms by which cobalt might induce polycythemia have been discussed by Underwood (*244*). No clear evidence of the mechanism is yet available, but Underwood favoured the idea that formation of cobalt complexes with those thiol-containing amino acids which may reverse effects of cobalt (*288*) was a likely explanation of respiratory interference associated with cobalt toxicity. Cobalt-induced polycythemia is apparently similar to high altitude polycythemia, and this suggests that oxygen shortage is a possible factor. Cobalt forms complexes with several compounds which are able to absorb and give up molecular oxygen reversibly. This reaction was first discovered by Calvin, Bailes, and Wilmarth (289) and Burk, Hearson, Caroline, and Shade (290). Burk *et al.* (290) showed that histidine, which is known to chelate cobalt strongly, forms a reversibly oxygenated complex, but this also undergoes further irreversible reaction with oxygen. Gilbert, Otey, and Price (291) found that several peptides also form complexes with cobalt which are able to undergo reversible oxygenation and do not apparently suffer secondary changes like the histidine complex. It is possible that these compounds interfere with the normal transfer of molecular oxygen by hemoglobin and lead to local anoxia. Histidine might be able to counteract cobalt excess because the oxygen reaction is not continuously reversible and cobalt would be immobilized.

A second possibility for a cobalt toxicity mechanism is the reaction of cobalt with the protoporphyrin metal-inserting enzyme described by Labbe and Hubbard (136, 143). It has been shown that cobalt is inserted nearly as well as iron into protoporphyrin and some aspect of hem metabolism may be involved when excess cobalt is present. Underwood (244) noted, however, that no cobalt methemoglobin is detected in cobalt-induced polycythemia and hemoglobin is apparently normal.

b. Copper. Chronic copper toxicity is known as an endemic condition in sheep in Australia. A full description of the condition under which copper toxicity occurs and the symptoms that result have been given by Bull (292). Merino sheep are more resistant than English breeds. Chronic copper poisoning which occurs on soils rich in available copper probably reflects effects of prolonged intake of excessive amounts of copper from herbage. Cases also occur where prolonged Bordeaux spraying has been carried out. In other soils, chronic copper poisoning is not clearly related to soil copper or herbage copper, and there is a distinct seasonal effect. Bull (292) reached the conclusion that the high copper/molybdenum ratio associated with subterranean clover grown in acidic pastures was an important factor. The Cu/Mo ratio in clover and feces also rose sharply from 10–20 in May to 400–600 in October in these two types of samples. A third condition related to copper toxicity is associated with consumption of *Heliotropium europaeum*. In many instances the liver appears to show an increased capacity for copper storage when heliotrope poisoning occurs, and symptoms of chronic copper poisoning are often associated with this condition. Copper toxicity results in sudden hemolysis—the "hemolytic crisis" associated with liver necrosis, and death. The high copper/molybdenum ratio may determine the extent to which the liver stores copper, and this seems to be a major factor in the disorder. Bull concluded that the concentration of soluble copper was the determining factor. There appears to be a reciprocal relationship between molybdenum and copper, but in molybdenosis the high copper concentrations that occur in blood and other tissues when high sulfate is given indicate an immobilization of copper. It might be, therefore, that copper toxicity and induced deficiency reflect the controlling effect of molybdenum on copper availability. Mills (private communication) queried whether molybdenum may mediate copper incorporation into protein as a nonavailable form.

c. Zinc. Zinc toxicity is not common in animals. Experimentally induced zinc poisoning in rats was described by Sutton and Nelson (*293*). Up to 0.5% zinc in the diet was necessary to produce symptoms which include loss of appetite and anemia. This is microcytic and hypochromic according to Smith and Larson (*294*). Van Reen (*295*) showed that there is some evidence that zinc toxicity resembles copper deficiency with respect to the anemia, decreased cytochrome oxidase, and to a lesser extent catalase which are also depressed by simple copper deficiency (*296, 297*). The depressed activity of the hemoproteins is restored by increasing the level of dietary copper uptake in either condition. Zinc excess resembles molybdenum excess in inducing an abnormally high activity of liver alkaline phosphatase (*295, 298*). At the same time there is a decrease in intestinal phosphatase (*298*), which is associated with decreased phosphate absorption and poor mineralization of bone (*299*).

d. Manganese. Manganese poisoning is rare in animals (*244*) as compared with plants. A possible connection with lactation tetany has been suspected by Blakemore, Nicholson, and Stewart (*300*). They observed that in certain areas where lactation tetany is prevalent there is a tendency for manganese uptake to be high because of high manganese accumulation by herbage plants growing on acid soils. Under these conditions the concentrations in serum of magnesium are low and of manganese, high. Feeding manganese results in a depression of serum magnesium concentration (*301*). Antagonism of magnesium and manganese has been observed in plants (Hewitt, unpublished) and is noted later in connection with a few enzyme systems.

Excess manganese was found by Matrone, Hartman, and Clawson (*302*) and Hartman, Matrone, and Wise (*303*) to depress hemoglobin formation in pigs, lambs, and rabbits. The conversion of ferrous iron to an unavailable form or antagonism of oxidation and reduction of iron in an enzyme was suggested as a possible reason. The work of Labbe and

Hubbard (*136, 143*) may be more relevant to this finding, since manganese was found to be a powerful competitive inhibitor of the enzyme which inserts iron into protoporphyrin; however, manganese is inserted at a very slow rate. A concentration *in vitro* of 5×10^{-5} M Mn^{2+}, which would approximate to 2.75 ppm fresh weight, inhibits the activity by 50%.

e. *Fluorine.* Endemic chronic fluorosis, in mammals particularly, occurs to varying degrees and is found in India, Australia (Queensland) (*304*), North America, and North Africa. Water and certain rock phosphates are the main sources. The bones and teeth are principally affected and show the greatest accumulation. The subject, which is extensive, is fully discussed by Underwood (*244*), and many aspects are not relevant to this chapter.

The association between fluorine and bones is possibly due to the affinity of fluorine to form a complex fluoroapatite. The reaction of fluorine with dental enamel occurs during deposition and does not occur in preformed teeth after emergence. In both teeth and bones the adsorption of fluorine onto hydroxyapatite has been shown by Volker *et al.* (*305*) to obey the Freundlich adsorption isotherm. White (*304*) stated that the fluorosis resembled calcium deficiency in bone structure, but Harvey (*306*) showed that the fluorosis was not reversed by giving extra calcium. It appears that the calcification is impaired in fluorosis of teeth, since Williams (*307*) earlier showed that fluorine impaired calcification of the enamel rods and of the interprismatic cement. Similarly, Robison and Rosenheim (*307a*) showed that calcification of cartilage *in vitro* in the presence of calcium and glycerophosphate was totally inhibited by 10^{-4} M fluoride and that fluorine was still inhibitory at 10^{-5} M, while glycerophosphatase was not inhibited at much higher concentrations. The relationships between fluorine inhibition of calcification and bone phosphatase are obscure (*244*). The enzymic effects of fluorine are described later.

f. *Boron in Animal Metabolism.* Borate toxicity in animal metabolism is not widely important. The limited literature on the subject is reviewed by Underwood (*244*), who pointed out that the excretion eliminates most of the boron absorbed. One of the main effects reported by Pfeiffer, Hallman, and Gersh (*307b*) is the injury to the brain tissues, where boron accumulates in white and gray matter of the central nervous system.

The pathological changes include increased numbers of small cells with dark, round or irregular nuclei. Shrinkage and vacuolation occur in the nerve cells of the spinal cord, and kidney cells are damaged.

III. ENZYMIC INTERACTIONS

A. General Effects of Cations and Anions

Before considering how cations and anions exert inhibitory effects on enzyme activity, it is convenient to review briefly the ways in which anions and cations react with proteins and then to relate these inter-actions with enzyme activity.

Most enzymes are markedly affected by salt concentrations. The amount of protein in solution is often a function of the total concentration and type of cation and anion. In general, proteins may be extracted from tissues at neutral or slightly alkaline pH values, preferably in buffered solutions with an ionic strength not exceeding 0.15 M sodium chloride. When using microorganisms from a marine environment, their disruption is readily achieved by suspending them in distilled water. It is usually necessary to add a buffered salt solution after cell breakage to maintain the activity of the enzymes.

A considerable selectivity of the type of enzyme extracted is achieved by a judicious choice of cations and anions, especially by varying their ratios. It is well known that salt linkages and hydrogen bonds may be largely dissociated by salts with univalent cations and multivalent anions. The solvent action of cations on proteins diminishes in the order $Li^+ > K^+ > Na^+$, and of anions in the order $P_2O_7^{4-} > B_4O_7^{4-} > PO_4^{3-} > CNS^- > HCO_3^- > I^- > Cl^-$ at neutral or alkaline pH, and in the acid range citrate $>$ acetate (308). Morton (308) considers that the most useful salt solutions for separation of enzymes in a heart muscle mince, in order of increasing effectiveness are 0.15 M sodium chloride, 0.02 or 0.05 M potassium phosphate buffer, 0.02 or 0.05 M sodium pyro-phosphate buffer at pH 7.4–7.8, and for the acid range 0.02 M sodium citrate buffer at pH 5.5. Pyrophosphate buffer is recommended for ex-traction of some enzymes since (a) it buffers over a wide pH range ($pK_{a3} = 6.54$, $pK_{a4} = 8.44$), (b) it effectively dissociates hydrogen bonds and salt linkages, (c) it chelates many cations that might inhibit enzyme activity, e.g. Cu^{++}, and (d) it has a specific protective effect on some enzymes, e.g., succinic dehydrogenase. At pH values below 6, citrate buffer has similar advantages to pyrophosphate, and in addition it strongly chelates calcium ions (308). An unusual effect of an anion was shown by Astrup and Stage (309) when 1 M thiocyanate was used for preparation of fibrinokinase from pig heart mince, presumably because of its marked dissociation effect on salt linkages.

In addition to dissociation by weakening electrostatic and hydrogen bonds, salts can stabilize extraction of enzymes by chelating with toxic metals. Thus, pyrophosphate and tris buffers are useful for this purpose, as are additions of Na EDTA and glutathione or cysteine to phosphate buffers. These chelate with free metals and prevent them from inhibiting enzymes. A good example is the use of Na EDTA and glutathione to offset inhibition by free copper ions of nitrate reductase extracted from bacteria, fungi, and green plants (23, 23a, 24).

Many metal-protein complexes are insoluble, and the addition of glycine and glycylglycine has been used to get them into solution (310). Neuberg and Mandl (311) have exploited the fact that ATP forms chelates with metals and that this facilitates solution of metal-protein complexes. An excess of calcium ions removed from casein by either citrate or Versene will allow it to dissolve in buffer solutions. Since proteins are large charged molecules they are affected by salt concentrations. Thus, small amounts of ions shield protein molecules from each other by coming between opposing charges, thus increasing solubility. This is often termed "salting in" of proteins. High concentrations of salts, however, decrease solubility of proteins; thus, a "salting out" occurs due to the dehydration of the protein molecule, but the salt effect is not well understood. It is known that slight changes in groups attached to the iron atoms markedly affect the solubility of hemoglobins; even a change in the valence state of iron atoms change the amounts of dissolved protein.

The classic work of Hardy (312) and Mellanby (313) with serum globulin, and of Osborne and Harris (314) with edestin showed that globulins were relatively insoluble at their isoelectric points and that their solubility increased on adding salt. Mellanby (313) recognized that solution of globulin by neutral salt was due to forces exerted by its free ions. Ions with equal valences, whether positive or negative, were equally efficient. All proteins have a minimum solubility at their isoelectric points in solutes of constant ionic strength. At low concentrations of electrolyte or in the absence of electrolyte some proteins are still insoluble, e.g., edestin and muscle phosphorylase. Since the majority of proteins become insoluble in the complete absence of an electrolyte, they are denatured. Green and Hughes (315) pointed out that should two proteins have the same isoelectric point and should one be more soluble at an electrolyte concentration just low enough to precipitate most of it, then lowering the electrolyte concentration by dialysis or by dilution will precipitate the second protein. Heavy metals, e.g., zinc or mercury, are also effective as protein precipitants.

The decrease in the logarithm of the solubility of a protein is a linear function of the increasing ionic strength, where the latter is defined as the square of the valence of the ions of the electrolyte [Eq. (10)]

$$\text{Log } S = -Ks'u \tag{10}$$

where S is the solubility of the protein; Ks' is the intercept constant (slope of line), salting-out constant; and u is the ionic strength of salt/1000 gm water.

In general, univalent salts are relatively ineffective in precipitating proteins. Salts of high valence produce much higher ionic strengths and are effective precipitants.

B. Activation and Inhibition of Enzymes by Cations

Notable publications that deal with metal-dependent enzymes are those of Lehninger (*316*), Calvin (*317*), Klotz (*318*), and Najjar (*319*). They have discussed the physicochemical properties of activating ions and the way in which they might be linked with active groups on proteins. Smith (*320*) has considered metal activation mechanisms for peptidases, and Lardy (*321*) has described the stimulatory effects of Mn^{++} and Mg^{++} and other ions in phosphorylation. McElroy (*322*) and McElroy and Nason (*323*) have reviewed the general problem of multiple metal effects on enzyme systems. Hewitt (*111, 324, 324a, 325*) and Nicholas (*10, 326–328*) have also considered the metabolism of micronutrients and their mode of action in plants and microorganisms.

The concept that metal catalysis of enzyme systems was due solely to the inherent chemical properties of the metal was based on early observations that metals alone react with enzyme substrates. Thus, Cu^{2+} ions oxidize ascorbic acid, and iron catalyzes the decomposition of hydrogen peroxide. It was soon found, however, that metals did not react readily with substrates unless the enzyme protein was present, and even those that did were far more active in association with enzymes, e.g., copper in ascorbic acid oxidase and iron in hemperoxidase. Copper and nonspecific proteins also catalyze the oxidation of ascorbic acid. Hellerman and Stock (*329*) and Smith (*320*) proposed that the metal links substrate to the enzyme by chelation, thus acting as a bridge bringing the two into close proximity for their interreaction. Najjar (*319*) has presented another hypothesis, that the metal combines with the substrate to form the "true active" substrate for the enzyme. He proposed that the metal of the substrate complex links it to the protein. This idea is of interest when considering multiple ion effects on enzymes. Provided an ion can combine with the substrate and orient it onto the enzyme, substitution of one metal by another for enzyme action should be feasible. This could explain the alternative metal requirements for certain enzymes and for the possible inhibition by a metal that occupies the active site but cannot bind substrate to protein. Examples of enzymes that are activated and inhibited by cations will now be considered. These include relationships between dissociable metal-activated enzymes and concentrations of the activating metal, and inhibition by nonactivating cations.

1. METAL ACTIVATION AND INHIBITION PATTERNS

a. Alternative Activating Metals. A number of enzymes are activated by more than one metal and are sometimes inhibited by concentrations of activating metals above the optimum for maximum activity. Patterns of metal activation and inhibition in several enzymes activated by magnesium or manganese as alternatives in dissociable systems were classified by Hewitt (*325*). Some examples are illustrated in Figs. 7–9. Figure 7 shows the patterns produced in the separate but related isocitric dehydro-

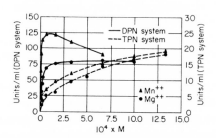

FIG. 7. Metal requirements of DPN- and TPN-isocitric dehydrogenases. The incubation mixtures contained 0.05 ml of tris(hydroxymethyl)aminomethane buffer (0.2 M, pH 7.5), 0.05 ml of d-isocitrate (0.015 M), and the chlorides of Mn^{2+} and Mg^{2+} as indicated. Also included in the DPN experiments were 0.05 ml of DPN (0.02 M), 0.05 ml of adenosine-5-phosphate (0.02 M), and DPN-isocitric dehydrogenase (0.05 ml of a 1:10 dilution of ammonium sulfate B). In the TPN experiments were included 0.20 ml of TPN (0.001 M) and TPN-isocitric hydrogenase (0.08 ml of a 1:5 dilution of the ethanol fraction dialyzed for 3 hours against running distilled water). From Kornberg and Pricer (*330*).

genases of yeast, described by Kornberg and Pricer (*330*), which use specifically either TPN or DPN. In the TPN enzyme, activation is progressive and similar with either magnesium or manganese. It shows no sharp optimum leading to inhibition at higher concentrations. In the DPN system manganese is far more effective than magnesium; it has a lower dissociation constant, but is inhibitory at concentrations above the optimum, in contrast to magnesium which does not inhibit. A similar pattern is shown by DPN kinase of pigeon liver described by Wang and Kaplan (*331*), except that the optimum concentration for manganese is much less than for magnesium. The DPN kinase enzyme of yeast described by Kornberg (*332*) (Fig. 8) shows a different pattern. Here

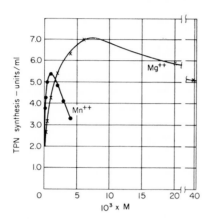

FIG. 8.   Effects of Mg^{2+} and Mn^{2+} on the TPN-synthesizing enzyme. The amount of purified enzyme present was 0.25 mg. From Kornberg (*332*).

the optimum concentration for manganese is much lower than for magnesium, but activation is also less; concentrations above the optimum are severely inhibitory for manganese and appreciably inhibitory for magnesium. The nicotinamide pyrophosphorylase enzymes of yeast and liver   (NMN + ATP $\leftrightarrows$ DPN + PP)   described by   Kornberg (*333*) show similar activation patterns by manganese and magnesium, but the activities are much greater and the dissociations are somewhat greater with magnesium than with manganese for both enzymes. Both metals inhibit above the optimum in the yeast enzyme, and neither is inhibitory in the liver enzyme.

The glutamine synthetase and glutamine transferase enzyme of pea, which was prepared in a highly purified state by Elliott (*334*), and the malic enzyme of pigeon liver studied by Viega-Salles and Ochoa (*335*) are especially interesting in connection with the present discussion. Each enzyme is considered to be a single protein which catalyzes two distinct reactions. The glutamine enzyme (*334*) catalyzes the synthesis of glutamine from glutamate and ammonia (synthetase reaction I) and the transfer or interchange of hydroxylamine or labeled ammonia with the amide group of glutamine (transferase reaction II). The metal activation patterns for the glutamine enzyme are shown in Figs. 9a and 9b. The activation pattern of the synthetase reaction I resembles that for DPN

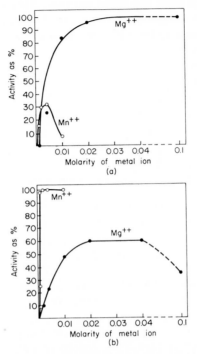

FIG. 9. *a*, Effect of Mg^{2+} and Mn^{2+} on glutamine synthetase. *b*, Effect of Mg^{2+} and Mn^{2+} on glutamine transferase activity. From Elliott (*334*).

kinase of yeast, but the differences between effects of the two metals are more extreme, and magnesium shows no inhibitory effects. The activation pattern of a similar enzyme in brain (*336*) is almost identical to that of the pea enzyme. By contrast, the activation of the transferase reaction II presents an entirely different pattern. Here, manganese has a strikingly greater affinity than magnesium for the enzyme, is far more effective, and is not markedly inhibitory at 10 times the optimum concentration. Unlike some of the enzymes previously considered, the optimum concentrations for manganese or magnesium in the glutamine enzyme are much greater, by factors of ten- to a hundredfold. The fluoride sensitivity of the two reactions also varies; 10^{-3} *M* fluoride inhibits reaction I by 90% and reaction II by 40%, apparently when magnesium is used as activator (*334*). The presence of traces of manganese may account for this effect as noted for effects of manganese in the presence of fluoride (171); or the enzyme sites involved in the two reactions may be different. The dissociation constants for magnesium appear to be similar for the two reactions. The activation patterns of the malic enzyme (335) also differ for the two reactions concerned, but the differences are less spectacular. Differential sensitivity to fluoride has been shown by Mazelis (337) to occur for the adenylic kinase enzymes from the same plants when obtained from different tissues. The mitochondrial enzyme has a greater affinity for magnesium than the chloroplast enzyme and is less sensitive to fluoride. This relationship applies also to inhibition by other metal ions. The effect of copper on the activity of lipoic acid dehydrogenase, described by Veeger and Massey (338), is also of interest. It is able to catalyze two reactions, namely, DPN-lipoic dehydrogenase (I) and DPNH diaphorase (II). Reaction I is totally inhibited by 6×10^{-6} M Cu^{2+}, while under these conditions the activity for the diaphorase reaction II is greatly increased.

b. *Dual Metal-Activated Enzymes and Monovalent Cations.* The relative effects of alkali metals on enzymes dependent on both a monovalent and divalent cation are also interesting. Thus, in the pyruvic kinase system in animals and plants described by Kachmar and Boyer (339), Miller and Evans (193), and McCollum, Hageman, and Tyner (194), K^+, Rb^+, and NH_4^+ are effective activators, while Na^+ activates to a lesser extent but is not inhibitory (193, 194) or activates slightly and inhibits competitively (339). The affinity of the enzyme for potassium appears to differ with preparations from different species; in some, high potassium concentrations are inhibitory (193). In the acetic thiokinase of animal tissues (340) and of plants (195) potassium, rubidium, or ammonium ions activate, while sodium is not only inactive but is a noncompetitive inhibitor; lithium behaves similarly. An analogous contrast is revealed in protein synthesis; whereas potassium is required for amino acid incorporation into protein by pea ribosomes, rubidium inhibits, while sodium, ammonium, and lithium are without effect at the same concentrations (197). L-Amino acid oxidase (341) is inhibited by NH_4^+ ions, and an unusual alcohol dehydrogenase containing a cytochrome component (342) was inhibited 60–90% by about 10^{-3} M NH_4^+ but not at all by the same concentration of K^+ ions. Similarly, potassium is said to be required for photosynthetic phosphorylation (196); but ammonium ions inhibit strongly and reversibly (343).

An interesting relationship between activating metal ions and fructo-kinase was found by Hers (344). When potassium was low, the optimum enzyme activity was obtained with a Mg/ATP ratio of 0.5. By increasing the potassium concentration to 1 M the enzyme activity increased when the optimum Mg/ATP ratio was one. Sodium, however, stimulated only slightly. Hers showed that the Mg-ATP complex was the likely substrate of fructokinase and that the affinity of the enzyme for the complex was five times greater with K^+ than with Na^+ ions. High potassium concentration depressed activity and addition of magnesium and ATP reversed the inhibition in a competitive manner. Hers suggests that the enzyme has two reactive sites which combine with the metals. The active form of the enzyme has the Mg-ATP complex on one site and potassium on another. Any deviation from this optimal condition results in enzyme inhibition. The double ion requirement for enzymes supports the concept of metal-substrates proposed by Najjar (*319*).

   c. *Multiple Metal Activation and Competitive Inhibition.* Several enzymes are activated by alternative metals. Some examples have already been noted. Others include phosphatases and many enzymes of carboxylic acid and phosphorus metabolism. The phosphoenolpyruvic carboxykinase enzyme in higher plants studied by Mazelis and Vennesland (*345*) differed greatly with respect to the relative extents to which the enzyme is activated by manganese or magnesium. In some preparations magnesium was almost inactive and in others was equivalent to manganese. In the *Avena* isocitric dehydrogenase enzyme, Mn^{2+} or Co^{2+} ($K_m = 1.5 \times 10^{-4}\ M$) are equally effective, and Mg^{2+} gives 80% of their activity, but in the *Phaseolus* enzyme the K_m for Mn^{2+} was 5×10^{-5} and that for Mg^{2+} was 5×10^{-4} (*346*). The malic enzyme in wheat germ is also activated by either Mn^{2+} or Co^{2+} (*347*). The activation patterns and properties described here and in Sections III, B, 1*a* and 1*b* reveal possibilities for interaction between activating metals when present simultaneously at various concentrations. Thus, the high affinity of the glutamine enzyme (*334*) for manganese results in inhibitory competition by suboptimal concentrations of manganese in the presence of an optimal concentration of magnesium for the transferase activity (reaction II). It would be expected that in reaction I optimal concentrations of manganese would not greatly affect the rate in the presence of much higher optimal concentrations of magnesium because the affinities for the two metals are relatively similar. In the brain enzyme (*336*), however, manganese might well inhibit competitively in the presence of optimal concentrations of magnesium, as distinct from its noncompetitive inhibitory effects.

   Another example is the oxidation of citrate by an enzyme complex in kidney, described by Hartman and Kalnitsky (*348*), which is activated by manganese at low concentrations ($5 \times 10^{-5}\ M$) or by magnesium at higher concentrations (about $10^{-3} M$). In this system intermediate concentrations of magnesium inhibit competitively in the presence of optimum concentrations of manganese but produce progressively more activation as the magnesium concentration approaches the optimum. Copper also inhibits the action of manganese in the same system.

The yeast inorganic pyrophosphatase system which was thought by Bailey and Webb (349) to be specifically activated by magnesium (optimum, $2 \times 10^{-3} M$) was shown by Kunitz (350) to be activated also by cobalt at much lower concentrations (10^{-5}–$10^4 M$). At $10^{-4} M$, however, cobalt competes with magnesium and is inhibitory in the presence of optimum concentrations of the latter.

Bard and Gunsalus (350a) observed a similar activation pattern of aldolase from *Clostridium* by Fe^{2+} and Co^{2+} ions. The latter was the less effective and inhibited competitively in the presence of optimal concentrations of Fe^{2+} ions. Enolase of yeast is activated not only by Mg^{2+} but by Zn^{2+}, Mn^{2+}, and Fe^{2+} in relative values of $1.0 : 0.3 : 0.29 : 0.09$. However, in the presence of Mg^{2+}, at optimal concentration, Zn^{2+} behaves in an inhibitory manner, (350b) because, although less effective, it has an affinity about 100 times greater than Mg^{2+} for the enzyme.

d. Competition by Inactive Metals. The competition between magnesium and a nonactivating metal, namely, calcium, was also demonstrated for yeast inorganic pyrophosphatase by Bailey and Webb (349). They showed that inhibition by calcium was a function of the Ca/Mg ratio and increased from zero to 100% inhibition over about a hundredfold range in the Ca/Mg ratio in the presence of adequate magnesium. The inhibitory effect of calcium was independent of the concentration of magnesium present, provided the enzyme was supplied with sufficient to saturate it under normal conditions.

Inhibitions of yeast alkaline pyrophosphatase by beryllium or manganese was reversible by increasing the substrate concentration but was mainly independent of magnesium concentration. The effect of zinc was intermediate, and inhibitory effects appeared to depend on both magnesium and substrate concentrations. Calcium is also a potent competitive inhibitor of pyruvic kinase (193, 339). The effect is complex, as a noncompetitive aspect is involved in relation to potassium activation of the muscle enzyme (339), and in the plant enzyme Miller and Evans (193) found that magnesium and potassium each partly reversed a competitive effect, which may indicate why potassium only partially reversed the calcium effect in the muscle enzyme.

Nagana and Menon (*351*) described a similar competitive inhibition of erythrocyte pyrophosphatase for beryllium, barium, or calcium in increasing order of inhibitory effect. For each metal the inhibition was determined by the Be/Mg, Ba/Mg, or Ca/Mg ratios over a range of magnesium concentrations. It is interesting to note that in this system beryllium competed with magnesium as might be expected, but in the yeast pyrophosphatase (*349*) it was concluded that beryllium inhibition was reversed by pyrophosphate and not by magnesium. Potato alkaline pyrophosphatase is also competitively inhibited by calcium (*279*).

Adenosinetriphosphatase of myosin is activated by calcium or manganese but not by magnesium (inhibition was not tested) (*352*), while an ADPase in the same preparation was activated by manganese more than by magnesium and was inactive in the presence of calcium. Kielly and Meyerhof (*353*) separated a magnesium-activated ATPase which was inhibited by calcium from actin and myosin. Heppel and Hilmoe (*353a*) found that magnesium-specific 5′-nucleotidase of bull semen was inhibited competitively by calcium. Williams (*354*) has contributed a likely explanation of the unpredictable but obviously related effects of calcium and magnesium in ATP and phosphate ester-activating enzymes. He pointed out that calcium tends to coordinate more strongly than magnesium by coordinating with hydroxyl groups in addition to oxygen of phosphate and carboxyl of 2-phosphoglyceric acid. The greater stability of the calcium complex might thus explain why calcium inhibits enolase whereas magnesium activates. Similarly, calcium may coordinate all three phosphate groups of ATP through oxygen atoms, while magnesium may coordinate only two. In some instances this difference might reflect inhibition by calcium and activation by magnesium. If, however, other protein groups (e.g. carboxyl) coordinate additional sites, then magnesium may coordinate only one phosphate oxygen, and calcium may coordinate two. Under these circumstances magnesium may be inactive, while calcium activates. A third possibility is that when magnesium coordinates two oxygen atoms, the third and perhaps other sites are occupied by water molecules; this arrangement permits activation of hydrolytic activity which would be inhibited by calcium where water does not occupy a coordinating site. The properties of apyrase and other ATPases appear to be explained better by the first two ideas rather than by the third.

Beryllium is chemically related to magnesium, and as already noted in the work of Nagana and Menon (*351*) a competitive inhibition of erythrocyte pyrophosphatase can be reversed by magnesium. The inhibition by beryllium of alkaline phosphatases of some animal tissues is very strong. Klemperer, Miller, and Hill (*354a*) found that 50% inhibition of hog kidney alkaline phosphatase occurred at $3 \times 10^{-6}\ M$ beryllium, and Grier, Hood, and Hoagland (*354b*) found that $10^{-5}\ M$ beryllium similarly inhibited rat intestinal alkaline phosphatase. Acid phosphatase was practically uninhibited by $10^{-4}\ M$ and only 15% inhibited by $10^{-3}\ M$ beryllium (*354a*). In both enzymes magnesium was unable to reverse the effect of beryllium, in contrast to the erythrocyte pyrophosphatase (*351*), but aging of the intestinal phosphatase decreased the extent to which beryllium inhibited the enzyme in the presence of magnesium.

Malmström (*350b*) showed that yeast enolase is inhibited competitively by Be^{2+}, Ca^{2+}, and Ni^{2+} with increasing order of affinity for the enzyme. In this example the value of K_i for Be^{2+} was $1.5 \times 10^{-3}\ M$, and was actually greater than the K_a ($3 \times 10^{-4}\ M$) for Mg^{2+}, the activating ion. It might be expected, here, that Zn^{2+} would reactivate better than Mg^{2+} when Be^{2+} ions are present because of the low value of K_a for Zn^{2+}, about $3 \times 10^{-6}\ M$.

2. INHIBITION BY CATIONS IN RELATION TO AFFINITIES FOR SPECIFIC GROUPS

A great many enzymes which depend upon thiol groups for their activity are sensitive to low concentrations of heavy metals, especially of mercury, and often also of copper, silver, lead, zinc, and cadmium. Other mechanisms of metal inhibition also occur. Examples of particularly sensitive enzymes include yeast alcohol dehydrogenase (*355*), urease (*356, 357*), saccharase (*358*), β-fructofuranosidase (*359*), malt amylase (*360*), and papain (*361*). Some of these enzymes are especially sensitive to silver, but the mechanisms of inhibition may be different. Thus, alcohol dehydrogenase, when in solution at a concentration of $6.7 \times 10^{-9}\ M$ is inactivated 50% by $8 \times 10^{-8}\ M\ Ag^+$, and the reaction appears to be with the free —SH groups of the enzyme. Myrbäck (*358*) concluded that in saccharase silver reacts with a pH-dependent group, probably a carboxyl group, K_i (Ag) $= 6 \times 10^{-8}$. Dixon and Webb (*362*) report the mechanism of silver inhibition of β-fructofuranosidase as due to combination between silver and a histidine group in the enzyme. The inhibition of enzymes by silver is often reversed by hydrogen sulfide, e.g. urease, regardless of the mechanism of the inhibition. Several other examples are given by Massart (*363*). The mechanism of silver inhibition of urease is not clear. Thus, Hellerman, Chinard, and Dietz (*364*) showed that urease, which has a molecular weight of **483,000**, contains a great many —SH groups. About **23** can be oxidized by ferricyanide or other reagents without loss of activity, and another **23** can be oxidized subsequently with a progressive and finally total loss of activity. On denaturation with urea another 40–70 —SH groups become reactive. In spite of this large number of reactive groups of different specificity, only 7 atoms of silver (356) or 3 to 4 silver equivalents per molecule of protein (357) are required for total inactivation, which can be reversed by immediate treatment with hydrogen sulfide. It is possible that some other group than a thiol is involved in this reaction. The metal sensitivity of papain and the formation of specific mercury compounds has been discussed elsewhere in this chapter in relation to the effects of cyanide and hydrogen sulfide.

The relative affinity of proteins for metals differs according to the nature of the specific binding groups involved, and this concept has been studied by Klotz (318) in relation to metal-enzyme activation. It may, however, apply also to the relative inhibitory effects of different metals and thus account for the differences in order of inhibition by metals observed with different enzymes. Thus, according to Klotz (318), in enzymes where free —SH groups are the binding sites, the order of affinity for metallosubstrate complexes reflects the relative magnitude of the solubility products of the metal sulfides, while in chelation reactions, the stability constants of metal chelates determine the relative affinities. The order of decreasing solubility products of metal sulfides is as follows (318, 365): Hg, Ag $\gg$ Cu $\gg$ Pb, Cd $>$ Zn $>$ Co, Ni $>$ Mn, and this corresponds precisely with the binding affinities of these metals with serum albumin (318).

Shaw (365, 365a) reviewed the results of several experiments on the inhibition of urease by metal ions and concluded that the order of metal sulfide insolubility was almost identical with the order of inhibitory effect. In a later paper (ref. 122a loc cit.) he considered that the order of organo-metallic complex stabilities closely reflected their effects on urease.

Arrigoni and Rossi (366) found that sulfoglutathione reductase of pea was inhibited 84, 36, and 15% by 10^{-5} M Zn^{2+}, Fe^{2+}, and Co^{2+}, respectively. This order would be consistent with the solubility products of these metal sulfides. Similarly, Turner and Turner (367) found that adenylic kinase of pea, which apparently depends on free —SH groups is inhibited 100, 100, and 23% by 10^{-5} M Hg^{2+}, 10^{-3} M Cu^{2+} and 5×10^{-3} M Zn^{2+}, respectively. The protein disulfide reductase of pea studied by Hatch and Turner (368), which is almost certainly dependent upon thiol groups, was inhibited in decreasing order by $Hg^{2+} > Zn^{2+} > Cd^{2+} > Ag^+$. This enzyme was shown to have a dithiol group (i.e., two associated adjacent thiol groups) as the active center, as revealed by inhibition by arsenite and low concentrations of Cd^{2+} ions, as described in connection with cadmium inhibition. The anomalous position of silver would be consistent with this property, since Ag^+ would not form the compounds with dithiols which would occur in the presence of the other divalent metals. The activity of zinc might seem anomalous. The protein disulfide reductase of yeast studied by Asaki, Bandurski, and Wilson (*369*) is also inhibited by cadmium but is less sensitive than the pea enzyme.

The combination of metals with thiol groups in proteins may be represented in the following possible ways [Eq. (11) and (12)].

(1) Where —SH groups are far apart:

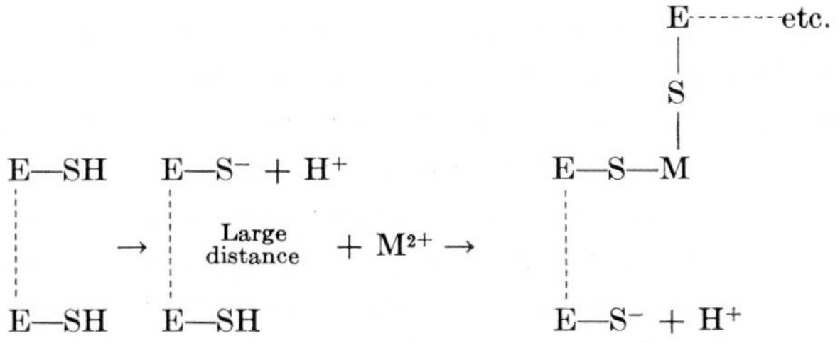

$$
\begin{array}{lll}
 & & \text{E} \text{------} \text{etc.} \\
 & & | \\
 & & \text{S} \\
 & & | \\
\text{E—SH} & \text{E—S}^- + \text{H}^+ & \text{E—S—M} \\
| & \xrightarrow{} \quad | \quad \substack{\text{Large}\\\text{distance}} \ + \ \text{M}^{2+} \rightarrow & | \\
\text{E—SH} & \text{E—SH} & \text{E—S}^- + \text{H}^+
\end{array}
\tag{11}
$$

(2) Where adjacent —SH groups form a dithiol:

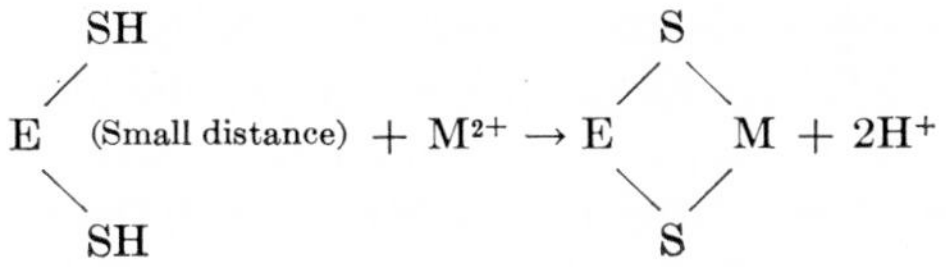

$$
\text{E}\begin{array}{l}{}^{\diagup\text{SH}}\\{}_{\diagdown\text{SH}}\end{array} \text{(Small distance)} + \text{M}^{2+} \rightarrow \text{E}\begin{array}{l}{}^{\diagup\text{S}}\diagdown\\{}_{\diagdown\text{S}}\diagup\end{array}\text{M} + 2\text{H}^+
\tag{12}
$$

The presence of other groups may modify the dissociation of the —SH groups. Reactions between divalent metals and isolated thiol groups may lead to an intermediate cross-linking of thiol groups as shown in reaction (11), while reactions between dithiol groups and monovalent metal ions [Eq. (13)] may be less stable than with divalent ions.

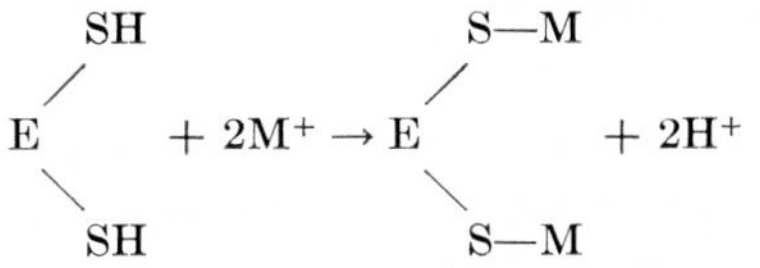

$$
\text{E}\begin{array}{l}{}^{\diagup\text{SH}}\\{}_{\diagdown\text{SH}}\end{array} + 2\text{M}^+ \rightarrow \text{E}\begin{array}{l}{}^{\diagup\text{S—M}}\\{}_{\diagdown\text{S—M}}\end{array} + 2\text{H}^+
\tag{13}
$$

Correspondingly, reaction between isolated thiol groups and monovalent ions may be more complete and also more readily reversible than with divalent metal ions.

Heavy metal toxicity is often reversed by hydrogen sulfide, monothiols, e.g., cysteine or GSH, and dithiols, e.g. 2,3-dimercaptopropanol (BAL), and metal inhibition of bacterial cells or fungal spores may be reversed in this way, as shown by Fildes (370), Yoder (371), and Janke, Beran, and Schmidt (372).

For several chelation complexes discussed in the physiological section the order, which varies at times for some metals with particular ligands as noted in Section I and as described by Williams (354), is in general $Cu^{2+} > Co^{2+} Ni^{2+} > Fe^{3+} > Zn^{2+} > Cd^{2-} > Fe^{2+} > Mn^{2+}$. For porphyrins Fe^{3+} and Co^{3+} have outstanding affinity and exceed Cu^{2+}. For a,a'-dipyridyl and o-phenanthroline Fe^{2+} and Fe^{3+} show reversed affinities, and the position of Co^{2+} may vary with different ligands. Klotz (318) pointed out that pH effects may be very important in relation to protein-metal binding in regard both to effects of pH on the general charge of the protein and on the dissociation of specific groups, such as phosphate, carboxyl, hydroxyl, imidazole, thio, and amido or guanidinium; Hg^{2+}, Cu^{2+}, and Ag^+ may combine at many of these sites, and Ca^{2+} binding, for example, appears to occur at carboxyl groups or phosphate groups. Differences between affinity for metals of —OH groups, on one hand, and =NH or C=O groups, on the other, may account for the activation of arginase by cobalt, ferrous iron, or nickel and its inactivation by copper, ferric iron, and mercury, which have very large solubility products with hydroxyl groups (318). In his intensive studies on the binding by metals of azopyridine dyes to serum albumin, Klotz found that the metal-protein-dye ternary complexes are formed, especially with Cu^{2+}, Hg^{2+}, Ni^{2+}, Co^{2+}, Zn^{2+}, and Mn^{2+}, but Ca^{2+} and Mg^{2+} were ineffective. All the active metals form chelates with the dye in the absence of proteins and promote combination of dye with serum albumin. Klotz concluded that chelate formation of metals with low molecular weight compounds might be a model of how metals chelate the various cofactors to a complex protein. Depending on the metal, it can either enhance enzymic reaction or else inhibit it completely by formation of electrostatic or coordinate bonds (318). Shaw (122a) gave diastase as another example of metal inhibition being related to metal-chelate stability constant values.

Hydrogen ion effects may be important also in nonspecific inhibition by ions. The sensitivity of urease to monovalent anions and cations was shown by Kistiakowsky and Shaw (373) to be nonspecific with regard to the ion under certain conditions, but to be accentuated by increasing pH. They suggested that the ionization of the protein as a whole or as a "zwitterion" was involved in this type of inhibition. Miyaji and Greenstein (374) have shown that in addition to the Mg^{2+} and Mn^{2+} ions, activation of deoxyribonuclease the following ions are also effective: Co^{2+}, Fe^{2+}, Ca^{2+}, Ni^{2+}, and Zn^{2+}. The optimum pH for the activation with Mg^{2+}, Co^{2+}, and Ca^{2+} was 6.5 and that for Fe^{2+} was 5.7, whereas two optima were observed (at 6.8 and 8.0) for activation by Mn^{2+}. It is of interest that when Mg^{2+} is effective, Fe^{2+} is not, and vice versa. Hellerman and Stock (*329*) had earlier observed a shift in the pH activity for arginase, depending on whether Mn^{2+}, Co^{2+}, or Ni^{2+} was used as an activator. This led them to postulate that a metal-enzyme complex was formed and that the pH curves represented the ability or otherwise of these complexes to form coordinate linkages with the substrate molecule.

Nygaard (*374a, 374b*) has published results of a detailed kinetic analysis of the inhibitory effects of salts and anions on the D- and L-lactic cytochrome c reductase of yeast. The effects of salts are considered here.

The activity (v) of the enzymes is represented by the general equation [Eq. (14)]

$$\frac{[E]}{v} = \emptyset_0 + \frac{\emptyset_1}{[S](\text{lactate})} + \frac{\emptyset_2}{[\text{Cyt c}]} \tag{14}$$

since substrate and acceptor are not mutually competitive. [E] is the enzyme concentration, and $\emptyset_0$, $\emptyset_1$, and $\emptyset_2$ are the reciprocals of the velocity constants. The apparent $K_m[S] = \emptyset_1/(\emptyset_0 + \emptyset_2/\text{Cyt c})$. The reaction mechanism was considered to involve two binary reactions in accordance with the observed kinetics [Eqs. (15) and (16)].

$$E + S \underset{k_2}{\overset{k_1}{\rightleftharpoons}} ES \overset{k_3}{\longrightarrow} EH \text{ (reduced enzyme)} + P \text{ (product)} \tag{15}$$

$$EH + Fe^{3+} \text{ Cyt c} \underset{k_2'}{\overset{k_1'}{\rightleftharpoons}} EHFe^{3+} \text{ Cyt c} \overset{k_3'}{\longrightarrow} E + Fe^{2+} \text{ Cyt c} + H^+ \tag{16}$$

From these reactions the constants $\emptyset_0$, $\emptyset_1$, and $\emptyset_2$ were given by the expressions in Eq. (17).

$$\emptyset_0 = \frac{1}{k_3 + k_3'}; \qquad \emptyset_1 = \frac{k_3 + k_2}{k_3 k_1}; \qquad \emptyset_2 = \frac{k_3' + k_2'}{k_3' k_1'} \tag{17}$$

The values of $\emptyset_0$ and $\emptyset_2$ are obtained from intercepts in the relationships between $1/V_{max}$ and $1/(Fe^{3+}Cyt\ c)$, while $\emptyset_1$ is obtained from the equation for $K_m(S)$. The effects of buffer concentration and of the ionic charge of various cations on the values of $\emptyset_0$, $\emptyset_1$, and $\emptyset_2$ were then determined. The parameter $\emptyset_2$, which is inversely related to saturation of the acceptor site by Fe^{3+}cytochrome c was increased strongly for the D(—)-lactate enzyme by phosphate and to a lesser extent by oxalate, and this effect was accentuated by the presence of cations, divalent ions (Ca^{2+}, Mg^{2+}, Co^{2+}) being more effective than monovalent ions (Na^+, K^+, NH_4^+, arginine+, and Tris+). The polyvalent cation protamine was most effective and produced severe inhibition. The values of $\emptyset_0$ and $\emptyset_1$ were scarcely affected by salt concentrations. Increasing ionic strength of cations and anions increased the competitive inhibition at the acceptor site for Fe^{3+}cytochrome c. Further analysis indicated that the inhibition for the D(—)-lactate enzyme at the acceptor site is of the type EI_3^- where three inhibitor molecules combine. It was thought that negatively charged carboxylic acid groupings were involved. The apparent dissociation constants K_i for the D(—)-enzyme were 10^{-5} for monovalent salts, 10^{-6}–10^{-7} for divalent salts, and 10^{-10} for the polyvalent protamine ion. The inhibition of the L(+)-lactate enzyme was not of the EI or EI_3 type but indicated a stepwise relationship with ionic strength which was thought to reflect the presence of several acceptor sites with differing salt sensitivities. Both D- and L-enzymes were inhibited in an EI manner by positively changed proteins at the acceptor site.

An unusual order of inhibitory activity by metals was reported for tryptophan synthetase in plants by Madhusudanan and Vaidyanathan (375). At $4 \times 10^{-4} M$ concentration the per cent inhibitions were as shown below:

Fe^{2+}	Ag^+	Cd^{2+}	Zn^{2+}	Co^{2+}	Mg^{2+}	Hg^{2+}	Mn^{2+}	Cu^{2+}
92	82	76	74	58	58	55	44	29

None of the orders for solubility products or stability constants mentioned previously is consistent with the relative effects shown here. Further investigation of this system might reveal some unexpected and interesting facts regarding protein-metal-substrate relationships or coordinating sites.

Inhibitory and toxic effects of cadmium are of interest. Before considering effects on specific enzymes, other aspects of cadmium as a physiologically active metal may be noted. An interesting protein named metallothioneine has been isolated by Kägi and Vallee (376, 377) from equine renal cortex. This contains 2.9% cadmium and 0.6% zinc in a molar ratio of 3:1. The protein is particularly rich in —SH groups, and these are present in a ratio of 3 —SH groups to 1 metal atom. Metallothioneine accounts for 60% of the total and usually high cadmium content of this tissue. Lawford (378) has found that in cases of experimental cadmium poisoning of rats an abnormal serum protein is produced with different electrophoretic properties; but the effect is not specific as the same band appears with mercury, beryllium, cadmium, copper, manganese, and zinc.

Cadmium at low concentrations has been proposed by Sanadi, Langley, and White (379) as a specific and confirmatory test for the presence of essential adjacent dithiol groups, following the observations of Jacobs et al. (380) that Cd^{2+} uncoupled oxidative phosphorylation by rat liver mitochondria. These workers found that $1.6 \times 10^{-6} M$ and $6 \times 10^{-6} M$ Cd^{2+} caused 50% inhibition and total inhibition, respectively, of coupled phosphorylation without affecting oxygen uptake. The cadmium was tightly bound to the protein but was removed by 2,3-dimercaptopropanol (BAL); mercury, zinc, copper, and lead did not produce this inhibition at the same concentrations. Jacobs et al. (380), Searls and Sanadi (381), Stein, Kauffman, and Kaplan (382) have shown that when cadmium inhibition of an adjacent dithiol center is suspected, inhibition may be expected to occur with arsenite. The effect of cadmium is reversible by BAL but not by monothiols like cysteine or glutathione. The enzymes concerned, α-ketoglutaric dehydrogenase, α-dihydrolipoic dehydrogenase, and transhydrogenase, are considered to function by oxidation and reduction of adjacent —SH groups, possibly present in a coenzyme state as a bound form of thioctic acid. An interesting point is that at least one of these enzymes is not inhibited by $10^{-2} M$ cyanide. Presumably, coenzyme-bound —S=S— groups are not susceptible to reduction by cyanide in the same way as protein-bound —S=S— groups, as discussed later. By contrast, xanthine oxidase and aldehyde oxidase, which, as pointed out later, show an irreversible inactivation by cyanide and are inhibited by arsenite, are not inhibited by Cd^{2+} ions, according to Peters and Sanadi (383). Presumably, protein-bound —S=S— groups are involved here, not coenzyme-bound groups, and are in some way protected from reaction with Cd^{2+} ions. This subject is discussed later.

The effects of metal inhibitors on phosphoglucomutase from muscle presents interesting features. This enzyme is known to be "activated" by chelating agents as well as by cysteine and magnesium. The problem which involves extreme sensitivity to some heavy metals, including zinc and copper, has been studied by Millstein (384, 385). Zinc inhibits the enzyme by competing very strongly with magnesium. The relative dissociation constants are very different, since the enzyme is saturated at about $1.5 \times 10^{-3} M$ Mg^{2+}, while it is almost totally inhibited by $10^{-10} M$ Zn^{2+} in the presence of magnesium; the value of K_i, for Zn^{2+}

is 3.9×10^{-14}. The inhibition is effected by Zn^{2+} ions, as shown by the use of histidine as a complexing agent, which gives identical results when calculated in terms of free Zn^{2+} ions.

Inhibition by copper is even more severe, but is also complex. By using the Lineweaver-Burk method of analysis, it was shown that copper inhibition is competitive with magnesium and also noncompetitive, suggesting that at least two Cu^{2+} ions or copper molecules are involved, since both V_{max} and the apparent Michaelis constants for magnesium were affected by copper. By applying a solution developed by Malström (*350b*) for kinetics of enolase inhibition, Millstein (*385*) showed that K_i (Cu^{2+}) for competitive inhibition is 2.3×10^{-17}, an exceptional avidity for ionic copper. K_i' for noncompetitive inhibition was also very small, but one order greater than K_i, i.e. 2.5×10^{-16}. The noncompetitive inhibition at other sites was therefore significant only at higher concentrations of magnesium.

Titration of the enzyme with *p*-chloromercuribenzoate in the presence and absence of zinc and results of other experiments indicated that —SH groups were not directly involved in activity or metal binding. Chelation with more than one group in the protein was considered likely, and imidazole, amino carboxyl, and phosphate groups were considered likely sites. Structural analysis of the protein by Millstein and Sangar (*386*) indicates that the active center of the enzyme contains a pentapeptide and that the imidazole group of a histidine residue may be oriented close to a phosphate group of phosphorylserine or, alternatively, to a carboxyl group, either arrangement could provide chelation of great stability.

A similar structural analysis of the yeast enzyme would be of great interest, as McCoy and Najjar (*387*) have shown that zinc can replace magnesium as an activating metal with about 60% efficiency at $10^{-3} M$. At higher concentrations ($10^{-2} M$) zinc inhibits totally but the difference between the two proteins with regard to metal sensitivity is nevertheless very great indeed.

Malmström (*350b*) investigated the inhibition of yeast enolase by different metal ions. Competitive inhibition in the presence of Mg^{2+} by active and inactive metal ions has been referred to previously. In addition to this type of inhibition which occurs at the active site of the enzyme, evidence was obtained that metal-substrate complexes were also formed and that their structure might be different for various inhibitory metals. In addition to this complication there was no clear relationship between the extent of inhibition and the order of metal stability constants. Malmström suggested that a carboxyl group and another group, possibly phenolic or imidazole, was involved in binding the metal to the protein. The lack of evidence for free —SH groups being involved makes the severe inhibition by Cd^{2+} difficult to explain.

3. TOXICITY OF CHELATED METALS

Although the primary effect of toxic concentrations of heavy metals is on enzymes within the cell, they also alter permeability barriers and block uptake of other essential nutrients. The case of entry of toxic metals into cells may also vary. The precise biochemical mechanisms involved are not understood, but chelation may be involved here (see *99, 145a*), and it must be remembered that chelate complexes may be charged and have opposite signs to those of the unchelated ions, and that chelate charge will be affected by pH.

In an earlier section the toxicity effects of chelates, in particular those of metal-oxine complexes on bacterial growth, was considered. Many cell metabolites readily chelate metals, e.g., hydroxy and amino acids, polyphosphates, peptides, and porphyrins, and for many of them biological activity is dependent on this reaction. Thus, Miller, McCallan, and Weed (*388*) showed that chelation of Mn was of prime importance for peptidase action. Calvin (*317*) considers that chelation is essential for the action of metal-dependent enzymes and that this mechanism can explain inhibition and interactions with metal-dependent enzymes. Albert (*37*) and Block (*389*) have put forward a possible mechanism for the action of oxine and its metal complexes in cell metabolism. They consider that the uncharged 1:2 chelate (XII) because of its higher lipid solubility enters the cell more rapidly than the charged 1:1 chelate (XI). This would be analogous to cell penetration by HN_3, HCN, and HF, as opposed to the dissociated ionic forms discussed later.

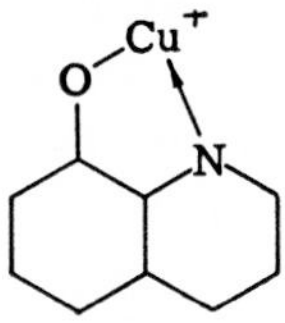

1:1 Complex   1:2 Complex

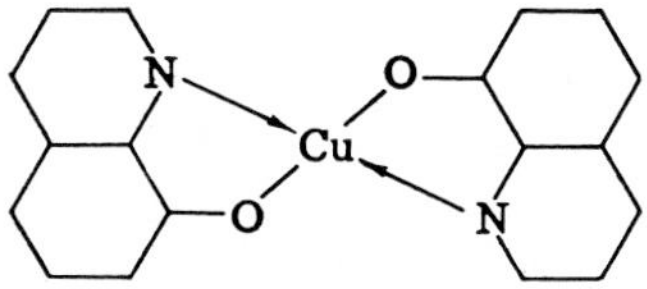

(XI)   (XII)

Within the cell it is likely that the 1:1 complex is the more toxic, presumably because it reacts directly with —SH groups and metal-binding sites. This hypothesis provides an explanation for the bimodal dose response curve for metal-oxine observed by Albert (*37*), Block (*389*), and Mason (*390*). There is little evidence, however, for the sites of the proposed reaction within the cell. Kaars Sijpesteyn and van der Kerk (*391, 392*) consider that the 1:1 copper chelate reacts with an enzyme normally linked with a metal, and that the available coordination positions of the copper in the 1:1 complex replace the metal on the enzyme.

C. Effects of Some Anions as Enzyme Inhibitors

1. GENERAL ASPECTS

a. Mechanisms Involved. Anions may inhibit or stimulate enzyme activity, and several different mechanisms may be involved. Anion inhibition may be due to (1) competition for an active site with a substrate anion, (2) complex formation at a reactive site producing a change in enzyme properties in relation to redox potential, structure, charge, or substrate affinity, (3) complex formation with a dissociable metal activator, thus preventing enzyme-metal combination, (4) competition with an activating metal for a reactive site, (5) alteration of dissociation of acidic or basic ionized groups in the enzyme, and (6) removal of a protein-bound metal.

Examples of these mechanisms are found in the discussion of effects of cyanide, azide, fluoride, sulfide, pyrophosphate, citrate, bicarbonate, borate, and other anions in the following section.

b. Effects of Anions on Ionized Groups. Massey (*393*) investigated the effects of monovalent and polyvalent anions on the activity of fumarase. It was found that the polyvalent anions, sulfate, citrate, borate, phosphate, and arsenate activated the enzyme with malate as substrate in increasing order of effectiveness and with an increasing value of the optimum pH, except for borate where the pH optimum was about the same as with phosphate and arsenate. With malate as substrate the shift in pH optimum induced by phosphate was about 0.5 units, whereas when fumarate was the substrate the pH shift was large, about 1.5 units. By contrast, monovalent anions, chloride, bromide, and thiocyanate, were inhibitory in increasing order of effectiveness. Lineweaver-Burk plots of activities in the presence or absence of phosphate or of thiocyanate, respectively, showed that the activation was not related to enzyme-substrate affinity and that the inhibition was not competitive.

From the different effects of polyvalent and monovalent anions on pH optima, shape of pH activity curves, and activity, Massey (*393*) developed a theory embracing both the activating and inhibiting effects of the

anions, which was based on the hypothesis of Michaelis and Davidsohn
(*394*) and Michaelis and Pechstein (*395*) that enzyme activity in relation
to pH is dependent upon the dissociation constants of both acidic and
basic groups.

In the presence of activating polyvalent anions the pH effects were
greatest for the alkaline values, indicating effects on the basic dissociation
constants of the protein. In the presence of the inhibiting monovalent
anions the acidic side of the pH-activity curve is mainly affected, and
acidic group dissociations are involved. Massey (*393*) postulated that
combination of the substrates (malate or fumarate) and protein occurred
at secondary sites adjacent to, but apart from, the active center, and that
this altered the dissociation of the ionizing groups of the active center.
Since the activating and inhibiting anions do not affect enzyme-substrate
affinities, it is concluded that they do not act on ionized groups at the
active center, but on adjacent subsidiary basic groups. On the basis of
this idea, combination of an anion with a basic group adjacent to the
activating basic group would increase the dissociation of the latter, raise
the pK value, and increase activation over the alkaline pH range. Similarly, combination of an anion with a basic group adjacent to an acidic
group responsible for activity would decrease the dissociation of the
latter, raise the pK value, and cause increased inhibition in the acid pH
range. What is not yet explained is why polyvalent anions combine with
basic groups adjacent to the activating basic group, while monovalent
anions combine with basic groups adjacent to the activating acidic group.
Massey suggested that ionic size or charge might be the determining
factors in this distinction.

Massey and Alberty (*396*) have described the pH relationships governing thiocyanate inhibition of fumarase. These indicate that the noncompetitive inhibition by thiocyanate depends upon the combination with an
anion-binding site with a pK of 7.0 when malate is the substrate and with
a pK of 6.0 when fumarate is the substrate. Owing to the effect of thiocyanate on the dissociation of the group (p$K = 7.0$) which is revealed by
a shift to more alkaline values of the acidic side of the curve relating
pH activity with malate, the presence of thiocyanate results in a slight
shift of the pH optimum for malate from 6.8 to 7.4. The effect of thiocyanate inhibition is therefore pH dependent. At a concentration of
$2.7 \times 10^{-2} M$, thiocyanate inhibits strongly at pH 6.0 (about 75%).
Inhibition decreases with increasing pH, and thiocyanate becomes stimulatory above about pH 7.2 for the reaction with fumarate. At pH 7.7
thiocyanate is stimulatory (30%) up to a concentration of about
$2 \times 10^{-2} M$ and then becomes progressively more inhibitory at higher

concentrations. The mechanism may be uncompetitive, as described in the next section since thiocyanate inhibits ceruloplasmin by this mechanism.

Inhibition by thiocyanate may also occur in enzymes containing a metal which reacts with CNS^- ions. Nicholas and Nason (23) observed that nitrate reductase is inhibited by thiocyanate. Presumably, the pentavalent state (Mo^{5+}) produced during functioning of the enzyme (25) is the reactive form, as Mo^{6+} does not form stable complexes with thiocyanate. Thiocyanate may be inhibitory to other enzymes not sensitive to cyanide, azide, Versene, or o-phenanthroline, as found by Avron and Jagendorf (397) for the TPNH-specific diaphorase in chloroplasts.

Nygaard (374a and 374b), whose work on the effects of salt concentration and ionic strength on the affinity for cytochrome c of the D- and L-lactic dehydrogenases has been described, also studied the effects of anions on the same enzymes as revealed by the value of $\emptyset_0$, $\emptyset_1$, $\emptyset_2$ obtained by the methods already specified (see Section III,B,2).

Anions of keto acids, such as α-ketoglutarate, oxaloacetate, pyruvate, and the aldehydic acid glyoxalate, inhibit reversibly at the substrate (lactate) site of the D-enzyme by increasing $\emptyset_1$ but have no effect on $\emptyset_0$ or $\emptyset_2$ and do not inhibit at the acceptor site. Oxalate increased both $\emptyset_1$ and $\emptyset_2$ and therefore inhibited at substrate and acceptor sites. The data for inhibition at the two sites are consistent with the theory that the mechanism of reaction involves two binary complexes, as already described. Since $\emptyset_0$ was not appreciably affected by anions or cations, it might be concluded that affinity or dissociation of enzyme and product of lactate oxidation or of enzyme and reduced cytochrome c is not sensitive to the presence of these ions.

By contrast with the D(−)-lactate enzyme the L(+)-lactate enzyme was affected to a negligible extent by the keto and aldehyde acids; and although oxalate inhibits, the K_i for oxalate is about 100 times greater for the L(+)- than for the D(−)-enzyme. The effect of long-chain fatty acids was also investigated. These inhibited both enzymes, and log K_i was linearly related to the number of $-CH_2-$ groups in the chain. The reaction appeared to be of the EI type with one acid molecule reacting at only one site binding the substrate. The free energy change for reaction with the D(−)-lactate enzyme was much greater than for the L(+)-enzyme.

c. *Anticompetitive or Uncompetitive Inhibition by Anions.* The term anticompetitive or uncompetitive inhibition was introduced by D. Burk in 1934 [ref. by Friedenwald and Mangwyn-Davies (398)] to account for effects which were neither competitive with nor independent of substrate or metal affinity. The inhibitor sometimes resulted in greater affinity between substrate and enzyme. This mechanism has been noted as a possibility in relation to the activation of arginase discussed by Klotz (*318*). The kinetic analysis of uncompetitive inhibition using the Lineweaver-Burk procedure has been fully described by Friedenwald and Mangwyn-Davies (*398*). An early example described was inhibition of arylsulfatase of *Alcaligenes metacaligenes* by cyanide (*399*). In these examples reciprocal plots of $1/v$ and $1/S$ are parallel for increasing concentrations of inhibitor and do not therefore intersect at infinite values of S or at the substrate axis. Curzon (*400*) studied the inhibition of ceruloplasmin by several monovalent anions and sulfate which inhibited in the order $CNS^- > F^- >> Cl^- > Br^- > SO_4^{2-}$ by a mechanism which was best interpreted as uncompetitive inhibition. As the enzyme is a copper-containing metalloenzyme, it might be expected that the anions combine with the metal but at the same time increase the substrate affinity. Borate inhibition of ceruloplasmin is considered later.

Tubbs (*400a*) studied the inhibitory effects of oxalate on D-α-hydroxy acid dehydrogenase of rabbit kidney mitochondria and reported several features which are relevant to this discussion. Where the substrate, lactate, contained a trace of oxalate as an impurity, the apparent value of $K_m[S]$ was decreased, i.e., the apparent affinity was increased. The value of K_i for oxalate was low, namely 5–10 μM. Pyruvate inhibition was competitive with respect to indophenol as the electron acceptor, but was apparently uncompetitive with respect to lactate, due to mixed inhibition (competitive with indophenol and noncompetitive with lactate). Other examples of this relationship were also given (*400a*). Cyanide as CN^- also inhibited competitively and reversibly with lactate, and potentiated the inhibitory effects of EDTA and *o*-phenanthroline. A metal component was inferred to be involved but was not identified.

d. Reaction of Anions with Metals in Metalloenzymes. Chance (*401*) studied the reaction between several anions and catalase and compared the kinetic requirements with the relationships between pH and inhibitor state (free acid or charged anion) with respect to several possible reaction mechanisms. Since a metalloenzyme was involved, the reactions listed by Chance (*401*) are shown below together with the mechanisms already proposed by Coryell, Stitt, and Pauling (*402*), and Lemberg and Legge (*403*). The reactions of catalase and other hemoproteins with several inhibitory anions are described separately later, but the possible mechanisms of reaction between metalloproteins and anions as a general phenomenon are included in the reactions (i)–(viii) below. Chance (*401*) distinguished two possible effects of pH on the reactions to be described.

These are (a) the effect of pH on the dissociation of the free acid to form the anion (governed by the pK of the acid), which may be low for a strong acid like formic acid or an acid of medium strength like hydrazoic acid and high for weak acids like carbonic acid, hydrogen sulfide, or hydrogen cyanide, and (b) the effect of pH on the ionization of reactive groups in the protein. Chance differentiated between these two effects by choosing a range of acids representative of low and high pK values and by correcting for free acid concentration at each pH used to study the relationships between pH and pK of the protein-inhibitor complex. The ratio of total acid to free acid is given by Eq. (18),

$$\frac{\text{Total acid}}{\text{Free acid}} = \frac{K}{(\text{H}^+)} + 1 \qquad (18)$$

where K is the dissociation constant of the acid. A table of percentage dissociations as determined by pK and pH is given by Albert (37). The values of pK for enzyme-inhibitor complexes are normalized to the basis of free acid by adding $\log [K/(\text{H}^+)] + 1$ and are plotted against pH. Horizontal lines indicate pH-independent reactions between enzyme and inhibitor when reacting as a free acid. The possible reactions between anion or free acid and metal-enzyme complex are as follows (401–403):

(i) $>\text{M}^+ + \text{HA} \rightleftharpoons >\text{MA} + \text{H}^+$

pH-dependent reaction with free acid and liberation of a proton

(ii) $>\text{M}^+ + \text{A}^- \rightleftharpoons >\text{MA}$

pH-dependent reaction with dissociated anion

(iii) $>\text{M}\cdot\text{OH} + \text{A}^- \rightleftharpoons >\text{MA} + \text{OH}^-$

pH-independent reaction with dissociated anion

(iv) $>\text{M}\cdot\text{OH} + \text{HA} \rightleftharpoons >\text{MA} + \text{H}_2\text{O}$

pH-independent reaction between free acid and OH group

(v) $>\text{M}\cdot\text{OH} + \text{HA} \rightleftharpoons >\text{MHA} + \text{OH}^-$

pH-dependent reaction with free acid; pH effect reverse of reactions (i) and (vii)

(vi) $>\text{M}\cdot\text{H}_2\text{O} + \text{A}^- \rightleftharpoons \text{MA}^- + \text{H}_2\text{O}$

pH-independent reaction with dissociated anion

(vii) $>\text{M}\cdot\text{H}_2\text{O} + \text{HA} \rightleftharpoons >\text{MA} + \text{H}_3\text{O}^+(\text{H}_2\text{O} + \text{H}^+)$

pH-dependent reaction with free acid; pH effect reverse of reaction (v)

(viii) $>\text{M}\cdot\text{H}_2\text{O} + \text{HA} \rightleftharpoons >\text{MHA} + \text{H}_2\text{O}$

pH-independent reaction with free acid

In a brilliant kinetic analysis, Chance (401) elucidated the reaction between catalase and several anions, including acetate, formate, fluoride, azide, and cyanide, in terms of the equations (i)–(viii) and concluded that the data were best explained by reaction (viii) but that reaction (iv) was possible if the enzyme had an ionizing OH group of very low pK (<3.0). This conclusion was contrary to the earlier views of Lemberg and Legge (403), who postulated reaction (iii). Agner and Theorell (403a) had shown that acetate and phosphate are relatively weakly inhibitory to catalase whereas formate and fluoride were strongly inhibitory. On Chance's theory all these react as free acids in a pH-independent manner. The strong inhibition of the formate and fluoride is then explained by the low dissociation constants of enzyme-acid complexes; $K = 6 \times 10^{-6}$ and 4×10^{-5}, respectively, compared with the high value of 9×10^{-3} for acetate. For reactions between methemoglobin or metmyoglobin and cyanide, Chance (401) concluded that reactions (viii) or (iv) were involved, but the reaction with fluoride appeared to involve reaction (vi).

Nicholls (403b) extended the work of Chance by investigating the reactions between the same anions and the catalase peroxide compounds and compared the reactions of catalase peroxide with those of the peroxidase and metmyoglobin peroxide compounds. The compounds formed between cyanide and the free catalase or peroxidase were considered to be covalent with HCN, and the compound between cyanide and metmyoglobin was considered to be also covalent but involving both HCN and CN^- ions. The fluoride complexes were regarded as ionic and involved similar free acid and ionic forms in the respective reactions. However, the dissociation constant for catalase fluoride was calculated at pH 5.0 as 3×10^{-3}, while the figure quoted by Chance (401) was 4×10^{-5}; the dissociation constant for formate was stated to be 1.3×10^{-4} in comparison with Chance's value of 6×10^{-6}; the differences were eighty- and twentyfold, respectively. The explanation of these differences is not apparent, but the concentration of free acids at pH 5 may be involved [see (458) and data in (37)]. Nicholls (403b) found that the affinity of the anions for the peroxide compounds or more strictly the higher oxidation state of compound III was similar to the affinity for the free catalase for azide, fluoride, acetate, and formate but was about 40 times smaller for cyanide. Metmyoglobin compound II showed a 5000 times lower affinity for cyanide and a 25 times lower affinity for fluoride than the free enzyme. Beers and Sizer (403c) also found that acetate, chloride, and azide inhibit catalase, but in a progressive manner apparently caused by the inhibition of the reduction of compound I to compound II, and that the progressive effect is independent of any immediate inhibition. The reactions of other metalloenzymes and other aspects of catalase inhibition are described later in the separate sections.

2. EFFECTS OF SOME IMPORTANT ANION INHIBITORS

a. Cyanide Inhibition of Enzyme Action. The effects of cyanide as an enzyme inhibitor are often associated with its importance as a respiratory poison. The cyanide molecule is very reactive and can produce enzyme inhibition in at least three ways, which can be partially distinguished by the pattern of inhibition. Cyanide is only weakly dissociated ($pK = 9.14$), and where cyanide ions are involved pH effects operate particularly over the range 6–9 as dissociation increases. Cyanide may react with metal enzymes as HCN or as CN^-, as described below. Extensive lists of enzymes inhibited by various concentrations of cyanide are given by James (*168*) and Dixon and Webb (*362*). Detailed examples are discussed below.

(i) *Metalloenzymes.* Cyanide is commonly considered to inhibit metalloenzymes containing metals which are complexed by cyanide. Important and classic examples are mentioned below. Cytochrome oxidase has possibly the greatest known sensitivity to cyanide; the concentration giving 50% inhibition is stated by Dixon and Webb (*362*) to be $10^{-8}\,M$. The relationships between respiration and cyanide are discussed later. Catalase and sundry peroxidases are also relatively sensitive and are mainly strongly inhibited at concentrations between 10^{-5} and $10^{-6}\,M$ [Dixon and Webb (*362*)]. Inhibition is reversible, and the cyanide complex of catalase is dissociated by crystallization.

The types of cyanide molecules concerned in the reaction may vary. Stannard and Horecker (*404*) concluded that inhibition of cytochrome oxidase involves the undissociated HCN molecule ($K_i = 5 \times 10^{-7}$), one order greater than the value quoted by Dixon and Webb. According to Horecker and Stannard (*405*) and Stannard and Horecker (*404*) combination between cyanide and methemoglobin and metmyoglobin involves the CN^- ion though this may not be correct, as indicated below (*401*). Thus, pH conditions affect inhibitions differently in the two groups. Reaction is reversible with these metal-proteins, and one molecule of enzyme reacts with one molecule of cyanide. These authors also found that where cyanide reacts with methemoglobins as CN^- ions, azide reacts also as the ionic form N_3^-. It is relevant here to note the comparison between effects of azide and cyanide observed by these workers (*304, 305*). Thus, azide as N_3^- reacts immediately with cytochrome c in the ferric form but is only weakly combined ($K_i = 0.15$); at $10^{-3}\,M$ azide (pH 7.4) only 0.6% of cytochrome c is combined. Cyanide as CN^- combines only slowly, but avidly $(K_i = 2 \times 10^{-6})$, and at 10^{-3} M CN- (pH 7.4) 87% of cytochrome c is complexed (*406*). Unlike cytochrome c, cytochrome oxidase combines avidly with free hydrazoic acid (HN_3) $(K_i = 7 \times 10^{-7})$ (*404*). The kinetic analysis made by Chance (*401*) for combination of anions with catalase has been described. Cyanide reacts as the undissociated HCN, and there is no formation of H^+ ion. As the reacting group does not show evidence of a dissociation value for pK above pH 3, Chance favored the idea that cyanide displaces a molecule of water. Keilin and Hartree (*407*) have estimated that cyanide inhibits catalase 50% at 4.3×10^{-6} M. Contrary to the earlier conclusions of Stannard and Horecker (*404*), Chance (*401*) concluded that the relationships between pH and inhibition of methemoglobin (ferrihemoglobin) by cyanide were one order less than would be expected for reaction with the CN^- ion and that, as the rate of combination of cyanide with methemoglobin was independent of pH, the inhibiting form was considered to be HCN. Nicholls (*403b*) stated that both HCN and CN^- react with metmyoglobin at pH 8.0 and that the compound is covalent, as also are those formed between catalase or peroxidase and the HCN molecule. A point of comparison of reaction between cytochrome oxidase and different inhibitors was emphasized by Keilin and Hartree (*408*). They showed from spectroscopic studies that whereas fluoride, hydrogen sulfide, and azide react only with the Fe^{3+} state, cyanide reacts with both Fe^{3+} and Fe^{2+} states. They concluded, however, that the reaction with the latter occurs only under entirely anaerobic conditions. The complex is highly autoxidizable, and the ferric complex which is produced is very stable. Wainio (*409*) and Wainio and Cooperstein (*410*) concluded differently that cytochrome oxidase is combined in the ferrous form with cyanide as the stable complex. Joan Keilin (*411*) studied the reactions between hemoproteins and hydrogen cyanide, methyl cyanide, and methyl isocyanide (CH_3NC) and concluded that cyanide combines through the carbon and not the nitrogen atoms. The reactions between the hemoproteins and several inhibitors, including cyanide, azide, fluoride, hydrogen sulfide, carbon monoxide, nitric oxide, and hydroxylamine, are characterized by important changes in the light absorption spectra. The spectral shifts are often used to identify the nature of the heme pigments present. Spectral shifts induced by cyanide have been described at different times by Lemberg and Legge (*403*), Keilin and Hartree (*408*, *412*, *413*), J. Keilin (*411*), and Chance (*413a*, *413b*) for cytochrome pigments, peroxidases, catalase, methemoglobin, and metmyoglobin.

The reactions between cyanide and peroxidase with details of the spectral changes involved were described by Keilin and Hartree (*412*, *413*). Peroxidase, and also catalase and methemoglobin all react reversibly with cyanide, azide, fluoride, and nitric oxide, with one molecule of anion per atom of iron. Peroxidase can be reduced by dithionite to ferroperoxidase which then combines with cyanide in the ferrous state (*413*). Stabilities differ greatly: for Fe^{2+}peroxidase CN, $K_i = 1.3 \times 10^{-3}$ at pH 9; and for Fe^{3+}peroxidase CN, $K_i = 2 \times 10^{-6}$ at pH 9. Ferroperoxidase cyanide is also dissociable by light.

At pH 6.0 or below $PerFe^{2+}$ cyanide spontaneously changes to $PerFe^{3+}$ cyanide. One may speculate that the reaction is as follows: $PerFe^{2+}$ CN + H^+ → $PerFe^{3+}$ HCN, since at that pH CN^- ions are in negligible concentration. $PerFe^{3+}$ would then react like catalase (*401*), and the reaction with ferriperoxidase is independent of pH (*413*). Since $PerFe^{3+}$ HCN cannot be reduced by dithionite at a pH below 5–6 it is possible that combination of ferriperoxidase and cyanide provides an example of a change in redox potential when a metalloenzyme reacts with an inhibitor, in this instance a decrease.

The reactions between cyanide and peroxidase, catalase, and metmyoglobin are also complex in other respects. George (*413c*) showed that cyanide combines with peroxidase (hydrogen peroxide) compound II and activates its reduction by endogenous hydrogen donors to peroxidase but inhibits the reduction of compound I to compound II. The combination of metmyoglobin or catalase with cyanide shows affinities of between 5×10^3 and 1.7×10^4 times the affinities between cyanide and the compound II forms of either enzyme (*403b*). George (*413c*) has concluded that compound II is not a compound with peroxide but is a separate redox state of the heme group, and Nicholls (*403b*) emphasized that a very interesting question regarding the change in affinity arises when a covalent ligand (HCN) is involved but not when an ionic ligand (HF) is formed.

Uricase which is almost certainly a copper-containing metalloenzyme (*414*) is also relatively sensitive (*415*), being 80% inhibited at 3×10^{-5} M cyanide. Colowick and Kalckar (*416*) and Mahler (*414*) concluded that cyanide reacts with the metal rather than with a carbonyl group because, of all other carbonyl reagents, only hydroxylamine showed any inhibitory effect. Keilin and Hartree (*415*) showed that cyanide inhibition of uricase was fully reversible by dialysis followed by competitive removal of residually associated cyanide with horse methemoglobin. When methemoglobin was added before dialysis to remove cyanide, there was a competitive partition between the two metalloproteins, and only partial reactivation of uricase occurred under these conditions.

The phenol oxidases and ascorbic acid oxidase are also copper-dependent metalloenzymes and are inhibited by cyanide, but mainly at higher concentrations (around $10^{-3} M$). The classic work of Kubowitz (417–419) showed that dialysis of purified potato tyrosinase against cyanide resulted in removal of the protein-bound copper with loss of activity, which was restored on adding copper to the dialyzed protein after removal of the cyanide. Meiklejohn and Stewart (420) showed by a similar technique that copper could be removed from and restored to ascorbic acid oxidase, and Tissières showed the same effect with laccase (421–422).

A similar technique was used by Nicholas and Nason (23, 23a) to show the presence of protein-bound molybdenum in the cyanide-sensitive nitrate reductases from *Neurospora* and soybean. These experiments show that cyanide can remove a particular protein-bound metal from certain enzymes, e.g. copper from tyrosinase or ascorbic acid oxidase, or molybdenum from nitrate reductase, but not the copper from uricase (414–416), where the metal appears to remain protein bound. Mahler (414) has postulated that cyanide combines with the copper by replacing the hydroxyl group in the "aquo hydroxo complex" form of the free enzyme.

Amine oxidase of pea seedlings has been shown by Mann (423) to contain copper which can be removed by diethyl dithiocarbamate. The cyanide inhibition of amine oxidase appears, however, to have complex features (424). Thus, whereas cyanide inhibits the oxidation of 1,4-diaminobutane 27% and 90% at concentrations of 10^{-4} and $10^{-3} M$, respectively, the oxidation of lysine or ethanolamine was unaffected at $10^{-3} M$ and that of β-phenylethylamine was inhibited 25%. At $10^{-2} M$ oxidation of all four substrates was totally inhibited. A competitive effect may be involved where the diamine requires a two-point attachment, and its oxidation is therefore more easily inhibited than that of the monoamines, which may compete with differing success with the cyanide-inhibited site.

Erythrocyte carbonic anhydrase is reversibly inhibited by cyanide and is highly sensitive (425–427), 85% inhibition occurring at $4 \times 10^{-6} M$ (425); cyanide was concluded to inhibit by combining with the prosthetic metal zinc (426). The plant enzyme is also cyanide sensitive but at much higher concentrations ($10^{-3} M$) (427).

Carboxypeptidase is cyanide sensitive, and it was concluded by Smith and Hanson (428, 429) that combination with a metal is involved. Inhibition was reversible in part by dialysis and was completely reversed when the residual cyanide was removed by competitive association with horse methemoglobin, a technique introduced by Keilin and Hartree (415) for tests on uricase. Smith and Hanson (429) applied the formula $KI^n =$

$(a - x)/x$, where K is the equilibrium constant for inhibitor-enzyme complex, I is the molar concentration of inhibitor, n is the number of moles of inhibitor per mole enzyme at saturation, a is the concentration of enzyme, and x is the concentration of active enzyme. The value for n was found to be 2 for cyanide and 1 for hydrogen sulfide. Later work by Vallee and Neurath (430), Coleman and Vallee (431), and Vallee *et al.* (432) showed that natural carboxypeptidases are zinc proteins and do not contain magnesium as was thought by Smith and Hanson. Their work showed that cyanide combined with but could not remove the zinc (429). Coleman and Vallee (431) showed, however, that zinc can be removed from carboxypeptidase A by dialysis at a low pH or against *o*-phenanthroline. Restoration to carboxypeptidase A of zinc or cobalt, particularly, and also of manganese or nickel restored activity (432). Folk and Gladner (433) similarly observed reactivation of metal-free carboxypeptidase B by cobalt or cadmium as well as by zinc.

The application of inhibitor studies with cyanide to remove metals involves some points which require consideration before a full interpretation of the results can be undertaken, and some special care is required. Thus, the conclusion reached by Mahler (434) that butyryl CoA dehydrogenase contains copper because the green color was discharged by dialysis against cyanide now appears to be a mistake, since Steyn-Parvé and Beinert (435) have shown that this enzyme does not contain or depend upon copper. The replacement of the natural protein-bound metal by others after dialysis of carboxypeptidases has been noted (432, 433), and Nicholas and Nason (23) showed that a real danger of uncontrolled restoration of a metal existed with nitrate reductase unless reagents purified from molybdenum were used for the dialysis treatment. The fact that cyanide combines with but may not remove metals, e.g., copper or zinc, which may be removed by other reagents also shows where confusion can arise. Furthermore, the enzyme yeast succinic dehydrogenase contains 4 iron atoms (436) but is not cyanide inhibited, possibly for steric reasons. It must also be noted that failure to observe inhibition by cyanide is not necessarily evidence that a transition metal is absent.

(ii) *Carbonyl groups.* Cyanide as HCN combines reversibly with carbonyl groups of aldehydes or ketones to form cyanohydrins [Eq. (19)].

$$
\begin{array}{c}
R \\
\diagdown \\
C{=}O + HCN \rightleftharpoons \\
\diagup \\
R'
\end{array}
\qquad
\begin{array}{cc}
R & OH \\
\diagdown \; \diagup \\
C \\
\diagup \; \diagdown \\
R' & CN
\end{array}
\qquad (19)
$$

The reaction with protein is dependent on the presence of undissociated HCN and was shown to be reversible by dilution (437) or possibly by competitive combination with pyruvate by analogy with reversal of hydroxylamine inhibition (438). Relatively high concentrations are required for this addition reaction, and susceptible enzymes would be expected to combine with other carbonyl reagents, e.g., bisulfite, semicarbazide, and hydroxylamine, as pointed out by James (168). These factors permit some conclusion as to whether cyanide inhibition involves a carbonyl grouping. Cyanide may also inhibit by combining with a substrate or cofactor where a carbonyl group is involved, e.g., a keto acid, an aldehyde, or a pyridoxyl derivative (362). Here also, relatively high concentrations and substrate-reversible characteristics will indicate the nature of the inhibition. This is presumably the basis for inhibition of amino acid decarboxylases which require pyridoxyl phosphate as a coenzyme and are inhibited by 10^{-3} M levels of cyanide. It must be noted, however, that Hurwitz (439), who examined the reaction between cyanide and pyridoxal, found that at pH 7.4 the reaction is only 60% complete when equivalent amounts of cyanide and pyridoxal are present; the reaction is easily reversed. The optimum pH for reaction is 5.5, and a spectral shift occurs in extinction from 325 to 345 mμ.

(iii) *Disulfide groups and activation of papain.* Mauthner (440) early discovered that sodium cyanide reacts with disulfide bonds irreversibly to give a thiol salt and a thiocyanate [Eq. (20)].

$$RS=SR + NaCN \rightarrow RSNa + RSCN \qquad (20)$$

This reaction was reinvestigated by Fraenkel-Conrat (441), who showed that a high pH is required for the reaction with nonprotein disulfide compounds. It is slow, progressive, and irreversible. Papain is activated by cyanide, as was discovered very early by Mendel and Blood (442). Fruton and Bergman (443) and Irving et al. (444) found a similar effect for cathepsin, and it was suggested that this activation is due to disulfide bond reduction. The question of activation of papain by cyanide reaction with protein disulfide bonds was considered unanswered by Fraenkel-Conrat, as the pH of the reaction may be below 6.0 for papain.

Krebs (361) suggested that removal of metals could also explain this effect, since he showed that pyrophosphate, citrate, and cysteine also reactivated and that when purified (metal-free) gelatin was used there was no inhibition. It may be noted that the idea of activation based on disulfide groups reacting with cyanide requires an irreversible activation. The work of Irving et al. (444) and Mendel and Blood (442) showed that cyanide effect was reversible. Murray (445) partly resolved the controversy by showing that metal inactivation and reductive activation of papain were independent effects, and that the effects of cyanide or hydrogen sulfide and of citrate or pyrophosphate were additive. Kimmel and Smith (446) in a recent analysis of the phenomenon concluded from a study of reactions with mercury that papain has one functional —SH group, one inactive (unreactive) —SH group, and 6 groups reacting with p-chloromercuribenzoate. Under these circumstances there is scope for speculating on the mechanism of reversible reaction between cyanide and temporary S—S bonds. Each cycle of activation and inhibition should lead to 50% loss of activity unless inactive dimeric and active nonomeric states are produced in a reversible reaction.

(iv) *Studies with succinic dehydrogenase and xanthine and aldehyde oxidases.* The possibility that cyanide inhibits succinic dehydrogenase by reaction with protein disulfide bonds in the manner already described was suggested by Keilin and King (447) on the basis of the slow reaction and its completeness and irreversibility. The question as to whether the —S—S— group was structural or derived from reversible oxidation of adjacent —SH groups during functioning of the enzyme was left open. A kinetic study of succinic dehydrogenase inhibition by cyanide was made by Guiditta and Singer (448). The soluble enzyme from heart muscle was found to be insensitive to cyanide under all conditions. The particulate enzyme was inhibited by cyanide in a pH-dependent manner with evidence for two reactions being involved. It was found that inhibition due to loss of activity at infinite substrate concentration (V_{max}) and decrease in affinity (increase in K_m) for the electron carrier, e.g., phenazine methosulfate, were prevented by the presence of succinate, DPNH, or dithionite (hydrosulfite), while only decrease in electron carrier affinity was reversible by the reducing agents, including succinate. Affinity for the substrate, succinate, was independent of the presence of cyanide. The sites of reaction were considered to be either a disulfide group or an iron atom. Guiditta and Singer considered that the protective effect of reducing agents, the previously unreported pH dependence of cyanide inhibition (based on V_{max} estimations), and reversibility with respect to electron carrier affinity were not compatible with the idea of a disulfide reaction but were consistent with reaction with ferric iron involving the CN^- ion. The maximal inhibition produced by cyanide was 50% with phenazine methosulfate but 100% with cytochrome c or methylene blue at $2 \times 10^{-2} M$ cyanide. When the reverse reaction with fumarate was tested with reduced FMN, there was no inhibition of maximal activity

(V_{max}) but a major decrease in affinity for FMN. When reduced methyl-viologen was used for fumarate reduction, there was no effect on dye affinity but a 50% decrease in V_{max}. Comparison of pH dependence of inhibition of methylene blue and phenazine methosulfate showed a difference suggesting action of cyanide at different sites. By contrast with the heart particulate preparation, brain and yeast succinic dehydrogenases were quite unaffected by cyanide, although the latter closely resembled the heart enzyme in other properties.

Guiditta and Singer (448) concluded that slow secondary changes in the heart enzyme brought about by the initial rapid reaction with cyanide were the more likely explanation of irreversible inactivation and were consistent with the high energy of activation for cyanide inhibition reported by Tsou (449).

The inhibition of liver aldehyde oxidase by cyanide was studied by Hurwitz (439). This enzyme contains molybdenum (450) and possibly iron also (450) and catalyzes oxidation of several aldehydes, including pyridoxal.

Hurwitz (439) calculated that at $3 \times 10^{-5} M$ cyanide, where only 3% of the pyridoxal present could be combined as cyanohydrin, there was an instantaneous and consistent inhibition of 15–20% of activity. This was irreversible in the presence of methemoglobin. Further incubation of the enzyme with the same concentration of cyanide resulted in total inhibition after a period of 60 minutes. Methemoglobin delayed the effect of cyanide during a short period of incubation by competing for the limited amount of cyanide present in the system. No conclusions were drawn regarding the significance of the results. It would appear that two sites may be involved in addition to lesser effects of reaction with pyridoxal. A possibility is that in aldehyde oxidase there is a mutual oxidation and reduction by similar groups produced during oxidation of the substrate. The second slower reaction might be between iron and cyanide, by analogy with ideas proposed for succinic dehydrogenase (448); the similarity between the inhibition of the two enzymes was noted by Hurwitz (439). As aldehyde oxidase does not require the molybdenum component for direct oxidase action with molecular oxygen (450), the reaction between cyanide and molybdenum would appear to be excluded from this aspect of the inhibition although it is complete at low concentrations. Hurwitz (439) did not favor the possibility that aldehyde oxidase inhibition was due to reaction with —S=S— groups, as inhibition by 2,3-dimercaptopropanol (BAL) was decreased when incubated under anaerobic conditions, while with cyanide these had no effect.

Mahler et al. (450) stated that if the molybdenum-free enzyme was treated with cyanide (or azide) the addition of molybdenum overcame the inhibition, but no data were given and the effects on immediate and progressive inhibition were not distinguished. It was found, however, that reduction of cytochrome c was inhibited instantaneously, while reduction of dyes by substrates other than DPNH was inhibited only after incubation. These differences reflect the two types of inhibition observed by Hurwitz (*439*) for pyridoxal oxidation by oxygen. It is possible that his preparation contained cytochrome c and that both cytochrome c peroxidase and 2-electron transfer reactions were involved in pyridoxal oxidation.

Xanthine oxidase of milk, which is also a molybdoflavoprotein (*280, 451*), shows a more complex pattern of inhibition by cyanide. This was first described by Dixon and Keilin (*452*), who showed that the reaction was not immediate, and was irreversible and substrate protected. Mackler *et al.* (*280*) showed that, while cyanide inhibited the reaction between cytochrome c and DPNH when the enzyme was incubated with cyanide for 60 minutes, there was no inhibition when DPNH was oxidized by methylene blue. Cyanide also inhibited oxidation of hypoxanthine or xanthine regardless of the electron acceptor used, including oxygen, 2-electron acceptor dyes, or cytochrome c. Azide did not inhibit cytochrome c reduction by any of the substrates, while aldehyde oxidase was sharply inhibited by azide to the extent of 70% at $5 \times 10^{-6} M$. The relative effects of these two inhibitors is therefore reversed with the two enzymes. The effects of cyanide on liver xanthine oxidases appears to be similar, according to studies of Doisy, Richert, and Westerfeld (*452a*). Fridovich and Handler (*281*) pointed out that as incubation of xanthine oxidase with cyanide led to a decrease in free —SH groups the irreversible inhibition was unlikely to be due to the rupture of —S=S— bonds but might be caused by rupture of a metal-thiol group. The reaction products might then be as shown in Eq. (*21*).

$$
\begin{array}{ccc}
\quad\ \ \text{S} & & \quad\ \ \text{SCN} \\
\diagup\ \Big| & & \diagup \\
\text{E}\quad\ \Big| \quad + \text{HCN} \rightarrow \text{E} & & \quad + \text{(M)} \quad \text{? charge} \\
\diagdown\ \Big| & & \diagdown \\
\quad\ \ \text{M} & & \quad\ \ \text{H}
\end{array}
\qquad (21)
$$

Alternatively, if a carbon-thiol group were involved, the reaction would be

$$
\begin{array}{ccc}
\quad\ \ \text{S} & & \quad\ \ \text{SCN} \\
\diagup\ \Big| & & \diagup \\
\text{E}\quad\ \Big| \quad + \text{HCN} \rightarrow \text{E} & & \\
\diagdown\ \Big| & & \diagdown \\
\quad\ \ \text{C} & & \quad\ \ \text{C—H} \\
\quad\ \ \| & & \quad\ \ \| \\
\end{array}
\qquad (22)
$$

and this could be followed by irreversible thiazolidine formation with an adjacent amino group, as described by Calvin (*453*). The first reaction does not seem attractive in terms of known behavior. Fridovich and Handler (*454*) made a further study of the reactions between cyanide and xanthine oxidase and showed that inhibition was in fact reversible under certain conditions. It was concluded that CN^- ions are involved, as inhibition is favored by a high pH. Pretreatment of the enzyme with dithionite prevented the development of inhibition, and the cyanide-inhibited enzyme was reactivated by dialysis in the presence of dithionite. Normally, the purified enzyme reacts with one molecule of cyanide for each molecule of FAD. In the presence of hypoxanthine or dithionite the ratio is changed to 0.5 mole of cyanide to 1 mole of FAD. In the light of these findings it was concluded that the enzyme contains two flavin molecules which are attached to metal-thiol groups (XIII).

$$
\begin{array}{ccc}
 & \diagdown & \\
 & \text{Fe—S} & \\
\diagup & & \diagdown \\
\text{FAD} & & \text{FAD} \\
\diagdown & & \diagup \\
 & \text{S—Fe} & \\
 & & \diagdown \\
\end{array}
$$

XIII

One flavin accepts electrons from the substrate and is directly reducible by substrate, and the other reduces oxygen at a different potential. Cyanide inhibits by combining as a stable complex with the ferric iron and ruptures the metal-thiol bonds, but does not combine avidly with the ferrous state. The reversibility in the presence of dithionite is explained on this basis. Fridovich and Handler (*454*) suggested that rupture of a ferric iron-thiol bond or combination across this grouping was a likely explanation of the irreversible inactivation of succinic dehydrogenase and of the protection afforded by reducing agents.

A point of some interest is that although cyanide inhibits nitrate reductase (*156*) and can extract the prosthetic molybdenum atom (*23*), Kinsky and McElroy (*455*) found no inhibition of cytochrome c reductase in the similar *Neurospora* nitrate reductase preparations. By contrast, cyanide inhibits single-electron transfer to cytochrome c in xanthine oxidase (*450*) and aldehyde oxidase (*280*).

b. *Azide.* (i) *Reactive forms of azide and stability of complexes.* Azide may inhibit by combining with a metal site either as the free acid HN_3 or as the ionic compound N_3^-, as described below. Hydrazoic acid is relatively strong ($pK = 4.7$), compared with many metal-combining anions like cyanide or hydrosulfide. When azide ions are involved, there is relatively little effect of pH over the upper part of the physiological range (5.5–8.5), as pointed out by Stannard and Horecker (*404*). When the free undissociated acid is concerned, the pH effect, as emphasized by James (*168*), may be large, and inhibition is increased by decreasing pH. Examples of this effect are provided by uricase, for which Keilin and Hartree (*415*) found 40% inhibition by $5 \times 10^{-3} M$ azide at pH 6.8 and 28% at pH 7.8, and by catechol oxidase of *Psalliota*, for which Keilin (*456*) found that 70% inhibition at pH 5.9 was decreased to nil at pH 7.3. The spectrographic and kinetic studies by Chance (*401*), already noted in connection with the reaction between catalase and cyanide, also indicated that azide reacts with catalase as the free acid HN_3. Stannard and Horecker (*404*) concluded from a kinetic study that cytochrome oxidase also reacts with azide as HN_3 (*404*).

The reaction between D-amino acid oxidase and azide, which produces 50% inhibition at pH 6.8 and slight stimulation at pH 7.8, also indicates reaction in the undissociated form. The reaction may be atypical and not due to combination with a metal, since none is thought to occur in this enzyme. Krebs (*457*) showed that it was insensitive to cyanide, and its inhibition by hydrogen sulfide (*415*), described later, is also atypical.

Azide reacts with other hemoproteins as the dissociated ion. This was concluded from kinetic studies by Horecker and Stannard (*405*) for cytochrome c. The reaction is fully reversible, and one molecule of ferricytchrome c reacts with one azide ion, N_3^-. Ferric azide catalyzes the autoxidation of ferrocytochrome c (*405*). Methemoglobin and metmyoglobin also react with the azide ion, according to Stannard and Horecker (*404*). The reaction of horse-radish peroxidase with azide has not been clearly established but was shown by Keilin and Hartree (*412*) to occur only between pH 4 and 4.5. It is reversible by hydrogen peroxide. The dissociation constant is also fairly high, about 10^{-3}. These data suggest that azide combines with horse-radish peroxidase as the undissociated acid HN_3. According to Lenhoff and Kaplan (*458*), cytochrome c peroxidase of *Pseudomonas fluorescens* also combines with azide as HN_3, and the dissociation constant appears to be about 10^{-3}.

Most of the reactions between hemoproteins and cyanide or azide therefore appear to be with the free acids, but clear exceptions, e.g., cytochrome c, also occur. The reactions with peroxidase (*459*), metmyoglobin, catalase, cytochrome c, and cytochrome oxidase involve one molecule of azide for each atom of iron (*404, 405, 412*). The stability of azide complexes is often less than the stability of those formed with cyanide, and higher concentrations are required for inhibition. The relative affinities (K_i) for cytochrome c are 1.5×10^{-1} for azide (N_3^-) and 2×10^{-6} for cyanide (CN^-), according to Horecker and Stannard (*405*). For catalase the relative affinities (K_i) appear to be 8×10^{-7} for cyanide and $1.2-6 \times 10^{-4}$ (*403, 407*) for azide; similar differences in relative inhibition occur with horse-radish peroxidase (*412, 459a*). The anomaly of catalase sensitivity to azide is discussed later, and the possibility that the true affinity for the free acid is much greater is noted below. Exceptions also occur. Thus, whereas the dissociation constants for mammalian cytochrome oxidase complexes with cyanide and azide are similar at 5 and 7×10^{-7}, respectively (*404*), and the stabilities of azide and cyanide complexes of methemoglobin are similar (*403*), the order is clearly reversed for cytochrome oxidase of *Azotobacter vinelandii* studied by Layne and Nason (*460*). Azide inhibited 78% at $10^{-5} M$ and pH 7.5, whereas according to Lenhoff and Kaplan (*458*) over 99% would be present as N_3^-, while cyanide inhibited 56% at $10^{-4} M$, but practically all would have been present as HCN. As no kinetic studies were reported (*460*), the relative significance of the two inhibitors cannot be further elucidated here. In fact, it must be recognized that in all comparisons between azide and cyanide the large differences in pK values which affect the extremes of the physiological pH range may confuse the interpretation of relative affinity unless the effects of pH on the concentrations of free acid and ionic forms are also taken into consideration. This point is illustrated by the data of Keilin and Hartree (*407*) and of Chance (*401*) and Nicholls (*403b*), respectively, which show that the apparently high value of 6×10^{-4} is probably incorrect and that values for HN_3 are about 3×10^{-6} or 1.5×10^{-5}. A similarly reversed order of apparent affinity was found by Mahler *et al.* (*450*) for liver aldehyde oxidase for oxidation of cytochrome c, where azide inhibits 70% at $5 \times 10^{-6} M$. This reaction with xanthine oxidase of milk is not inhibited by azide (*280*), and neither is the reaction with oxygen (*415*). Both these enzymes, however, appear to contain iron as well as molybdenum.

Azide inhibition of the copper enzymes appears to be less severe than that of the iron enzymes, and is less severe than the effects of cyanide. Thus, amine oxidase which is a copper protein (*423*) is inhibited only 8% by $10^{-2} M$ azide but is completely inhibited by the same concentration of cyanide (*424*). Similarly, uricase is inhibited 28–40% by azide at $5 \times 10^{-3} M$ and is inhibited 83% by cyanide at $3 \times 10^{-5} M$ (*415*). According to Holmberg (*461*), azide inhibition of uricase is only temporary and soon disappears.

Inhibition of the zinc enzymes by azide is relatively weak. Pancreatic carboxypeptidase, which is not inhibited by azide according to Smith and Hanson (*428, 429*), is nevertheless severely inhibited by both cyanide and hydrogen sulfide. Carbonic anhydrase, which is inhibited 85% by $4 \times 10^{-6} M$ cyanide (*425*), is much less sensitive to azide with which only partial inhibition occurred at $2 \times 10^{-3} M$ with the preparation of Meldrum and Roughton (*462*); hydrogen sulfide was as effective as cyanide.

Azide inhibition is usually readily reversible. Azide inhibition of aldehyde oxidase of potato, measured by reduction of nitrate to nitrate with acetaldehyde under anaerobic conditions, is readily reversed by dialysis against water without loss of initial activity (*463*); $10^{-3} M$ azide at pH 6.0 produced 80% inhibition, and $5 \times 10^{-4} M$ provided 45% inhibition of the enzyme. Although irreversibly inhibited by cyanide, no other metal-chelating agents inhibit, and the presence of a metal is uncertain.

Tubbs (*400a*) found that, although CN^- ions inhibited D-α-hydroxy acid dehydrogenase of rabbit kidney mitochondria, azide had no effect at similar pH values. As EDTA and *o*-phenanthroline were also inhibitory, the presence of a metal in the prosthetic group was considered likely.

(ii) *Reaction with nitrite.* A point of importance regarding the use of azide as an inhibitor in reactions involving the production or loss of nitrite requires emphasis. Villanueva (*464*) and Hewitt and Hallas (*463*) pointed out that azide interferes with the estimation of changes in nitrite concentration due to the reaction between azide and nitrite which occurs in acid solutions produced during the Griess-Ilosway method of estimation [Eq. (23)].

$$NO_2^- + N_3^- + 2H^+ = N_2 + N_2O + H_2O; \quad \text{or} \quad HONO + HN_3 = H_2O + N_2O + N_2$$

$$(23)$$

Villanueva (*464*) suggested that several reports of azide inhibition of nitrate-reducing systems might require reinvestigation for this reason. The concentrations of nitrite and of azide involved are in fact frequently of a similar order. Thus, in estimations of nitrite reductase the substrate concentrations are often around $2 \times 10^{-4} M$, and when nitrite formation from nitrate is being measured, concentrations observed are usually between 5×10^{-6} and $5 \times 10^{-5} M$; azide concentrations have ranged from 5×10^{-6} to $10^{-3} M$. Azide at $5 \times 10^{-4} M$ will cause almost total loss, analytically, of nitrite present at $5 \times 10^{-5} M$ (*463*). Villanueva (*464*) showed that $3.3 \times 10^{-3} M$ azide caused 92% loss of nitrite present at a concentration of about $1.2 \times 10^{-3} M$. The azide inhibition of nitrate reductase obtained by Sadana and McElroy (*465*) was observed to be

50–100% at concentrations of 10^{-3} and $3 \times 10^{-2}\,M$, respectively, under conditions where cyanide showed no inhibition in the presence of reduced benzylviologen as electron donor. The high concentrations of azide involved suggest that the possibility of chemical interference requires investigation before the unusual difference between azide and cyanide is accepted.

Hewitt and Hallas (463) showed that by using a manometric estimation of nitrite-reducing activity with larger amounts of enzyme and substrate and longer reaction times, azide inhibition could be demonstrated without analytical interference. The method consisted in measurement of nitrite produced when estimated by reaction with azide in acid solution at the end of the incubation period, either with or without the presence of azide as an inhibitor during enzymic reaction under physiological pH conditions.

The method is approximately twice as sensitive as the manometric method using sulfamic acid (466). The nitrite concentration present is related to the volume of gas measured under the experimental conditions by previous calibration.

(iii) *Azide and reactions with catalase and peroxidases.* The study of the inhibition of catalase, peroxidase, methemoglobin, and metmyoglobin by azide and also by hydroxylamine has elucidated general points of considerable interest which are summarized here.

Keilin and Hartree (407) pointed out that, whereas the relative affinities of catalase for cyanide, azide, and hydroxylamine are in the ratio of 10,000:67:40, respectively, the concentrations producing 50% inhibition are 4.3×10^{-6}, 6.3×10^{-8}, and 6.3×10^{-7}, respectively. This observation was clearly inconsistent with the known relationships between reversible enzyme inhibitors and the kinetics of enzyme-inhibitor complex formation.

Keilin and Hartree (407) developed the view supported by numerous lines of circumstantial evidence that the iron in catalase (407, 467–469) and in methemoglobin (412, 468, 470) and metmyoglobin (412, 470) undergoes reversible oxidation and reduction during functioning as peroxidases with hydrogen peroxide, but this view regarding catalase was not accepted by Theorell and Ehrenberg (471).

Keilin and Hartree and Theorell and Ehrenberg showed that catalase and methemoglobin (468, 469, 471) catalyzed the peroxidation of azide to nitrogen and nitrous oxide (471) with the formation also of traces of nitric oxide or nitrite (468, 469). Hydroxylamine is also oxidized to give nitric oxide and other products in the presence of catalase and hydrogen peroxide (468). Whereas, however, azide-methemoglobin is very stable, does not react with peroxide, and is not reduced by hydrogen peroxide (412), peroxide-methemoglobin rapidly peroxidates azide (468). The catalase-azide complex, which is much less stable, by contrast reacts readily with azide in the presence of hydrogen peroxide, and the catalase iron *when present as an azide complex* is reduced to the ferrous state (407, 468, 471) by hydrogen peroxide. Catalase iron-hydroxylamine complex is also reduced to the ferrous state by peroxide (407) but not by dithionite.

Keilin and Hartree (468), following the discovery by Theorell and Ehrenberg (471) that azide is oxidized by peroxide in the presence of catalase, identified the mechanism of azide inhibition of catalase as due not to azide-Fe^{3+} or azide-Fe^{2+} complexes but to nitric oxide production. The nitric oxide combines specifically and avidly with the iron and stabilizes ferrous catalase in the ferrous state as the nitric oxide complex. The same reaction was shown in the oxidation of azide by methemoglobin and peroxide, which resulted in the hemoglobin-nitric oxide complex being formed. This reaction cannot occur to any appreciable extent when the azide-methemoglobin is formed first because of its great stability ($K_i = 3 \times 10^{-6}$, approximately) unlike the less stable ($K_i = 10^{-4}$, approximately) and more easily reduced azide-catalase complex which functions as an autoxidizable system (407). The same mechanism accounts for the inhibition of catalase by hydroxylamine, where Keilin and Hartree (468, 469) observed that nitric oxide is produced. An early observation by Keilin and Hartree (472) that the reaction between azide, hydrogen peroxide, and catalase was inhibited under nitrogen was at first held by them to indicate prevention of autoxidation of the ferrous-azide-catalase complex. Reinvestigation (468, 469) of this work in a commendably open and unbiased approach revealed the part played by nitric oxide produced during "purification" of nitrogen by passage over apparently pure copper at a temperature over 400° C. It was found that ferrocatalase-azide is extremely sensitive to NO, and this provided the clue to the whole mechanism described above.

An interesting point concerns the severe inhibition of catalase by hydroxylamine as a result of peroxidation to nitric oxide, although at 10^{-3} M hydroxylamine may inhibit purpurogallin formation by peroxidase 40% (459). Cresswell and Hewitt (473) showed that peroxidase and hydrogen peroxide with manganese and monophenolic cofactors led to the rapid oxidation of hydroxylamine as a substrate without inhibition. The difference may be explained by the fact that whereas catalase-iron may be assumed to undergo reduction to the ferrous state which combines with the nitric oxide with great avidity by analogy with hemoglobin (403,

474) the iron of peroxidase remains in the ferric state. The NO-ferric catalase complex is reversible and does not combine with the nitric oxide so avidly, as shown by Keilin and Hartree (*475*) and Stern (*476*); ferric hemoglobin reacts weakly (*474*), and therefore little inhibition would be expected to occur by this mechanism. The failure of catalase to inhibit the reaction described by Cresswell and Hewitt (*473*) might also be due to inhibition of catalase itself by the hydroxylamine used as a substrate for the peroxidase, with formation of some nitric oxide, since nitrite formation also occurred (*473*). Peroxidase and metmyoglobin differ from methemoglobin and catalase in that the peroxidation of azide by the first two is apparently slow or negligible (*469*) compared with the reaction with catalase (*468, 469*) or methemoglobin (*468*); but some chemical destruction of azide also occurs in the presence of hydrogen peroxide alone (*469*).

c. *Effects of Fluoride on Enzyme Activity.* Fluoride ions form complexes with several metal-enzyme systems including those dependent on iron, calcium, and magnesium. Mechanisms and examples have been reviewed by Borei (*477*), Reiner (*478*), James (*168*), and Hackett (*169*).

(i) *Enolase and phosphoglucomutase.* Fluoride inhibition of enolase, which catalyzes the reaction between 2-phosphoglyceric acid and enol-phosphopyruvic acid was elucidated by Warburg and Christian (*479*). They showed that magnesium is required for the enzymic reaction and that in the presence of phosphate or arsenate an inactive dissociable magnesium fluorophosphate complex is formed. The product of the function $[Mg] [PO_4] [F]^2 \times$ (fractional activity)/inhibition was a constant equal to about 3.2×10^{-12}. As a consequence the fluoride concentration producing 50% inhibition was decreased as magnesium concentration was increased.

An analogous but slightly different mechanism was found to occur with phosphoglucomutase, studied by Najjar (*480*). This enzyme catalyzes the reversible reaction between glucose-1-phosphate and glucose-6-phosphate with glucose-1.6-diphosphate as a coenzyme. Here, a magnesium fluoride complex with glucose-1-phosphate is formed with the enzyme. Fluoride inhibition also depends upon magnesium concentration. Najjar (*480*) applied the formula of Warburg and Christian (*479*), substituting glucose-1-phosphate for phosphate, and obtained a constant; $K = 1.7 \times 10^{-12}$.

(ii) *Phosphatase, pyrophosphatase, and phosphorylase enzymes.* It might be expected that many enzymes that are dependent on magnesium are inhibited by fluoride, especially in the presence of phosphate. The particular susceptibility, however, differs considerably among different enzymes.

The polynucleotide phosphorylase enzymes which depend specifically on magnesium are entirely insensitive to fluoride, according to Grunberg-Manago Ortiz, and Ochoa (481). Alkaline phosphatases are often unaffected by fluoride unless only magnesium is present (482) or they are exposed to a low pH (483).

The magnesium-dependent 5-nucleotidases are, however, inhibited by fluoride, as reported by Heppel and Hilmoe (353a). Fluoride inhibition of alkaline phosphatases, when observed, may be a nonspecific anion effect similar to that described earlier, since phosphate, arsenate, and borate also inhibited (353a, 482, 484). Acid phosphatases are usually particularly fluoride sensitive, as shown by Sizer (485), Kutscher (486), Belfanti et al. (483); these include acid phosphatases in spinach (487) and in potato (279).

In contrast to the somewhat differential effects of fluoride on acid and alkaline phosphatases, the acid and alkaline pyrophosphatases of potato described by Nagana et al. (279) are both inhibited (86 and 91%, respectively) by $10^{-3} M$ fluoride, although the acid pyrophosphatase is inhibited by magnesium, while the same metal is specifically required by the alkaline pyrophosphatase. Erythrocyte pyrophosphatase with a pH optimum of 8.0, studied by Nagana and Menon (351), was inhibited 50% by only $2 \times 10^{-5} M$ fluoride and 95% at $2 \times 10^{-4} M$. Similar enzymes from different parts of the same organism may show different sensitivity to fluoride (337), and this may be related to the differing affinities of the enzymes, adenylic kinase, for magnesium.

The mechanism of acid phosphatase inhibition by fluoride may be quite complex, as was shown by Reiner, Tsuboi, and Hudson (488) for human prostatic acid phosphatase. Maximum fluoride inhibition was found to occur at intermediate concentrations of about $0.01 M$; higher and lower concentrations produced markedly less inhibition. The magnitude of the inhibition and the effect of fluoride concentration also vary with the nature and concentration of the phosphate ester substrate. A theory was derived by mathematical means to explain these observations. The curve relating inhibition to fluoride concentration was thought to represent the effect of combination of two types of fluorine compounds with the enzyme.

A plot of the reciprocal of fractional inhibition, defined as in [Eq. (24)] with (i) as fractional inhibition,

$$i = 1 - \frac{V_{\text{fluoride}}}{V_{\text{control}}} \qquad (24)$$

where V is velocity, against the reciprocal of the square of fluoride concentration $[F]^2$ was linear with intercepts at unity for both phenyl phosphate and adenylic acid as substrates, at the low fluoride concentrations below maximal inhibition.

This indicated that fluoride was most effective in a form dependent on a dimeric state. It was supposed that fluoride combines as the dimer $(HF_2)^-$ with the electropositive reactive site, in competition with the substrate. A higher polymer, possibly $(HF_2)_2^{-2}$, also combines at this site, but less avidly, and can be displaced by the substrate, thus explaining the decreased inhibition at the higher fluoride concentrations. The electropositive site could be produced by Mg^{2+} or other activating metals, but no evidence for these was obtained, and guanidinium or amino groups were considered possible sites. The inhibition by fluoride was also dependent on the presence of other anions. Monovalent anions tended to accentuate fluoride inhibition or had no effect, while divalent or polyvalent anions tended to decrease inhibition, their effectiveness being in order of the magnitude of their second dissociation constants. Citrate had an outstanding effect in reversing fluoride inhibition.

The theory regarding this effect is that the divalent anion competes with fluoride, but does not prevent substrate combination with the enzyme, and functions like the partly protective $(HF_2)_2^{-2}$, but more effectively. The fluoride as $(HF_2)^-$ was considered possibly to complex with two adjacent, positively charged amino groups. The fluoride inhibition of the unusual dual function glutamine synthetase and transferase enzyme of lupin described by Elliott (*334*) is interesting, as the synthetase reaction is inhibited 90% and the transferase reaction 40% by $10^{-3} M$ fluoride, presumably in the presence of magnesium. The difference in sensitivity could, however, be due to traces of manganese, as has already been suggested (see Sections II,C,2,c and III,B,1,a).

(iii) *Inhibition of metalloenzymes.* Fluoride inhibition of succinic dehydrogenase, studied by Slater and Bonner (*489*), shows another aspect of the complexity of fluoride inhibition. Unlike enolase (*479*) or acid phosphatase (*488*), where two or more fluorine atoms are involved, the inhibition of succinic dehydrogenase involves only one fluoride ion (F^-) per enzyme molecule. Inhibition by fluoride alone is weak and so also is that by phosphate alone. Inhibition by fluoride and phosphate together in 1:1 ratio is very strong and is competitive with succinate. It may be that the ferric iron atom in succinic dehydrogenase indicated by the work of Massey (*490*) is the combining center and forms a ferric fluorophosphate complex analagous to that between enolase and magnesium but involving only a single dissociable fluoride ion.

Fluoride combines with many hemoprotein enzymes, and well-defined spectral changes are usually associated with the reaction. These spectral shifts are described by Lemberg and Legge (*403*), Keilin and Hartree (*408, 412*), Chance (*413b*), Keilin and Mann (*459*), and Stern (*476*). The reaction is with the ferric iron state of cytochrome oxidase (*408*), peroxidase, catalase, and methemoglobin (*412, 476*); it is freely reversible and involves one atom of iron for one fluoride molecule.

The reaction between catalase and anions, including fluoride, has already been described; it was concluded that the free acid HF reacts with the hydrated group of ferric catalase (Fe—H_2O + HF $\leftrightharpoons$ FeHF + H_2O) in a pH-independent reaction. Lemberg and Legge (*403*) previously depicted the reaction as Fe—OH + F $\leftrightharpoons$ FEF + OH^-. The reaction between methemoglobin and fluoride was, however, considered to involve the fluoride iron in a pH-independent reaction (*401*). The affinity of methemoglobin, metmyoglobin, and catalase for fluoride are relatively low (*403, 403b, 475*), by contrast with those for sulfide and cyanide, and are reversed by hydrogen peroxide, as also is the complex with peroxidase (*412*). The reaction between peroxidase and fluoride is complex. George (*413c*) has shown that fluoride accelerates the decomposition of peroxidase compound II by reduction by endogenous hydrogen donor to form peroxidase fluoride. Excess hydrogen peroxide and fluoride lead to the production of peroxidase compound I due to the rate-limiting reaction between compound I and endogenous reducing agents to produce compound II.

Nicholls (*403b*) described a kinetic study of the reactions between catalase or catalase-peroxide compounds and anions, including fluoride, and compared these reactions with those observed with peroxidase and metmyoglobin. The reaction with fluoride was concluded to involve the free acid HF in an ionic reaction with catalase or peroxidase and to involve both HF and F^- with metmyoglobin. The dissociation constants for catalase fluoride and catalase compound II fluoride are similar, unlike the great difference for the cyanide compounds. Peroxidase differs from catalase because in the former fluoride inhibits reduction of compound I to II (*413c*), but in the latter formation and decomposition of compound II are both accelerated. Acetate acts in a similar manner, but formate, which shows this effect, has a complicating factor because it also reacts as a 2-electron donor with compound I (*403b*). Metmyoglobin differs from peroxidase and catalase in that fluoride has no effect on the reactions of metmyoglobin peroxide over a wide pH range. An anomaly also arises in the apparent dissociation of the fluoride complex of catalase which Nicholls (*403b*) gives as 3 × 10^{-3} from the effects of dissociation between catalase and fluoride at pH 5, whereas Chance (401) gives a value of 4×10^{-5} for HF as a pH-independent value (see Section III,C,1,d). The reactions of fluoride with other metalloenzymes are relatively weak. Thus, uricase is not inhibited by fluoride (415), and neither is carbonic anhydrase (462). Neither nitrate reductase (157) nor the other molybdoflavoproteins which also contain iron (450, 451) are reported to be appreciably sensitive to fluoride.

(iv) *Fluoro analogues.* Fluorine replaces hydrogen in a number of organic compounds. This subject is discussed principally elsewhere, but mention may be made of the fluorocitric and fluoroacetic acids which are involved in "lethal synthesis," a term introduced by Peters (491), and blocking of the tricarboxylic acid cycle. Fluoroacetic acid occurs as the natural toxin of *Dichapetalum cymosum* and was identified by Peters (492). Fluorocitrate behaves as an inhibitor of aconitase, as shown by Morrison and Peters (493). Brady (494) prepared fluoroacetyl CoA and showed that oxalacetate reacts enzymically with it to produce fluorocitrate in the presence of crystalline condensing enzyme from pigeon liver. Fluoroacetyl CoA competes strongly with acetyl CoA for the condensing enzyme. The respective Michaelis constants were 1.3×10^{-6} and 2.2×10^{-5}. The condensation reactions with methyl groups such as citric acid synthesis were decreased in rate but not in equilibrium by fluoroacetyl CoA, whereas carboxyl condensations, such as acetylation of mercaptoethanol by an enzyme from *Clostridium kluyveri* were not inhibited. Reactions such as ethylacetoacetate synthesis were inhibited to an intermediate extent. Whereas pigeon liver enzymes cannot activate fluoroacetate with condensing enzyme systems, the enzymes from rabbit kidney can activate fluoroacetate, and fluoride ions can inhibit this reaction but not the reaction with acetate.

d. Sulfide. Enzyme inhibitions by hydrogen sulfide (H_2S) or hydrosulfide (HS^-) may involve two aspects of the reactions of sulfide with proteins. In this form the compound behaves as a weak acid ($pK_1 = 7.14$) intermediate between azide and cyanide. Hydrogen sulfide may reduce disulfide bonds in some proteins and cause inactivation. Roche (495) pointed out that sulfide and cyanide inhibit the metal-dependent alkaline phosphatases, but Shuster (496) showed that both acid and alkaline phosphatases (i.e., 3'-nucleotidase of rye grass, which does not require a metal, and 5'-nucleotidase of semen, which is activated by magnesium) are inhibited by cyanide and cysteine at pH values between 6 and 9 and are activated by both of these over the pH range between 6 and 4. He was inclined to dismiss reduction of disulfide bonds as the explanation of these effects. The effect of cysteine was not competitive and was related to the probable formation of a dissociated or ionic compound. Shuster (496) did, however, consider that rupture of —S=S— bonds might lead to progressive denaturation of the enzyme, but kinetic studies were not made on this point. With 5′-nucleotidase a synergistic effect of magnesium and cysteine was observed, since at pH 7.5 cysteine alone was inhibitory; but with magnesium, cysteine had a stimulatory effect.

The second and more general mechanism of sulfide inhibition concerns its reaction with metals. The hemoproteins as a class are generally highly sensitive to hydrogen sulfide. The details of effective concentrations are given by Lemberg and Legge (403), Dixon and Webb (362), and James (168) for several enzymes, including the hemoproteins.

The reactions of sulfide with hemoproteins have been summarized by Lemberg and Legge (403), and spectral changes involved are given by them and by Keilin (497), Keilin and Hartree (408, 415, 475), and Keilin and Mann (459). The reaction with sulfide occurs with the ferric and not the ferrous stage, according to Keilin and Hartree (408). Sulfide is a powerful inhibitor of catalase (475) and of the peroxidative activity of methemoglobin; the compound is reversible but has a small dissociation constant of 10^{-5} (497).

Nicholls (498) has recently described the reactions between metmyoglobin, myoglobin, or catalase, and sulfide. The compounds metsulfmyoglobin and sulfcatalase are covalent. The reactions are complex and can only be summarized here. The literature on earlier work has also been reviewed by Nicholls, and spectral data are illustrated.

Myoglobin ($MbFe^{2+}$) and hydrogen sulfide form myoglobin sulfide, $MbSFe^{2+}$. This is oxidized by ferricyanide to metsulfmyoglobin ($MbSFe^{3+}$), but with hydrogen peroxide oxymyoglobin is produced ($MbSFe^{2+} + H_2O_2 \rightarrow MbFe^{2+}O_2 + H_2S?$). When H_2S is added to metmyoglobin peroxide, metsulfmyoglobin and sulfmyoglobin are produced ($2MbFeO^{2+} + 2H_2S \rightarrow MbSFe^{2+} + MbSFe^{3+} + 2H_2O + e^-$). Metsulfmyoglobin reacts with peroxide like metmyoglobin and behaves as a peroxidase, i.e., it is not appreciably inhibited. It is reduced by H_2S and forms complexes with azide, cyanide, and fluoride. Catalase reacts with hydrogen sulfide to give sulfcatalase; here, sulfur reacts with the porphyrin group in an irreversible manner. The ferric iron of sulfcatalase also reacts reversibly with hydrogen sulfide to give sulfide-sulfcatalase. There are thus two reactions involved in the inhibition. Sulfcatalase cannot form peroxide compounds I or II but can be converted with some losses to catalase by oxidizing agents such as oxygen or ethylhydrogen peroxide but not by ferricyanide. Ferric sulfcatalase cannot be reduced to the ferrous form by dithionite but is converted to free ferric catalase with losses and formation of unknown sulfur compounds. Catalase compound II with Fe^{4+} iron is reduced by H_2S to ferrosulfcatalase with Fe^{2+} iron, and this is converted to free ferrous catalase by dithionite. The ferrous catalase is then rapidly autoxidized to ferricatalase. Catalase compound I will not react with H_2S, or at least no such reaction can be detected. This is in contrast to the reaction of catalase I with azide to give nitric oxide ferrocatalase where a three-electron reduction reaction occurs (*403b, 407, 468*).

Ferrous sulfcatalase combines with carbon monoxide in a light-reversible reaction. Cyanide, azide, and fluoride combine to form stable compounds with ferric sulfcatalase but catalyze the production of free ferric catalase from ferrous sulfcatalase, possibly by autoxidation. Carbon monoxide inhibits this reaction, and formate is inactive. Nicholls draws attention to the natural occurrence of sulfhemoglobin in cases of septicemia and TNT poisoning, which is common in certain circumstances. Peroxidase differs from catalase in that it oxidizes H_2S as a substrate. Addition of ammonium sulfide to peroxidase compound I or II regenerates free peroxidase [Eq. (25)].

$$\text{Per II} + H_2S \rightarrow \text{Per } Fe^{3+} + SH^{\bullet} \tag{25}$$

The reactions and extent of inhibition with sulfide in metalloenzymes are often compared with those of azide and cyanide and frequently found to be similar; there are, however, also differences. The reaction between D-amino acid oxidase and H_2S and its insensitivity to cyanide constitute one example, but the nature of H_2S inhibition, as described below, is not typical. Uricase, which is a copper protein (*414*), is relatively sensitive to cyanide and rather less so to azide; in a nontypical manner it is not appreciably inhibited by sulfide or by fluoride (*415*). By contrast, the copper proteins of ascorbic acid oxidases of drumstick (*Moringa pterygosperma*) and of squash (*499–501*) are inhibited by sulfide as well as by cyanide to about equal extents, and ascorbic oxidases of cauliflower and squash were found by Stotz, Harrer, and King (*502*) to be 91–96% inhibited by 2.5×10^{-5} M Na_2S. Laccase is also inhibited by H_2S (*503*) and so also is polyphenol oxidase (tyrosinase) from *Psalliota* (*504*). The zinc proteins, animal carboxypeptidase and animal carbonic anhydrase, are inhibited about equally by cyanide and sulfide, according to Meldrum and Roughton (*462*) and Smith and Hanson (*428, 429*), whereas azide is much less inhibitory, and fluoride not at all. Xanthine oxidase is not inhibited by sulfide (*415*), but nitrate reductase of *Achromobacter fischeri* is completely inhibited at 5×10^{-4} M Na_2S (*465*).

Sulfide inhibition also occurs in some systems dependent on freely dissociable metal complexes. Maschmann (505) has shown that the dipeptidase of *Bacillus histolycus*, which is activated by ferrous iron and cysteine together, is reversibly inhibited by cyanide and severely inhibited by H_2S, for which reversibility was not tested.

D-Amino acid oxidase of liver, which is insensitive to cyanide (457), is irreversibly inhibited by hydrogen sulfide. The effect of H_2S on D-amino acid oxidase is not a typical reaction and is not directly due to H_2S. Keilin and Hartree (415) showed that, whereas inhibition in air is progressive and irreversible, there is no inhibition when the enzyme and H_2S are incubated anaerobically and then separated before testing the activity. An oxidation product of sulfide is probably involved, possibly as a result of hydrogen peroxide formation during initial substrate oxidation.

e. Pyrophosphate and Citrate. Pyrophosphate and citrate may produce inhibition for similar reasons in two different ways.

(i) *Chelation or competition.* Chelation of a metal component site may occur where iron, manganese, calcium, or magnesium are involved. Thus, both citrate and pyrophosphate inhibit DPNH-cytochrome c reductase, due to competition with cytochrome c for a binding site which may involve iron, according to Mahler (434, 506). Extra cytochrome c reverses the inhibition. The inhibition of lactic cytochrome c reductase by anions has been described earlier (374a, 374b).

Pyrophosphate inhibits aldehyde oxidase of liver (450) and xanthine oxidase (280) under certain circumstances by competing with phosphate when this anion is involved (280, 450, 506a). As the latter is required only for the single-electron transfer reactions involving molybdenum, the inhibition by pyrophosphate affects reduction of cytochrome c or nitrate but not that of oxygen as terminal electron acceptor. This accounts for earlier statements by Keilin and Hartree (415) and Dixon and Elliott (507) that xanthine oxidase was not inhibited by pyrophosphate because only the direct oxidase activity was being measured. Molybdenum cannot reverse pyrophosphate inhibition of xanthine oxidase. Citrate inhibits aldehyde oxidase (450) 60% at $10^{-3} M$, and this may be a competitive effect with phosphate; but the kinetics have not been described. The phosphate requirement for aldehyde and xanthine oxidases was also observed by Nicholas and Scawin (507a) and Kinsky and McElroy (455) for nitrate reductase and to a lesser extent for cytochrome c reductase. Pyrophosphate was slightly inhibitory (455) to nitrate reductase but not to cytochrome c reductase, and citrate had no effect. In one experiment phosphate was replaceable by both tungstate and arsenate but not by silicate. In the other experiment, however, silicate partially replaced phosphate. There is a specific effect of phospho- or silicomolybdates on reduction of cytochrome c by aldehyde oxidase, observed by Glenn and Crane (507b). The replacement of phosphate by tungstate (455) is not always observed (507a) and is in contrast also with the antagonistic effect of tungstate to molybdate in nitrogen fixation noted later. Sulfate, tellurate, and selenate were also able to replace phosphate.

(ii) *Chelation and redox effects.* The effect of pyrophosphate and citrate on some reactions involving manganese and peroxidation systems is of interest. The mechanism was first elucidated by Kenten and Mann (105–107), who showed that peroxidase, together with added hydrogen peroxide or that generated by amine oxidase, xanthine oxidase, or D-amino acid oxidase and a monophenol such as p-cresol, catalyzed the oxidation of Mn^{2+} to Mn^{3+}, which could be identified in the presence of pyrophosphate by its accumulation as stable trivalent manganipyrophosphate. Andreae (212) showed that light, oxygen, and riboflavin also induced the oxidation of manganese in the presence of a monophenol and pyrophosphate, which stabilized the Mn^{3+} as manganipyrophosphate.

Kenten and Mann (109) showed that illuminated chloroplasts would catalyze oxidation of manganese in the presence of pyrophosphate, probably by a similar mechanism, and later Kenten and Mann (110) demonstrated the accumulation of manganipyrophosphate *in vivo* in pea plants grown with high manganese levels; see also Section II,C,1,a.

The basic system elucidated by Kenten and Mann was later found to provide a mechanism for the manganese and monophenol-catalyzed peroxidation of a wide range of substrates of which two may be noted here, namely, many dicarboxylic acids studied by Kenten and Mann (508) and indoleacetic and indolepropionic acids studied by Kenten (509, 510), Waygood and his associates (511–513), Stutz (514), Ray (515) and others, whose work has been reviewed by Hewitt (324a, 325) and Ray (515).

Kenten (509, 510), Waygood and co-workers (511–513), and Stutz (514) showed that pyrophosphate severely inhibited the oxidation of indoleacetic acid and indolepropionic acid by peroxidase in the presence of manganese and a monophenol. Kenten (509) also found a considerable extension in the initial lag period before oxidation occurred when the manganese level was increased to $10^{-4}\,M$ in the presence of pyrophosphate.

The reactivity of manganipyrophosphate or, alternatively, the capacity of pyrophosphate to inhibit systems of the type noted above differs in the presence of various substrates. Thus, whereas pyrophosphate inhibits the oxidation of indoleacetic acid and indolepropionic acid presumably because the redox potential of the manganipyrophosphate complex is not high enough for the purpose, manganipyrophosphate is rapidly reduced by o-diphenols, as shown by Kenten and Mann (106, 107), and these compounds therefore prevent manganipyrophosphate accumulation. Cresswell (unpublished work with E. J. Hewitt) has also found that pyrophosphate does not inhibit the manganese and phenol-catalyzed peroxidation of hydroxylamine described by Cresswell and Hewitt (473). On the other hand, manganiversenate was shown by Waygood (516) to cause immediate oxidation of indoleacetic acid, and Cresswell (unpublished work) has shown a similar reaction with hydroxylamine.

Citrate also severely inhibits the oxidation of indoleacetic acid and indolepropionic acid by the manganese-catalyzed enzymic system (509–514), and citrate increased the lag period in a similar manner to that observed with pyrophosphate. It is suggested that the manganicitrate complex also has too low a redox potential to function in these systems, and Mn^{3+} thereby accumulates as inactive manganicitrate. Waygood (516) gave the relative potentials of manganipyrophosphate and manganicitrate at pH 6.0 as $E'_o = 0.6$ volt, while at pH 6.2 the E'_o for manganiversenate is 0.71 and increases to 0.81 at pH 4.2. In the experiments of Kenten (509) the inhibitory effects of pyrophosphate and citrate were dependent on the presence of manganese. Stutz (514) found the same for the effect of citrate, whereas pyrophosphate was inhibitory with or without manganese. The effective inhibitory concentrations of citrate and pyrophosphate in these systems are about $10^{-3} M$.

f. Bicarbonate. Miller and Evans (146, 147) found that bicarbonate inhibited strongly the cytochrome oxidase activity obtained from soybean or spinach roots when tested as crude particulate preparations; 0.15 N bicarbonate inhibited the activities by about 75 and 55%, respectively, compared with activity in the presence of the same normality of sodium chloride. Similar effects were reported for oat, wheat, tobacco, and pig heart preparations. The inhibition was shown to be a competitive one with cytochrome c. Ranson, Walker, and Clarke (517) reported that carbon dioxide inhibited the oxidation of succinate by castor bean mitochondria, and this was investigated further by Bendall, Ranson, and Walker (518).

Bendall, Ranson, and Walker (518) examined the effects of carbon dioxide content of gas phase on the activity of succinic dehydrogenase (succinic-cytochrome c reductase), DPNH-cytochrome c reductase, and cytochrome oxidase in mitochondria obtained from *Ricinus* endosperms. The succinic dehydrogenase was most sensitive and was inhibited from 8% CO_2 upward; it was 86% inhibited at 46% CO_2 in air. DPNH-cytochrome c reductase was intermediate and was inhibited 25% at this concentration of CO_2. Cytochrome oxidase was not inhibited at this concentration; it was stimulated 2.65 times normal at 17% CO_2, but was inhibited 75% when 78% CO_2 was present. The inhibition of the succinic dehydrogenase system was competitive with respect to succinate, and inhibitions of all three systems were reversible. The competition with succinate was therefore not comparable with competition with cytochrome c observed in other systems.

Bicarbonate inhibition of a possibly different type was described by Ball and Cooper (519) and by Bonner (520) for heart particulate succinic oxidase. This inhibition, which amounted to 80%, was found by Ball and Cooper (519) to be partially prevented by the previous treatment of the enzyme with phosphate buffer, whereas phosphate buffer could not reverse the inhibitory effects of incubating the preparations with bicarbonate solutions. Bonner (520) found that the bicarbonate inhibition was reversed by the addition of denatured globin and was unable to repeat the results of Ball and Cooper with respect to nonreversal by phosphate after incubation in bicarbonate. Bonner (520) suggested that bicarbonate inhibition was due to a change in the colloidal structure of the protein which could be reversed by a colloid such as denatured globin. The effect of bicarbonate or saturated solutions of carbon dioxide on protein solubility (521) seems relevant to the effects described by Ball and Cooper (519) and Bonner (520). The weak dissociation of ferrous bicarbonate also may be related to possible effects of bicarbonate as an inhibitory anion.

g. Borate. The inhibitory effects of borate have been observed in several enzyme systems. Several workers (202–205) have, as already mentioned in the physiological section on plants, observed inhibition of the polyphenol oxidase, tyrosinase groups of enzymes by borate ions. Fifty per cent inhibition occurs between 4×10^{-3} and $10^{-2} M$ and is competitive in the oxidation of dihydroxyphenylalanine by tyrosinase. A complex between borate and the phenolic substrate has been suggested as the possible mechanism.

Roush and Norris (522) have found that borate inhibits oxidation of xanthine competitively in milk xanthine oxidase ($K_i = 8 \times 10^{-3}$). The theory is that both borate and xanthine react with the hydroxyl groups of the ribityl part of the flavin coenzyme, a function of ribityl compounds described by Zittle (206).

A possibly analagous inhibition by borate also occurs in a specific phosphatase hydrolyzing adenosine-5-phosphate, reported by Heppel and Hilmoe (353a), and in the nucleotide pyrophosphatase of potato, described by Kornberg and Pricer (507a), which reacts with ATP, nicotinamide mononucleotide, FAD, TPN, and DPN. Kornberg and Pricer found that inhibition occurred at pH 8.5 but not at pH 7.4 and concluded that borate ions were involved.

Recently, Roush and Gowdy (523) have observed a marked inhibition of yeast alcohol dehydrogenase by borate ions: 50% at $7.5 \times 10^{-4} M$. The inhibition is competitive with DPN. For the effects of various concentrations of alcohol as substrate for oxidation, K_i was 6×10^{-5}, while for varying DPN concentrations K_i was 4.1×10^{-4}. These different values suggest that borate competes at two sites on the enzyme, one of which binds ethanol and the other DPN. Roush and Gowdy suggested that borate inhibition of DPN-dependent alcohol dehydrogenase would be observed as the coenzyme has a ribityl group which forms a complex with borate (206). In this respect DPN resembles riboflavin phosphate, TPN, and adenosine-5-phosphate.

Roush and Gowdy (523), however, also considered whether the borate effect is that of an anion by analogy with the inhibitory effects of other anions observed with liver alcohol dehydrogenase by Theorell, Nygaard, and Bonnischen (524). Both enzymes are zinc proteins, and the evidence that borate inhibits at two sites, since its competitive effects differ with DPN or ethanol, is consistent with the recent account of the probable mechanism of zinc-coenzyme and ethanol binding described by Theorell and McKinley-McKee (525). In this theory no mention is made of any function of the hydroxyl groupings of the ribityl part of the coenzyme. Borate probably acts as an anion in an ionic linkage when it behaves as a competitive inhibitor of liver alkaline phosphatase (206).

A recent discovery of some interest, which relates the chemistry of borate ions to a specific inhibitory effect, has been reported by Osaki (526). Pig blood contains an enzyme ceruloplasmin. This is a copper protein containing also about 2% by weight of glucose, mannose, and xylose, which are an integral part of the enzyme, which catalyzes the oxidation of p-phenylenediamine and other substrates. Activity is reversibly and noncompetitively inhibited by borate ions, and inhibition is 50% at $2 \times 10^{-2} M$. The dissociation curve between borate and enzyme indicates a constant which is of the same order as the stability constants for sugar-borate complexes, and the mechanism is considered to involve this type of reaction.

h. *Molybdenum, Tungsten, and Vanadium.* Inhibitory and interacting effects of these elements have been observed in two respects, namely, in phosphatase activity and nitrogen metabolism.

Molybdate has been shown to be a fairly general inhibitor of acid phosphatase from several plants, including potato [investigated by Bossard (277)] and tomato; the effect was shown by Spencer (278) to operate *in vivo* and *in vitro*. The effect of molybdate depended partly on the substrate and ranged from 50 to 90% inhibition at $10^{-4} M$ molybdate. The enzyme in cauliflower is similarly inhibited (unpublished work of E. J. Hewitt and D. P. Hucklesby).

Nicholas and Commissiong (276) studied enzyme changes in *N. crassa* at different optimal and toxic levels of molybdenum, copper, and iron and interactions between them. Thus, cytochrome c oxidase enhanced by increasing copper was decreased by increasing molybdate in the basal culture solution; the reverse was obtained for nitrate reductase. Cytochrome c oxidase and nitrate reductase were depressed, however, by amounts of copper and molybdenum which were toxic to growth; the effects were additive. Molybdate was shown to inhibit acid phosphatase competitively

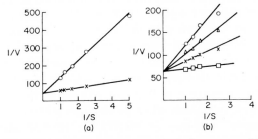

FIG. 10. *a*, Lineweaver-Burk (1934) plot of the competitive inhibition of acid phosphatase activity by sodium molybdate. Assay mixtures consisted of 1 ml acid phosphatase reagent, 0.05 ml enzyme extract, and 0.05 ml of either distilled water or a solution of Na_2MoO_4 of 8 μg Mo/ml. The mixtures were incubated at 38° for 30 minutes, and then 3.9 ml 0.06 N NaOH was added to make a final volume of 5 ml. The intensity of the *p*-nitrophenol color developed was read on the Spekker Absorptiometer at 540 mμ. $1/V$, reciprocal of the intensity of the *p*-nitrophenol at 540 mμ $\times$ 10^4; $1/S$, reciprocal of substrate concentration, where the normal substrate concentration is considered as unity; X—X, no inhibitor; O—O, with molybdate. From Nicholas and Commissiong (276). *b*, Lineweaver-Burk (1934) plot showing competitive inhibition of copper by molybdate on acid phosphatase (*in vitro*). Assay mixtures consisted of 1 ml acid phosphatase reagent, 0.05 ml enzyme extract, 0.05 ml $Na_2MoO_4 \cdot 2H_2O$ at 0, 1.0, 2.1, or 5.2×10^{-6} M-$Na_2MoO_4 \cdot 2H_2O$ and 0.05 ml $CuSO_4 \cdot 5H_2O$ at 0.6, 0.9, 1.2, and 1.5×10^{-5} M. The mixtures were incubated at 38° for 30 minutes, and then 3.85 ml 0.06 N NaOH was added to make a final volume of 5 ml. The intensity of the *p*-nitrophenol color developed was read on the Spekker absorptiometer at 540 mμ. $1/V$, reciprocal of the intensity of the *p*-nitrophenol at 540 mμ, $\times$ 10^4; $1/S$, reciprocal of the amount of copper added per assay; □—□, no molybdenum; X—X, 1.0×10^{-6} M $Na_2MoO_4 \cdot 2H_2O$; Δ—Δ, 2.1×10^{-6} M $Na_2MoO_4 \cdot 2H_2O$; O—O, 5.2×10^{-6} M $Na_2MoO_4 \cdot 2H_2O$. From Nicholas and Commissiong (276).

in vitro, as shown in Fig. 10, presumably by forming a molybdophosphate addition compound with the substrate. Copper dispersed this complex and restored the enzyme activity to normal. Vanadate or tungstate had a similar effect to molybdate in depressing the enzyme, and copper again reversed the inhibition. Naganna *et al.* (*279*) found that both acid phosphatase and an acid pyrophosphatase of potato were inhibited by molybdate or tungstate about equally, and 70–80% inhibition was observed with as little as $10^{-6} M$ concentration of either anion. Alkaline pyrophosphatase was not inhibited, and fluoride, sulfate, chloride, cyanide, and thiocyanate were either much less effective or were ineffective. Hiltz, Kittler, and Knape (*526a*) found that $4 \times 10^{-3} M$ molybdate markedly inhibited sulfate reduction in the presence of ATP by a yeast enzyme system by inhibiting the reaction between sulfate and ATP.

The other aspect of molybdenum or vanadium and tungsten interactions concerns nitrogen metabolism. The inhibition of nitrate reductase by vanadium but not by tungsten (*159*) has been mentioned, as has also the antagonism of vanadium to molybdenum in nitrogen fixation by *A. glutinosa*. Takahashi and Nason (*528*) showed that tungstate is a competitive inhibitor of molybdate for the growth of *A. vinelandii* on nitrate or atmospheric nitrogen as the sole sources of nitrogen. Inhibition was overcome by increasing sodium molybdate in the medium, but the latter did not affect inhibition when ammonium sulfate or glutamate was the nitrogen source. Addition of $NaNO_3$ at $10^{-4} M$ also inhibited N_2 fixation, but small amounts of nitrate (1.5–$3 \times 10^{-5} M$) did not overcome the inhibitory effect of tungstate. Similar results were reported by Keeler and Varner (*528a*), and the same behavior was later observed for *A. Chroococcum* (*528b*).

3. Effects of Cyanide, Azide, and Fluoride on Metabolism *in vivo*

The effects of enzyme inhibitors *in vitro* on isolated systems may not always resemble their apparent effects on more complex metabolic systems when studied in living cells. This type of discrepancy has been noted on several occasions in relation to the effects of cyanide, azide, and fluoride as respiratory inhibitors and has at times led to the idea that cytochrome oxidase may mediate only a part, and even only a small part, of total tissue respiration. The significance and interpretation of observations of this sort have been fully reviewed by Dixon (*529*), Commoner (*530*), Winzler (*531*), Lemberg and Legge (*403*), James (*167, 168*), Hackett (*169, 532*), Hill and Hartree (*533*), and Hartree (*534*). It is not possible here to deal in any detail with this subject, and there is little doubt that in some organs or at certain stages of development the proportion of respiratory activity that is mediated by cytochrome oxidase may vary. It is also apparent (*168, 530–534*) that in most circumstances cytochrome oxidase mediates the major proportion, and perhaps all, of the respiratory oxygen uptake.

It is evident, however, that circumstances may affect the interpretation of the apparent effect of respiratory inhibitors when it is observed that cyanide or azide, for example, do not inhibit oxygen uptake as much as might be expected. In the first place it is necessary to know if the inhibitor reaches the sensitive system; pH effects may determine whether this occurs, as it has been shown that respiratory inhibition by azide is sensitive to pH. Hill and Hartree (*533*) pointed out that, where weak acids such as fluoride, azide, and cyanide are involved, penetration is often limited to the undissociated free acid. This has been observed by Stenlid (*535*) for azide penetration into barley roots and by Keilin (*459a*) for azide penetration of yeast cells, while Beevers and Simon (*536*) observed a pH dependence of fluoride inhibition. This last point may be subject to other interpretations in view of the observations of Fitzgerald and Bernheim (*537*). They showed that the effect of fluoride on respiratory oxygen uptake by *Mycobacterium* was dependent on substrate and pH in a complex manner, as seen in Fig. 11. At pH 7.8 fluoride had no

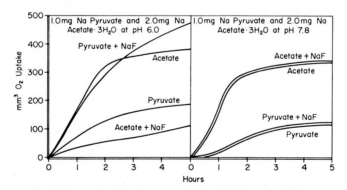

FIG. 11.   The effect of 2.0 mg NaF on the oxidation of pyruvate and acetate at pH 6.0 and 7.8 by *Mycobacterium* BCG. The respective control uptakes, with and without fluoride, have been subtracted. From Fitzgerald and Berheim (*537*).

effect on acetate or pyruvate respiration, but at pH 6.0 fluoride depressed oxygen uptake with acetate and stimulated it (possibly adaptively) with pyruvate. The effects of fluoride on oxidation of fructose or glucose (Fig. 12) were entirely reversed from inhibition to stimulation over a pH range of 6.0–6.7. Fluoride was therefore metabolically active at pH

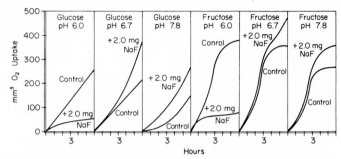

FIG. 12.   The effect of 2.0 mg NaF on the oxidation by *Mycobacterium* BCG of glucose and fructose at 3 hydrogen ion concentrations. The respective control uptakes, with and without fluoride, have been subtracted. From Fitzgerald and Bernheim (*537*).

values well above 6.0 but was not usually inhibitory at the higher values. If penetration was involved, this phenomenon was modified by the respiratory substrate, or perhaps HF inhibited and F⁻ was stimulatory. This could happen if uncoupling effects were also involved.

When pH effects are important in the respiratory effects of weak acids, Simon (*538*) and Simon and Beevers (*539*) conclude that the maximum effects of the inhibitor are to be observed only at pH values two units less than the pK of the inhibitor acid. The pK values for fluoride, azide, and cyanide (3.2, 4.9, and 9.8, respectively) would indicate that maximum inhibition could be observed only at pH values of 1–2, 3, and 7–8, respectively. Clearly, one might expect few complications with cyanide in most experiments, yet this compound has been shown not always to inhibit *in vivo* in the manner to be expected if cytochrome oxidase is the principal terminal acceptor. Two points may be considered in explanation of this particular problem. First, it was pointed out by Winzler (*531*), from the results of a thorough kinetic analysis described below, and by Hill and Hartree (*533*) that, if an intermediate respiratory step is rate limiting but not particularly cyanide sensitive, cyanide will not have such a marked effect on respiration. Cyanide-inhibited ferrocytochrome oxidase is autoxidizable, and this reaction is not rate limiting. When carbon monoxide is present, the cytochrome oxidase is held in the ferro form, and inhibition may then be observed (see *533*, p. 130). Secondly, it must be remembered that, although cytochrome oxidase is inhibited by HCN, cytochrome c is inhibited by CN⁻, and opposite pH effects are involved to those favoring penetration. Similar reservations apply to the effects of azide and their interpretation.

A possible way of accentuating cyanide or azide sensitivity when the terminal oxidase is not rate limiting is to limit the step until its rate becomes that of the rate-limiting reaction. Thus, sensitivity to cyanide *in vivo* is greatly affected by the metal status of the cells. Tissières (*540*) showed that respiration of *Aerobacter aerogenes* is sharply inhibited by cyanide or CO when deficient in iron but is relatively insensitive when grown in an iron-rich medium. Ducet and Rosenberg (*541*) observed a similar effect in regard to carbon monoxide sensitivity of respiration in leaves of maize, beet, and tomato plants grown with or without iron. The view that rate-limiting reactions *in vivo* cause a decreased sensitivity to cyanide but not to azide was favored by Darby and Goddard (*542*) as a result of their experiments with *Myrothecium verucaria*, but other possibilities, including structural protective effects and alternative respiratory mechanisms, were also regarded as possible explanations. Commoner (*530*) presented an early but still admirable account of the relationships known up to 1939 between cyanide and respiration in animal, plant, and microorganism cells. This study is too extensive to incorporate here, but some interesting or important general points are emphasized here.

Since cyanide-sensitive respiration, which is mediated normally by cytochrome oxidase, is dependent on substrate availability, the apparent ratio of cyanide-sensitive to -insensitive respiration will vary with substrate supply.

By plotting the original values of respiration against cyanide-inhibited respiration a linear relationship was obtained with an intercept of original respiration. Commoner showed that the percentage of inhibition of cyanide-sensitive respiration approached 100% as respiration rate was increased. Normally, the ratio of cyanide-sensitive to cyanide-insensitive respiration is about 9.5:1, and the absolute value of the cyanide-insensitive respiration is nearly constant regardless of the value of this ratio.

Statement of relative cyanide sensitivity is therefore without meaning unless substrate saturation and potential activity are taken into account. Whereas the maximum Q_{O_2} values ranged from 33 to 0.2, for different animal tissues $Q_{O_2}^{CN}$ ranged from 0.1 to 3.0 and was usually between 0.3 and 1.0. In comparing the two types of respiration for *Lathyrus* embryo it was shown that, whereas cyanide-sensitive respiration varied from Q_{O_2} 4.3 to 0.8, the cyanide-stable respiration $Q_{O_2}^{CN}$ ranged only from 1.1 to 0.6 in relation to age, light, or morphological part used.

Cyanide-sensitive respiration is affected by light, age, buffer, temperature, pO_2, species, organ, and substrate supply to a much greater extent than cyanide-stable respiration. The latter may often be associated with the oxidation of a fatty substrate rather than of carbohydrates and is associated frequently with relatively low RQ values of 0.7–0.8.

Winzler (531) studied the effects on the respiration of yeast cells of azide and cyanide, singly and in combination with each other or with carbon monoxide. From the application of Michaelis-Menten kinetic analysis he concluded that cyanide reacts with at least three sites in the respiratory chain and that an intermediate enzyme system which possesses about half the equivalent activity of cytochrome oxidase is the rate-limiting system for over-all respiration. Azide was thought to react only with the terminal oxidase in the oxidized form. Reciprocal Lineweaver-Burk plots showed that the maximal velocity of respiration of the cyanide-inhibited over-all system was the same as the observed maximal rate in the absence of cyanide. Thus, cyanide inhibits the rate-limiting enzyme. It was also found that cyanide inhibition was non-competitive with oxygen uptake and that the Q_{O_2} was approximately double in the presence of cyanide. The presence of cyanide therefore increased the dependence of the respiratory system on oxygen tension.

Reciprocal plots for azide as an over-all inhibitor showed that V_{max} of the inhibited system was twice the observed maximum respiration rate, and azide therefore inhibits the terminal cytochrome oxidase but not the rate-limiting reaction. It is similar in this respect to carbon monoxide but reacts with the ferric instead of the ferrous state. This relationship led to the consequence that at moderate concentrations azide was a more potent inhibitor than cyanide, but at very low concentrations cyanide was equally or more effective as an inhibitor. The inhibition by azide also differed from that by cyanide in being independent of oxygen tension.

When azide was tested as an inhibitor at different concentrations in the presence or absence of cyanide, it was found that both V_{max} and observed maximum respiration (R_{max}) were decreased by cyanide, showing that cyanide inhibited both the rate-limiting and the azide-sensitive systems. The dissociation constants for cyanide for both systems could thus be calculated. The slopes of the reciprocal plots for azide concentration were the same in the presence or absence of cyanide. Conversely, when effects of cyanide concentration were tested in the presence or absence of azide, it was found that cyanide still affected the rate-limiting system until the azide inhibition of the faster reaction became the rate-limiting factor. By using the appropriate values for K_i of azide, it was shown independently that cyanide and azide both inhibit the fast reaction, while cyanide also inhibits the rate-limiting reaction.

The values for K_i calculated for azide and cyanide were as follows: for the rate-limiting reaction K_i for cyanide was 3.7×10^{-5}; for the fast reaction (terminal oxidase) K_i for cyanide was 1.4×10^{-5}, and K_i for azide was 2.2×10^{-6}. These values may require to be corrected for effects of dissociation on the reactive forms.

The effects of azide on growth and reproduction of microorganisms have been studied by Tissières (540) with A. aerogenes and by Aubel and Szulmajster (543), Rosenberg (544), and Aubel, Rosenberg, and Szulmajster (545) with Escherichia coli.

The work on Aerobacter was done because this organism has an atypical cytochrome spectrum with a very strong cytochrome a_2 spectrum and can also be made to show effects of metal deficiencies, especially of iron. The cytochrome a_2 was considered to function in place of the normal cytochrome oxidase. Azide was found not to combine with any of the cytochrome components of Aerobacter, unlike cyanide, which combined with cytochrome a_2. Azide at concentrations of 3×10^{-3} M more than doubled oxygen uptake and carbon dioxide output in the presence of glucose and increased anaerobic oxidation of methylene blue fourfold. Azide had no effect on methylene blue reduction with fructose or galactose and decreased it by 60% when succinate or acetate was used as a substrate. These observations were in agreement with those of Aubel and Szulmajster (543) and Aubel, Rosenberg, and Szulmajster (545), who found with E. coli that azide and fluoride inhibited fermentation but not respiration with pyruvate or glucose in resting cells, whereas they inhibited respiration with succinate, pyruvate, or hexose phosphate in proliferating cells. Cyanide also inhibited respiration with these substrates but not with pyruvate. Tissières (540) referred to the effects of azide as an inhibitor of oxidative phosphorylation. As uncoupling of oxidation from phosphorylation often results in increased oxygen uptake, the effects of azide found by Tissières might have been due to this relationship. It is relevant that, whereas cyanide inhibits both growth and regeneration of some microorganisms, azide may inhibit only regeneration, and this aspect of metabolism is certainly dependent on phosphorylation (546). Rosenberg (544) found that azide inhibits the deamination of glucosamine by E. coli but not its oxidation. When phosphate is omitted, the glucosamine is not deaminated. These results also point to an effect of azide on phosphorylation.

The effects of azide on carrot leaf respiration were studied by Stenlid (547, 548), who showed that the pH-independent inhibition shown by young leaves gave way to a pH-dependent effect where inhibition was observed only at pH values of about 4.5 and where stimulation of O_2 uptake occurred at pH 7.0. Stenlid concluded that, as dinitrophenol showed similar effects, some aspect of oxidative phosphorylation was involved in older tissues, while in young leaves an oxidative reaction was concerned. The independence of pH and inhibition in these young leaves contrasts with the pH dependence found for effects with barley roots.

The inhibitory effects of azide on phosphorylation have been described by Hotchkiss (549), Case and McIlwain (550), Loomis and Lipman (551), and Spiegelman, Kamen, and Sussman (552). The last group concluded that triosephosphate dehydrogenase may be involved. As this enzyme probably contains zinc (427), the azide may react with the metal. It is also a key enzyme in fermentation. As Hatch and Turner (553) have shown that it may be the key enzyme in the operation of the Pasteur effect, an increase of oxygen uptake when this enzyme is inhibited would be expected in organisms which respire by the hexose monophosphate shunt or pentose phosphate cycle, as fully described recently by Turner (554). Robertson and Boyer (555), however, regard the effects of azide on phosphorylation as indirect and independent of phosphate or acceptor availability, and according to Rakestraw and Roberts (556), phosphorylation may be increased or decreased without affecting respiration by *Azotobacter*. Recently, Suelter *et al.* (557) have shown that azide inhibits the accumulation of an unidentified intermediate of oxidative phosphorylation by rat liver mitochondria.

IV. CONCLUSION

In brief, it appears that a particular anionic or cationic inhibitor may act in one or more ways. It may compete with a substrate, block an active site in one of several ways, alter the redox potential, react as an ionized or nonionized enzyme-inhibitor-substrate complex. It may inhibit competitively or noncompetitively or uncompetitively, react at one or more sites, function specifically or nonspecifically, or indirectly after transformation. It may vary greatly in affinity for related enzymes or in different mechanisms in the same enzyme, and it may activate one enzyme but inactivate another closely related one.

It is therefore clear that conclusions regarding active sites and reaction mechanisms are of little value in many instances unless kinetic analyses and confirmatory tests are undertaken. The use of analytical amounts of the homogeneous enzymes in these tests is also desirable. The use of inhibitor studies can however, provide fundamental information regarding the mechanism of enzyme action, enzyme structure, and, perhaps, also, in problems of cellular differentiation and *in vivo* pathways of metabolism.

REFERENCES

1. D. I. Arnon, *in* "Trace Elements in Plant Physiology," pp. 31-39. Chronica Botanica, Waltham, Massachusetts, 1950.
2. S. Ahmed and H. J. Evans, *Biochem. Biophys. Research Communs.* 1, 271 (1959).
3. S. Ahmed and H. J. Evans, *Soil Sci.* 90, 205 (1960).
4. R. H. Lowe, H. J. Evans, and S. Ahmed, *Biochem. Biophys. Research Communs.* 3, 675 (1960).
5. H. M. Reisenauer, *Nature* 186, 375 (1960).
6. S. H. Hutner, L. Provasoli, A. Schatz, and C. P. Haskins, *Proc. Am. Phil. Soc.* 94, 152 (1950).
7. G. C. Gerloff, G. P. Fitzgerald, and F. Skoog, *Am. J. Botany* 37, 217 (1950).
8. D. I. Arnon, P. S. Ichioka, G. Wessel, A. Fujiwara, and J. T. Woolley, *Plant Physiol.* 8, 538 (1955).
9. D. Bertrand, *Bull. Am. Museum Nat. Hist.* 94, 407 (1950).
10. D. J. D. Nicholas, *Ann. Rev. Plant Physiol.* 12, 63 (1961).
11. R. A. MacLeod and E. E. Snell, *J. Biol. Chem.* 176, 39 (1948).
12. R. A. MacLeod and E. E. Snell, *J. Bacteriol.* 59, 783 (1950).
13. R. A. MacLeod, *J. Bacteriol.* 62, 337 (1951).
14. E. E. Snell, *in* "Trace Analysis" (J. H. Yoe and H. J. Koch, eds.), p. 547. Wiley, New York, 1957.
15. A. Pirson, *Ann. Rev. Plant Physiol.* 6, 71 (1955).
16. V. W. Cochrane, "Physiology of Fungi." Wiley, New York, 1958.
17. H. Bortels, *Arch. Mikrobiol.* 1, 333 (1930).
17a. C. K. Horner, D. Burk, F. E. Allison, and M. S. Sherman, *J. Agr. Research* 65, 173 (1942).
18. J. Bové, C. Bové, and D. I. Arnon, *Plant Physiol.* 32, Suppl. 23 (1957).
19. D. J. D. Nicholas, D. J. Fisher, W. J. Redmond, and M. A. Wright, *J. Gen. Microbiol.* 22, 191 (1960).
20. R. A. Steinberg, *Botan. Rev.* 5, 327 (1939).
21. R. A. Steinberg and J. D. Bowling, *J. Agr. Research* 58, 717 (1939).
22. D. J. D. Nicholas, A. Nason, and W. D. McElroy, *J. Biol. Chem.* 207, 341 (1954).
23. D. J. D. Nicholas and A. Nason, *J. Biol. Chem.* 207, 352 (1954).
23a. D. J. D. Nicholas and A. Nason, *Plant Physiol.* 30, 135 (1955).
24. D. J. D. Nicholas and A. Nason, *J. Bacteriol.* 69, 580 (1955).
25. D. J. D. Nicholas and H. M. Stevens, *Nature* 176, 1066 (1955).
26. H. J. Evans and N. S. Hall, *Science* 122, 922 (1955).
27. P. W. Wilson, *in* "Handbuch der Pflanzenphysiologie" (K. Mothes, ed.), Vol. 8, p. 9. Springer, Berlin, 1958.
28. B. R. Holland and W. W. Meinke, *J. Biol. Chem.* 178, 7 (1949).
29. G. Bertrand and M. Javillier, *Compt. rend. acad. sci.* 152, 225 (1911).
30. R. A. Steinberg, *Am. J. Botany* 6, 330 (1919).
31. R. A. MacLeod and E. E. Snell, *Ann. N.Y. Acad. Sci.* 52, 1249 (1950).
32. J. Lavollay and F. Laborey, *Compt. rend. acad. sci.* 204, 1686 (1937).
33. J. Lavollay, *Compt. rend. Acad. sci.* 28, 350 (1942).
34. J. Lavollay, *in* "VI Congres International de Microbiologie." *Extrait Rev. gen. sci.* 62, (3-4a), 1.

34a. J. Lavollay, *Bull. soc. franc. physiol. veg.* 5, No. 2, 29 (1959).

34b. P. H. Abelson and E. Aldous, *J. Bacteriol.* 60, 401 (1950) [quoted by Adiga (34d)].

34c. K. Sivarama Sastry, P. R. Adiga, V. Venkatasubramanyan, and P. S. Sarma, *Abstr. Comm. Vth Inst. Congr. Nutrition, Washington, D.C.*, No. 182, 40 (1960) [quoted by Adiga (34d)].

34d. P. R. Adiga, K. Sivarama Sastry, V. Venkatasubramanyan, and P. S. Sarma, *Biochem. J.* 81, 545 (1961).

35. J. B. Walker, *Arch. Biochem. Biophys.* 46, 1 (1953).

36. J. B. Walker, *Arch. Biochem. Biophys.* 53, 1 (1954).

37. A. Albert, "Selective Toxicity," 2nd ed. Methuen, London, 1960.

38. A. Albert, S. D. Rubbo, R. J. Goldacre, and B. G. Balfour, *Brit. J. Exptl. Pathol.* 28, 69 (1947).

39. G. A. Zentmyer, *Science* 100, 294 (1944).

40. S. Rubbo, A. Albert, and M. Gibson, *Brit. J. Exptl. Pathol.* 31, 425 (1950).

41. A. Albert, M. Gibson, and S. D. Rubbo, *Brit. J. Exptl. Pathol.* 34, 120 (1953).

42. G. Greathouse, S. Block, E. Kovach, D. Barnes, C. Byron, G. Long, D. Gerber, and J. McLenny, "Research on Chemical Compounds for Inhibition of Fungi." U.S. Corps of Engineers, Fort Belvoir, Virginia.

43. B. Nordbring-Hertz, *Physiol. Plantarum* 8, 691 (1955).

44. S. S. Block, *J. Agr. Food Chem.* 4, 1042 (1956).

45. A. Albert, C. W. Rees, and A. J. H. Tomlinson, *Brit. J. Exptl. Pathol.* 37, 500 (1956).

46. J. Goksøyr, *Nature* 175, 820 (1955) ; *Physiol. Plantarum* 8, 719 (1955).

47. A. K. Sijpesteijn, M. J. Janssen, and G. J. M. van der Kerk, *Biochim. et Biophys. Acta* 23, 55 (1957).

48. E. D. Weinberg, *Bacteriol. Revs.* 21, 46 (1957).

49. A. Albert, *Biochem. J.* 54, 646 (1953).

50. J. Cymerman-Craig, S. D. Rubbo, D. Willis, and J. Edgar, *Nature* 176, 35 (1955).

51. A. Albert, *Nature* 177, 525 (1956).

52. A. Albert and C. W. Rees, *Nature* 177, 433 (1956).

53. A. K. Saz and J. Marmur, *Proc. Soc. Exptl. Biol. Med.* 82, 783 (1953).

54. A. K. Saz and R. B. Slie, *J. Biol. Chem.* 210, 407 (1954).

55. A. P. Mathews, *Am. J. Physiol.* 10, 290 (1904).

56. J. R. E. Jones, *J. Exptl. Biol.* 17, 408 (1940).

57. J. F. Danielli and J. T. Davies, *Advances in Enzymol.* 11, 35 (1951).

58. E. Somers, *Nature* 184, 475 (1959).

59. E. Somers, *Nature* 187, 427 (1960).

60. E. Somers, *Ann. Appl. Biol.* 49, 246 (1961).

61. L. P. Miller, *Nature* 185, 545 (1960).

62. L. P. Miller and R. M. Weed, *Contribs. Boyce Thompson Inst.* 17, 151 (1953).

63. L. P. Miller and S. E. A. McCallan, *Proc. Intern. Conf. Peaceful Uses Atomic Energy, Geneva, 1955* A/Conf. 8/5/100 (1955).

64. H. Martin. "The Scientific Principles of Plant Protection with Special Reference to Chemical Control," 3rd ed. Edward Arnold, London, 1940.

65. J. G. Horsfall, "Principles of Fungicidal Action." Chronica Botanica, Waltham, Massachusetts, 1956.
66. Plant Protection Conference 1956. Proc. 2nd Intern. Conf., Fernhurst Research Station, England. Butterworths, London, 1957.
67. J. Bodnár and T. Terényi, Z. physiol. Chem. Hoppe-Seyler's 186, 157 (1930).
68. L. P. Miller and S. E. A. McCallan, J. Agr. Food Chem. 5, 116 (1957).
69. J. H. Brewer, in "Antiseptics, Disinfectants, Fungicides and Chemical and Physical Sterilization," (G. F. Reddish, ed.), p. 212. Lea & Febiger, Philadelphia, Pennsylvania, 1954.
70. G. J. M. van der Kerk and J. G. A. Luitjen, J. Appl. Chem. 4, 314 (1954).
71. J. Bodnár and Terényi, Z. physiol. Chem. Hoppe-Seyler's 207, 78 (1932).
72. W. Biedermann and E. Müller, Phytopathol. Z. 18, 307 (1951).
73. S. E. A. McCallan, Botan. Rev. 15, 629 (1949).
74. R. W. Marsh, J. Pomol. Hort. Sci. 7, 237 (1929).
75. F. Wilcoxon and S. E. A. McCallan, Contribs. Boyce Thompson Inst. 4, 415 (1932).
76. S. E. A. McCallan and C. Setterstrom, Contribs. Boyce Thompson Inst. 11, 325 (1940).
77. L. P. S. Miller, S. E. A. McCallan, and R. M. Weed, Contribs. Boyce Thompson Inst. 17, 151 (1953).
78. G. S. Weissman and S. F. Trelease, Am. J. Botany 42, 489 (1955).
79. A. Shrift, Am. J. Botany 4, 377 (1953).
80. W. P. Kelley, Hawaii Agr. Exptl. Sta., Bull. 26, (1912).
81. W. T. McGeorge, Soil Sci. 16, 269 (1923).
82. M. O. Johnson, Hawaii Agr. Expt. Sta., Bull. 52, (1924).
83. M. O. Johnson, Ind. Eng. Chem. 20, 724 (1928).
84. E. F. Hopkins, V. Pagan, and F. J. Ramirez-Silva, J. Agr. Univ. Puerto Rico 28, 43 (1944).
85. T. Wallace and E. J. Hewitt, J. Pomol. Hort. Sci. 22, 133 (1946).
86. E. J. Hewitt, Long Ashton Research Sta. Ann. Rept., 1948, p. 66 (1949).
87. E. J. Hewitt, Nature 161, 489 (1948).
88. E. J. Hewitt, J. Exptl. Botan. 4, 59 (1954).
89. C. R. Millikan, J. Australian Inst. Agr. Sci. 13, 180 (1947).
90. C. R. Millikan, Proc. Roy. Soc. Victoria [N.S.] 61, 25 (1949).
91. E. S. Twyman, New Phytol. 45, 18 (1946).
92. E. S. Twyman, New Phytol. 50, 210 (1951).
93. D. J. D. Nicholas, J. Hort. Sci. 25, 60 (1949).
94. D. J. D. Nicholas, Long Ashton Research Sta. Ann. Rept. p. 96 (1950).
95. D. J. D. Nicholas, Long Ashton Research Sta. Ann. Rept. p. 87 (1951).
96. W. A. Forster, Long Ashton Research Sta. Ann. Rept. p. 108 (1950).
97. D. J. D. Nicholas and W. D. E. Thomas, Plant and Soil 5, 67 (1953).
98. D. J. D. Nicholas and W. D. E. Thomas, Plant and Soil 5, 182 (1954).
99. P. C. De Kock, Ann. Botany (London) [N.S.] 20, 133 (1956).
100. O. Vergnano and J. G. Hunter, Ann. Botany (London) [N.S.] 17, 317 (1952.)
101. I. I. Somers and J. W. Shive, Plant Physiol. 17, 582 (1942).
102. I. I. Somers, S. G. Gilbert, and J. W. Shive, Plant Physiol. 17, 317 (1942).
103. K. Noack and H. Liebeck, Naturwissenschaften 302, (1940).

104. S. Granick, *in* "Trace Eelements" (C. A. Lamb, O. G. Bentley, and J. M. Beattie, eds.), pp. 365-382. Academic Press, New York, 1958.
105. R. H. Kenten and P. J. G. Mann, *Biochem. J.* 45, 255 (1949).
106. R. H. Kenten and P. J. G. Mann, *Biochem. J.* 46, 67 (1950).
107. R. H. Kenten and P. J. G. Mann, *Biochem J.* 52, 125 (1952).
108. P. George, *Biochem J.* 54, 267 (1953).
109. R. H. Kenten and P. J. G. Mann, *Biochem. J.* 61, 279 (1955).
110. R. H. Kenten and P. J. G. Mann, *Biochem. J.* 65, 179 (1956).
110a. G. W. Leeper, *J. Australian Inst. Agr. Sci.* 10, 186 (1944).
111. E. J. Hewitt, *Ann. Rev. Plant Physiol.* 2, 25 (1951).
112. W. M. Latimer, "The Oxidation States of the Elements and their Potentials in Aqueous Solutions." Prentice-Hall, Englewood Cliffs, New Jersey, 1952.
113. P. Pfeiffer, H. Thielert, and H. Glaser, *J. prakt. Chem.* 152, 145 (1939).
114. D. P. Mellor and L. Maley, *Nature* 159, 370 (1947).
115. D. P. Mellor and L. Maley, *Nature* 161, 436 (1948).
116. H. Irving and R. J. P. Williams, *Nature* 162, 746 (1948).
117. H. Ackerman, J. E. Prue, and G. Schwarzenbach, *Nature* 163, 723 (1949).
118. K. Yamasaki and K. Sone, *Nature* 166, 998 (1950).
119. A. Albert, *Biochem. J.* 50, 690 (1952).
120. L. Maley and D. P. Mellor, *Nature* 165, 453 (1950).
121. A. Albert, *in* "The Strategy of Chemotherapy," p. 112 (S. T. Cowan and E. Rowatt, eds.). Cambridge Univ. Press, London and New York, 1958.
122. J. G. Hunter and O. Vergnano, *Ann. Appl. Biol.* 40, 761 (1955).
122a. W. H. R. Shaw, *Nature* 192, 755 (1961).
123. P. Koenig, *Landwirtsch Jahrb.* 39, 775 (1910).
124. C. R. Millikan, *Australian J. Sci. Research* B3, 450 (1950).
125. K. Warington, *Ann. Appl. Biol.* 38, 624 (1951).
126. K. Warington, *Ann. Appl. Biol.* 41, 1 (1954).
127. K. Warington, *Ann. Appl. Biol.* 43, 709 (1955).
128. E. J. Hewitt, *Long Ashton Research Sta. Ann. Rept.* 1950, p. 64.
129. E. J. Hewitt, *J. Exptl. Botany* 5, 110 (1955).
130. W. M. Crooke, J. G. Hunter, and O. Vergnano, *Ann. Appl. Biol.* 41, 311 (1954).
131. W. M. Crooke, *Ann. Appl. Biol.* 43, 465 (1956).
132. W. M. Crooke and A. M. Knight, *Ann. Appl. Biol.* 43, 454 (1955).
132a. S. Granick, *Bull. N.Y. Acad. Med.* 30, 81 (1954). Cited in Granick (*134*).
133. C. P. Sideris and H. Y. Young, *Plant Physiol.* 24, 416 (1949).
134. S. Granick, *J. Biol. Chem.* 172, 717 (1948).
135. S. Granick, *J. Biol. Chem.* 175, 333 (1948).
136. R. F. Labbe and N. Hubbard, *Biochim. et Biophys. Acta* 41, 185 (1960).
137. J. H. C. Smith, *J. Am. Chem. Soc.* 69, 1492 (1947).
138. H. E. Davenport, *Proc. 4th Intern. Congr. Biochem., Vienna, 1958* 2, Section 11, No. 51 (1958).
139. H. C. Eyster, *Plant Physiol.* 25, 630 (1950).
140. P. C. De Kock, K. Commissiong, V. C. Farmer, and R. H. E. Inkson, *Plant Physiol.* 35, 599 (1960).
141. S. C. Agarwala, A. Kumar, and C. P. Sharma, *Nature* 191, 726 (1961).

141a. W. B. Healy, Sze-Chuh Cheng, and W. D. McElroy, *Arch. Biochem. Biophys.* 54, 206 (1955).
142. D. Wang and E. R. Waygood, *Can. J. Botany* 37, 743 (1959).
143. R. F. Labbe and N. Hubbard, *Biochim. et Biophys. Acta* 52, 130 (1961).
144. F. E. Bear, ed., "Symposium on Bicarbonates." *Soil Sci.* 89, 241-302 (1960).
145. G. W. Miller, *Soil Sci* 89, 241 (1960).
145a. V. Q. Hale and A. Wallace, *Soil Sci.* 89, 285 (1960).
146. G. W. Miller and H. J. Evans, *Nature* 178, 974 (1956).
147. G. W. Miller and H. J. Evans, *Plant Physiol.* 131, 363 (1956).
148. E. Bayer, *Experientia* 12, 365 (1956).
149. R. C. Warner and I. Weber, *J. Am. Chem. Soc.* 75, 5094 (1953).
150. W. A. Rhoads and A. Wallace, *Soil Sci.* 89, 248 (1960).
151. W. S. Iljin, *Jahrb. wiss. Botan.* 90, 464 (1942).
152. W. S. Iljin, *Plant and Soil* 3, 339 (1951).
153. W. T. McGeorge, *Soil Sci.* 68, 381 (1949).
154. P. C. De Kock and R. I. Morrison, *Biochem. J.* 70, 272 (1958).
155. B. Åberg, *Ann. Roy. Agr. Coll. Sweden* 15, 39 (1948).
156. A. Nason and H. J. Evans, *J. Biol. Chem.* 202, 665 (1953).
157. H. J. Evans and A. Nason, *Plant Physiol.* 28, 233 (1953).
157a. H. Lees and J. H. Quastel, *Nature* 155, 276 (1945).
158. J. H. Quastel, M. Stephenson, and M. D. Whetham, *Biochem. J.* 19, 304 (1925).
159. D. Spencer, *Australian J. Biol. Sci.* 12, 181 (1959).
159a. H. Lees and J. R. Simpson, *Biochem. J.* 59, i (Proc.) (1955).
160. J. C. Lewis and W. L. Powers, *Plant Physiol.* 16, 393 (1941).
161. M. Cotton, *Torrey Botan. Club. Bull.* 57 (1930).
162. R. H. Hageman, E. S. Hodge, and J. S. McHargue, *Plant Physiol.* 17, 465 (1942).
163. P. George, *J. Biol. Chem.* 201, 413 (1953).
164. R. P. Bartholemew, *Soil Sci.* 40, 203 (1935).
165. I. B. McNulty, and D. W. Newman, *Plant Physiol.* 36, 385 (1961).
166. D. F. Adams and R. A. Solberg, *Am. J. Botany* 43, 755 (1956).
167. W. O. James, "Plant Respiration." Oxford Univ. Press (Clarendon), London and New York, 1953.
168. W. O. James, *Ann. Rev. Plant Physiol.* 4, 59 (1953).
169. D. P. Hackett, *in* "Handbuch der Pflanzenphysiologie" (W. Ruhland, ed.) Vol. 12, Part 2, pp. 23-41. Springer, Berlin, 1960.
170. W. D. Bonner, Jr., and K. V. Thimann, *Am. J. Botany* 37, 66 (1950).
171. R. Nillson, F. Alm, and D. Burström, *Arch. Mikrobiol.* 12, 353 (1942).
172. E. J. Hewitt, *Long Ashton Research Sta. Ann. Rept.* 1947, p. 82. (1948).
173. E. J. Hewitt, *Long Ashton Research Sta. Ann. Rept.* 1948, p. 58. (1949).
174. E. J. Hewitt, *Intern. Soc. Soil Sci., Dublin, 1952, Trans.*, IA, 107 (1953).
175. W. J. Rees and G. H. Sidrak, *Plant and Soil* 14, 101 (1961).
176. K. E. Wright, *Plant Physiol.* 12, 173 (1937).
177. K. E. Wright, *Plant Physiol.* 18, 708 (1943).
178. K. E. Wright and B. A. Donahue, *Plant Physiol.* 28, 674 (1953).
179. E. F. Wallihan, *Am. J. Botany* 35, 106 (1948).
180. E. M. Chenery, *Ann. Botany (London)* [N.S.] 12, 121 (1948).

181. G. E. Hutchinson, *Soil Sci.* **60**, 29 (1945).
181a. P. J. Randall and P. B. Vose, *Plant Physiol.* **38**, 403 (1963).
182. P. F. Brownell and J. G. Wood, *Nature* **179**, 635 (1957).
183. M. C. Williams, *Plant Physiol.* **35**, 500 (1960).
184. E. J. Hewitt, *in* "Plant Physiology" (F. C. Steward, ed.), Vol. III, Chapter 2. Academic Press, New York, 1962.
185. F. M. Eaton, *J. Agr. Research* **64**, 399 (1942).
186. O. C. Magistad, *Botan. Rev.* **11**, 181 (1945).
187. F. J. Richards and Sheng-Han Shih, *Ann. Botany (London)* [N.S.] **4**, 165 (1940).
188. F. J. Richards and Sheng-Han Shih, *Ann. Botany (London)* [N.S.] **4**, 403 (1940).
189. A. R. C. Haas, *Botan. Gaz.* **87**, 630 (1929).
190. D. G. Aldrich, A. P. Vanselow, and G. R. Bradford, *Soil Sci.* **71**, 291 (1951).
191. F. J. Richards, *Ann. Botany (London)* [N.S.] **5**, 263 (1941).
192. F. J. Richards, *Ann. Botany (London)* [N.S.] **8**, 323 (1944).
193. G. Miller and H. J. Evans, *Plant Physiol.* **32**, 346 (1957).
194. R. E. McCollum, R. H. Hageman, and E. H. Tyner, *Soil Sci.* **86**, 325 (1958).
195. A. J. Hiatt and H. J. Evans, *Plant Physiol.* **35**, 673 (1960).
196. E. Latzko, *Agrochimica* **3**, 148 (1959).
197. G. C. Webster, *Biochim. et Biophys. Acta* **20**, 565 (1956).
198. F. J. Richards and E. Berner, *Ann. Botany (London)* [N.S.] **18**, 15 (1954).
199. R. G. Coleman and F. J. Richards, *Ann. Botany (London)* [N.S.] **20**, 393 (1956).
200. F. M. Eaton, *J. Agr. Research* **69**, 237 (1944).
201. H. S. Reed, *Hilgardia* **17**, 377 (1947).
202. R. MacVicar and R. H. Burris, *Arch. Biochem.* **17**, 31 (1948).
203. R. M. Klein, *Arch. Biochem. Biophys.* **80**, 207 (1951).
204. A. Nason, H. A. Oldewurtel, and L. M. Propst, *Arch. Biochem. Biophys.* **38**, 1 (1952).
205. K. T. Yasunobu and E. R. Norris, *J. Biol. Chem.* **227**, 473 (1957).
206. C. A. Zittle, *Advances in Enzymol.* **12**, 493 (1951).
207. A. R. Spurr, *Science* **116**, 421 (1952).
208. H. J. Perkins and S. Aronoff, *Arch. Biochem. Biophys.* **64**, 506 (1956).
209. W. M. Dugger, Jr. and T. E. Humphries, *Plant Physiol.* **32**, 364 (1957).
210. W. M. Dugger, Jr. and T. E. Humphries, *Plant Physiol.* **35**, 523 (1960).
210a. S. S. Cohen, *J. Biol. Chem.* **201**, 71 (1953).
210b. M. H. Pubols, J. C. Zahnley, and B. Axelrod, *Plant Physiol.* **38**, 457 (1963).
211. E. J. Hewitt, *Long Ashton Research Sta. Ann. Rept.* 1946, p. 51.
212. W. A. Andreae, *Arch. Biochem. Biophys.* **55**, 584 (1955).
213. O. Vergnano and J. G. Hunter, *Ann. Botany (London)* [N.S.] **17**, 317 (1952).
214. M. B. Ahmed and E. S. Twyman, *J. Exptl. Botany* **4**, 164 (1953).
215. T. Pfeiffer, W. Scinenermacher, and A. Rippel, *Fühling's Landwirtsch. Ztg.* **67**, 313 (1918).

216. W. E. Brenchley, "Inorganic Plants and Poisons," 2nd ed. Cambridge Univ. Press, London and New York, 1927.
217. W. E. Brenchley, *J. Agr. Sci.* 22, 704 (1932).
218. W. E. Brenchley, *Ann. Appl. Biol.* 25, 671 (1938).
219. E. Haselhoff, F. Haun, and W. Elbert, *Landwirtsch. Vers.-Sta.* 110, 283 (1930).
220. K. Scharrer, "Biochemie der Spuren Element." Paul Parey, Berlin, 1941.
221. K. Warington, *Ann. Appl. Biol.* 24, 475 (1937).
222. K. Warington, *Ann. Appl. Biol.* 33, 249 (1946).
223. S. C. Agarwala and E. J. Hewitt, *J. Hort. Sci.* 29, 278 (1954).
224. E. W. E. Macfarlane, *Exptl. Cell. Research* 5, 375 (1933).
225. E. W. E. Macfarlane, N. G. Schmock, and Miessing, (Sister Alma Marie), *Proc. Soc. Exptl. Biol. Med.* 82, 115 (1953).
226. E. W. E. Macfarlane, *Growth* 15, 241 (1950).
227. W. Crocker, "Growth of Plants," p. 459. Reinhold, New York, 1948.
228. K. R. Bock, J. B. D. Robinson, and G. T. Chamberlain, *Nature* 182, 1607 (1958).
229. C. M. Keaton, *Soil Sci.* 43, 401 (1937).
230. F. S. Hammett, *Protoplasma* 4, 183 (1928).
231. F. S. Hammett, *Protoplasma* 4, 187 (1928).
232. F. S. Hammett, *Protoplasma* 5, 135 (1929).
233. F. S. Hammett, *Protoplasma* 5, 535 (1929).
234. F. S. Hammett and E. S. Justice, *Protoplasma* 5, 543 (1929).
235. F. S. Hammett and E. S. Justice, *Protoplasma* 5, 547 (1929).
236. P. F. Smith, *Botan. Gaz.* 114, 426 (1953).
237. S. C. Brooks, *Science* 75, 105 (1932).
238. M. M. McCool, *Contribs. Boyce Thompson Inst.* 5, 289 (1933).
239. J. E. McMurtrey, *Science* 76, 86 (1932).
240. A. S. Crafts, *Science* 79, 62 (1935).
241. A. S. Crafts, *Hilgardia* 10, 377 (1936).
242. S. Pratt, J. Babicka and I. Polivkova, *Publ. Fac. Sci. Charles Univ. (Prague)* C121, 1 (1932).
243. A. L. Moxon, *in* "Trace Elements" (C. A. Lamb, O. G. Bentley, and J. M. Beattie, eds.), Chapter 12, pp. 175-191. Academic Press, New York, 1958.
244. E. J. Underwood, "Trace Elements in Human and Animal Nutrition." Academic Press, New York, 1956.
245. T. Walsh, G. Flemming, R. O'Connor, and A. Sweenay, *Nature* 168, 881 (1951).
246. A. L. Moxon, *South Dakota Agr. Expt. Sta. Bull.* 311 (1937).
247. A. L. Moxon, H. D. Anderson, and E. P. Painter, *J. Pharmacol. Exptl. Therap.* 63, 357 (1938).
248. H. L. Klug, D. F. Petersen, and A. L. Moxon, *Proc. South Dakota Acad. Sci.* 28, 117 (1949).
249. A. L. Moxon and M. Rhian, *Physiol. Rev.* 23, 305 (1943).
250. S. F. Trelease and O. A. Beath, "Selenium, Its Geological Occurrence, and Its Biological Effects in Relation to Botany, Chemistry, Agriculture, Nutrition and Medicine." Prentice-Hall, Englewood Cliffs, New Jersey, 1949. Cited by Moxon (*243*).

251. K. W. Franke, *J. Nutrition* 8, 597 (1934).
252. K. W. Franke and V. R. Potter, *J. Nutrition* 8, 615 (1934).
253. K. W. Franke and W. C. Tully, *Poultry Sci.* 14, 273 (1935).
254. K. W. Franke, A. L. Moxon, W. E. Poley, and W. C. Tully, *Anat. Record* 65, 15 (1936).
255. E. P. Painter and K. W. Franke, *J. Biol. Chem.* 111, 643 (1935).
256. K. P. McConnell, D. M. Roth, and R. D. Dallam, *Nature* 183, 183 (1959).
256a. H. Zalkin, A. L. Tappel, and J. P. Jordan, *Arch. Biochem. Biophys.* 91, 117 (1960).
257. H. S. Olcott, W. D. Brown, and J. Van der Veen, *Nature* 191, 1201 (1961).
258. W. S. Ferguson, A. H. Lewis, and S. J. Watson, *Nature* 141, 553 (1938).
258a. W. S. Ferguson, A. H. Lewis, and S. J. Watson, *J. Agr. Sci* 33, 44 (1943).
259. A. T. Dick, *in* "Inorganic Nitrogen Metabolism" (W. D. McElroy and B. Glass, eds.), pp. 445-473. Johns Hopkins Press, Baltimore, Maryland, 1956.
260. I. J. Cunningham, *New Zealand J. Sci. & Technol.* 27A, 372 (1946).
261. H. R. Marston, *in* "Copper Metabolism" (W. D. McElroy and B. Glass, eds.), pp. 230-245. Johns Hopkins Press, Baltimore, Maryland, 1950.
262. I. J. Cunningham, *in* "Copper Metabolism" (W. D. McElroy and B. Glass, eds.), pp. 246-273. Johns Hopkins Press, Baltimore, Maryland, 1950.
263. C. L. Comar, L. Singer, and G. K. Davis, *J. Biol. Chem.* 180, 913 (1949).
264. G. K. Davis, *in* "Copper Metabolism" (W. D. McElroy and B. Glass, eds.), pp. 216-229. Johns Hopkins Press, Baltimore, Maryland, 1950.
265. L. F. Gray and G. H. Ellis, *J. Nutrition* 40, 441 (1950).
266. L. F. Gray and L. J. Daniel, *J. Nutrition* 53, 43 (1954).
267. L. R. Arrington and G. K. Davis, *J. Nutrition* 51, 295 (1953).
268. A. T. Dick, *Australian Vet. J.* 29, 18 (1953).
269. A. T. Dick, *Australian Vet. J.* 29, 233 (1953).
270. L. J. Daniel and L. F. Gray, *Proc. Soc. Exptl. Biol. Med.* 83, 487 (1953).
271. R. Van Reen and M. A. Williams, *Arch Biochem. Biophys.* 63, 1 (1956).
271a. A. Ramaiah and E. R. B. Shanmugasundrum, *Biochim. et Biophys. Acta* 60, 373 (1962).
272. C. F. Mills, K. J. Monty, A. Ichihara, and P. B. Pearson, *J. Nutrition* 65, 129 (1958).
273. R. Van Reen, *Arch. Biochem. Biophys.* 53, 77 (1954).
274. A. W. Halverson, J. H. Phifer, and K. J. Monty, *J. Nutrition* 71, 95 (1960).
275. C. F. Mills, *Proc. Nutrition Soc.* 19, 162 (1960).
275a. L. M. Siegel and K. J. Monty, *J. Nutrition* 74, 167 (1961).
276. D. J. D. Nicholas and K. Commissiong, *J. Gen. Microbiol.* 17, 699 (1957).
277. M. Bossard, *Bull. soc. Chim. biol.* 29, 218 (1947)
278. D. Spencer, *Australian J. Biol. Sci.* 7, 151 (1954).
279. B. Naganna, A. Raman, B. Venugopal, and C. E. Sripathi, *Biochem. J.* 60, 215 (1955).
280. B. Mackler, H. R. Mahler, and D. E. Green, *J. Biol. Chem.* 210, 149 (1954).
281. I. Fridovich and P. Handler, *in* "Inorganic Nitrogen Metabolism" (W. D. McElroy and B. Glass, eds.), pp. 539-551. Johns Hopkins Press, Baltimore, Maryland, 1956.

282. E. Kun and D. W. Fanshier, *Biochim et Biophys. Acta* 32, 338 (1959).
283. B. H. Sörbo, *Acta Chem. Scand.* 7, 1129 (1953).
284. R. L. Blackley and I. E. Coop, Cited by Coop (*285*).
285. I. E. Coop, *in* "Plant and Animal Nutrition in Relation to Soil and Climatic Factors," British Commonwealth Scientific Official Conference. Specialist Conference in Agriculture, pp. 335-342. H. M. Stationery Office, London, 1951.
286. K. Waltner and K. Waltner (1929). Cited by Underwood (*244*).
287. W. C. Grant and W. S. Root, *Physiol. Rev.* 32, 449 (1952).
288. W. H. Griffith, C. L. Parcek, and D. J. Mulford, *J. Nutrition* 23, 603 (1942).
289. M. Calvin, R. H. Bailes, and W. K. Wilmarth, *J. Am. Chem. Soc.* 68, 2254 (1946).
290. D. Burk, J. Hearson, L. Caroline, and A. L. Shade, *J. Biol. Chem.* 165, 723 (1946).
291. J. B. Gilbert, M. C. Otey, and V. E. Price, *J. Biol. Chem.* 190, 377 (1951).
292. L. B. Bull, *in* "Plant and Animal Nutrition in Relation to Soil and Climatic Factors," H. M. Stationery Office, London, 1957. Proceedings British Commonwealth Scientific Official Conference (1949). Specialist Conference in Agriculture, pp. 300-310.
293. W. R. Sutton and V. E. Nelson, *Proc. Soc. Exptl. Biol. Med.* 36, 211 (1937).
294. S. E. Smith and E. J. Larson, *J. Biol. Chem.* 163, 29 (1946).
295. R. Van Reen, *Arch. Biochem. Biophys.* 46, 337 (1953).
296. M. O. Schultze, *J. Biol. Chem.* 129, 729 (1939).
297. M. O. Schultze, and K. A. Kuiken, *J. Biol. Chem.* 137, 727 (1941).
298. V. Sadasivan, *Biochem. J.* 52, 452 (1952).
299. V. Sadasivan, *Biochem. J.* 48, 527 (1951).
300. F. Blakemore, J. A. Nicholson, and J. Stewart, *Vet. Record* 49, 415 (1937).
301. P. Fain, J. Dennis, and F. G. Harbaugh, *Am. J. Vet. Research* 13, 348 (1952).
302. G. Matrone, R. H. Hartman, and A. J. Clawson, *J. Nutrition* 67, 309 (1958).
303. R. H. Hartman, G. Matrone, and G. H. Wise, *J. Nutrition* 57, 429 (1955).
304. M. White, *in* "Plant and Animal Nutrition in Relation to Soil and Climatic Factors," Proceedings British Commonwealth Scientific Official Conference (1949). Specialist Conference in Agriculture, pp. 316-318. H. M. Stationery Office, London, 1951.
305. J. F. Volker, H. C. Hodge, H. G. Wilson, and S. N. Van Voorkis, *J. Biol. Chem.* 134, 543 (1940).
306. J. M. Harvey, *Queensland J. Agr. Sci.* 9, 47 (1952).
307. J. Williams, *J. Dental Research* 5, 117 (1923).
307a. R. Robison and A. H. Rosenheim, *Biochem. J.* 28, 684 (1934).
307b. C. C. Pfeiffer, L. F. Hallman, and I. Gersh, *J. Am. Med. Assoc.* 128, 266 (1945).
308. R. K. Morton, *in* "Methods in Enzymology" (S. P. Colowick and N. O. Kaplan, eds.), Vol. 1, p. 25. Academic Press, New York, 1953.
309. T. Astrup, and A. Stage, *Nature* 170, 929 (1952).

310. E. J. Cohn, F. R. N. Gurd, D. M. Surgenor, B. A. Barnes, R. K. Brown, G. Derouaux, J. M. Gillespie, F. W. Kahnt, W. F. Lever, C. H. Liu, D. Mittelman, R. F. Mouton, and E. Uroma, *J. Am. Chem. Soc.* **72**, 465 (1950).

311. C. Neuberg and I. Mandl, *Arch. Biochem.* **23**, 499 (1949).

312. W. B. Hardy, *J. Physiol. (London)* **33**, 251 (1905).

313. J. Mellanby, *J. Physiol. (London)* **33**, 338 (1905).

314. T. B. Osborne and I. Harris, *Am. J. Physiol.* **14**, 151 (1905).

315. A. A. Green and W. L. Hughes, *in* "Methods in Enzymology" (S. P. Colowick and N. O. Kaplan, eds.), Vol. 1, p. 67. Academic Press, New York, 1955.

316. A. L. Lehninger, *Physiol. Revs.* **30**, 393 (1950).

317. M. Calvin *in* "Mechanisms of Enzyme Action" (W. D. McElroy and B. Glass, eds.), p. 221. Johns Hopkins Press, Baltimore, Maryland, 1954.

318. I. M. Klotz, *in* "Mechanism of Enzyme Action" (W. D. McElroy and B. Glass, eds.), pp. 257-285. Johns Hopkins Press, Baltimore, Maryland, 1954.

319. V. A. Najjar, *in* "Phosphorus Metabolism" (W. D. McElroy and B. Glass, eds.), p. 500. Johns Hopkins Press, Baltimore, Maryland, 1951.

320. E. Smith, N. C. Davis, E. Adams, and D. H. Speckman, *in* "Mechanism of Enzyme Action," p. 291 (W. D. McElroy and B. Glass, eds.). Johns Hopkins Press, Baltimore, Maryland, 1954.

321. H. A. Lardy, *in* "Phosphorus Metabolism" (W. D. McElroy and B. Glass, eds.), p. 477. Johns Hopkins Press, Baltimore, Maryland, 1951.

322. W. D. McElroy, *in* "Symposium on Nutrition" (R. M. Herriott, ed.), p. 262. Johns Hopkins Press, Baltimore, Maryland, 1953.

323. W. D. McElroy and A. Nason, *Ann. Rev. Plant Physiol.* **5**, 1 (1954).

324. E. J. Hewitt, *Biol. Revs.* **34**, 333 (1959).

324a. E. J. Hewitt, *Nature* **180**, 1020 (1957).

325. E. J. Hewitt, *in* "Handbuch der Pflanzenphysiologie" (W. Ruhland, ed.), Vol. 4, pp. 427-481. Springer, Berlin, 1958.

326. D. J. D. Nicholas, *Proc. 4th Intern. Congr. Biochem., Vienna, 1958* XIII Colloquia, p. 307 (1959).

327. D. J. D. Nicholas, *Symposia Soc. Exptl. Biol.* **13**, 1 (1959).

328. D. J. D. Nicholas, *Nature* **179**, 800 (1957).

329. L. Hellerman and C. C. Stock, *J. Biol. Chem.* **125**, 771 (1938).

330. A. Kornberg and W. E. Pricer, Jr., *J. Biol. Chem.* **189**, 123 (1951).

331. T. P. Wang and N. O. Kaplan, *J. Biol. Chem.* **206**, 311 (1954).

332. A. Kornberg, *J. Biol. Chem.* **182**, 805 (1950).

333. A. Kornberg, *J. Biol. Chem.* **182**, 779 (1950).

334. W. H. Elliott, *J. Biol. Chem.* **201**, 661 (1953).

335. J. B. Veiga-Salles and S. Ochoa, *J. Biol. Chem.* **187**, 849 (1950).

336. W. H. Elliott, *Biochem. J.* **49**, 106 (1951).

337. M. Mazelis, *Plant Physiol.* **31**, 37 (1956).

338. C. Veeger and V. Massey, *Biochim et Biophys. Acta* **37**, 181 (1960).

339. J. F. Kachmar and P. D. Boyer, *J. Biol. Chem.* **200**, 669 (1952).

340. R. W. Von Korff, *J. Biol. Chem.* **203**, 265 (1953).

341. M. Blanchard, D. E. Green, V. Nocito, and S. Ratner, *J. Biol. Chem.* **155**, 421 (1944).

342. T. Nakayama, *J. Biochem. (Tokyo)* 49, 240 (1961).
343. D. W. Krogmann, A. T. Jagendorf, and M. Avron, *Plant Physiol.* 34, 272 (1959).
344. H. G. Hers, *Biochim. et Biophys. Acta* 8, 424 (1952).
345. M. Mazelis and B. Vennesland, *Plant Physiol.* 32, 591 (1957).
346. J. Berger and G. S. Avery, Jr., *Am. J. Botany* 31, 11 (1944).
347. E. E. Conn, B. Vennesland, and L. M. Kraemar, *Arch. Biochem.* 23, 179 (1949).
348. W. J. Hartman and G. Kalnitsky, *Arch. Biochem.* 26, 6 (1950).
349. K. Bailey and E. C. Webb, *Biochem. J.* 38, 394 (1944).
350. M. Kunitz, *J. Gen. Physiol.* 35, 423 (1952).
350a. R. C. Bard and I. C. Gunsalus, *J. Bacteriol.* 59, 387 (1950).
350b. B. G. Malmström, *Arch. Biochem. Biophys.* 58, 381 (1955).
351. B. Nagana and V. K. N. Menon, *J. Biol. Chem.* 174, 501 (1948).
352. K. Bailey, *Biochem. J.* 36, 121 (1942).
353. W. W. Kielley and O. Meyerhof, *J. Biol. Chem.* 176, 591 (1948).
353a. L. A. Heppel and R. J. Hilmoe, *J. Biol. Chem.* 188, 665 (1951).
354. R. J. P. Williams, *in* "The Enzymes" (P. D. Boyer, H. Lardy, and K. Myrbäck, eds.), Vol. 1, pp. 391-441. Academic Press, New York, 1959.
354a. F. W. Klemperer, J. M. Miller, and C. J. Hill, *J. Biol. Chem.* 180, 281 (1949).
354b. R. S. Grier, M. B. Hood, and M. B. Hoagland, *J. Biol. Chem.* 180, 289 (1949).
355. P. J. Snodgrass, B. L. Vallee, and F. L. Hoch, *J. Biol. Chem.* 235, 504 (1960).
356. J. B. Sumner and K. Myrbäck, *Z. physiol. Chem. Hoppe-Seyler's* 189, 218 (1930).
357. J. F. Ambrose, G. B. Kistiakowsky, and A. G. Kridl, *J. Am. Chem. Soc.* 73, 1232 (1951).
358. K. Myrbäck, *Z. physiol. Chem. Hoppe-Seyler's* 158, 4 (1926).
359. K. Myrbäck, *Arkiv Kemi.* 11, 47 (1957). Cited by Dixon and Webb (*362*).
360. U. Olsson, *Hoppe-Seyle Z. physiol. Chem.* 114, 51 (1921).
361. H. A. Krebs, *Biochem. Z.* 220, 289 (1930).
362. M. Dixon and E. C. Webb, "The Enzymes." Academic Press, New York, 1958.
363. L. Massart, *in* "The Enzymes" (J. B. Sumner and K. Myrbäck, eds.), Vol. I, Part 1, pp. 307-342. Academic Press, New York, 1950.
364. L. Hellerman, F. P. Chinard, and V. R. Dietz, *J. Biol. Chem.* 147, 443 (1943).
365. W. H. R. Shaw, *J. Am. Chem. Soc.* 76, 2160 (1954).
365a. W. H. R. Shaw, *Science* 120, 361 (1954).
366. O. Arrigoni and G. Rossi, *Biochim et Biophys. Acta* 46, 121 (1961).
367. D. H. Turner and J. F. Turner, *Biochem. J.* 79, 143 (1961).
368. M. D. Hatch and J. F Turner, *Biochem J.* 76, 556 (1960).
369. T. Asaki, A. S. Bandurski, and L. G. Wilson, *J. Biol. Chem.* 236, 1830 (1961).
370. P. Fildes, *Brit. J. Exptl. Pathol.* 21, 67 (1940).
371. D. M. Yoder, The Toxicity of Heavy Metals to Fungus Spores and Its

Reversal by Sulphydryl Containing Compounds. Ph.D. Thesis, Cornell University (1950).

372. A. Janke, F. Beran, and G. Schmidt, *Pflanzenschutz Ber.* 8, 161 (1952).
373. G. B. Kistiakowsky and W. H. R. Shaw, *J. Am. Chem. Soc.* 75, 2751 (1953).
374. T. Miyaji and J. P. Greenstein, *Arch. Biochem. Biophys.* 32, 414 (1951).
374a. A. P. Nygaard, *J. Biol. Chem.* 236, 2128 (1961).
374b. A. P. Nygaard, *J. Biol. Chem.* 236, 2779 (1961).
375. N. Madhusudanan and C. S. Vaidyanathan, *Arch. Biochem. Biophys.* 93, 262 (1961).
376. J. H. R. Kagi and B. L. Vallee, *J. Biol. Chem.* 235, 3460 (1960).
377. J. H. R. Kagi and B. L. Vallee, *J Biol. Chem.* 236, 2435 (1961).
378. D. J. Lawford, *Nature* 187, 946 (1960).
379. D. R. Sanadi, M. Langley, and F. White, *J. Biol. Chem.* 234, 183 (1959).
380. E. E. Jacobs, M. Jacobs, D. R. Sanadi, and L. B. Bradley, *J. Biol. Chem.* 223, 147 (1956).
381. R. L. Searls and D. R. Sanadi, *Biochem. Biophys. Research Communs.* 2, 189 (1960).
382. A. M. Stein, B. T. Kaufman, and N. O. Kaplan, *Biochem. Biophys. Research Communs.* 2, 354 (1960).
383. J. M. Peters and D. R. Sanadi, *Arch. Biochem. Biophys.* 93, 312 (1961).
384. C. Millstein, *Biochem. Biophys. Research Communs.* 3, 292 (1960).
385. C. Millstein, *Biochem. J.* 79, 591 (1961).
386. C. Millstein, and F. Sanger, *Biochem. J.* 79, 456 (1961).
387. E. E. McCoy and V. A. Najjar, *J. Biol. Chem.* 234, 3017 (1959).
388. L. P. Miller, S. E. A. McCallan, and R. M. Weed, *Contribs. Boyce Thompson Inst.* 17, 151 (1953).
389. S. S. Block, *J. Agr. Food Chem.* 3, 229 (1955).
390. C. L. Mason, *Phytopathogy* 38, 740 (1948).
391. A. Kaars Sijpesteyn and G. J. M. van der Kerk, *Biochim et Biophys. Acta* 13, 545 (1954).
392. A. Kaars Sijpesteyn and G. J. M. van der Kerk, *Biochim et Biophys. Acta* 15, 69 (1954).
393. V. Massey, *Biochem. J.* 53, 67 (1953).
394. L. Michaelis and H. Davidsohn, *Biochem. Z.* 35, 386 (1911).
395. L. Michaelis and H. Pechstein, *Biochem. Z.* 58, 77 (1914).
396. V. Massey and R. A. Alberty, *Biochim et Biophys. Acta* 13, 354 (1954).
397. M. Avron and A. T. Jagendorf, *Arch. Biochem. Biophys.* 65, 475.
398. J. S. Friedenwald and G. D. Mangwyn-Davies, *in* "Mechanism of Enzyme Action" (W. D. McElroy and B. Glass, eds.), pp. 154-179. Johns Hopkins Press, Baltimore, Maryland, 1956.
399. K. S. Dodgson, B. Spencer, and K. Williams, *Nature* 177, 432 (1956).
400. G. Curzon, *Biochem. J.* 77, 66 (1960).
400a. P. K. Tubbs, *Biochem. J.* 82, 36 (1962).
401. B. Chance, *J. Biol. Chem.* 194, 483 (1952).
402. C. D. Coryell, F. Stitt, and L. Pauling, *J. Am. Chem. Soc.* 59, 633 (1937).
403. R. Lemberg and J. W. Legge, "Haematin Compounds and Bile pigments." Wiley (Interscience), New York, 1949.
403a. K. Agner and H. Theorell, *Arch. Biochem.* 10, 321 (1946).

403b. P. Nicholls, *Biochem. J.* **81**, 365 (1961).
403c. R. F. Beers, Jr. and I. W. Sizer, *Arch. Biochem. Biophys.* **60**, 115 (1960).
404. J. N. Stannard and B. L. Horecker, *J. Biol. Chem.* **172**, 599 (1948).
405. B. L. Horecker and J. N. Stannard, *J. Biol. Chem.* **172**, 589 (1948).
406. B. L. Horecker and A. Kornberg, *J. Biol. Chem.* **165**, 11 (1946).
407. D. Keilin and E. F. Hartree, *Biochem. J.* **39**, 148 (1945).
408. D. Keilin and E. F. Hartree, *Proc. Roy. Soc.* **B127**, 167 (1939).
409. W. W. Wainio, *J. Biol. Chem.* **212**, 723 (1955).
410. W. W. Wainio and S. J. Cooperstein, *Advances in Enzymol.* **17**, 329 (1956).
411. J. Keilin, *Biochem. J.* **45**, 440 (1949).
412. D. Keilin and E. F. Hartree, *Biochem. J.* **49**, 88 (1951).
413. D. Keilin and E. F. Hartree, *Biochem. J.* **61**, 153 (1955).
413a. B. Chance, *J. Cellular Comp. Physiol.* **22**, 33 (1943).
413b. B. Chance, *Arch. Biochem.* **21**, 416 (1949).
413c. P. George, *Biochem. J.* **55**, 220 (1953).
414. H. R. Mahler, *in* "Trace Elements," (C. A. Lamb, O. G. Bentley and J. M. Beattie, eds.), pp. 311-335. Academic Press, New York, 1958.
415. D. Keilin and E. F. Hartree, *Proc. Roy. Soc.* **B119**, 114 (1936).
416. C. P. Colowick and H. M. Kalckar, *J. Biol. Chem.* **148**, 117 (1943).
417. F. Kubowitz, *Biochem. Z.* **292**, 221 (1937).
418. F. Kubowitz, *Biochem. Z.* **296**, 443 (1938a).
419. F. Kubowitz, *Biochem. Z.* **299**, 32 (1938a).
420. G. T. Meiklejohn and C. P. Stewart, *Biochem. J.* **35**, 755 (1941).
421. T. Tissiéres, *Nature* **162**, 340 (1948).
422. T. Tissiéres, *Nature* **163**, 480 (1949).
423. P. J. G. Mann, *Biochem. J.* **79**, 623 (1961).
424. P. J. G. Mann, *Biochem. J.* **59**, 609 (1955).
425. D. Keilin and T. Mann, *Biochem. J.* **34**, 1163 (1940).
426. D. Keilin and T. Mann, *Nature* **153**, 107 (1940).
427. F. L. Hoch and B. L. Vallee, *in* "Trace Elements" (C. A. Lamb, O. G. Bentley and J. M. Beattie, eds.), pp. 337-363. Academic Press, New York, 1958.
428. E. L. Smith and H. T. Hanson, *J. Biol. Chem.* **176**, 997 (1948).
429. E. L. Smith and H. T. Hanson, *J. Biol. Chem* **179**, 803 (1949).
430. B. L. Vallee and H. Neurath, *J. Biol. Chem.* **217**, 253 (1955).
431. J. E. Coleman and B. L. Vallee, *J. Biol. Chem.* **235**, 390 (1960).
432. B. L. Vallee, J. A. Rupley, T. L. Coombs, and H. Neurath, *J. Biol. Chem.* **235**, 64 (1960).
433. J. E. Folk and J. A. Gladner, *Biochim. et Biophys. Acta* **48**, 139 (1961).
434. H. R. Mahler, *J. Biol. Chem.* **206**, 13 (1953).
435. E. P. Steyn-Parvé and H. Beinert, *J. Biol. Chem.* **233**, 853 (1958).
436. T. P. Singer, V. Massey, and E. B. Kearney, *Arch. Biochem. Biophys.* **69**, 405 (1957).
437. E. F. Gale and H. M. R. Epps, *Biochem. J.* **38**, 232 (1944).
438. H. Blaschko, *Advances in Enzymol.* **5**, 67 (1945).
439. J. Hurwitz, *J. Biol. Chem.* **212**, 757 (1955).
440. I. Mauthner, *Z. Physiol. Chem. Hoppe-Seyler's* **78**, 28 (1912).
441. H. Fraenkel-Conrat, *J. Am. Chem. Soc.* **63**, 2533 (1941).

442. L. B. Mendel and A. F. Blood, *J. Biol. Chem.* **8**, 177 (1910).
443. J. S. Fruton and M. Bergman, *J. Biol. Chem.* **133**, 153 (1940).
444. G. W. Irving, Jr., J. S. Fruton, and M. Bergmann, *J. Biol. Chem.* **139**, 569 (1941).
445. D. R. P. Murray, *Biochem. J.* **27**, 541 (1933).
446. J. R. Kimmel and E. L. Smith, *Advances in Enzymol.* **19**, 267 (1957).
447. D. Keilin and Tsoo E. King, *Biochem. J.* **69**, 32P (1958).
448. A. Guiditta and T. P. Singer, *J. Biol. Chem.* **234**, 666 (1959).
449. C. C. Tsou, *Biochem. J.* **49**, 512 (1951).
450. H. R. Mahler, B. Mackler, D. E. Green, and R. M. Bock, *J. Biol. Chem.* **210**, 465 (1954).
451. P. G. Avis, F. Bergel, R. C. Bray, and K. V. Shooter, *in* "Inorganic Nitrogen Metabolism" (W. D. McElroy and B. Glass, eds.), pp. 552-564. John Hopkins Press, Baltimore, Maryland, 1956.
452. M. Dixon and D. Keilin, *Proc. Roy Soc.* **B119**, 159 (1936).
452a. R. J. Doisy, D. A. Richert, and W. W. Westerfeld, *J. Biol. Chem.* **217**, 307 (1955).
453. M. Calvin, *in* "Glutathione" (S. P. Colowick *et al.*, eds.), p. 3. Academic Press, New York, 1954.
454. I. Fridovich and P. Handler, *J. Biol. Chem.* **231**, 899 (1958).
455. S. C. Kinsky and W. D. McElroy, *Arch. Biochem.* **73**, 466 (1958).
456. D. Keilin, *Proc. Roy. Soc.* **B121**, 165 (1937).
457. H. A. Krebs, *Biochem. J.* **29**, 1620 (1935).
458. H. M. Lenhoff and N. O. Kaplan, *J. Biol. Chem.* **220**, 967 (1956).
459. D. Keilin and T. Mann, *Proc. Roy. Soc.* **B122**, 119 (1937).
459a. D. Keilin, *Proc. Roy. Soc.* **B121**, 165 (1936).
460. E. C. Layne and A. Nason, *J. Biol. Chem.* **231**, 889 (1958).
461. C. G. Holmberg, *Biochem. J.* **33**, 1901 (1939).
462. N. U. Meldrum and F. J. W. Roughton, *J. Physiol. London* **80**, 113 (1933).
463. E. J. Hewitt and D. G. Hallas, *Nature* **184**, 1485 (1959).
464. J. R. Villanueva, *Nature* **184**, 549 (1959).
465. J. C. Sadana and W. D. McElroy, *Arch. Biochem. Biophys.* **67**, 16 (1957).
466. J. Robinson, *Arch. Biochem. Biophys.* **52**, 148 (1954).
467. D. Keilin and E. F. Hartree, *Proc. Roy. Soc.* **B121**, 123 (1936).
468. D. Keilin and E. F. Hartree, *Nature* **173**, 720 (1954).
469. D. Keilin and E. F. Hartree, *Biochem. J.* **60**, 310 (1955).
470. D. Keilin and E. F. Hartree, *Nature* **166**, 513 (1050).
471. H. Theorell and A. Ehrenberg, *Arch. Biochem. Biophys.* **41**, 462 (1952).
472. D. Keilin and E. F. Hartree, *Nature* **152**, 626 (1943).
473. C. F. Cresswell and E. J. Hewitt, *Biochem. Biophys. Research Communs.*
474. D. Keilin and E. F. Hartree, *Nature* **139**, 548 (1937).
475. D. Keilin and E. F. Hartree, *Proc. Roy. Soc.* **B121**, 173 (1936).
476. K. G. Stern, *J. Gen. Physiol.* **20**, 631 (1937).
477. H. Borei, *Arkiv Kemi, Mineral. Geol.* **A20**, 215 pp. (1945).
478. J. M. Reiner, *Proc. Soc. Exptl. Biol. Med.* **63**, 81 (1946).
479. O. Warburg and W. Christian, *Biochem. Z.* **310**, 384 (1942).
480. V. A. Najjar, *J. Biol. Chem.* **175**, 281 (1948).
481. M. Grunberg-Manago, P. J. Oritz, and S. Ochoa, *Biochim. et Biophys. Acta* **20**, 269 (1956).

482. J. Roche and N-v. Thoai, *Advances in Enzymol.* **10**, 83 (1950).
483. S. Belfanti, A. Contardi, and A. Ercoli, *Biochem. J.* **29**, 843 (1935).
484. C. A. Zittle and E. S. Della Monica, *Arch. Biochem.* **26**, 112 (1950).
485. I. W. Sizer, *J. Biol. Chem.* **145**, 405 (1942).
486. W. Kutscher, *Biochem. Z.* **310**, 292 (1941).
487. S. G. Wildman and J. Bonner, *Arch. Biochem.* **14**, 381 (1947).
488. J. M. Reiner, K. K. Tsuboi, and P. B. Hudson, *Arch. Biochem. Biophys.* **56**, 165 (1955).
489. E. C. Slater and W. D. Bonner, Jr., *Biochem. J.* **52**, 185 (1952).
490. V. Massey, *Biochim. et Biophys. Acta* **30**, 500 (1958).
491. R. A. Peters, *Proc. Roy. Soc.* **B139**, 143 (1952).
492. R. A. Peters, *Advances in Enzymol.* **18**, 113 (1957).
493. J. F. Morrison and R. A. Peters, *Biochem. J.* **58**, 473 (1954).
494. R. O. Brady, *J. Biol. Chem.* **217**, 213 (1955).
495. J. Roche, *in* "The Enzymes" (J. B. Sumner and K. Myrbäck, eds.), Vol. I, Part 1, Academic Press, New York, 1950.
496. L. Shuster, *Arch. Biochem. Biophys.* **75**, 345 (1958).
497. D. Keilin, *Proc. Roy. Soc.* **B113**, 393 (1933).
498. P. Nicholls, *Biochem. J.* **81**, 374 (1961).
499. H. Tauber and I. S. Kleiner, *Proc. Soc. Exptl. Biol. Med.* **32**, 577 (1935).
500. M. Srinivasan, *Biochem. J.* **30**, 2077 (1936).
501. C. R. Dawson and W. B. Tarpley, *in* "The Enzymes" (J. B. Sumner and K. Myrbäck, eds.), Vol. II, Part 1, pp. 457-498. Academic Press, New York, 1951.
502. E. Stotz, C. J. Harrer, and C. G. King, *J. Biol. Chem.* **119**, 511 (1937).
503. D. Keilin and T. Mann, *Nature* **143**, 23 (1939).
504. D. Keilin and T. Mann, *Proc. Roy. Soc.* **B125**, 187 (1938).
505. E. Maschmann, *Biochem. Z.* **307**, 1 (1941).
506. H. R. Mahler, *J. Am. Chem. Soc.* **75**, 3288 (1953).
506a. H. R. Mahler, *Advances in Enzymol.* **17**, 233 (1959).
507. M. Dixon, and K. A. C. Elliott, *Biochem. J.* **23**, 872 (1929).
507a. D. J. D. Nicholas, and J. H. Scawin, *Nature* **178**, 1474 (1956).
507b. J. L. Glenn and F. L. Crane, *Biochim. et Biophys. Acta* **22**, 111 (1956).
507c. A. Kornberg and W. E. Pricer, Jr., *J. Biol. Chem.* **182**, 763 (1950).
508. R. H. Kenten and P. J. G. Mann, *Biochem. J.* **53**, 498 (1953).
509. R. H. Kenten, *Biochem. J.* **59**, 110 (1955).
510. R. H. Kenten, *Biochem. J.* **61**, 353 (1955).
511. E. R. Waygood, and G. A. Machlachlan, *Physiol. Plantarum* **9**, 607 (1956).
512. E. R. Waygood, A. Oaks, and G. A. Machlachlan, *Can. J. Botany* **34**, 54 (1956).
513. E. R. Waygood, A. Oaks, and G. A. Machlachlan, *Can. J. Botany* **34**, 905 (1956).
514. R. E. Stutz, *Plant Physiol.* **32**, 31 (1957).
515. P. M. Ray, *Ann. Rev. Plant Physiol.* **9**, 81 (1958).
516. E. R. Waygood, *Physiol. Plantarum* **9**, 321 (1956).
517. S. L. Ranson, D. A. Walker, and I. D. Clarke, *Biochem. J.* **66**, 57P (1957).
518. D. S. Bendall, S. L. Ranson, and D. A. Walker, *Nature* **181**, 133 (1958).
519. E. G. Ball and O. Cooper, *J. Biol. Chem.* **180**, 113 (1949).
520. W. D. Bonner, Jr., *Nature* **165**, 757 (1950).

521. M. A. Mitz, *Biochim. et Biophys. Acta* **25**, 426 (1957).

522. A. H. Roush and E. R. Norris, *Arch. Biochem.* **29**, 344 (1950).

523. A. H. Roush and B. B. Gowdy, *Biochim. et Biophys. Acta* **52**, 200 (1961).

524. H. Theorell, A. P. Nygaard, and R. Bonnischen, *Acta Chem. Scand.* **9**, 1148 (1955).

525. H. Theorell, and J. S. McKinley-McKee, *Nature* **192**, 46 (1961).

526. S. Osaki, *J. Biochem. (Tokyo)* **50**, 29 (1961).

526a. H. Hiltz, M. Kittler, and G. Knape, *Biochem. Z.* **332**, 151-166 (1959).

527. C. C. Pfeiffer, L. F. Hallman, and I. Gersh, *J. Am. Med. Assoc.* **128**, 266 (1945).

528. H. Takahashi and A. Nason, *Biochim. et Biophys. Acta* **23**, 433 (1957).

528a. R. F. Keeler and J. E. Varner, *Arch. Biochem. Biophys.* **70**, 585 (1957).

528b. R. F. Keeler and J. E. Varner, in "Trace Elements" (C A. Lamb, O. G. Bentley, and J. M. Beattie, eds.), pp. 297-309. Academic Press, New York, 1958.

529. M. D. Dixon, *Biol. Revs.* **4**, 352 (1929).

530. B. Commoner, *Biol. Revs.* **15**, 168 (1940).

531. R. J. Winzler, *J. Cellular Comp. Physiol.* **21**, 229 (1943).

532. D. P. Hackett, *Ann. Rev. Plant Physiol.* **10**, 113 (1959).

533. R. Hill and E. F. Hartree, *Ann. Rev. Plant Physiol.* **4**, 115 (1953).

534. E. F. Hartree, *Advances in Enzymol.* **18**, 1 (1957).

535. G. Stenlid, *Physiol. Plantarum* **1**, 185 (1948).

536. H. Beevers and E. W. Simon, *Nature* **163**, 408 (1949).

537. R. J. Fitzgerald and F. Bernheim, *J. Bacteriol.* **55**, 677 (1944).

538. E. W. Simon, *Nature* **166**, 343 (1950).

539. E. W. Simon and H. Beevers, *New Phytologist* **51**, 163 (1952).

540. A. Tissiéres, *Biochem. J.* **50**, 279 (1951).

541. G. Ducet and A. J. Rosenberg, *Ric. sci.* **25**, 3 (1955).

542. R. T. Darby and D. R. Goddard, *Physiol. Plantarum* **3**, 435 (1950).

543. E. Aubel and J. Szulmajster, *Compt. rend. acad. sci.* **224**, 680 (1947).

544. A. J. Rosenberg, *Compt. rend. acad. sci.* **226**, 1751 (1948).

545. E. Aubel, A. J. Rosenberg, and J. Szulmajster, *Biochim. et Biophys. Acta* **5**, 228 (1950).

546. F. Moog and S. Spiegelman, *Proc. Soc. Exptl. Biol. Med.* **49**, 392 (1942).

547. G. Stenlid, *Physiol. Plantarum* **2**, 61 (1949).

548. G. Stenlid, *Physiol. Plantarum* **2**, 350 (1949).

549. R. D. Hotchkiss, *Advances in Enzymol.* **4**, 153 (1944).

550. E. M. Case and H. McIlwain, *Biochem. J.* **48**, 1 (1951).

551. W. F. Loomis and F. Lipmann, *J. Biol. Chem.* **179**, 503 (1949).

552. S. Spiegelman, M. D. Kamen, and M. Sussman, *Arch. Biochem.* **18**, 409 (1948).

553. M. D. Hatch and J. F. Turner, *Biochem. J.* **75**, 66 (1960).

554. J. F. Turner, in "Handbuch der Pflanzenphysiologie" (W. Ruhland, ed.), Vol. 12, Part 2, pp. 42-87. Springer, Berlin, (1960).

555. H. E. Robertson and P. D. Boyer, *J. Biol. Chem.* **214**, 295 (1955).

556. J. A. Rakestraw and E. R. Roberts, *Biochim. et Biophys. Acta* **24**, 388 (1957).

557. C. H. Suelter, M. De Luca, J. B. Peter, and P. D. Boyer, *Nature* **192**, 43 (1961).

CHAPTER 30

Polyanionic Inhibitors

Peter Bernfeld

I. INTRODUCTION

Surface active agents and certain other groups of organic anions have long been known to act as metabolic inhibitors. Their common feature is the presence in their molecules of strongly electronegative charges which occur either in conjunction with certain other functions, such as lipophilic groups in surface active compounds, or which repeat themselves many times in the same molecule, as in macromolecular polyanions.

The structural analogy between surface active agents and macromolecular polyanions, such as sulfated polysaccharides, becomes more striking when one considers the well-known ability of fatty acids and of their analogues to form oriented multilayers (*1, 2*) and micelles. In such laminar structures the hydrophobic groups of one layer are directed toward the hydrophobic groups of a second layer, while in turn the hydrophilic groups of one layer are in contact with the hydrophilic groups of another layer. In an aqueous medium this leads to aggregated particles or micelles of surface active compounds in which each micelle is covered by a multitude of negatively charged groups and thus closely resembles a macromolecular polyanion (*3, 4*). Because of this analogy, surface active agents and macromolecular polyanions exhibit many similarities in their biological behavior, and this group of substances will be referred to in the following discussion for short as "polyanions."

It appears that the strongly electronegative nature of polyanions is responsible for their high affinity toward a large variety of substances carrying opposite charges. Among biological materials, proteins are the principal targets, independent of whether or not they possess biological activity. The interaction of polyanions with proteins causes various changes in the physicochemical and biological behavior of the latter substances and appears to be the principal reason for the ability of polyanions to function as metabolic inhibitors.

The following discussion will deal with the phenomena which lead to metabolic inhibition by surface active agents, by other low or medium molecular weight organic sulfones and sulfate esters, and by macromolecular polyanions.

II. SURFACE ACTIVE AGENTS AS METABOLIC INHIBITORS

Surface active compounds are substances capable of lowering surface tension in gas-liquid systems, and interfacial tension in liquid-liquid systems. The common feature in their chemical structure is the presence of both hydrophilic and hydrophobic groups, especially at distant points or at opposite ends of the molecule. They are mainly used as detergents or wetting agents, and the number of surface active agents commercially available in this country well exceeds 200 (*5, 6*). Although soap is no doubt the most widely used detergent, and while the classic studies by Langmuir (*7*) on the phenomena underlying detergency, i.e., the orientation of detergent molecules on a liquid surface, have been carried out with fatty acids, the surface active agents to be discussed in this chapter are essentially sulfate esters of long-chain aliphatic alcohols; cationic detergents will not be included.

A. Denaturation of Proteins

The denaturation of proteins by sulfated alkyl detergents was first described by Bull and Neurath (8). Among a number of anionic detergents of varying chain length, Anson (9) found that sodium dodecyl sulfate (SDS) possesses the highest potency to denature beef methemoglobin or other proteins. These effects are due, no doubt, to complex formation which, in the case of the interaction between crystalline horse serum albumin and SDS, has been found to result from stoichiometric combination (10). On the other hand, complex formation between protein and detergent may also lead to the opposite effect, namely to protection against denaturation, as in the case of the complex of β-lactoglobulin with SDS (11). This complex is crystallizable and has been found to contain two equivalents of firmly bound detergent (12). The basic requisites for structure of stabilizing agents of human serum proteins against heat have been studied by Boyer et al. (13). An anionic function with a nonpolar group attached to it has been found essential; fatty acids are less effective than the corresponding sulfate esters, and the presence of carboxyl or hydroxyl groups has been observed to decrease the effectiveness.

B. Complex Formation with Proteins

A mechanism for the complex formation between protein and detergent has been proposed by Lundgren (3) and is based upon the tendency of

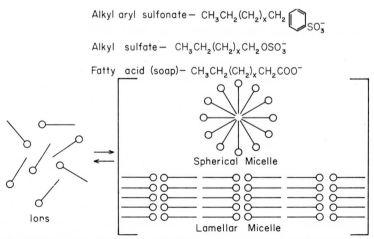

Alkyl aryl sulfonate— $CH_3CH_2(CH_2)_xCH_2$〈 〉SO_3^-

Alkyl sulfate— $CH_3CH_2(CH_2)_xCH_2OSO_3^-$

Fatty acid (soap)— $CH_3CH_2(CH_2)_xCH_2COO^-$

Spherical Micelle

Ions

Lamellar Micelle

FIG. 1. Structural properties of organic detergents in aqueous media; the long-chain hydrocarbon anions appear to associate to give spherical or lamellar micelles, according to Lundgren (3).

detergents in aqueous media to exist in the form of multilayer aggregates (see Fig. 1). This mechanism suggests a structure of the protein-detergent complex in which several peptide chains are connected to one another by a detergent aggregate through electrostatic forces, whereas the detergent aggregate itself is held together by nonpolar bonds (see Fig. 2).

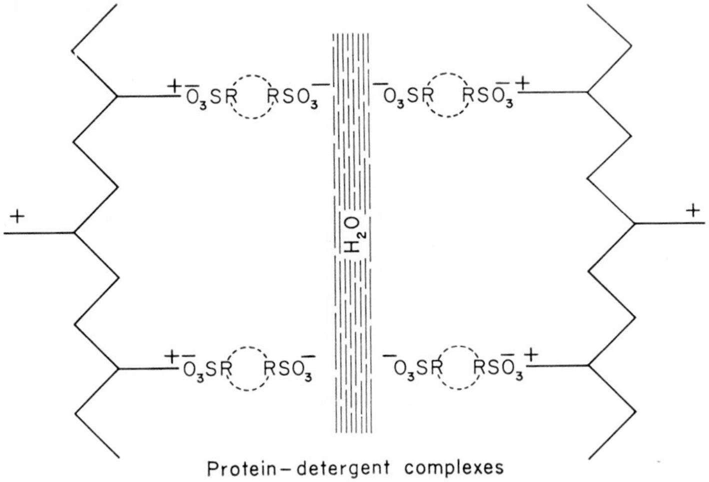

Protein – detergent complexes

FIG. 2. Proposed structure of protein-detergent complexes, according to Lundgren (3).

Since this type of complex formation is predominantly due to electrostatic attraction forces between the component parts, the interaction is greatly dependent, among many other factors, on the number of electropositive charges of the protein molecule and hence on the pH of the medium. The pH dependence of the protein-detergent complexes has been studied by Putnam and Neurath (14). Maximum precipitation is generally attained at a pH near the isoelectric point of the protein, as seen from the data in Table I. The precipitation ceases abruptly on the alkaline side of the isoelectric point of the protein, indicating that only the cationic form of the latter is precipitated. However, the formation of soluble complexes takes place also on the alkaline side of the isoelectric point, as evidenced by ultracentrifugal, diffusion, and electrophoretic studies (14, 15). Such soluble complexes are probably of a structure somewhat different from the one suggested by Lundgren, and they more closely resemble those obtained at high detergent concentrations near the isoelectric point, which are equally soluble (14). Under these circumstances, detergent aggregates will combine with protein, without, however, con-

TABLE I

RELATIONSHIP BETWEEN ISOELECTRIC POINTS AND MAXIMUM PRECIPITATION OF
PROTEINS BY SODIUM DODECYL SULFATE[a]

Protein	Isoelectric point	pH of maximum precipitation
Pepsin	2.7	2.7
Egg albumin	4.6	4.6
Horse serum albumin	4.75	4.85
Beef serum albumin	4.8	4.8
β-Lactoglobulin	5.2	5.2
Horse pseudoglobulin GI	6.0	5.9
Human carboxyhemoglobin	7.1	6.4

[a] According to Putnam and Neurath (14).

necting several protein molecules to each other, either because less positively charged groups are available on the protein (on the alkaline side of the isoelectric point) or because of the presence of an excess of detergent.

Numerous are the observations of interactions between proteins and detergents, and this subject has been extensively reviewed (4, 16). Only a few cases will be mentioned in addition to the complex formation of SDS with the proteins listed in Table I. Egg albumin has been reported to form complexes with sodium lauryl sulfate, a reaction proceeding in several steps, whereby the detergent is at first adsorbed at the surface of an albumin film and penetrates this film only during the later stages of the reaction (17). Ovalbumin interacts with dodecybenzenesulfonate (18, 19), insulin with Duponol, a commercial mixture of sulfated aliphatic alcohols, with chain lengths ranging from C_8 to C_{18} (15), and serum a- and β-lipoproteins form complexes with SDS or with the arylalkyl sulfonated detergent Lakeseal (20).

In the case of proteins possessing biological activity, such as enzymes, proteohormones, toxins, antibodies, and many antigens, or in the case of more complicated biological systems in which proteins play a major part, such as in viruses, bacteria, and erythrocytes, an inhibition of the biological function will be the ultimate consequence of the interaction with surface active agents. Valko (21) describes the sequence of events in the action of surface active agents on various biological systems in the following way. Surface active agents possess a strong affinity for proteins and cause combination. As a result, the balance of the electrostatic forces and of the noncoulombic cohesion in the molecule is upset, while profound changes occur in the interaction of the protein with solvent molecules.

Then bonds between components of conjugated proteins may be disrupted, and, finally, denaturation and unfolding of the protein occurs, resulting in the inactivation of enzymes, viruses, and bacteria.

C. Inhibition of Enzymes

At pH 2, a 0.5% solution of SDS has been reported to inhibit peptic activity completely (22). This inhibition takes place at a pH slightly on the acid side of the isoelectric point of the enzyme, i.e., in a medium more acid than that at which maximum precipitation with SDS occurs (see Table I); this is in good agreement with the type of complex formation discussed above. It has been reported, however, that pepsin can also be inactivated by SDS at pH 4.0 (23). Marini and Levey (24) observed that SDS is able to inhibit both the proteolytic and the milk-clotting activity of crystalline pepsin, while other inhibitors of the type of macromolecular polyanions, e.g., chondroitin sulfate, inhibited only the proteolytic activity, but *increased* the clotting activity.

Trypsin was found to be inactivated by SDS (25), sodium decyl sulfate, and sodium octyl sulfate, in order of decreasing effectiveness (26). Octylbenzenesulfonate and decylbenzenesulfonate were also inhibitors. In contrast to these observations, Wills stated that the tryptic hydrolysis of serum proteins was stimulated by SDS, but that of casein was hardly affected (27).

Urease is completely inhibited by 0.001 M SDS at pH 5.0, but the inhibition falls sharply with increasing pH (27). At pH 5.4 and at higher pH values, urease activity is no longer affected by 0.001 M SDS (28). A decrease in detergent concentration reduces the sensitivity of the enzyme toward the anion. While the inhibition is irreversible at 0.001 M detergent concentration, it becomes reversible at 0.0005 M SDS (27).

Malt amylases have been reported to be inhibited by SDS (29, 30). It is generally agreed that β-amylase is more strongly inhibited than α-amylase. The inhibition of pancreatic α-amylase by SDS has also been observed (25). Measuring the triolein hydrolysis, Wills (31) found that pancreatic lipase could be inhibited by the majority of anionic detergents. He also observed that SDS inhibited triacetin hydrolysis, but stimulated tributyrin hydrolysis.

Other enzyme systems which could be inhibited by SDS were ribonuclease (32), lecithinase of human serum (33), acetylcholinesterase from bovine erythrocytes (34), and invertase (27). The inhibition of the latter enzyme could be abolished by 0.067 M fructose, but not by glucose.

Keilin and Hartree (35) noted a reversible change in cytochrome c activity under the influence of SDS. Since the absorption spectrum was modified, they concluded that the change was due to an effect on the heme-protein linkage. Cytochrome oxidase is inhibited by SDS and also by laurate or oleate, but only slightly by stearate, palmitate, and sorbitan esters of fatty acids or their polyoxyalkylene derivatives (the Spans and Tweens) (36).

The inhibition of succinic dehydrogenase by sodium cetyl sulfate or sodium isopropylnaphthalenesulfonate does not appear to be dependent on the anionic nature of the detergent (37). In fact, neutral substances, such as cetylpolyethylene oxide, or cationic compounds, like cetyltri-methylammonium chloride, also inhibit this enzyme; and anionic substrate analogues which are obviously in competition with the substrate, in particular 1,2-ethanedisulfonic acid and β-sulfopropionic acid, are strong inhibitors of succinic dehydrogenase (38). It may be assumed, therefore, that the inhibition of succinic dehydrogenase by anionic detergents does not necessarily follow the same pattern as that of many other enzymes.

Finally, the oxidative and phosphorylative systems of rat liver mito-chondria are inhibited by SDS (39).

D. Other Modes of Action with Enzymes

The transformation of protyrosinase to tyrosinase can be accomplished in several ways, i.e., by dialysis, by heating to 65° C for 10 minutes, or by treatment with SDS (40). It appears likely that this mechanism is due to a rearrangement of the protein molecule.

Lactic dehydrogenase has been reported not to lose, but to gain activity by the treatment with SDS (41).

E. Inhibition of Other Biological Materials

The tendency of anionic surface active agents to form complexes with proteins is reflected by their ability to decrease, abolish, or sometimes to enhance biological activity wherever the latter is attached to proteic material. Thus, among proteohormones, sheep pituitary gonadotropin is precipitated by SDS in a slightly acid medium (42), and insulin dis-sociates under the influence of a mixture of sulfated aliphatic alcohols with chain lengths ranging from C_8 to C_{18} (15). The latter hormone is partially inactivated by SDS; the activity of the former is slightly stimu-lated by SDS (42). Lactogenic hormone is also inhibited by anionic deter-gents (43).

Diphtheria toxin is neutralized by SDS (*44*). This detergent also prevents the precipitin reaction of serum proteins with their specific antibodies (*45*).

Numerous animal and plant viruses are inactivated by anionic detergents. SDS splits tobacco mosaic, tomato bushy stunt, and potato X viruses into the nucleic acid and protein moieties, entailing loss of activity (*46–50*). SDS and other anionic detergents have been reported to inactivate vaccinia virus (*51, 52*) and many other animal viruses. In many of these cases, cationic detergents were also capable of inactivation.

F. Antibacterial Activity

According to Bayliss, only gram-negative organisms may be lysed by SDS (*53*). Other authors have stated, however, that anionic detergents exert germicidal action only against gram-positive organisms although the effect of cationic detergents on these microorganisms is much more pronounced (*54*). Among the straight-chain derivatives, SDS, and myristyl and cetyl sulfates were the most active compounds. A secondary alcohol sulfate with a branched chain, i.e., 3,9-diethyltridecanol-6-sulfate, produced a strong inhibition (*54*).

The germicidal action of anionic detergents depends on the pH in a manner analogous to that observed with the interaction between enzymes or other proteins and polyanions. Maximum inhibitory effects were found in an acid medium, whereas cationic detergents inhibited mostly in the alkaline range (*55*).

Actively growing cultures of *Escherichia coli* resisted to a concentration of 0.2% SDS (*56*). Only after the cell metabolism had been inhibited by potassium cyanide was the detergent able to lyse the cells. This was accompanied by an extraction of lipoprotein from the cell walls.

At subbacteriostatic concentrations, SDS retarded the growth of *Staphylococcus aureus* and prevented the culture from reaching the maximum number of cells (*57*).

According to Hotchkiss (*58*) the antibacterial activity of synthetic detergents is due to a succession of events. At first, positively charged groups on the bacterial surface combine with the polyanion. This stage is followed by damage to the membrane which results in cytolysis and autolysis. Finally, the detergent acquires access to the metabolic systems of the cell, causing inactivation of enzymes. Dubos (*59*) remarks that the effect of detergents is not limited to interference with one single enzyme but depends on a nonspecific effect on cell membranes and proteins.

G. Miscellaneous Physiological Inhibitory Actions

Surface active agents have also been observed to inhibit the mobility, fructolysis, and respiration of spermatozoa (60, 61). Both anionic and cationic detergents were found to be active. A more physiological example of the function of anionic detergents is the inhibition of gastric acid secretion by 0.5–6% SDS, which supposedly acts directly and selectively on parietal cells (62).

H. Specificity and Mechanism of Inhibition

It is evident that the inhibition of biologically active proteins by sulfated alkyl detergents is a general and totally unspecific reaction. Practically every kind of protein or protein-containing material is susceptive to inactivation by these substances. Hydrolytic, desmolytic, oxidative, and phosphorylative enzyme systems, proteohormones, toxins, antibodies, viruses, bacteria, etc. have been observed to be more or less strongly inhibited, and, in addition, a number of proteins with no known biological activity have been found to be denatured by or to undergo complex formation with many of these detergents. A small number of exceptions exists, however, where activation has been observed, such as the case of lactic dehydrogenase (41) and the tryptic hydrolysis of serum proteins (27).

While sodium dodecyl sulfate is generally considered to be the strongest inhibitor of this class of substances, homologue compounds with longer or shorter chain length, as well as certain branched-chain alcohol sulfate esters are also known to possess marked inhibitory action. In a great many cases, the phenomenon is by no means limited to sulfate esters of aliphatic alcohols alone; fatty acids, a few nonpolar, water-soluble alkyl derivatives, e.g., cetyl polyethylene oxide and polyoxyalkylene derivatives of sorbitan esters of fatty acids (Tweens), as well as cationic detergents have frequently been found to behave in a similar fashion.

It thus appears that this type of inhibition is due to a completely unspecific interaction between proteins and, in most cases, polar substances. That electrostatic forces appear to play an important role in the resulting soluble or insoluble complexes follows from the marked dependency of the inhibition on the pH. The anionic detergents act only on the acid side of the isoelectric points of each protein, where the number of positive charges is predominant. Direct evidence for complex formation has been obtained in numerous instances by the observation of precipita-

tion and of changes in the physicochemical behavior, such as electrophoretic mobility, ultracentrifugal sedimentation, diffusion constant, and
spreading characteristics.

The inhibition may be due to denaturation, to blocking of essential
electropositively charged groups of the protein, to precipitation of the
protein as a complex with the anionic detergent, or to other modes of
interaction. Whether additional nonelectrostatic forces are involved in the
complex formation is not known. It is likely, however, that the mechanism of inhibition of one protein may differ in this respect from that of
another protein.

III. INHIBITION OF ENZYMES BY ORGANIC MONO- OR POLYSULFONATES

This group of substances includes mainly the following compounds:
suramin with six sulfonate groups per molecule, trypan red with five
sulfonate groups, trypan blue with four, Congo red and the β-naphtha-
lenedisulfonic acids with two sulfonate groups each, and methyl orange
and taurocholate with one sulfonate group per molecule. Five out of these
seven substances contain, in addition, more or less strong basic groups.

Although these compounds are not considered to be of macromolecular
structure—the molecular weight of suramin sodium is 1429 and is the
highest in this group—they assume an intermediate position between the
low molecular anionic detergents and the macromolecular polyanions to
be discussed later on. While the former are known to exist in aqueous
media as oriented aggregates or micelles of considerable particle size, they
usually do not contain other functional groups besides the sulfate ester
residues. Like many of the naturally occurring macromolecular polyanions, the mono- and polysulfonates contain one or several additional
functional groups, such as hydroxyl, amino, dimethylamino, or carboxyl-
amino. Hydrogen bonding may add, therefore, to the polar bonds in the
formation of complexes between these polyanions and proteins.

The interaction of crystalline bovine serum albumin and of other proteins with acid dyes has been studied by Klotz et al. (63). These workers
observed that the interaction is accompanied by an electrostatic effect,
and that the binding follows the principles of the law of mass action. They
also reported that the complex formation is reflected by spectral changes
(64). Bile acids were found by Anson (9) to denature beef methemoglobin
and other proteins, but SDS was more active in this respect than sodium
glycocholate and sodium taurocholate.

Quastel (65) reported the inhibition of fumarase by suramin, trypan red, trypan blue, Congo red, and β-aminonaphthalenedisulfonic acids.

A great deal of work on the inhibition of enzymes by suramin has been carried out by Wills and his co-workers. Urease was inhibited at pH 5.0 but not at pH 7.5; trypsin lost activity at pH 8.5 (66). The inhibition of trypsin by $M/1920$ suramin at pH 8.9 shows that suramin concentrations of the magnitude found in plasma after intravenous injection of the drug may have inhibitory effects (67). The pH was found to be of high importance in the inhibition of urease, carboxylase, hexokinase, succinic dehydrogenase, cytochrome oxidase, cholinesterase, tyrosinase, arginase, D-amino acid oxidase, and catalase (68). The pH dependence of suramin inhibition has been used to estimate the isoelectric points of a number of enzymes (69, 70), and good agreements with determinations of the isoelectric point made by physicochemical methods were found for a number of enzymes (see Table II).

TABLE II

COMPARISON OF ISOELECTRIC POINTS OBTAINED BY THE SURAMIN METHOD WITH THOSE DETERMINED BY PHYSICOCHEMICAL PROCEDURES[a]

Enzyme	Isoelectric point (pH)	
	By the suramin method	Values recorded in the literature, obtained by physicochemical methods
Urease	5.1	5.0–5.1
Catalase		
Ox liver	5.8	5.7
Horse liver	5.2–5.3	5.4
Amylase		
Human saliva (α)	5.3	5.0–5.5
Hog pancreas (α)	5.2	5.2–5.6
Malt (α)	5 0	5.7
Malt (β)	5.7	5 75
Carbonic anhydrase		
Ox blood	5.2–5.4	5.3
Peroxidase	4.9	7.2
Tyrosinase		
Potato	4.3	5.4
Mushroom	3.9[b]	5.0
Invertase	4.1	4.42
β-Glucosidase	4.4	5.7–5.8

[a] Data from Wills (69).
[b] Using catechol as substrate.

Suramin has also been reported to inhibit ribonuclease (*32*), and sodium taurocholate has been found to inhibit acetylcholinesterase (*34*), as well as the oxidative and phosphorylative enzyme systems of rat liver mitochondria (*39*). Mono- and disulfonic derivatives of polycyclic hydrocarbons were observed to inhibit certain enzyme systems, such as the pyruvate-triosephosphate system of rabbit skeletal muscle, the oxalacetate-triosephosphate system of the same preparation, and also lactic and succinic dehydrogenases (*71*). Sulfated or phosphorylated derivatives of hesperidin were shown to be powerful inhibitors of hyaluronidase (*72*). This inhibition could be reversed by the addition of salmine. Obviously, the reversal was due to a competition of electropositive groups of salmine with positive groups of the enzyme for negative charges of the inhibitor.

There exists a considerable analogy between the inhibition of enzymes by alkyl sulfate esters and by organic mono- or polysulfonates. In both cases, the inhibition is totally unrelated to the nature of the enzyme, as well as to the chemistry of the organic anion, while the pH dependency is the same for both groups of inhibitors. It appears, therefore, that the presence of one or several strongly electronegative groups per molecule is a sufficient requisite for the structure to give organic substances the capacity of inhibiting the biological activity of proteins. Occasionally, the negative charge of carboxyl groups may be sufficient, as in the case of the methemoglobin denaturation by glycocholate, and of the inhibition of cytochrome oxidase by fatty acids. Most frequently, however, sulfonate or sulfate ester groups are necessary for the inhibition.

IV. MACROMOLECULAR POLYANIONS AS METABOLIC INHIBITORS

The interaction of proteins with high molecular weight polyanions is an extremely widespread phenomenon. Macromolecular polyanions of greatly varying structure have been investigated in this respect, and their number exceeds considerably that of the anions discussed in the two preceding sections of this review. A considerable number of papers on this subject matter has appeared in the literature, in particular on enzyme inhibition by a large variety of macromolecular polyanions.

A. Macroanionic Enzyme Inhibition

The inhibition of enzymes by macromolecular polyanions is an unspecific phenomenon which has been observed with a great number of enzymes and with a large variety of polyanions. Because of the lack of specificity and general nature of this phenomenon, Spensley and Rogers (73) have introduced the term "macroanionic enzyme inhibition" for the general effect.

1. CLASSIFICATION OF MACROMOLECULAR POLYANIONIC INHIBITORS

Three main classes of macromolecular polyanions can be distinguished, according to the chemical nature of the groups carrying the negative charges. The first group consists of sulfate esters and sulfones, the second group is made up of phosphate esters, and the third group includes the carboxylic acids. It is convenient to further subdivide the first group into two subgroups, i.e., those polysulfates which do not contain additional functional groups (with the exception of hydroxyl) and those which do contain other groups, such as carboxyl, N-acetyl, and others. Consequently, the enzyme inhibition by macromolecular polyanions has been summarized in four separate tables (Tables III–VI).

In Table V the salts of two inorganic heteropolyacids, i.e., phosphomolybdate and silicotungstate, were included. Although these substances are neither polyphosphates nor polymers, their inclusion in this table appeared justified because their molecular weights are quite elevated (2348 and 3420, respectively, for the crystalline, hydrated, free acids) and because they bear certain analogies with the polyphosphates. These heteropolyacids resemble macromolecular polysufate esters not only with regard to the inhibition of enzymes, but also with respect to other biological functions, such as the prolongation of clotting time and the *in vivo* induction of plasma lipemia-clearing factor (117).

Polymetaphosphate has also been mentioned in Table V because it is usually considered to be a true high polymer (118), and molecular weights from 150,000 to 2,500,000 have been reported for this substance (119). It appeared logical to include also tetrametaphosphate in the same table because of its close structural relationship to polymetaphosphate.

2. pH DEPENDENCE OF INHIBITION

Most attempts to inhibit enzymes by macromolecular polyanions have been made near the optimum pH of the enzymic action. The pH dependence of the inhibition has been studied, however, in a few cases. Berdick and Morawetz (116) observed that catalase is not appreciably precipitated by low concentrations of polyacrylic acid and by other polycarboxylic polymers below pH 4.3 and above 5.3, but that as much as 97% of the enzyme is precipitated at pH 5.0 by 0.0125 mg/ml of the polyanion. Thus, very little precipitation is achieved near the isoelectric point of

TABLE III

INHIBITION OF ENZYMES BY MACROMOLECULAR POLYSULFATES AND POLYSULFONES CONTAINING NO ADDITIONAL FUNCTIONAL GROUPS EXCEPT HYDROXYL

Enzyme	Inhibitor[a]								
	Amylose sulfate	Amylopectin sulfate	Dextran sulfate	Cellulose sulfate	Synthetic polyglucose sulfates	Polyvinyl sulfate	Polyethylene sulfonate	Polystyrene sulfonate	Polysulfonic acid-aldehyde polymers
Acid phosphatase							74	74	
β-Glucuronidase								75	73
α-Amylase		76, 77					80	73, 76, 77	81
Hyaluronidase				78	79				83
Lysozyme					79, 82				
Ribonuclease	84	84	84, 85, 86	84	79, 82	84	84, 87		73
Deoxyribonuclease							87		73
Pepsin	91a					91a			83
Lipoprotein lipase	88, 89	88, 89	88, 89			89	90	89	
Fumarase						91			
Lactic dehydrogenase								91	
Aldolase								91	

a The figures refer to references in which inhibition has been described.

TABLE IV

INHIBITION OF ENZYMES BY MACROMOLECULAR POLYSULFATES CONTAINING ADDITIONAL FUNCTIONAL GROUPS

Inhibitor[a]

Enzyme	Carboxymethyl cellulose sulfate	Pectic acid sulfate	Pectin sulfate	Polygalacturonic acid sulfate methyl ester[b]	Sulfated pectic acid amide	Chitin sulfate	Chitosan sulfate	Sulfated hyaluronate	Chondroitin-4-sulfate	Heparin
Acid phosphatase							74		74	74
Alkaline phosphatase										93, 94
α-Amylase		76, 77								95
Hyaluronidase						78		96	97	76, 77, 98, 99
Lysozyme										100
Pepsin										
Trypsin									24, 105a	105a, 91a, 101
Ribonuclease	84	84	86, 102	87	86	84	84			84, 87, 102, 103, 104
Deoxyribonuclease	88, 89	88, 89		87						
Lipoprotein lipase						89		89		89, 105c
Fumarase									90	90

[a] The figures refer to references in which inhibition has been described.
[b] Treburon, described by Mangieri et al. (92)
[c] Inhibition at high concentrations of heparin; activation at low concentrations

TABLE V

INHIBITION OF ENZYMES BY MACROMOLECULAR POLYPHOSPHATES

Enzyme	Inhibitor[a]										
	Tetrameta-phosphate	Polymeta-phosphate	Ribonucleate	Deoxyribonucleate	Polyhydroquinone phosphate	Polyxenyl phosphate	Phosphates of poly-phloretin and related polyphenols	Phosphate polymers of various aromatic hydroxy and amino compounds	Polyestradiol phosphate	Phosphomolybdate	Silicotungstate
Acid phosphatase		74			74	74	106		107		
Alkaline phosphatase							106		107		
β-Amylase							106				
Hyaluronidase				77			106	108	107		
Lysozyme			109	109							
Urease							106				
Arginase			110								
Chymotrypsin						74					
Ribonuclease	102					74, 111		102		86	
Deoxyribonuclease						74	106				86
Hexokinase			90								
Fumarase						74					
Glyceraldehyde phosphate dehydrogenase						74					
Catalase						74					

[a] The figures refer to references in which inhibition has been described.

TABLE VI

INHIBITION OF ENZYMES BY MACROMOLECULAR CARBOXYLIC ACIDS

Enzyme	Inhibitor[a]							
	Hyaluronate	Poly-L-aspartate	Polyglutamate	Polyacrylate	Polymethacrylate	Maleic anhydride-styrene copolymer	Maleic anhydride-vinyl methyl ester copolymer	Polyhydroxybenzoic acid-formaldehyde polymers
β-Glucuronidase					75			
Hyaluronidase					76, 77			112, 113, 114
Lysozyme	109		109					
Trypsin			115					
Ribonuclease		102						
Catalase				116		116	116	

[a] The figures refer to references in which inhibition has been described.

the enzyme (pH 5.6–5.7). The addition of barium ions shifts the pH of maximum precipitation to a slightly more alkaline region and causes substantially greater precipitation near the isoelectric point (116). Kidney alkaline phosphatase was found to be more strongly inhibited by polyphloretin phosphate on the acid side of the pH optimum (106). Bacterial hyaluronidase was inhibited by the same polyanion at pH 6, but not at pH 7 (106). The inhibition of ribonuclease (cyclic phosphatase activity) by polyxenyl phosphate was most striking between pH 6 and 7, while the inhibitory effect became insignificant above pH 8 (111). The RNA-depolymerizing activity of RNase was moderately inhibited by this polyanion at pH 5, but no inhibition was noted at pH 5.8 (111).

The marked pH dependence of the inhibition and the preference in many cases of a pH on the acid side of the isoelectric point of the enzyme are analogous with the conditions of enzyme inhibition by anionic detergents. It appears likely, therefore, that the macroanionic enzyme inhibition is due to interaction of cationic groups of the enzyme protein with anionic groups of the inhibitor. Complex formation through electrostatic forces will ensue and will lead to either precipitation of the enzyme or to blocking of the active sites of the enzyme. Unlike the case of sodium dodecyl sulfate and suramin, inhibitory effects of the macromolecular polyanions are also noticeable, though weaker, on the alkaline side of the isoelectric point of the enzyme (106), where both enzyme and inhibitor have negative charges, e.g., in the case of the cyclic phosphatase activity of RNase (111) the isoelectric point of which is at pH 7.8. In contrast to enzyme inhibition by SDS and suramin, other than polar forces must be assumed to contribute also to the interaction between enzymes and macromolecular polyanions.

3. SPECIFICITY OF INHIBITION

Considerable quantitative differences in the strength of the various inhibitors, as well as in the susceptibility of the individual enzymes have been noted. Thus, polysaccharide sulfates are more potent inhibitors of ribonuclease than the inorganic heteropolyacids (86). Heparin, pectin sulfate, and poly-p,p'-dioxydibenzyl phosphate inhibit ribonuclease more strongly than poly-L-aspartate and considerably more strongly than tetrametaphosphate (102). Polyvinyl sulfate, cellulose sulfate, and amylose sulfate proved to be more powerful inhibitors of ribonuclease than a number of other polysaccharide sulfates, including amylopectin sulfate, dextran sulfate, heparin, and others (84). Acid phosphatase was most strongly inhibited by polyxenyl phosphate, followed in order of decreasing potency by polyhydroquinone phosphate, chitosan sulfate, polystyrenesulfonate, polydiphenyldimethylmethane phosphate, heparin, and poly-metaphosphate (74). Lysozyme is approximately 100 times more inhibited by polyglucose sulfate than by ribonucleate (79), and the potency of macroanionic inhibitors on hyaluronidase decreases in the following order: polystyrenesulfonate, heparin, sulfated pectic acid, polymethacrylate, and amylopectin sulfate (77).

The comparison of the action of a given inhibitor (polyxenyl phosphate) toward a number of different enzymes on the acid side of their pH optimum, where the protein-polyanion interaction is supposedly favored, showed that acid phosphatase was most strongly inhibited, followed by glyceraldehydephosphate dehydrogenase, chymotrypsin, deoxyribonuclease, ribonuclease, and catalase, which was only slightly inhibited, while the activity of pepsin remained unaffected by the same concentrations of the polyanion (74). Although polymethacrylate is a strong inhibitor of β-glucuronidase (75) and of hyaluronidase (76, 77), liver esterase has been found not to be inhibited by the same polyanion (120). Some enzymes require a contact period with the polyanion (polyphloretin phosphate) in order to be inhibited, e.g., urease, β-amylase, and brain hexokinase (106).

The long list of enzyme-polyanion inhibitions (Tables III–VI) documents that there appears to exist no general rule governing the relationship between the chemical or physicochemical nature of the polyanion and the potency of enzyme inhibition, nor between the specificity of the enzyme and the nature of the inhibitor. The reasons for such a lack of relationship may be manifold, but they may possibly be explained, at least in part, by the conditions found in the case of two enzymes, i.e., hyaluronidase and β-glucuronidase, which will be described below (Section III, B). These conditions may very well also prevail in other enzyme systems.

4. POLYCATIONIC DEINHIBITION

In the case of β-glucuronidase and hyaluronidase, the macroanionic inhibition was observed to be closely interlinked with other phenomena, one of which is the reversal of the inhibition by polycations (75, 77). Actually, the inhibition of these two enzymes by polyanions appeared to be a secondary effect only, whereas the action of polycations on the enzymes was found to be a true activation. This "activator-competitive" enzyme inhibition will be discussed later on in more detail. It is noteworthy, however, that the reversal of macroanionic enzyme inhibition by polycations, frequently also called deinhibition, is a more general phenomenon. Vandendriessche (102) abolished the inhibitory effect of heparin on ribonuclease by the addition of protamine, and that of poly-L-aspartic acid by poly-L-ornithine. The inhibition of alkaline phosphatase and hyaluronidase by polyphoretin phosphate and related polyphenol phosphates could be reversed by protamine or by methyl gelatin (*106*). Hummel *et al.* (*74*) showed that the addition of protamine, globin, salmine, or ovalbumin considerably weakened the inhibition of acid phosphatase by polyxenyl phosphate. That the inhibition of ribonuclease, lysozyme, and hyaluronidase by polyglucose sulfates can be completely reversed by protamine has been demonstrated by Mora and Young (*79*). A large number of polycations have been reported by Bernfeld *et al.* (*75*) to reverse the inhibition of β-glucuronidase by polymethacrylate. These polycations consisted mainly of positively charged or amphoteric macromolecular substances, such as chitosan, deacetylchondroitin sulfate, crystalline bovine serum albumin, crystalline β-lactoglobulin, and crystalline ovalbumin, but included also low molecular weight cations like 1,10-diamino-*n*-decane. Even certain preparations of deoxyribonucleate proved to possess sufficient positive charges to counteract the inhibitory effect of the polyanion. Hyaluronidase inhibition by polystyrene sulfonate was reversed by protamine, poly-L-lysine, chitosan, or 1,10-diamino-*n*-decane (*76, 77*).

5. MACROANIONIC VERSUS MACROCATIONIC INHIBITION

In a few enzyme systems the roles of polycations and polyanions are reversed. Thus, Katchalski, Berger, and Neumann (*121*) have found that pepsin is inhibited at pH 1.7 and 6.0 by poly-L-lysine and that the inhibition is overcome by heparin. In a similar way, Person and Fine (*122*) observed that heart muscle cytochrome c oxidase is inhibited by basic proteins, such as protamine, histone, lysozyme, or ribonuclease, whereas polyglucose sulfate completely reverses the inhibition of this enzyme. Whether an enzyme is inhibited by a polyanion or a polycation probably depends on its chemical and physicochemical nature. Pepsin has been reported, however, to be inhibited by polycations (*121*) and polyanions as well (*83*).

In the light of the experience obtained with β-glucuronidase (*75*) and hyaluronidase (*76, 77*), where the activation was the primary effect and the inhibition by polyelectrolytes of opposite charge consisted in the sequestration of the activator, the *in vitro* activation of lipoprotein lipase by heparin (*105*) and its reversal by protamine seemed to follow the same pattern as the effect of polyelectrolytes on pepsin and on cytochrome c oxidase. Actually, the case of lipoprotein lipase is different because its *in vitro* activation is strictly specific for only those polyanions bearing sulfoamino groups, like heparin (*88, 89*).

The inhibition of trypsin by polyglutamic acid can also be reversed by a large excess of the polyanion until the activity of the enzyme is actually enhanced (*115*). Similarly, pepsin inhibition by poly-L-lysine is abolished by an excess of the polypeptide (*115*). The activation of lipoprotein lipase by heparin has been found to turn into inhibition when high concentrations of the polyanion are present (*105*). Dellert and Stahmann (*115*) believe that the mechanism for this behavior, at least in the case of the two proteolytic enzymes, is the same. They assume complex formation at low polypeptide concentrations, probably due to electrostatic attraction, which leads to aggregation and precipitation. At high peptide concentrations, the complex would dissolve and enzyme activity would be restored. It should be emphasized, however, that the reversal of the effect of polyelectrolytes by higher concentrations of the same substance is limited to a few cases only, whereas the large majority of enzyme inhibitions by polyanions cannot be abolished, reversed, or even weakened by an excess of the same polyanion.

B. "Activator-Competitive" Enzyme Inhibition

It is generally taken for granted that the mechanism of macroanionic enzyme inhibition lies in a direct interaction between negative groups of the inhibitor and positive functions of the enzyme protein; this interaction is then assumed to lead to complex formation through coulombic forces, which in turn causes a decrease in enzyme activity as a consequence of precipitation of the complexor of masking the active sites of the enzyme.

A different mechanism has been found to prevail in the case of at least two enzymes and is believed to be applicable to a much larger number of enzyme systems. Testicular hyaluronidase and mammalian β-glucuronidase have been observed to be inhibited by macroanions without necessarily interacting directly with the inhibitors. This mechanism is based upon two other phenomena, (1) the decrease of specific enzyme activity upon dilution and (2) the reversibility of this decrease of specific activity by the addition of polycations.

1. DECREASE OF SPECIFIC ENZYME ACTIVITY UPON DILUTION

Loss of enzyme activity upon dilution has been described to occur with prostatic acid phosphatase (*124, 125*) and with carbonic anhydrase (*122a*).

Kinetic studies on the specific activity (ratio of enzyme activity over quantity of enzyme protein) of hyaluronidase (*76, 77*) and of β-glucuronidase (*123*) have been carried out over a wide range of enzyme dilutions. Highly purified preparations of β-glucuronidase from calf liver and spleen exhibit marked losses of specific activity when the enzyme is diluted below concentrations of 100 μg/ml, as seen from curve A in Fig. 3.

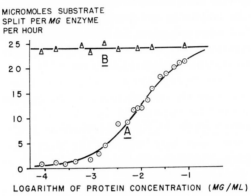

MICROMOLES SUBSTRATE SPLIT PER *MG* ENZYME PER HOUR

LOGARITHM OF PROTEIN CONCENTRATION (*MG/ML*)

FIG. 3. Reversible decrease of specific activity (ordinates) of highly purified calf liver β-glucuronidase, measured with phenolphthalein glucuronoside as subtrate, as a function of the logarithm of enzyme concentration (abscissas). Curve A: without added activator; curve B: in the presence of 100 μg chitosan/ml.

At enzyme concentrations of 0.1 μg/ml, the specific activity drops to less than 10% of the original value. Commercial preparations of testicular hyaluronidase or preparations of this enzyme which had been partially purified by zone electrophoresis showed the same phenomenon at enzyme concentrations below 1 USP unit/ml (*77*). In both cases, the specific enzyme activity decreased progressively upon dilution, and this behavior followed the law of mass action.

It was possible to rule out experimentally the participation of surface forces during this effect, and the most likely interpretation of the decrease of specific enzyme activity upon dilution is the assumption that the active enzyme protein dissociates during dilution into enzymically inactive products. While it appears evident that the bonds which are severed upon dilution are essential for the enzymic activity, it is not possible, however, at the present state of our knowledge, to decide whether the dissociation involves the cleavage of inter- or intramolecular bonds, and whether the nature of the bonds in question is polar or is of the secondary or tertiary protein structure.

The phenomenon of dissociation of active enzymes into enzymically inactive subunits has now been recognized to occur, also, under various other conditions. Bovine pancreatic ribonuclease was found to undergo reversible intramolecular dissociation by reduction and oxidative reconstitution of disulfide bonds (*123a–e*). Stellwagen and Schachman (*123f*) as well as Deal and Van Holde (*123g*) demonstrated that rabbit muscle aldolase reversibly dissociates into three subunits when the enzyme is exposed to urea, to acid, or to sodium dodecyl sulfate. Similar phenomena of reversible dissociation accompanied by loss and recovery, respectively, of enzyme activity were also observed with lysozyme, fungal a-amylase (*123h*), and with alkaline phosphatase (*123i*).

2. REVERSIBILITY OF THE DILUTION EFFECT BY POLYCATIONS

The dissociation of active enzyme into inactive products has been shown to be reversible (*76, 77, 123*). Unfortunately, the reversion could not be achieved by simply concentrating the highly diluted enzyme solutions, because of the marked instability of the dissociation products toward freeze-drying.

However, the addition to the diluted enzyme solutions of polycationic substances, mostly of macromolecular nature, was capable of restoring the specific enzyme activity. Consequently, the specific activity remained independent of the enzyme concentration when the enzyme was diluted in the presence of polycations (see curve B in Fig. 3). The latter substances thus proved to be activators of the diluted enzymes. Since this type of activation is the reversal of a dissociation upon dilution, the extent of activation also depends greatly on the enzyme concentration. It becomes less and less important as the enzyme concentration is increased, and is practically nil at high enzyme concentrations where no dissociation occurred at all, as seen from the decreasing difference at rising enzyme concentration between curves A and B in Fig. 3. A threshold of specific activity is reached for each enzyme preparation and will not be exceeded by further increases of either enzyme or activator concentrations.

This phenomenon will be called macrocationic enzyme activation, in analogy to the term macroanionic enzyme inhibition (*73*). All of the enzyme activators of this group but one are indeed macromolecular substances. The one exception is 1,10-diamino-n-decane (and related a,ω-diaminoparaffins), which is, however, a considerably less potent activator than the substances of high molecular weight. The latter include chitosan and other deacetylated mucopolysaccharides, such as deacetylhyaluronate and deacetylchondroitin-4-sulfate, further basic proteins like protamine, but also less basic proteins like crystalline bovine serum albumin, and finally also basic polypeptides, e.g. poly-L-lysine.

Macrocationic enzyme activation and reversible dissociation on dilution has also been found to occur with crystalline β-amylase from sweet potatoes (91).

3. STABILIZATION OF ENZYMES BY POLYCATIONS

While the decrease of specific enzyme activity of β-glucuronidase and hyaluronidase upon dilution has been found to be a reversible effect, another phenomenon has been observed to occur simultaneously with β-glucuronidase (75) and, to a lesser degree, also with hyaluronidase. It has been noted that highly diluted solutions of these enzymes lose their specific activity slowly but irreversibly, unless the solutions are protected against the contact with rough surfaces, such as glass, in particular scratched glass, quartz sand, or filter cel. Such rough surfaces will be provided under normal working conditions by the container material. The use of containers with smooth surfaces, such as polyethylene or silicone-coated glass, has actually been found to prevent the irreversible surface inactivation of the enzymes.

On the other hand, it has been possible to stabilize the diluted enzyme solutions, even in glass containers, by the addition of any of the polycationic substances which had been found to activate the dilute enzymes (75). It appears reasonable to assume, therefore, that the irreversible inactivation is due to an interaction between the products of enzyme dissociation and the surface of the container. Whether such an interaction produces irreversible adsorption or denaturation of the enzyme cannot be decided. It should be emphasized, however, that the decrease of specific activity upon dilution and the irreversible surface inactivation are two distinctly different phenomena. The first occurs independently of the container material, is a fast process, and is completely reversible. The second is dependent on the presence of rough surfaces, is a relatively slow action, and can be prevented but not reversed by polycations.

The protective effect of polycations has also been reported in other cases. Jeffree (124) found that polyamines are capable of protecting prostatic alkaline phosphatase against surface denaturation. It is possible that the same polyamines may also activate this enzyme under proper conditions (125).

4. REVERSAL OF THE EFFECT OF POLYCATIONS BY MACROANIONS

The inhibition of hyaluronidase and of β-glucuronidase by macromolecular polyanions, such as polystyrenesulfonate, amylopectin sulfate, pectic acid sulfate, heparin, and polymethacrylate, has been found to be a reversal of the activation of these enzymes by polycations (75–77). A plot of the reciprocal of enzyme activity versus the reciprocal of the activator concentration (see Fig. 4) indicates a complete abolition of the inhibitory

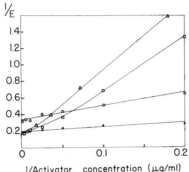

FIG. 4. Plot of the reciprocal of specific activity (ordinates) of highly puri-fied calf liver β-glucuronidase, measured with phenolphthalein glucuronoside as subtrate, versus the reciprocal of the polyanionic activator concentration (abscissas). The activator was salmon milt deoxyribonuclease ranging in con-centration from 5 to 1000 μg/ml. Triangles: with 50 μg/ml of polysulfonic polymer extracted from finely ground Amberlite IR-120; rectangles: with 1 μg/ml polymethacrylic acid; open circles: with 15 μg potassium saccharate; black dots: without inhibitor (75).

effect of polyanion when sufficiently high concentrations of polycationic activator are added. In analogy to the graphic representation of enzyme inhibition by Lineweaver and Burk (126), where the inverse value of enzyme activity is plotted as a function of the inverse value of the sub-strate concentration, the data in Fig. 4 denote an activator-competitive type of enzyme inhibition (75). For the purpose of comparison, the inhibition of β-glucuronidase by saccharolactone has been studied as a function of activator concentration. While this substance is known to be a substrate-competitive inhibitor of β-glucuronidase (127), it can be clearly seen that it is a noncompetitive inhibitor with respect to the activator concentration (see Fig. 4).

Obviously, the macromolecular polyelectrolytes of opposite charges interact with each other through electrostatic forces, whereby soluble and, in some instances, insoluble complexes are formed. The mechanism of the activator-competitive type of inhibition is, therefore, the sequestration of activator by the polyanion. Consequently, this leads to a promotion of the dissociation of the enzyme and, hence, to the loss of specific enzyme activity (see schematic representation in Fig. 5). The protection of

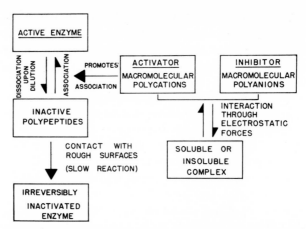

FIG. 5. Schematic representation of the interrelationships among reversible dissociation, activation by polycations, inhibition by polyanions, and stabilization against irreversible inactivation through contact with rough surfaces, as observed for the enzymes hyaluronidase and β-glucuronidase (75).

enzyme by polycations against surface inactivation can be explained by the same mechanism, and polyanions would therefore be expected to cause irreversible inactivation of highly diluted enzyme in the presence of rough surfaces. This has actually been observed (75).

The activator-competitive inhibition of hyaluronidase and β-glucuronidase by macromolecular polyanions is therefore a process during which the enzyme and the polyanion do not necessarily have to interact or get in direct contact with each other. Whether there is an additional mechanism by which a small portion of the enzyme also forms a complex with the inhibitor is not known. It appears likely, however, that the activator-competitive type of inhibition is not limited to these two enzyme systems, and that it may be a much more general type of inhibition, especially in view of the large number of enzymes which have been reported in the literature to lose activity in the presence of macromolecular polyanions (see Tables III–IV). Negative results in this regard were obtained, however, with crystalline aldolase and lactic dehydrogenase, both from rabbit muscle; neither enzyme exhibited any loss of specific activity upon dilution, although both of them were markedly inhibited by polystyrene sulfonate and sodium dodecyl sulfate (91). These two enzymes were not inhibited by most of the other polyanions, and none of the polysaccharide sulfates listed in Table III and IV had any effect on their activity; the only other polyanion which was found to inhibit lactic dehydrogenase was polyvinyl sulfate, but this substance had no influence on the activity of aldolase. The inhibition of aldolase and lactic dehydrogenase by polystyrene sulfonate appears to be significantly different, therefore, from both the activator-competitive enzyme inhibition and from the common macro-anionic inhibition characterized by a broad spectrum of the chemical nature of the inhibitors.

Irreversible enzyme inhibition by polyanions at low enzyme concentrations may be due in many other instances to a dissociation phenomenon and to the presence of rough surfaces.

The number of both polyanionic inhibitors and polycationic activators is large, and their chemical nature is highly diversified. The affinity between any two polyelectrolytes of opposite charges and their tendency to undergo complex formation must be expected, therefore, to be subject to very large variations. Consequently, it is not surprising for a given polyanion to act as an inhibitor in the presence of a certain polycationic activator, but not to affect the activity of this enzyme in the presence of a different activator. Since partially purified enzyme preparations must be assumed to be contaminated by potential polycationic activators, for instance, by other proteic material, and since partially purified enzyme preparations obtained by different purification procedures are expected to contain polycationic activators of different chemical nature, it appears logical that a given polyanion may be an inhibitor of one enzyme preparation, but not of a preparation of the same enzyme obtained by a different method. Among the numerous observations of this nature, it may be worth while to mention that Becker and Friedenwald (128) have reported the inhibition of calf liver β-glucuronidase by heparin, whereas heparin did not inhibit β-glucuronidase preparations purified in the writer's laboratory.

C. Inhibition of Other Biological Materials by Macromolecular Polyanions

In a considerable number of instances, macromolecular polyanions have been reported to inhibit more complex biological systems. These include the well-known anticoagulant action of heparin and of many other sulfated polysaccharides, which has been reviewed by Walton (129), Stefanini (130) and others, as well as the growth inhibitory effect of heparin in tissues (131–133), the inhibition of cell division by heparin (134–136), the thromboplastic action of heparin, which was interpreted as a binding of the polyanion on the surface of intact live leucocytes (137), the reduction of the infectivity of tobacco mosaic virus by poly-L-glutamate, polyacrylate, and pectate (138), the effect of amylose sulfate, dextran sulfate, and polyvinyl sulfate on the hyperchromicity of beef pancreas ribosomes (138a), and the irreversible loss of viability of T2 bacteriophage by polyglucose sulfate (139). The latter process has been studied with S^{35}-labeled polyanion which was found to complex directly with the phage. Among the possible mechanisms suggested for this inhibition was the blocking of the penetration enzyme, lysozyme, by the polyanion (139).

Polyanetholsulfonate, polyvinyl alcohol sulfonate, and dextran sulfate have been found to produce lesions in rabbits indistinguishable from those of the generalized Shwartzman reaction (140). This phenomenon is probably an intravascular precipitation of fibrinogen by the polyanions and can be prevented by heparin (141). Naturally occurring macromolecular polyanions have also been observed to cause hemorrhagic necrosis in animal tumors (142–145). Some of these substances which were obtained from culture filtrates of *E. coli* and *Serratia marcescens* (145) have been identified to be phospholipid-containing acid polysaccharide-protein complexes (146, 147).

Polyethylenesulfonate has been reported to possess tumor-inhibiting effects in mice (148), and moderate inhibition of mouse tumors has been observed with polyxenyl phosphate (149). The latter polyanion had been labeled with P^{32} and was thus found to be accumulated in the tumor tissue (149), while other macromolecular polyanions, especially dextran sulfate (150) and heparin (151), are known to collect predominantly in the liver, spleen, lung, and kidney. That polyxenyl phosphate combines directly with the tumor cells was also demonstrated by the fact that this polyanion is capable of increasing the electronegative charges of the cells when added *in vitro*, as shown by their increased electrophoretic mobility and by the loss of their amphoteric character (152).

It appears most likely that the previously mentioned effects of macromolecular polyanions on complete biological systems, such as living cells, viruses, or phages, are the consequence of unspecific polyanion-protein interactions which take place on the surface of the particles or cells. The tendency of complex formation of macromolecular polyanions is not limited, therefore, to *in vitro* conditions or to protein particles which are in a state of high molecular dispersion, as in solution.

D. Mechanism of Protein-Macromolecular Polyanion Interactions

The principal features leading to the complex formation of proteins with macromolecular polyanions are, no doubt, coulombic attraction forces between groups of opposite charges in the two classes of substances, as has been pointed out by many workers, for instance, Chargaff, Ziff, and Moore (*153*), Jacques (*154*), Gorter and Nanninga (*155*), Meyer (*156*), and others. In this respect, the interaction closely resembles, therefore, the complex formation of proteins with surface active compounds and other polyanions of low or medium molecular weight. The marked pH dependence of the complexes, as well as the characteristic effect of concentrated salt solutions which tend to dissociate the complexes into their component parts, is sufficient evidence for the electrostatic nature of these interactions.

In contrast to the protein complexes with surface active agents and other polyanions of low molecular weight, however, marcromolecular polyanions have been found to produce some inhibitory effects on enzymes also on the alkaline side of their isoelectric points, where the negative charges are predominant in both participants of the interaction (*106*, *111*). In addition to the electrostatic attraction, nonpolar forces must be expected, therefore, to be involved in the complex formation of proteins with macromolecular polyanions. Some light on this aspect has been cast by studies on the interaction of β-lipoproteins with macromolecular polyanions, which has been found to result in at least three different types of complexes, according to the nature of the polyanion (*157*). The presence of carboxyl, N-acetyl, or N-sulfatyl groups in the polyanion, as well as the molecular weight and degree of branching of the latter, appears to influence considerably the solubility of the complexes and to determine the affinity of their component parts for one another (*158*). Hydrogen bonding is assumed, therefore, to contribute markedly to the complex formation and is likely to be also responsible, at least in part, for the inhibition of enzymes by macromolecular polyanions and for the differences in inhibitory potency of various polyanions.

V. SUMMARY AND CONCLUSIONS

Polyanions are defined in this review as those substances which contain a large number of negatively charged groups on each *particle*. They thus include not only high polymer substances which possess acidic functions, such as polysaccharides containing uronic acid residues or sulfate ester groups, the nucleic acids, and synthetic macromolecular polyanions, but they also involve low molecular weight carboxylic acids and acid sulfate esters, such as anionic surface active agents which are known to form aggregated particles or micelles in aqueous media where the surface of each particle is covered by a multitude of negatively charged groups. Some nonpolymer organic mono- and polysulfonates of medium molecular weight, like suramin and other acid drugs or dyes, are related in many respects to the macromolecular polyanions and to the surface active agents by similarities in their structure and biological behavior, and have been included in the present discussion.

Polyanions interact with proteins to form complexes of various degrees of solubility. In many cases of biologically active proteins, this complex formation leads to reversible or irreversible loss of the biological activity. Polyanions have thus been found to inhibit a great number of enzymes; they also have been reported to inhibit proteohormones, toxins, antibodies, antigens, virus infectivity, bacterial growth, blood coagulation, mitosis, tumor growth, etc. Polyanions with strongly acid functions, like poly-sulfate or polyphosphate esters, are more frequently found to possess inhibitory action than polycarboxylic acids.

The mechanism of inhibition may vary from one system to another, but in many instances it is believed that the electrostatic attraction between groups of opposite charges on the protein and on the polyanion is the principal force causing complex formation. Consequently, interaction and inhibition are greatly dependent on the number of electropositive charges of the protein and, hence, on the acidity of the medium. As it would be expected from this simple mechanism of protein-polyanion interaction, the resulting inhibition is rather unspecific, both with respect to the nature or biological activity of the protein and to the chemical or physicochemical structure of the polyanion. Thus, as an example, the inhibition of many enzymes by sodium dodecyl sulfate and by sulfopolysaccharides appears to bear a considerable analogy.

In contrast to most surface active agents, macromolecular polyanions frequently contain other groups in addition to their sulfate ester, phosphate ester, or carboxylic acid functions. In the case of acid polysaccharides, these neutral functions mainly include hydroxyl or N-acetyl groups. These also contribute, although to a lesser degree than the acid groups, to the complex formation and, hence, to the inhibition, probably through hydrogen bonding. The inhibitory action of many macromolecular polyanions is, thus, slightly more specific than that of surface active agents with the effect that in many instances the inhibitory potency toward a given enzyme system has been found to vary considerably for different macromolecular polyanions. Likewise, the pH dependency of the inhibition is somewhat weaker for macromolecular polyanions than for surface active agents, and slight macroanionic enzyme inhibition on the alkaline side of the isoelectric point is not infrequent.

The addition of polycationic substances is capable of reversing the inhibitory action of polyanions if the affinity of the added polycation for the inhibitor is higher than that of the biologically active protein or if the added polycation is present in a large excess. A few instances are known where the roles of polycations and polyanions are reversed. Pepsin and cytochrome oxidase are inhibited by polycations, whereas certain polyanions may counteract the inhibition, and may even enhance the activity. Polycations also abolish the activating effect of heparin on lipoprotein lipase and, thus, produce inhibition of this enzyme.

In at least two enzyme systems, the inhibition by macromolecular polyanions has been found to be due to a sequestration of polycationic activators of the enzymes, rather than to a direct interaction between enzyme and polyanion. The activity of hyaluronidase and β-glucuronidase is subject to a sequence of events. These two enzymes dissociate upon dilution into inactive components, their dissociation is reversed by polycations which thus reactivate the dilute enzymes, and they lose their activity again through the addition of polyanions which offset the action of the polycations by complex formation. Present and future research will show whether this mechanism applies to a larger number of enzyme systems.

ACKNOWLEDGMENT

Some of the work published in this review has been supported in part by Research Grants RG-5664 and H-3850 from the National Institutes of Health, U. S. Public Health Service, and G 13257 and 23772 from the National Science Foundation.

REFERENCES

1. I. Langmuir, *J. Franklin Inst.* 218, 143 (1934).
2. K. B. Blodgett, *J. Ann. Chem. Soc.* 57, 1007 (1935).
3. H. P. Lundgren, *Textile Research J.* 15, 335 (1945).
4. F. W. Putnam, *Advances in Protein Chem.* 4, 79 (1948).
5. F. J. Van Antwerpen, *Ind. Eng. Chem.* 35, 126 (1943).
6. A. M. Schwarz and J. W. Perry, "Surface Active Agents." Interscience, New York, 1949.
7. I. Langmuir, *J. Am. Chem. Soc.* 39, 1848 (1917).
8. H. B. Bull and H. Neurath, *J. Biol. Chem.* 118, 163 (1937).
9. M. L. Anson, *J. Gen. Physiol.* 23, 239 (1939).
10. F. W. Putnam and H. Neurath, *J. Am. Chem. Soc.* 66, 1992 (1944).
11. M. L. Groves, N. J. Hipp, and T. L. McMeekin, *J. Am. Chem. Soc.* 73, 2790 (1951).
12. T. L. McMeekin, B. D. Polis, E. S. Della Monica, and J. H. Custer, *J. Am. Chem. Soc.* 71, 3606 (1949).
13. P. D. Boyer, F. G. Lum, G. A. Ballou, J. M. Luck, and R. G. Rice, *J. Biol. Chem.* 162, 181 (1946).
14. F. W. Putnam and H. Neurath, *J. Am. Chem. Soc.* 66, 692 (1944).
15. G. L. Miller and K. J. I. Andersson, *J. Biol. Chem.* 144, 475 (1942).

16. I. M. Klotz, *in* "The Proteins" (H. Neurath and K. Bailey, eds.), Vol. I, p. 727. Academic Press, New York, 1953.
17. H. B. Bull, *J. Am. Chem. Soc.* **67**, 10 (1945).
18. J. T. Yang and J. F. Foster, *J. Am. Chem. Soc.* **75**, 5560 (1953).
19. J. F. Foster and J. T. Yang, *J. Am. Chem. Soc.* **75**, 5743 (1953).
20. S. Grundy, H. L. Dobson, and A. C. Griffin, *Proc. Soc. Exptl. Biol. Med.* **98**, 313 (1958).
21. E. I. Valko, *Ann. N. Y. Acad. Sci.* **46**, 451 (1946).
22. D. Shoch and S. J. Fogelson, *Proc. Soc. Exptl. Biol. Med.* **50**, 304 (1942).
23. J. A. Cooper and H. B. Bull. *Abstr. Papers Presented at the 107th Meeting Am. Chem. Soc., Cleveland, Ohio, 1944.*
24. M. Marini and S. Levey, *Proc. Soc. Exptl. Biol. Med.* **88**, 611 (1955).
25. B. Fuchs, F. J. Ingelfinger, and M. Ellis, *Gastroenterology* **27**, 802 (1954).
26. T. Viswanatha, M. J. Pallansch, and I. E. Liener, *J. Biol. Chem.* **212**, 301 (1955).
27. E. D. Wills, *Biochem. J.* **57**, 109 (1954).
28. E. D. Wills, *Congr. intern. biochim., Résumés communs., 2ᵉ Congr., Paris, 1952* p. 237.
29. H. Katagiri and M. Ikemiya, *Kôso Kagaku Shinpojiumu,* **12**, 5 (1957); see *Chem. Abstr.* **51**, 16605.
30. M. Ikemiya, *Bull. Inst. Chem. Research, Kyoto Univ.* **35**, 81 (1957–1958); see *Chem. Abstr.* **52**, 11998.
31. E. D. Wills, *Biochem. J.* **60**, 529 (1955).
32. N. Grubhofer, *Z. physiol. Chem., Hoppe-Seyler's* **302**, 217 (1955).
33. G. Cuzzocrea, *Giorn. biochim.* **4**, 363 (1955).
34. W. M. Doizaki, I. E. Liener, C. M. Stowe, and C. E. Stevens, *Arch. Biochem. Biophys.* **73**, 425 (1958).
35. D. Keilin and E. F. Hartree, *Nature* **145**, 934 (1940).
36. K. Setälä, S. Lundbom, and P. Holsti, *Z. Krebsforsch.* **61**, 681 (1957).
37. D. Hockenhull, *Nature* **162**, 850 (1948).
38. I. M. Klotz and F. Tietze, *J. Biol. Chem.* **168**, 399 (1947).
39. F. E. Hunter, Jr. and L. Ford, *J. Biol. Chem.* **216**, 357 (1955).
40. J. H. Bodine and L. D. Carlson, *Proc. Natl. Acad. Sci. U.S.* **40**, 513 (1954).
41. A. P. Nygaard, *Acta Chem. Scand.* **10**, 397 (1956).
42. F. Bischoff, *Am. J. Physiol.* **145**, 123 (1945).
43. C. H. Li, *J. Biol. Chem.* **155**, 45 (1944).
44. M. Bayliss, *J. Infectious Diseases* **59**, 131 (1936).
45. L. F. Holmes, *Yale J. Biol. Med.* **14**, 155 (1941).
46. F. C. Bawden and N. W. Pirie, *Proc. Roy. Soc.* **B123**, 274 (1937).
47. M. Sreenivasaya and N. W. Pirie, *Biochem. J.* **32**, 1707 (1938).
48. F. C. Bawden and N. W. Pirie, *Brit. J. Exptl. Pathol.* **19**, 66 (1938).
49. F. C. Bawden and N. W. Pirie, *Biochem. J.* **34**, 1278 (1940).
50. G. L. Miller, *J. Biol. Chem.* **146**, 339 (1942).
51. T. Shedlovsky and J. E. Smadel, *J. Exptl. Med.* **72**, 511 (1940).
52. M. Klein, S. S. Kalter, and S. Mudd, *J. Immunol.* **51**, 389 (1945).
53. M. Bayliss, *J. Lab. Clin. Med.* **22**, 700 (1937).
54. Z. Baker, R. W. Harrison, and B. F. Miller, *J. Exptl. Med.* **73**, 249 (1941); **74**, 611 (1941).
55. L. Gershenfeld and M. Ibsen, *Am. J. Pharm.* **114**, 281 (1942).

56. A. Bolle and E. Kellenberger, *Schweiz. Z. allgem. Pathol. u. Bakteriol.* **21**, 714 (1958).
57. S. Lambin, J. Bernard, and A. Desvignes, *Compt. rend. soc. biol.* **151**, 659 (1957).
58. R. D. Hotchkiss, *Ann N. Y. Acad. Sci.* **46**, 479 (1946).
59. R. J. Dubos, "The Bacterial Cell." Harvard Univ. Press, Cambridge, Massachusetts, 1945.
60. H. H. Kœfoed-Johnsen and T. Mann, *Biochem. J.* **57**, 406 (1954).
61. T. Mann, *Proc. Soc. Study Fertility No.* **6**, 41 (1954).
62. R. F. Grover, C. A. Maaske, L. L. Hardt, and J. B. Henderson, *Gastroenterology* **22**, 263 (1952).
63. I. M. Klotz, F. M. Walker, and R. B. Pivan, *J. Am. Chem. Soc.* **68**, 1486 (1946).
64. I. M. Klotz, *J. Am. Chem. Soc.* **68**, 2299 (1946).
65. J. H. Quastel, *Biochem. J.* **25**, 1121 (1931).
66. B. W. Town, E. D. Wills, and A. Wormall, *Nature* **163**, 735 (1949).
67. B. W. Town and A. Wormall, *Biochem. J.* **44**, xxxviii (1949).
68. E. D. Wills and A. Wormall, *Biochem. J.* **44**, xxxix (1949).
69. E. D. Wills, *Biochem. J.* **50**, 421 (1952).
70. E. D. Wills and A. Wormall, *Nature* **165**, 813 (1950).
71. D. Hockenhull, *Nature* **162**, 813 (1948).
72. J. M. Beiler and G. J. Martin, *J. Biol. Chem.* **174**, 31 (1948).
73. P. C. Spensley and H. J. Rogers, *Nature* **173**, 1190 (1954).
74. J. P. Hummel, D. O. Anderson, and C P. Patel, *J. Biol. Chem.* **233**, 712 (1958).
75. P. Bernfeld, S. Jacobson, and H. C. Bernfeld, *Arch. Biochem. Biophys.* **69**, 198 (1957).
76. P. Bernfeld and L. P. Tuttle, *Federation Proc.* **18**, 191 (1959).
77. P. Bernfeld, L. P. Tuttle, and R. W. Hubbard, *Arch. Biochem. Biophys.* **92**, 232 (1961).
78. T. Astrup and N. Alkjaersig, *Nature* **166**, 568 (1950).
79. P. T. Mora and B. G. Young, *Arch. Biochem. Biophys.* **82**, 6 (1959).
80. K. Myers, *Physiol. Revs.* **27**, 344 (1947).
81. H. J. Rogers and P. C. Spensley, *Biochim. et Biophys. Acta* **13**, 293 (1954).
82. P. T. Mora and B. G. Young, *Nature* **181**, 1402 (1958).
83. H. Heymann, T. Ginsberg, Z. R. Gulick, and R. L. Mayer, *Proc. Soc. Exptl. Biol. Med.* **100**, 279 (1959).
84. J. Fellig and C. E. Wiley, *Arch. Biochem. Biophys.* **85**, 313 (1959).
85. K. W. Walton, *Brit. J. Pharmacol.* **7**, 370 (1952).
86. S. R. Dickman, *Science* **127**, 1392 (1958).
87. J. S. Roth, *Arch. Biochem. Biophys.* **44**, 265 (1953).
88. P. Bernfeld and T. F. Kelley, *Federation Proc.* **19**, 231 (1960).
89. P. Bernfeld and T. F. Kelley, *J. Biol Chem.* **238**, 1236 (1963).
90. A. Fischer and H. Herrmann, *Enzymologia* **3**, 180 (1937).
91. P. Bernfeld, B. J. Berkeley, and D. Ehrenfeld, manuscript in preparation.
91a. L. J. Ravin, J. G. Baldinus, and M. L. Mazur, *J. Pharm. Sci.* **51**, 857 (1962).

92. C. N. Mangieri, R. Engelberg, and L. O. Randall, *J. Pharmacol. Exptl. Therap.* **102**, 156 (1951).
93. L. M. Buruiana, *Naturwissenschaften* **44**, 306 (1957).
94. L. M. Buruiana and E. Hadarag, *Naturwissenschaften* **45**, 293 (1958).
95. K. Myrbäck and B. Persson, *Arkiv. Kemi* **5**, 177 (1952).
96. E. A. Balazs, B. Högberg, and T. C. Laurent, *Acta Physiol. Scand.* **23**, 168 (1951).
97. D. McClean, *J. Pathol. Bacteriol.* **54**, 284 (1942).
98. H. J. Rogers, *Biochem. J.* **40**, 583 (1946).
99. J. Seifter, D. H. Baeder, and A. J. Begany, *Proc. Soc. Exptl. Biol. Med.* **72**, 277 (1949).
100. G. P. Kerby and G. S. Eadie, *Proc. Soc. Exptl. Biol. Med.* **83**, 111 (1953).
101. M. K. Horwitt, *Science* **92**, 89 (1940).
102. L. Vandendriessche, *Arch. Biochem. Biophys.* **65**, 347 (1956).
103. N. Zöllner and J. Fellig, *Naturwissenschaften* **39**, 523 (1952).
104. G. DeLamirande, G. Weber, and A. Cantero, *Am. J. Physiol.* **184**, 415 (1956).
105. E. D. Korn, *J. Biol. Chem.* **215**, 1 (1955).
105a. S. Levey and S. Sheinfeld, *Gastroenterology* **27**, 625 (1954).
106. E. Diczfalusy, O. Fernö, H. Fex, B. Högberg, T. Linderot, and T. Rosenberg, *Acta Chem. Scand.* **7**, 913 (1953).
107. O. Fernö, H. Fex, B. Högberg, T. Linderot, S. Veige, and E. Diczfalusy, *Acta Chem. Scand.* **12**, 1675 (1958).
108. O. Fernö, H. Fex, B. Högberg, T. Linderot, and T. Rosenberg, *Acta Chem. Scand.* **7**, 921 (1953).
109. R. C. Skarnes and D. W. Watson, *J. Bacteriol.* **70**, 110 (1955).
110. S. Moss, *Science* **115**, 69 (1952).
111. J. P. Hummel, M. Flores, and G. Nelson, *J. Biol. Chem.* **233**, 717 (1958).
112. L. Hahn, *Nature* **170**, 282 (1952).
113. L. Hahn and J. Fekete, *Acta Chem. Scand.* **7**, 798 (1953).
114. L. Hahn and E. Frank, *Acta Chem. Scand.* **7**, 806 (1953).
115. E. E. Dellert and M. A. Stahmann, *Nature* **176**, 1028 (1955).
116. M. Berdick and H. Morawetz, *J. Biol. Chem.* **206**, 959 (1954).
117. J. H. Bragdon and R. J. Havel, *Science* **120**, 113 (1954).
118. K. H. Meyer, "Natural and Synthetic High Polymers," p. 112. Interscience, New York, 1950.
119. H. Malmgren and O. Lamm, *Z. anorg. u. allgem. Chem.* **245**, 103 (1940); **252**, 256 (1944).
120. H. Morawetz and W. L. Hughes, *J. Phys. Chem.* **56**, 64 (1952).
121. E. Katchalski, A. Berger, and H. Neumann, *Nature* **173**, 998 (1954).
122. P. Person and A. Fine, *Science* **132**, 43 (1960).
122a. J. Stolkowski and A. J. Rosenberg, *Bull. soc. chim. biol.* **35**, 529 (1953).
123. P. Bernfeld, H. C. Bernfeld, J. S. Nisselbaum, and W. H. Fishman, *J. Am. Chem. Soc.* **76**, 4872 (1954).
123a. M. Sela, F. H. White, Jr., and C B. Anfinsen, *Biochim. et Biophys. Acta* **31**, 417 (1959).
123b. E. Haber and C. B. Anfinsen, *J. Biol. Chem.* **236**, 422 (1961).
123c. F. H. White, Jr., *J. Biol. Chem.* **236**, 1353 (1961).
123d. C. B. Anfinsen and E. Haber, *J. Biol. Chem.* **236**, 1361 (1961).

123e. C. B. Anfinsen, E. Haber, M. Sela, and F. H. White, Jr., *Proc. Natl. Acad. Sci. U. S.* **47**, 1309 (1961).

123f. E. Stellwagen and H. K. Schachman, *Biochemistry* **1**, 1056 (1962).

123g. W. C. Deal and K. E. Van Holde, *Federation Proc.* **21**, 254 (1962).

123h. T. Isemura, T. Takagi, Y. Maeda, and K. Imai, *Biochem. Biophys. Res. Commun.* **5**, 373 (1961).

123i. C. Levinthal, E. R. Signer, and K. Fetherolf, *Proc. Natl. Acad. Sci. U. S.* **48**, 1230 (1962).

124. G. M. Jeffree, *Biochim. et Biophys. Acta* **20**, 503 (1956).

125. G. M. Jeffree, *Nature* **175**, 509 (1955).

126. H. Lineweaver and D. Burk, *J. Am. Chem. Soc.* **56**, 658 (1934).

127. G. A. Levy, *Biochem. J.* **52**, 464 (1952).

128. B. Becker and J. S. Friedenwald, *Arch. Biochem.* **22**, 101 (1949).

129. K. W. Walton, *Brit. Med. Bull.* **11**, 62 (1955).

130. M. Stefanini, *An. J. Med.* **14**, 64 (1953).

131. A. Fischer, *Arch. pathol. Anat. u. Physiol., Virchow's* **279**, 94 (1930–1931).

132. A. Goerner, *J. Lab. Clin. Med.* **16**, 369 (1931).

133. A. Fischer, *Protoplasma* **26**, 344 (1936).

134. L. V. Heilbrunn and W. L. Wilson, *Proc. Soc. Exptl. Biol. Med.* **70**, 179 (1949).

135. A. Balazs and H. J. Holmgren, *Proc. Soc. Exptl. Biol. Med.* **72**, 142 (1949).

136. J. Runnstrom and G. Krizat, *Exptl. Cell Research* **1**, 497 (1950).

137. A. Fischer, *Skand. Arch. Physiol.* **75**, 121 (1936).

138. M. A. Stahmann and S. S. Gothoskar, *Phytopathology* **48**, 362 (1958).

138a. J. T. Madison and S. R. Dickman, *Biochemistry* **2**, 326 (1963).

139. P. T. Mora and B. G. Young, *Abstr. of Papers Presented at the Meeting Am. Chem. Soc., New York, 1960*, p. 51C.

140. L. Thomas, J. Brunson, and R. T. Smith, *J. Exptl. Med.* **102**, 249 (1955).

141. L. Thomas, R. T. Smith, and R. Von Korff, *J. Exptl. Med.* **102**, 263 (1955).

142. G. Shwartzman and N. Michailovsky, *Proc. Soc. Exptl. Biol. Med.* **29**, 737 (1931–32).

143. H. B. Andervont and M. J. Shear, *Proc. Soc. Exptl. Biol. Med.* **34**, 673 (1936).

144. J. L. Hartwell, M. J. Shear, and J. R. Adams, Jr., *J. Natl. Cancer Inst.* **4**, 107 (1943).

145. M. J. Shear, *J. Natl. Cancer Inst.* **4**, 461 (1944).

146. P. Rathgeb and B. Sylvén, *J. Natl. Cancer Inst.* **14**, 1099 (1954).

147. P. Rathgeb and B. Sylvén, *J. Natl. Cancer Inst.* **14**, 1109 (1954).

148. W. Regelson and J. F. Holland, *Nature* **181**, 46 (1958).

149. C. Muehlbaecher, J. V. Straumfjord, Jr., J. P. Hummel, and W. Regelson, *Cancer Research* **19**, 907 (1959).

150. K. W. Walton, *Brit. J. Pharmacol.* **9**, 1 (1954).

151. H. B. Eiber, I. Danishefsky, and F. J. Borrelli, *Proc. Soc. Exptl. Biol. Med.* **98**, 672 (1958).

152. J. V. Straumfjord, Jr. and J. P. Hummel, *Cancer Research* **19**, 913 (1959).

153. E. Chargaff, M. Ziff, and D. H. Moore, *J. Biol. Chem.* **139**, 383 (1941).

154. L. B. Jacques, *Biochem. J.* **37,** 189 (1943).
155. E. Gorter and L. Nanninga, *Koninkl. Ned Akad. Wetenschap., Proc., Ser.*
      C55, 341, 351 (1952); *Discussions Faraday Soc. No.* **13,** 205 (1953).
156. K. Meyer, *Discussions Faraday Soc. No.* 13, 271 (1953).
157. P. Bernfeld, V. M. Donahue, and M. E. Berkowitz, *J. Biol. Chem.* **226,** 51
      (1957).
158. P. Bernfeld, J. S. Nisselbaum, B. J. Berkeley, and R. W. Hanson, *J. Biol.
      Chem.* **235,** 2852 (1960).

CHAPTER 31

Inhibitions in the Citric Acid Cycle

J. H. Quastel

I. INTRODUCTION

Studies of the biological oxidation of succinate and of its products, fumarate and L-malate, gave rise to observations fundamental for the development of modern concepts of the mechanisms involved in respiratory processes, particularly those embraced by the citric acid cycle. The demonstration (1) that pyruvic acid is a normal product of the biological oxidation of fumaric acid and therefore of its precursor, succinic acid (2–5), led to a study of the relations existing between succinic and fumaric acid. This resulted in the finding, with bacterial suspensions (5), that a reversible equilibrium exists between succinate and fumarate in presence of succinic dehydrogenase, and later in the observation that substances exist, other than the substrates succinate and fumarate, that have an affinity for this enzyme. It was found (6) that molecules related chemically in structure to the substrate may have an affinity for the enzyme [or, as then designated, its active center (7)] and may compete with the natural substrate and thus inhibit its metabolism. This observation was the foundation of the principle of competitive inhibition, which was early used in an investigation of the effects of succinate and its analogues on the growth of *Escherichia coli* (8).

Various substances of the structure $R \cdot CH_2COOH$ inhibit the activity of succinic dehydrogenase, but of these malonic acid (6) is the best known. It inhibits the enzyme competitively (6), and its high specificity of action has made it an important tool in the investigation of respiratory processes. Its action as a competitive inhibitor of succinic dehydrogenase, shown originally with suspensions of *E. coli*, was found to apply to mammalian tissues (9) and to soluble succinic dehydrogenase (10–12). There are, however, wide differences between the degrees of inhibition of the rates of oxygen consumption brought about by malonate in the presence of succinate with different organisms and tissues, these being largely due to the differences between rates of oxidation of succinate and of fumarate (or L-malate) with these cells. When the latter rate is large, relatively little effect of malonate on the rate of total oxygen uptake is seen, owing to the fact that, in spite of the inhibition of succinic dehydrogenase, sufficient fumarate (or L-malate) is formed to enable subsequent oxidative reactions to proceed optimally (9). Thus, malonate exercises but little inhibition of oxygen consumption of suspensions of *Bacillus subtilis* or *Micrococcus lysodeikticus* in the presence of succinate under conditions where it almost completely suppresses the rate of oxygen consumption of rabbit muscle or brain tissue. The observations (13) that malonate inhibition of respiration may be overcome by the addition of fumarate, that fumarate has a catalytic effect on cell respiration (13, 14), that malonate inhibition leads aerobically to the formation of succinate, that in the presence of malonate a variety of substrates, e.g., malate, oxalacetate, citrate, and α-ketoglutarate, is converted to succinate, and that oxalacetate and pyruvate together can give rise to citrate in the presence of tissues, led to the formulation of the citric acid cycle (15, 16) as a major respiratory process.

The fact that succinic dehydrogenase is the only enzyme that is inhibited to a marked extent by malonate at low concentrations (up to 1 mM) at physiological succinate concentrations is supported by the observation that injection of malonate leads to the accumulation of succinate in animal tissues and body fluids (17, 18).

II. INHIBITORS OF SUCCINIC DEHYDROGENASE

A. Malonate

Study of the properties of succinic dehydrogenase may be simplified by replacement of methylene blue (19) as hydrogen acceptor by ferricyanide (20), whose reduced product is not autoxidizable and whose reduction, measured either manometrically or spectroscopically, makes it possible to assay affinities of succinate or its analogues to the enzyme. Using ferricyanide as a hydrogen acceptor, it was found (21) that the K_m of succinic dehydrogenase in six different heart muscle preparations has values ranging from $2.5 \times 10^{-4}\,M$ to $5.3 \times 10^{-4}\,M$, while the inhibitory constant K_i of malonate has values ranging from $5.4 \times 10^{-6}\,M$ to $9.8 \times 10^{-6}\,M$. The ratio of affinities of malonate and succinate varies from 4.7 to 60, depending on the nature and concentration of the hydrogen acceptor. The variations are explained as being due to differences in the values of the rate constant for decomposition of the enzyme-substrate complex to give the products of reaction. It was concluded (21) that the true ratio of affinities of succinic dehydrogenase for malonate and succinate, in the absence of further reactions of succinate, is about 3. Ferricyanide may react, however, at several points in the succinic oxidase chain, and it is considered that phenazine methosulfate provides a more reliable means for assay of succinic dehydrogenase activities in a variety of preparations (22, 23). The kinetic constants, using the phenazine methosulfate method, of succinic dehydrogenase at pH 7.6 and 38° are given (10) as follows: K_m values for succinate, for heart, yeast, and *Proteus vulgaris* are $1.3 \times 10^{-3}\,M$, $1.0 \times 10^{-3}\,M$, and 1.3–$2 \times 10^{-3}\,M$, respectively, while the K_m values at 38° for fumarate for these preparations are $1.9 \times 10^{-3}\,M$, $1.03 \times 10^{-3}\,M$, and $1.8 \times 10^{-3}\,M$, respectively. The corresponding value for malonate K_i is given as $4.1 \times 10^{-5}\,M$ at 38°

and $2.5 \times 10^{-5} M$ at 20° for beef heart succinic dehydrogenase, and as $1 \times 10^{-5} M$ at 38° for a purified yeast enzyme (10).

With an isolated soluble succinic dehydrogenase preparation (10, 12) (and ferricyanide at pH 7.8 with bovine serum albumin present) at 20–23°, it was found (11) that K_m (succinate) is $1.2 \times 10^{-3} M$, and K_i (malonate) is $4.5 \times 10^{-5} M$. The ferricyanide method was chosen to avoid the complication due to the formation of hydrogen peroxide during the reoxidation of reduced phenazine methosulfate. Some values, collected by Keilin and King (11), for the Michaelis constants of succinic dehydrogenase are given in Table I. The affinities of the soluble enzyme for malonate and pyrophosphate differ from those reported with earlier preparations of the enzyme (24), the affinity for malonate being about five times that for pyrophosphate (11).

The affinity of malonate to succinic dehydrogenase is also shown by its ability (in common with succinate and fumarate) to protect the sulfhydryl groups of the dehydrogenase from oxidation by oxidized gluta-thione (25, 26). Cystine is also inhibitory to the succinoxidase system (27), the extent of inhibition in tissue homogenates being dependent on the concentration of the dicarboxylic acids present, particularly fumarate and malonate (28). It had earlier been shown that fumarate and its analogues (e.g., succinate, malate) can protect the enzyme fumarase from the toxic action of dyestuffs and certain trypanocidal agents (29, 30). Such protection indicates an affinity for the enzyme active center, if combination between the protector molecule and the toxic agent does not occur. The protection of succinic dehydrogenase by malonate takes place with very low concentrations of the latter, much lower than those necessary for the inhibition of the succinic dehydrogenase (26). Protection also occurs, as would be expected, with succinate and fumarate. Pyrophosphate also protects, but with less efficiency.

B. Effects of Thiol Reactants

Copper ions, maleic acid, and alloxan are inhibitory to the enzyme, presumably through their combination with the thiol groups of succinic dehydrogenase (26); malic, lactic, and α-glycerophosphate dehydro-genases are much less sensitive to these inhibitors.

Succinic dehydrogenase is also inhibited by sodium diethyldithiocar-bamate (DDC), this being due, not to chelation with a metal, but to the oxidized form of DDC, namely, tetraethyldithiocarbamyl disulfide $[(C_2H_5)_2NCS \cdot SS \cdot SCN(C_2H_5)_2]$ derived from DDC by an oxidation catalyzed by the cytochrome system (31). The oxidized product is

TABLE I

MICHAELIS CONSTANTS OF SUCCINIC DEHYDROGENASE

Substrate	$K_m{}^a$	$K_m{}^b$		$K_m{}^c$	
	20°–23°C	20°–23°C	38°C	0°C	38°C
Succinate	$1.2 \times 10^{-3}\ M$	$5.2 \times 10^{-4}\ M$	$1.3 \times 10^{-3}\ M$	$1.9 \times 10^{-3}\ M$	$5.8 \times 10^{-4}\ M$
Malonate	$4.5 \times 10^{-5}\ M$	$2.5 \times 10^{-5}\ M$	$4.1 \times 10^{-5}\ M$	—	—
Pyrophosphate	$2.3 \times 10^{-4}\ M$	—	—	—	—

a Keilin and King (11).
b Singer et al. (10).
c Wang et al. (12).

inhibitory, presumably by its ability to oxidize the thiol groups of the enzyme (11). Tetrathionate is also inhibitory presumably for the same reason.

The well-known thiol reactant p-chloromercuribenzoate inactivates soluble succinic dehydrogenase. The enzyme may be reactivated by a short incubation with cyanide (10). Thus, conclusions as to the thiol nature of succinic dehydrogenase obtained from studies with particulate preparations of the enzyme are confirmed by studies with the soluble enzyme preparation.

Alloxan inhibition of the citric acid cycle (32), which occurs at low concentrations, e.g., 0.03 mM, is not wholly due to a suppression of succinic oxidase activity. Succinate oxidation is less sensitive to alloxan than that of pyruvate, a-ketoglutarate, or L-malate by rat kidney homogenates. Protection against inhibition may be brought about by the presence of 0.15 mM nicotinicadenine dinucleotide (NAD) or 0.6 mM glutathione. Alloxan inhibition of yeast fermentation (33) is also suppressed by the addition of NAD, and the diabetogenic action of alloxan in rats may be diminished by preliminary injection of nicotinamide, an effect probably due to an elevation of the NAD level (34, 35). These facts point to an interference of alloxan with NAD-linked metabolic systems, and may account for the uncoupling action of alloxan on oxidative phosphorylation (32, 36). Conceivably, alloxan may compete with NAD as a hydrogen acceptor for some dehydrogenase system. It should be noted that moderately high concentrations of NADH and NAD have been held to be competitive inhibitors with respect to ferricyanide (37), which can act at more than one point in the NADH oxidase chain, either directly with NADH (20, 38) or at a site probably identical with that taken by cytochrome c (37).

C. Effects of Fluoride

Fluoride and phosphate each have weak inhibitory effects on succinic dehydrogenase and compete with succinate for the enzyme; a mixture of the two may be strongly inhibitory (40). A study of the kinetics of the inhibitions indicates that one phosphate ion and one fluoride ion are involved in the inhibition. It is pointed out (40) that inhibitions by fluoride often involve two fluoride ions, e.g., that of enolase (41) and the oxidation of quinol by cytochrome c and cytochrome oxidase (42). It has been suggested (43) that succinic dehydrogenase is a manganese compound on the basis of the fluoride inhibition, but this seems unlikely as managanese ions have but little effect on the enzyme activity (40). The suggestion that the enzyme is a calcium complex (44), both because of the fluoride inhibition and of the activating action of calcium ions, is also unlikely, as it is known that the calcium activation is connected with the manner in which the enzyme preparation is made (31, 45) (for instance, no activating effect of calcium is seen with the enzyme in presence of phosphate-free buffers). Aluminum and chromium ions and those of the rare earths (46, 47) increase the rate of oxidation of succinate in the presence of a variety of tissue preparations. The suggestion was made (48) that the activating effect of calcium on succinic dehydrogenase is due to its activation of an enzyme hydrolyzing NAD [whose presence produces oxalacetate, a potent inhibitor of succinic dehydrogenase (45, 49)], but opposed to this suggestion was the demonstration that calcium ions are able to exert their effects in the absence of NAD from the enzyme preparation (31).

Fluoride, in comparison with other inhibitors, is not a particularly powerful inhibitor of succinic dehydrogenase; but if the substrate, succinate, is used at the low concentrations normally found in cells, fluoride becomes a strong inhibitor. It is conceivable, in fact, that the entire inhibitory effect of fluoride on cell respiration (42) may be due to its effect on succinic dehydrogenase (40). It has been concluded (40) that succinic dehydrogenase is the only component of the succinic oxidase system which is susceptible to fluoride, although the isolated enzyme is apparently less sensitive than the complete respiratory system, possibly because the enzyme within the cell is not working at optimal activity.

D. Effects of Cyanide

Cyanide, in low concentrations, inhibits the oxidation of succinate by the cell oxidase system by combination with cytochrome oxidase (cytochrome a_3). It therefore prevents the reoxidation of other components of the cytochrome system (cytochrome b, c_1, c, and a). It has no effect on the anaerobic oxidation of succinate by methylene blue and other hydrogen (or electron) acceptors. However, cyanide, at a relatively high concentration (0.1 M) brings about a considerable inhibition (50%) of succinic dehydrogenase activity (50). It appears (51) that the enzyme is slowly and irreversibly inactivated by cyanide, the rate depending on temperature and concentration of cyanide. It may be protected from such inactivation by succinate (in its role as hydrogen donor) or by sodium dithionite, but not by malonate or by fumarate. The inactivation is due (11) to a reaction of cyanide with a disulfide group of the succinic dehydrogenase, which is independent of the thiol groups already known to be implicated in the activity of the enzyme (25, 26). Thus, the enzyme needs for its activity not only flavin adenine nucleotide, two or four iron atoms, and two thiol groups per molecule but an additional disulfide group (10–12). The succinic dehydrogenase of a particulate preparation of brain tissue or of yeast cells, unlike that of a heart muscle preparation, is not affected by incubation with cyanide (52). This is held (11) to be due to a more efficient protection of the enzyme's disulfide group, which may play a role as a carrier of hydrogen via the flavin prosthetic group to the cytochrome system.

Cyanide may therefore react with the components of the succinic oxidase system in the following ways: (a) rapid reversible reaction with the trivalent iron of cytochrome oxidase, (b) slow and reversible reaction with the trivalent iron of cytochrome c, and (c) slow and irreversible reaction with a disulfide group of succinic dehydrogenase.

E. Effects of Action of Iron Chelators

While the role of the iron in succinic dehydrogenase activity is still problematical (53), it is known that certain iron-chelating agents exert inhibitory effects. Thus, 8-oxyquinoline, O-phenanthroline, and a,a'-dipyridyl as well as crystalline β_1-globulin are inhibitory (54). It is suggested (10) that O-phenanthroline, for example, forms a ternary complex with the enzyme, the complex having about 70% of the original activity in assays requiring the participation of the enzymic iron (e.g., with ferricyanide, phenazine methosulfate) and full activity in those assays where the carrier reacts with the flavin (FMN, diethylsafranine). Possibly, the iron may be the immediate electron donor to ferricyanide and phenazine methosulfate (10) [see, however (53)].

It should be noted that hematin inhibits succinic dehydrogenase activity, concentrations of $3 \times 10^{-4} M$ and $6 \times 10^{-4} M$ inhibiting the activity of a soluble preparation by 75% and 100%, respectively (11). Its mode of action is unknown.

F. Effects of High Oxygen Tension

Brain cell respiration is inhibited at high tensions of oxygen, the rate of respiration falling off to a greater extent in the presence of oxygen than in air, particularly when the respiration is allowed to occur in the presence of glucose, lactate, or pyruvate (55). Apparently, the most vulnerable enzyme is the thiol enzyme, pyruvic oxidase (55). Respiration in presence of succinate is also sensitive to the inhibitory effect of oxygen. Protection may be afforded by the presence of malonate (1 mM) or manganese ions (0.25 mM) (*56*). It is reported that, at pressures of 4–7 atmospheres oxygen, the thiol groups of succinate are slowly oxidized (*56–58*).

G. Effects of Arsenicals

Investigations reported to the Medical Research Council (U.K.) in 1940, showed that trivalent organic arsenoso compounds are highly inhibitory to thiol enzymes, particularly pyruvic oxidase, choline dehydrogenase, and succinic dehydrogenase (*59, 60*). 2-Amino-4-arsenosophenol is a highly effective inhibitor, its effects being neutralized by the addition to the arsenoso compound of thiol compounds such as glutathione and cysteine. The pentavalent arsenic compounds, such as tryparsamide or atoxyl, are inert until they are reduced to the trivalent form. The organic arsenoso compounds establish an equilibrium with the thiol enzymes as their toxicities do not increase with time, and the activities of some of the enzymes are restored by addition of thiol compounds (*59, 60*). The inhibitory effects of the organic arsenoso compounds are greater than those due to arsenite at equivalent concentrations. Succinate protects its dehydrogenase from inactivation by the arsenoso compound (*59, 60*).

Many thiol enzymes are attacked by trivalent arsenicals (*59–61*), but of these the brain pyruvic oxidase system seems to be most sensitive, 50% inhibition occurring with 17 μM lewisite (*62*). The trivalent organic arsenicals were first used as thiol reagents in 1935 (*63*); their addition compounds with the thiol compounds readily dissociate on increase of pH. With dithiol compounds, such as reduced lipoic acid, the trivalent arsenicals form stable ring structures, the combination not being reversed by subsequent addition of a monothiol compound. The inhibition of pyruvate oxidase by a trivalent arsenical such as lewisite, which is presumably due to an attack on the lipoate cofactor, cannot be reversed by subsequent addition of cysteine (*64*). It can, however, be reversed by certain dithiol compounds, notably 2,3-dimercaptopropanol (BAL) (*65*).

H. Effects of Iodoacetate

While iodoacetate, a well-known thiol reagent, has little or no effect on the activity of succinic dehydrogenase, its ester, ethyl iodoacetate, is a highly effective inhibitor (inhibition occurring at 0.7 mM) (*66*). For information on the effects of lachrymators and chemical warfare substances on thiol enzymes, the reader is referred to a variety of reviews (67–73) on this subject, details of which are outside the scope of this chapter.

I. Effects of Quinones

Succinic oxidase is inhibited by quinones (74), benzoquinone (5 × $10^{-5} M$) bringing about 80% inhibition (61). The inhibition is suppressed by the addition of glutathione (2 mM). p-Benzoquinone inhibition takes place noncompetitively in a heart muscle preparation in which the succinate-methylene blue system is mediated by ubiquinone and other active quinones (75).

Doubtless, the quinones are largely effective by their reactions with enzyme thiol groups (76, 77). A large number of naphthoquinone derivatives (antimalarials) have been tested on a succinic oxidase preparation, but no correlation of the inhibitors with their therapeutic effects has been found (78).

J. Effects of Pyrophosphate

Pyrophosphate, known as an inhibitor of cell respiration (79), inhibits succinic dehydrogenase competitively. It appears to act in a manner similar to that of malonate, by competition with succinate by virtue of its adjacent acid groups (24, 51). Kinetic studies with a soluble succinic dehydrogenase preparation confirm the fact that pyrophosphate is a competitive inhibitor of succinate (11), and a value for K_m (pyrophosphate) is given in Table I.

K. Effects of Oxalacetate

Since the observation of the competitive inhibitory action of malonate on succinic dehydrogenase, many studies have been made of the effects of other succinic acid analogues. The most important of these is oxalacetic acid.

Oxalacetate is probably the most potent competitive inhibitor of succinic dehydrogenase both in its soluble and its particulate form (45, 80–82) [K_i 1.5 × $10^{-6} M$ (82)]. Under conditions in which oxalacetate accumulates, succinate oxidation is inhibited (83, 84).

The importance of the inhibitory action of oxalacetate lies in the fact that, because of this, the substance may exert a rate-controlling effect on cell respiration, or that aspect of it controlled by the citric acid cycle.

It is known (45, 49) that the addition of NAD to a suspension of washed and ground pig heart greatly reduces its succinic dehydrogenase activity. This is attributed (45) to the formation of oxalacetate from succinate by the action of succinic dehydrogenase and of malate dehydrogenase in conjunction with NAD. The oxalacetate formed, even in very small quantities, inhibits succinic dehydrogenase. The addition of NADase (85) to the heart preparation removes the inhibitory effect due to NAD (86), but the inhibitory effect is retained if nicotinamide is added at the same time to diminish the activity of the NADase (86). The addition of NAD to a brain preparation has no effect on the latter's succinic dehydrogenase activity, and this was attributed to a rapid breakdown of oxalacetate (45). It is more likely, however, that the lack of effect is due to the high NADase activity of the brain preparation. In the presence of nicotinamide, the inhibitory effect of NAD on brain succinic dehydrogenase is evident (86).

The rate-limiting effect of oxalacetate on succinate metabolism in the intact cell is seen in a study of the conversion of succinate-2,3-C^{14} into radioactive amino acids in brain cortex slices in the absence and presence of glucose (87). In the presence of an ample supply of acetyl CoA, such as is afforded by the presence of glucose, the yields of radioactive CO_2 and amino acids, particularly glutamate and glutamine, are much increased above those found in the absence of glucose. The fraction of radioactive succinate converted to radioactive CO_2 is increased threefold by the addition of glucose, and at the same time the yield of labeled aspartate (formed by transamination of oxalacetate) is almost halved. These results are satisfactorily explained by the conclusion that succinate metabolism is retarded by the formation of oxalacetate, whose removal by condensation into the citric acid cycle allows succinate metabolism to be enhanced, aspartate yield to be reduced, and glutamate and glutamine formation to be increased.

Inhibition of succinic oxidase by oxalacetate (0.2 μM) may be prevented (48) by addition of L-glutamate, which converts it to aspartate by transamination.

L. Mitochondrial Respiration in Presence of Succinate and the Effects of Metabolic Inhibitors

Although, as already pointed out, the effects of glucose on the oxidation of succinate, and on the conversion of the latter to aspartate, to glutamate, and to glutamine in brain cortex slices, may be explained by the conclusion that the formation of oxalacetate is a controlling factor in succinate metabolism (87), the use of cell fractions, such as mitochondria, makes it possible to study in more detail the somewhat complicated factors involved in succinate oxidation and the effects of inhibitors.

Succinate brings about the reduction of NAD in mitochondria and it has been suggested that this involves a reversal of oxidative phosphorylation (87a–k). A different mechanism, competition between succinate and NADH for a common rate-limiting component of the respiratory chain, has also been suggested (87l, m), and it has been disputed as to whether a reversal of oxidative phosphorylation plays a major role in succinate oxidations in mitochondria or homogenates (87n). Competition between substrates for oxidizing catalysts presumably plays an important role in cell oxidations although this may be more observable in cell fractions than in the intact cell. Many years ago (87o) it was observed that when a mixture of succinate and lactate was added to minced guinea pig brain, the oxidation of succinate was retarded by an amount proportional to the oxidation of the lactate. The explanation given at that time was that there was competition between the substrates for an intracellular hydrogen carrier.

Recent observations have given rise to the conclusion that the reduction of NAD by succinate requires energy made available by oxidative phosphorylation, but not necessarily in the form of ATP, as such reduction can occur (39) in the presence of concentrations of oligomycin which can inhibit synthesis of ATP but not that of energy-rich intermediates which precede ATP formation (111, 112, 114). In the absence of oligomycin, a competition for an energy-rich intermediate possibly occurs between a reaction leading, on one hand, to the formation of ATP and a reaction (involving succinate and NAD) leading, on the other hand, to the formation of NADH$_2$. Thus, according to this hypothesis, the continued utilization of NADH$_2$ (as, for example, in the reductive amination of a-ketoglutarate to L-glutamate) leads to a diminution in the rate of formation of ATP (39, 114).

When beef heart mitochondria are incubated anaerobically with a mixture of succinate, NAD, and ATP, the rate of formation of NADH$_2$ is dependent on the concentration of ATP (87q). This may be suppressed by suitable concentrations of Amytal, oligomycin, and uncouplers of oxidative phosphorylation. Both the ATP-dependent reduction of NAD by succinate and the fumarate oxidation of NADH$_2$ are inhibited by malonate, Amytal, and high concentrations of antimycin (*87r*), the results supporting the concept of reversible oxidative phosphorylation in the NADH region of the respiratory chain. The NADH dehydrogenase system would appear to be implicated as Amytal is known to inhibit the reduction of coenzyme Q_1 by NADH (*87s*).

The proposition (*87t*) that aerobic oxidation of succinate by rat liver mitochondria requires ATP is supported by the finding that preincubation of the mitochondria in an arsenate medium (free of phosphate) leads to depression of succinic oxidase activity when measured in the presence of 2,4-dinitrophenol or dicoumarol, and that addition of ATP, after the preincubation, restores the oxidation. However, the restoration by ATP occurs only after a time lag; the inactivation is not specific for succinate oxidation nor is the reactivation specific for ATP (*87u*). Moreover, the reactivation by ATP is not sensitive to oligomycin. It has been suggested (*87u*) that the phenomena in question are due to changes in mitochondrial structure.

Doubt, however, is thrown on the possibility that succinate oxidation in mitochondria is necessarily linked with oxidative phosphorylation by the demonstration that a mixture of 0.5 mM dinitrophenol and 1.25 mM Amytal, which strongly inhibits oxidative phosphorylation, may not inhibit the reduction of acetoacetate by succinate (*87n*). 2,4-Dinitrophenol stimulates respiration of a rat liver homogenate in presence of succinate at 0.05 mM and inhibits it at 0.5 mM.

Amytal, which does not normally inhibit succinate oxidation, abolishes both the stimulatory and inhibitory effects of dinitrophenol on the respiration of liver homogenate and on succinate oxidation (*87n*). It does not reverse the inhibition of oxidative phosphorylation by dinitrophenol. In this connection, it may also be observed that barbiturates suppress the stimulated respiration of rat brain cortex slices (in a glucose-saline medium) brought about by the addition of 2,4-dinitrophenol (*87v*). It is possible to explain this by the known suppression by barbiturates and other anesthetics of ADP-dependent $NADH_2$ oxidation (see Chapter 33).

The stimulation of liver homogenate respiration brought about by Amytal in presence of succinate and an *inhibitory* concentration of 2,4-dinitrophenol is abolished by the addition of ATP. The evidence (*87n*) supports the conclusion that, in presence of Amytal, electron transport from NADH is no longer controlled by ADP or phosphate or both (see also Chapter 33). The activity of purified succinic dehydrogenase is not affected by dinitrophenol.

The steady-state concentration of oxalacetate controls the rate of oxygen uptake in isolated mitochondria in presence of succinate or

L-malate (*87p*), and the removal of oxalacetate by transamination with L-glutamate stimulates the rate of oxygen consumption (*87p*). The addition of ATP (magnesium salt) prevents the inhibition by added oxalacetate of the oxidation of succinate in rat kidney homogenates (*83*; see also *82*). It is held that this may be due to diminished penetration of oxalacetate into the mitochondria (*39*).

The suggestion that oxalacetate may be the immediate cause of the inhibition of succinate oxidation by the presence of a relatively high concentration of dinitrophenol (*87w*) is apparently not borne out by experiment which shows that less than 0.05 mM oxalacetate accumulates under these conditions (*87n*). But, it should be pointed out that, with guinea pig liver mitochondria, the addition of glutamate greatly stimulates the rate of oxidation of L-malate, and it is evident that undetectable concentrations (less than 0.03 mM) of oxalacetate are able to inhibit malate dehydrogenase (*87x*).

There is a large increase in the rate of oxygen uptake in presence of succinate when oxidative phosphorylation is uncoupled, both with guinea pig (*87x*) and rat liver mitochondria (*87z*), and the evidence obtained from studies of guinea pig liver mitochondria indicates that oxidation of succinate is controlled by the rate of formation of ATP (*87x*). Moreover, in presence of 2,4-dinitrophenol, added oxalacetate (which normally gives only a limited inhibition of succinate oxidation by mitochondria) gives a complete suppression of succinate oxidation. There, thus, appears to be an energy requirement for local removal of oxalacetate at the succinate oxidase site (*83, 87x, 87y*). In mammary gland mitochondria the oxidation of succinate is controlled by the rate of removal of oxalacetate (*87x*).

M. Inhibitive Effects of Various Succinic Acid Analogues

It was pointed out (*6*) in the study of bacterial succinic dehydrogenase that other structures related to succinate, besides malonate, had inhibitory effects on this enzyme, though malonate was the most effective of those tested. Among such substances were glutaric acid, β-phenylpropionic acid, phenylacetic acid, and tricarballylic acid.

Alkylsuccinic acids are inhibitory, the inhibition varying with the length of the alkyl chain (*88*). 1,2-Ethanedisulfonate and β-sulfopropionate in concentrations between 3.3 mM and 20 mM inhibit succinic dehydrogenase almost as well as malonate (*89*).

Arsenoacetic acid ($COOH \cdot CH_2 \cdot As \cdot O_3H_2$) acts as a competitive inhibitor of protozan succinic dehydrogenase (90), but it is apparently without effect on a succinic dehydrogenase preparation from mouse or rat (91).

The additions of competitive inhibitors (e.g., maleate, itaconate, or malonate) to a soluble succinic dehydrogenase preparation give changes in the absorption spectrum of the enzyme preparation that are similar to those brought about by fumarate (92, 93). Malate and oxalacetate have relatively large effects, but pyrophosphate has no action. These results suggest the possibility that the spectrum is that of a flavin semiquinone (92, 93).

Malondialdehyde has a slight inhibitory effect on succinate and oxalacetate utilization by rat liver homogenate (93a).

N. Antimycin A Inhibition

Antimycin A inhibits the flow of electrons from succinate (or DPNH) to cytochrome c but not to other acceptors in mitochondrial preparations (94, see also 95), and there appears to be an equivalence between the flavin content of the enzyme preparation and the antimycin titer (96). This evidence, taken together with the inhibitory effects of ethyl urethan at high concentrations [for 0.36 M ethyl urethan inhibits oxidation through the cytochrome system by about 90% and through phenazine methosulfate by about 40% (11)] and those of 2,3-dimercaptopropanol (BAL) in the presence of oxygen (97–99), suggests the existence of one or more carriers additional to cytochrome b and c. These inhibitions have been believed to be associated with the same factor (commonly known as the "Slater" factor) in the respiratory chain, but there seems to be evidence that the antimycin- and BAL-sensitive sites are not identical (100). Antimycin A is also held to inhibit electron flow between succinate and DPN (101). The Slater factor has been identified at various times with either cytochrome b or c; but this is unlikely to be the case, as antimycin A interferes with the reaction between cytochrome b and c without affecting the spectrum of either (102). The inhibition of succinic acid oxidation in the respiratory chain by antimycin A in fact appears to be localized between cytochromes b and c_1 (11, 103). With 0.3 mg of a soluble preparation of succinic dehydrogenase, 0.1 mg antimycin A had no effect on the oxidation of succinate (11) by phenazine methosulfate as an autoxidizable hydrogen acceptor (see also 104–107). However, it affects the properties of cytochrome b in disrupted beef heart mitochondria (103).

O. Oligomycin Inhibition

Succinate-linked pyridine nucleotide reduction may occur in mitochondria, and this is inhibited by small concentrations of Amytal (see also Chapter 33). Oligomycin can also affect the NAD reduction [except in the presence of glutamate (108)], but partial or complete oligomycin insensitivity depends on the concentrations of ATP or internal high energy intermediates (109–111); the latter are supplied during succinate oxidation. Oligomycin interferes with ATP formation (112, 113) and blocks the interaction of ATP with components of the respiratory chain (112). It can, in fact, prevent the stimulating action of ATP on metabolic processes dependent on malate oxidation (114). Respiratory inhibition by oligomycin in rat liver slices is largely released by 2,4-dinitrophenol suggesting that, as in isolated mitochondria, the oligomycin-sensitive respiration is coupled to the formation of intermediates of oxidative phosphorylation (114a).

III. FUMARATE CONVERSION TO L-MALATE; INHIBITIONS OF FUMARASE

Fumarase plays an essential role in the citric acid cycle by bringing about the conversion of fumarate to L-malate. It is very widely distributed in bacteria, molds, yeasts, and animal tissues and even in red blood cells (115); in fact, human blood is one of the richest sources of fumarase. Most cells seem to be so amply supplied with the enzyme that it is unlikely to play any rate-limiting role in the citric acid cycle. Specific inhibitors of the enzyme would have to be very effective indeed to bring about marked diminutions in the rate of operation of the citric acid cycle.

Phosphate ions bring about a marked activation of fumarase (115–117), but the activation varies according to the preparation of the enzyme and the pH (115). They have a protective effect against the toxic action of certain dyestuffs [e.g. brilliant green (115)].

A variety of anions, di- or trivalent (e.g., arsenate, citrate) activates fumarase, the activation being a function of pH (118). This is held to be due to a combination of the anion with a basic group adjacent to either of the two ionizable groups in the active center of fumarase (118).

Fumarase is particularly sensitive to the action of acid dyes such as Congo red, trypan blue, methyl violet. Congo red will exert inhibitory effects at a concentration of $1.2 \times 10^{-5} M$ (115). The presence of proteins diminishes the dye toxicity, owing to their rapid combination with the dyes. Substances related in structure to trypan blue or trypan red, such as Bayer 205 (suramin) and the S-carbamides of 2-naphthylamine-disulfonic acid, are highly inhibitory to fumarase (119), and there seems to be some relation between fumarase inhibition and trypanocidal activity. However, it must not be supposed that the toxicity of the higher S-carbamides to fumarase is any explanation for their trypanocidal activities, as some of them, which are toxic to fumarase, have no trypanocidal action (119). As reported in 1932 (30), fumarase is protected from the toxic action of dyes by its substrate fumarate and by its analogues, succinate and malate, that combine reversibly with the enzyme. Competitive inhibitors of fumarase are D-malate, citrate, D-tartrate, L,a-hydroxy-β-sulfopropionate, maleate, mesaconate, transaconitate, succinate, malonate, adipate, glutarate, glycine (120). Substances that are inactive as inhibitors include crotonate, acetoacetate, acetate, butyrate, and acetylenedicarboxylate (120). It would appear that the presence of two acidic groups is necessary for attachment to the active center of fumarase, but it is important to note that removal of the a-hydrogen atoms from fumarate (as in acetylenedicarboxylate) renders the substance inactive.

It seems possible that the high toxicity of acid (sulfonated) dyes, referred to previously, to fumarase may be due to combination with the receptor groups at the active center, with which the acid groups of fumarate and its analogues also combine.

Many investigations have been carried out on the activity of fumarase and its mode of action (115, 120–123), and it is evident that this enzyme presents many advantages for studies of the manner in which enzymic hydration of the double bond is brought about.

IV. INHIBITION OF MALATE METABOLISM

Just as the metabolism of lactate is inhibited by lactic acid analogues, e.g., pyruvic acid, tartronic acid, glyceric acid, glyoxylic acid, mandelic acid, meso-tartaric acid, oxalic acid (6), so is the metabolism of malate affected by malic acid analogues, which resemble both the lactic acid analogues and the succinic acid analogues.

Tartronate and oxalacetate are inhibitors of malate oxidation in a pig heart preparation (124); and in a partially purified pigeon liver preparation, using the anaerobic ferricyanide system, tartronate is approximately 1000 times more inhibitory of malate oxidation than in a pig heart preparation (125). It is of interest to note that, with the liver preparation, citric acid, maleic acid, isocitric acid, and malonic acid have inhibitory effects (*125*), indicating some affinity of these molecules to the malic dehydrogenase. Thus, isocitrate (10 mM) and malonate (20 mM) inhibit malate oxidation by 55% and 30%, respectively, in the presence of 20 mM DL-malate.

β-Fluorooxalacetate is a powerful inhibitor of malic dehydrogenase (and of glutamic-aspartic transaminase) (*126*). Relatively high concentrations of fluorooxalacetate also inhibit the reduction of triphosphopyridine dinucleotide (NADP) by L-malate at pH 7.4 by a preparation of "malic enzyme" of chicken liver. Moreover, the NADP-dependent decarboxylation of oxalacetate at pH 4.5 is inhibited by fluorooxalacetate (*127*). Apparently, this inhibitor reacts nonenzymically with NADH and NADPH, and with some analogues of these coenzymes, to form fluorescent addition compounds. Oxalacetate is inert in this respect (*127*). The addition compounds are without influence at pH 7.5 on the action of malic and glucose-6-phosphate dehydrogenases and of the malic enzyme.

The malic enzyme (*128*), which is very widely distributed and which catalyzes the reaction [Eq. (1)]

$$\text{Pyruvate} + CO_2 + \text{NADPH} + H^+ \rightleftarrows \text{Malate} + \text{NADP} \qquad (1)$$

tends to favor the synthesis of malate, rather than its breakdown, owing to the high value of the NADPH/NADP ratio in the cell. This enzyme is inhibited by the malic acid analogues oxalacetate, malonate, tartronate, oxalate, mesoxalate, *meso*-tartrate, and fluoromalate (*129–132*). In this connection, reference may be made to the inhibitory action of *meso*-tartrate on pyruvate metabolism, in rat kidney slices, and rat kidney mitochondria (*133*). This inhibition is reversed by the addition of small quantities of fumarate, malate, or citrate. The evidence indicates that *meso*-tartrate acts by inhibiting dicarboxylic acid formation from pyruvate.

Malate synthetase, which catalyzes formation of malate from glyoxylic acid and acetyl CoA (*134*), requires magnesium ions for maximal activity and is competitively inhibited by analogues of glyoxylic acid, viz., oxalate ($K_i = 1.9 \times 10^{-5}\ M$), fluoroacetate ($K_i = 2.5 \times 10^{-4}\ M$), and glycolate ($K_i = 3.1 \times 10^{-4}\ M$) (*135*). The K_m for glyoxylate was found to be $9.3 \times 10^{-5}\ M$ (in a preparation from yeast).

Mention may be made here of the enzyme isocitratase (*136*), which controls the reversible reaction between isocitrate and its products, succinate and glyoxylate. This enzyme is noncompetitively inhibited by succinate (*137*); the sensitivity to succinate varies with the source of the enzyme (*134*). Isocitratase is also powerfully inhibited by oxalacetate (*138*), but pyruvate, malate, fumarate, and aspartate are without effect.

V. OXALACETATE METABOLISM

It is reported that oxalacetate decarboxylase is inhibited by malonate (*139–141*), even at a concentration of 10 mM (*141*) and by D- and L-malate. At a concentration of 30 mM, malonate is reported as inhibiting the conversion of oxalacetate to citrate with a liver preparation (*82*).

Oxalacetate metabolism plays a basic role in the citric acid cycle, for oxalacetate acts as a catalyst in the oxidation of acetate to CO_2, in the conversion of L-glutamate to L-aspartate, in the synthesis of fatty acids from sugars, and in controlling the oxidation of succinate and L-malate. With guinea pig liver mitochondria (*87x*) its utilization is relatively constant under a variety of conditions, e.g., presence or absence of succinate or 2,4-dinitrophenol. Its removal by acetyl CoA to give citrate or malonyl CoA, or by glutamate to yield aspartate and α-ketoglutarate is important for determining the steady-state level.

VI. CITRATE BREAKDOWN; INHIBITION OF ACONITASE

The reversible transformations of citric acid into *cis*-aconitic acid and *d*-isocitric acid, catalyzed by aconitase (*142, 143*), are an essential part of the series of reactions involved in the citric acid cycle. As is well known, the key reaction of the cycle is the condensation of oxalacetate with acetyl CoA to form a tricarboxylic acid (*144–146*).

While the succinate cytochrome oxidase system is always found in mitochondria, aconitase is found mainly in the supernatant in the liver but exclusively in the mitochondria in brain (*147*).

The enzyme is inhibited by copper and mercury ions, cyanide, and sulfide at relatively low concentrations (*148*). Aconitase, in contrast to fumarase, is unstable in solution on storage even in the refrigerator (*148*). The enzyme substrates, citrate or *cis*-aconitate, protect it from inactivation. It is fairly stable in frozen tissues. It is reported to be dependent on ferrous ions for optimal activity.

The analogue, *trans*-aconitate, which is not activated by aconitase, inhibits the enzyme presumably competitively (*149*).

A. Fluoroacetate Inhibition

A good deal of literature has now accumulated on the subject of fluoroacetate inhibition of cell respiration, and much of it is summarized in a recent review (*150*). Only the outstanding facts that bear on the mechanism of fluoroacetate inhibition will be considered here.

Fluoroacetate, known as a rat poison because of a selective toxicity to rodents (*151*), inhibits the oxidation of acetate in animal tissues and causes an accumulation of acetate in the presence of pyruvate (*152*). It was thought to be a specific, perhaps competitive, inhibitor of acetate oxidation (*152*). However, an accumulation of citrate takes place in kidney homogenates in the presence of fluoroacetate (*153, 154*), and a very large accumulation of citrate takes place *in vivo* in a variety of tissues when fluoroacetate is injected into rats, pigeons, guinea pigs, and frogs (*155, 156*). It was suggested (*157–159*) that fluoroacetate is not directly responsible for the accumulation of citric acid but that there is enzymic synthesis to a component affecting the citric acid cycle, possibly fluorocitrate (*158*). Fluorocitrate was eventually identified as a product formed on incubation of tissue homogenates with oxalacetate or fumarate and fluoroacetate (*160*), and it was shown (*161*) that fluorocitrate specifically inhibits aconitase, thus accounting for citric acid accumulation. Fluoroacetate itself has no effect on aconitase (*162*). Apparently, fluorocitrate is more effective *in vivo* than *in vitro* using soluble preparations of aconitase (*62*). Fluorocitrate, which inhibits the enzyme competitively (*161*), has a lesser effect on a soluble preparation of the enzyme than in a mitochondrial preparation, and it is thought possible that this may be due to accumulation of fluorocitrate in the mitochondria (*163*). There is a lesser effect of synthetic fluorocitrate than enzyme-synthesized fluorocitrate, at equal concentrations, on citrate disappearance by a kidney preparation, and this is attributed to the presence in the former product of inactive isomers of fluorocitrate. On the other hand, synthetic fluorocitrate is a more powerful inhibitor of purified aconitase than the enzymic preparation (*150*).

Fluoroacetyl CoA reacts with oxalacetate in the presence of the purified condensing enzyme to form fluorocitrate (*164*). The initial reaction is slower than with acetyl CoA, and there is competitive inhibition. However, a pigeon liver acetate-activating system does not form fluorocitrate from fluoroacetate and oxalacetate (*150*). Acetate inhibits the synthesis of fluorocitrate by kidney particles in the presence of malate and fluoroacetate, but the evidence appears to indicate that fluoroacetate and acetate are not necessarily activated at the same enzyme (*150*). Pigeon brain tissue, when used as a homogenate, does not synthesize fluorocitrate from fluoroacetate; nor does the presence of fluorocitrate give rise to citrate accumulation. When the brain tissue is more finely ground and reinforced with ATP and magnesium ions, the presence of fluorocitrate causes citrate accumulation in the presence of pyruvate (*165*).

Acetate acts as a protector to some animals (e.g. mice) against the toxic effects *in vivo* of fluoroacetate, and ethanol is effective with mice, guinea pigs, and rabbits (*166*) but not in dogs. The most effective protectors are glycerol monoacetate and acetamide (*167, 168*). Presumably, these effects are due to competition between acetate (or acetyl CoA) and fluoroacetate (or fluoracetyl CoA).

Fluoroacetate also accelerates acetoacetate formation in liver *in vitro* (*169*), and this is held to be due to an inhibition in the citric acid cycle (*150*). An effect of fluoroacetate *in vivo* is to increase blood sugar levels (*170*), and in fact an injection of 8 mg/kg of sodium fluoroacetate into fasted rats gives a rise in ketone bodies followed by a rise in blood sugar (*171*). Possibly, these observations may be explained by an interference with the citric acid cycle preventing the normal utilization of acetyl CoA, so that more of the latter is converted to acetoacetate. It is already established (*172*) that malonate, added to liver slices in presence of acetate, causes accumulation of acetoacetate. This phenomenon was held, at first, to be due to inhibition of acetoacetate breakdown. Subsequent work showed, however, that inhibition of acetoacetate breakdown by rat kidney cortex slices by malonate was reversed by the addition of fumarate (*173*), indicating that the breakdown of acetoacetate is dependent on the operation of the citric acid cycle. The fact that the inhibition was reversed also by lactate and alanine is consistent with this view, as both substances give rise to pyruvate and thence to oxalacetate. It follows that inhibition of the citric acid cycle with a diminished utilization of acetyl CoA will affect acetoacetate formation.

The convulsive effects due to fluoroacetate administration appear not to be due to citrate accumulation (*150, 174*). Convulsions occur when there is little increase in citrate in the brain, and introduction of fluoroacetate or fluorocitrate directly into the cortex causes changes in the electrical patterns in various areas without increased citrate levels in these areas. Fluorocitrate convulsions in mice cannot be stopped by intravenous calcium administration (*175*). Nor is there evidence that convulsions are due to defective acetylcholine metabolism (*150, 176*), although bovine brain tissue is reported capable of forming fluoroacetylcholine from fluoroacetate (*177*). Fluoroacetate has little or no effect on the respiration of mammalian brain tissue (*178, 179*), and there seems to be no evidence that fluoroacetate gives rise to fluorocitrate in brain (*150*). In view of this it is difficult to understand cerebral effects of fluoroacetate as being due to significant inhibitions of the cerebral citric acid cycle.

It should be noted in this connection that the enzymes involved in the citric acid cycle and subsequent hydrogen transfer, as well as pyruvic oxidase, are unaffected by fluoroacetate (even at concentrations as high as 16.6 mM) (*152, 157*). The respiration of pigeon brain homogenate, in the presence of pyruvate, is unaffected by fluoroacetate (16.6 mM) (*157*).

A relatively large increase in the ammonia level of dog brain has been reported (*180, 181*) as preceding the onset of convulsions in fluoroacetate poisoning. Recent work (*182*) indicates that fluoroacetate, at concentrations (e.g. 0.1 mM) that have no effect on rat brain cortex respiration (stimulated or unstimulated) *in vitro*, greatly reduces glutamine formation from glucose and the cerebral utilization of ammonium ions. There is no inhibition of glutamate formation, indicating that there is little interference with the citric acid cycle, for glutamate is derived by transamination from a-ketoglutarate. The mechanism by which fluoroacetate affects cerebral utilization of ammonium ions is at present unknown. Possibly, this phenomenon is related to the convulsive effects of fluoroacetate administration.

A study (*183*) of the effects of fluoroacetate on the metabolism of *Rhodaspirillum rubrum* has shown that this substance (0.8 mM) strongly inhibits the photometabolism of butyrate, pyruvate, and oxalacetate, but it also affects the photoreduction of carbon dioxide by hydrogen, a process apparently independent of the citric acid cycle.

Fluoroacetate (1 mM) inhibits nitrogen fixation and ammonia metabolism in *Azotobacter* (*184*), a process counteracted by acetate, but not by a-ketoglutarate. Whether this inhibition is brought about by an inhibitory effect on the citric acid cycle is unknown.

In studies of the metabolism of *Aspergillus terreus*, it is shown (*185*) that fluoroacetate (0.2 mM) increases the molar conversion of both glucose and citrate to itaconate (arsenite, 10 mM, on the other hand, inhibits the conversion of glucose to itaconate, with accumulation of pyruvate and acetaldehyde).

B. Oxalomalate Inhibition

Oxalomalate, which may be formed nonenzymically from glyoxylate and oxalacetate, is a competitive inhibitor of aconitase (*186, 187*), and it is possible that inhibitory effects of glyoxylate on the oxidation of components in the citric acid cycle may be partly due to the formation of oxalomalate (*187*).

VII. METABOLISM OF α-KETOGLUTARATE

α-Ketoglutarate plays an important role in the operation of the citric acid cycle. It is not only broken down to succinate by mechanisms including the participation of guanosine diphosphate and adenosinediphosphate (so that for every molecule of α-ketoglutarate oxidized, one of ATP is formed), but it is transaminated to L-glutamate, the precursor of γ-aminobutyric acid and glutamine. Inhibitors of α-ketoglutarate metabolism may be expected, therefore, to affect the velocity of the citric acid cycle.

Parapyruvate $(COOH \cdot C(OH)(CH_3) \cdot CH_2 \cdot CO \cdot COOH)$, a structural analogue of α-ketoglutarate, inhibits specifically the oxidation of α-ketoglutarate in various tissue preparations (188–190). It diminishes respiration of muscle homogenates in presence of pyruvate, the inhibition being restored by the addition of succinate and fumarate, with accumulation of α-ketoglutarate (190). Apparently, those stages involved in the formation of α-ketoglutarate from fumarate in the citric acid cycle proceed more rapidly in the presence of parapyruvate and compensate for the loss of activity in the steps between α-ketoglutarate and fumarate. α-Ketoglutarate dehydrogenase activity is also inhibited by ions of heavy metals (191, 192), the inhibition being readily reversed by BAL. However, inhibitions of the enzyme by cobalt and copper ions are not reversed by BAL, and this may be explained by chelation with dihydrolipoic acid (193).

Arsenite is an effective inhibitor of α-ketoglutarate oxidation (108).

A method of selectively inhibiting one step in the citric acid cycle is to omit phosphate and add 2,4-dinitrophenol. Under these conditions, the step of α-ketoglutarate conversion to succinate is inhibited because the substrate-linked phosphorylation step, in contrast to respiratory-chain phosphorylation, is not uncoupled by 2,4-dinitrophenol (193a, 193b). It has been shown (87i) that the aerobic oxidation of α-ketoglutarate in rat liver mitochondria in presence of 2,4-dinitrophenol requires phosphate but not ADP for maximal activity. Arsenate, which abolishes α-ketoglutarate-linked phosphorylation, is able to replace phosphate. The lack of requirement of ADP is explained as being due to continuous regeneration of mitochondrially bound ADP from ATP by dinitrophenol-activated ATPase. Phosphate (and not ADP) is also needed for the optimal rate of α-ketoglutarate dismutation in presence of ammonium ions and rat liver mitochondria (193c).

VIII. ISOCITRATE OXIDATION

Estradiol increases the conversion of both pyruvate-2-C^{14} and acetate-1-C^{14} to $C^{14}O_2$ by slices of placenta, and homogenates of placenta also respond to the *in vitro* addition of estradiol, the production of α-ketoglutarate from citrate being increased about 50%. The estradiol apparently stimulates specifically isocitric dehydrogenase (*194, 195*) and activates the reversible reaction [Eq. (2)]

$$\text{Isocitrate} + \text{NAD} \rightleftharpoons \text{NADH} + \text{H}^+ + \text{CO}_2 + \alpha\text{-ketoglutarate} \tag{2}$$

Stilbestrol is an inhibitor of this system, apparently competing with estradiol for the receptor group on the enzyme (*194, 195*).

The activating agent is 17β-estradiol, and 17α-estradiol is a potent competitive inhibitor. It is suggested that estradiol combines with isocitric dehydrogenase, converting it from an inactive to an active form and thus affecting the operation of the citric acid cycle (*194, 195*).

In addition, it may be pointed out that crude extracts of *Aspergillus niger* contain both NAD- and NADP-linked isocitric dehydrogenases and that 2'-adenylic acid inhibits the NADP isocitric dehydrogenase but not the NAD-linked enzyme (*196*). The accumulation of citric acid is also reported to inhibit the isocitric dehydrogenase of *A. niger* (*197*).

A heart muscle preparation (from horse or pig) contains isocitrate dehydrogenase, requiring NAD (or NADP) and Mg^{++} needed for decarboxylation of oxalosuccinate. Magnesium ions may be replaced by catalytic amounts of acetyl CoA, which reacts with oxalosuccinate to form α-ketoglutarate and malonyl CoA which is a precursor of acetyl CoA (*198*).

REFERENCES

1. J. H. Quastel, *Biochem. J.* 18, 365 (1924).
2. F. Batelli and L. Stern, *Biochem. Z.* 30, 172 (1911).
3. T. Thunberg, *Zentr. Physiol.* 31, 98 (1916).
4. H. Einbeck, *Biochem. Z.* 95, 296 (1919).
5. J. H. Quastel and M. D. Whetham, *Biochem. J.* 18, 519 (1924).
6. J. H. Quastel and W. R. Wooldridge, *Biochem. J.* 22, 689 (1928).
7. J. H. Quastel and W. R. Wooldridge, *Biochem. J.* 21, 1224 (1927).
8. J. H. Quastel and W. R. Wooldridge, *Biochem. J.* 23, 115 (1929).
9. J. H. Quastel and A. H. M. Wheatley, *Biochem. J.* 25, 117 (1931).
10. T. P. Singer, E. B. Kearney, and V. Massey, *Advances in Enzymol.* 18, 65 (1957).
11. D. Keilin and T. E. King, *Proc. Roy. Soc.* B152, 163 (1960).
12. T. Y. Wang, C. L. Tsou, and Y. L. Wang, *Sci. Sinica (Peking)* 5, 73 (1956).

13. A. Szent-Györgyi, *Z. physiol. Chem. Hoppe-Seyler's* **236,** 1 (1935); **244,** 105 (1936).
14. F. J. Stare and C. A. Baumann, *Proc. Roy. Soc.* **B121,** 338 (1936).
15. H. A. Krebs and W. A. Johnson, *Enzymologia* **4,** 148 (1937).
16. H. A. Krebs and L. V. Egglestone, *Biochem. J.* **34,** 442 (1940).
17. H. A. Krebs, E. Salvin, and W. A. Johnson, *Biochem. J.* **32,** 113 (1938).
18. H. Busch and V. R. Potter, *J. Biol. Chem* **198,** 71 (1952).
19. T. Thunberg, *Skand. Arch. Physiol.* **40,** 1 (1920).
20. J. H. Quastel and A. H. M. Wheatley, *Biochem. J.* **32,** 936 (1938).
21. M. B. Thorn, *Biochem. J.* **54,** 540 (1953).
22. T. P. Singer and E. B. Kearney, *Biochim. et Biophys. Acta* **15,** 151 (1954).
23. T. P. Singer and E. B. Kearney, *J. Biol. Chem.* **219,** 963 (1956).
24. L. F. Leloir and M. Dixon, *Enzymologia* **11,** 81 (1937).
25. F. G. Hopkins and E. J. Morgan, *Biochem. J.* **32,** 611 (1938).
26. F. G. Hopkins, E. J. Morgan, and C. Lutwak-Mann, *Biochem. J.* **32,** 1829 (1938).
27. S. R. Ames and C. A. Elvehjem, *Proc. Soc. Exptl. Biol. Med.* **57,** 108 (1944).
28. S. R. Ames and C. A. Elvehjem, *Arch. Biochem.* **5,** 191 (1944).
29. J. H. Quastel, *Biochem. J.* **25,** 898 (1931).
30. J. H. Quastel, *Proc. Roy. Soc.* **B111,** 294 (1932).
31. D. Keilin and E. F. Hartree, *Biochem. J.* **44,** 205 (1949).
32. E. S. Younathan, *J. Biol. Chem.* **237,** 608 (1962).
33. C. J. Kensler, S. O. Dexter, and C. P. Rhoads, *Cancer Research* **2,** 1 (1942).
34. A. Lazarow, J. Liambies, and A. J. Tausch, *J. Lab. Clin. Med.* **36,** 249 (1950).
35. N. O. Kaplan, A. Goldin, S. R. Humphreys, M. M. Ciotti, and F. E. Stolzenbach, *J. Biol. Chem.* **219,** 287 (1956).
36. G. Bhattacharya, *Proc. Natl. Inst. Sci. India* **21B,** 210 (1955).
37. S. Minakami, R. L. Ringler, and T. P. Singer, *J. Biol. Chem.* **237,** 569 (1962).
38. E. Haas, *Biochem. Z.* **291,** 79 (1937).
39. E. C. Slater, *Chem. Weekblad* **58,** No. 52 (1962).
40. E. C. Slater and W. D. Bonner, *Biochem. J.* **52,** 185 (1952).
41. O. Warburg and W. Christian, *Biochem. Z.* **310,** 384 (1942).
42. H. Borei, *Arkiv. Kemi, Mineral. Geol.* **20A,** No. 8 (1945).
43. L. Massart, *Z. physiol. Chem. Hoppe-Seyler's* **258,** 190 (1939).
44. V. R. Potter and W. C. Schneider, *J. Biol. Chem.* **142,** 543 (1942).
45. D. Keilin and E. F. Hartree, *Proc. Roy. Soc.* **B129,** 277 (1940).
46. B. L. Horecker, E. Stolz, and T. R. Hogness, *J. Biol. Chem.* **128,** 251 (1939).
47. W. C. Schneider and V. R. Potter, *J. Biol. Chem.* **149,** 217 (1943).
48. K. F. Swingle, A. E. Axelrod, and C. A. Elvehjem, *J. Biol. Chem.* **145,** 581 (1942).
49. V. R. Potter, *Arkiv. Kemi, Mineral. Geol.* **13B,** No. 7 (1939).
50. I. Banga and E. Porges, *Z. physiol. Chem. Hoppe-Seyler's* **254,** 200 (1938).
51. C. L. Tsou, *Biochem. J.* **49,** 512 (1951).
52. A. Giuditta and T. P. Singer, *J. Biol. Chem.* **234,** 666 (1959).

53. V. Massey, *Biochim. et Biophys. Acta* **30**, 500 (1958).
54. T. P. Singer, E. B. Kearney, and V. Massey, *in* "Enzymes" (O. H. Gaebler, ed.), p. 417. Academic Press, New York, 1956.
55. P. J. G. Mann and J. H. Quastel, *Biochem. J.* **40**, 139 (1946).
56. F. Dickens, *Biochem. J.* **40**, 145–171 (1946).
57. W. Libbrecht and L. Massart, *Compt. rend. soc. biol.* **124**, 299 (1937).
58. W. C. Stadie and N. Haugaard, *J. Biol. Chem.* **161**, 153 (1945).
59. J. J. Gordon and J. H. Quastel, *Nature* **159**, 97 (1947).
60. J. J. Gordon and J. H. Quastel, *Biochem. J.* **42**, 337 (1948).
61. E. S. G. Barron and T. P. Singer, *J. Biol. Chem.* **157**, 221 (1945).
62. R. A. Peters, *2nd Intern. Congr. Biochem., Paris, 1952* p. 64.
63. T. Bersin, *Ergeb. Enzymforsch.* **4**, 68 (1935).
64. R. H. S. Thompson, *Biochem. Soc. Symposia (Cambridge, Engl.) No.* **2**, 28 (1948).
65. L. A. Stocken and R. H. S. Thompson, *Physiol. Revs.* **29**, 168 (1949).
66. M. Dixon, see (*64*).
67. R. A. Peters, L. A. Stocken, and R. H. S. Thompson, *Nature* **156**, 616 (1945).
68. R. L. Waters and C. Stock, *Science* **102**, 601 (1945).
69. M. Dixon and D. M. Needham, *Nature* **158**, 432 (1946).
70. A. Gilman and F. S. Phillips, *Science* **103**, 409 (1946).
71. R. A. Peters, *Nature* **159**, 149 (1947).
72. Z. M. Bacq, *Experientia* **2**, 349 (1946).
73. Z. M. Bacq and V. Desreux, *Exposés ann. biochim. méd.* **8**, 67 (1948).
74. V. R. Potter and K. P. DuBois, *J. Gen. Physiol.* **26**, 391 (1943).
75. E. R. Redfearn and P. A. Whittaker, *Biochim. et Biophys. Acta* **56**, 440 (1962).
76. E. E. Jacobs and F. L. Crane, *Biochem. Biophys. Research Communs.* **3**, 333 (1960).
77. A. L. Smith and R. L. Lester, *Biochim. et Biophys. Acta* **48**, 547 (1961).
78. H. Heymann and L. F. Fieser, *J. Biol. Chem.* **176**, 1359, 1363 (1948).
79. M. Dixon, K. A. C. Elliott, *Biochem. J.* **23**, 812 (1929).
80. T. P. Singer, E. B. Kearney, and P. Bernath, *J. Biol. Chem.* **223**, 599 (1956).
81. N. B. Das, *Biochem. J.* **31**, 1124 (1937).
82. A. B. Pardee and V. R. Potter, *J. Biol. Chem.* **176**, 1085 (1948); **178**, 241 (1949).
83. D. B. Tyler, *J. Biol. Chem.* **216**, 395 (1955).
84. N. Zollner and E. Rothemund, *Z. physiol. Chem. Hoppe-Seyler's* **298**, 97 (1954).
85. P. J. G. Mann and J. H. Quastel, *Nature* **147**, 326 (1941).
86. P. J. G. Mann and J. H. Quastel, *Biochem. J.* **35**, 502 (1941).
87. O. Gonda and J. H. Quastel, *Nature* **193**, 138 (1962).
87a. B. Chance and G. Hollunger, *Federation Proc.* **16**, 163 (1957).
87b. B. Chance and G. Hollunger, *Nature* **185**, 666 (1960).
87c. B. Chance and G. Hollunger, *J. Biol. Chem.* **236**, 1534, 1555, 1562, 1577 (1961).
87d. B. Chance and B. Hagihara, *Biochem. Biophys. Research Communs.* **3**, 6 (1960).

87e. B. Chance, *Nature* 189, 719 (1961) ; *J. Biol. Chem.* 236, 1544, 1569 (1961).
87f. B. Chance and U. Fugmann, *Biochem. Biophys. Research Communs.* 4, 317 (1961).
87g. M. Klingenberg, W. Slenczka, and E. Ritt, *Biochem. Z.* 332, 47 (1959).
87h. G. F. Azzone, L. Ernster, and M. Klingenberg, *Nature* 188, 552 (1960).
87i. G. F. Azzone and L. Ernster, *J. Biol. Chem.* 236, 1501, 1510 (1961).
87j. M. Klingenberg and P. Schollmeyer, *Biochem. Z.* 333, 335 (1960).
87k. M. Klingenberg and P. Schollmeyer, *Biochem. Biophys. Research Communs.* 4, 38, 323 (1961).
87l. L. M. Birt and W. Bartley, *Biochem. J.* 76, 427 (1960).
87m. R. G. Kulka, H. A. Krebs, and L. V. Eggleston, *Biochem. J.* 78, 95 (1961).
87n. H. A. Krebs and L. V. Eggleston, *Biochem. J.* 82, 134 (1962).
87o. J. H. Quastel and A. H. M. Wheatley, *Biochem J.* 26, 725 (1932).
87p. P. Borst, *Biochim. et Biophys. Acta* 57, 256 (1962).
87q. H. Löw, H. Krueger, and D. M. Ziegler, *Biochem. Biophys. Research Communs.* 5, 231 (1961).
87r. R. R. Sanadi and H. L. Fluhartz, *Biochemistry* 2, 523 (1963).
87s. Y. Hatefi, A. G. Haavik, and D. E. Griffiths, *J. Biol. Chem.* 237, 1676 (1962).
87t. G. F. Azzone and L. Ernster, *J. Biol. Chem.* 236, 1518 (1961).
87u. E. C. Slater and A. Kemp, *Biochem. J.* 84, 65P (1962).
87v. J. J. Ghosh and J. H. Quastel, *Nature* 174, 28 (1954).
87w. P. Schollmeyer and M. Klinjenberg, *Biochem. Biophys. Research Communs* 4, 43 (1961).
87x. E. A. Jones and H. Gutfreund, *Biochem. J.* 87, 639 (1963).
87y. E. C. Slater and W. C. Hülsmann, *Proc. Natl. Acad. Sci. U.S.* 47, 1109 (1961).
87z. J. B. Chappell, *Biochem. J.* 84, 62P (1962).
88. W. Francke and D. Siewerdt, *Z. physiol. Chem. Hoppe-Seyler's* 280, 76 (1944).
89. I. M. Klotz and F. Tietze, *J. Biol. Chem.* 168, 399 (1947).
90. G. R. Seaman, *Arch. Biochem. Biophys.* 35, 132 (1952).
91. F. Tietze and I. M. Klotz, *Arch. Biochem. Biophys.* 35, 355 (1952).
92. E. B. Kearney, *J. Biol. Chem.* 229, 363 (1957).
93. D. V. Dervartanian and C. Veeger, *Biochem. J.* 84, 65P (1962).
93a. D. E. Holtkamp and R. M. Hill, *Arch. Biochem. Biophys.* 34, 216 (1951).
94. K. Ahmad, H. G. Schneider, and F. M. Strong, *Arch. Biochem.* 28, 281 (1950).
95. J. M. Tager, J. L. Howland, and E. C. Slater, *Biochim. et Biophys. Acta* 58, 616 (1962).
96. D. E. Green, S. Mii, and P. M. Kohout, *J. Biol. Chem.* 217, 551 (1955).
97. E. C. Slater, *Biochem. J.* 45, 14 (1949) ; 46, 484 (1950).
98. E. C. Slater, *Advances in Enzymol.* 20, 147 (1958).
99. M. B. Thorn, *Biochem. J.* 63, 420 (1956).
100. D. H. Deul and M. B. Thorn, *Biochim. et Biophys. Acta* 59, 426 (1962).
101. B. Chance and T. Ito, *Nature* 195, 150 (1962).
102. D. Keilin and E. F. Hartree, *Nature* 176, 200 (1955).
103. A. M. Pumphrey, *J. Biol. Chem.* 237, 2384 (1962).
104. V. R. Potter and A. E. Reif, *J. Biol. Chem.* 194, 287 (1952).

105. A. E. Reif and V. R. Potter, *Arch. Biochem. Biophys.* **48**, 1 (1954).
106. A. E. Reif and V. R. Potter, *Cancer Research* **12**, 290 (1952) ; **13**, 49 (1953).
107. J. R. Copenhaver, Jr. and H. A. Lardy, *J. Biol. Chem.* **195**, 225 (1952).
108. E. C. Slater, J. M. Tager, and A. M. Snoswell, *Biochim. et Biophys. Acta* **56**, 177 (1962).
109. B. Chance, *Federation Proc.* **21**, 55 (1962).
110. B. Chance, *J. Biol. Chem.* **236**, 1573 (1961).
111. A. M. Snoswell, *Biochim. et Biophys. Acta* **52**, 216 (1961).
112. H. A. Lardy, D. Johnson, and W. C. McMurray, *Arch. Biochem. Biophys.* **78**, 587 (1958).
113. F. Huijing and E. C. Slater, *J. Biochem. (Japan)* **40**, 493 (1961).
114. J. M. Tager, *Biochem. J.* **84**, 64P (1962).
114a. G. D. V. van Rossum, *Biochem. J.* **84**, 35P (1962).
115. J. H. Quastel, *Biochem. J.* **25**, 898 (1931).
116. P. W. Clutterbuck, *Biochem. J.* **22**, 1193 (1928).
117. P. J. G. Mann and B. Woolf, *Biochem. J.* **24**, 427 (1930).
118. V. Massey, *Biochem. J.* **53**, 67 (1953).
119. J. H. Quastel, *Biochem. J.* **25**, 1121 (1931).
120. V. Massey, *Biochem. J.* **55**, 172 (1953).
121. R. A. Alberty, V. Massey, C. Frieden, and A. R. Fuhlbrigge, *J. Am. Chem. Soc.* **76**, 2485 (1954).
122. T. C. Farrar, H. S. Gutorowski, R. A. Alberty, and W. G. Miller, *J. Am. Chem. Soc.* **79**, 3978 (1957).
123. V. Massey and R. A. Alberty, *Biochim. et Biophys. Acta* **13**, 354 (1954).
124. D. E. Green, *Biochem. J.* **30**, 2095 (1936).
125. P. G. Scholefield, *Biochem. J.* **59**, 177 (1955).
126. E. Kun, D. R. Grassetti, D. Faushier, and R. M. Featherstone, *Biochem. Pharmacol.* **1**, 207 (1958).
127. E. Kun and H. G. Williams-Ashman, *Nature* **194**, 376 (1962).
128. S. Ochoa, A. H. Mehler, and A. Kornberg, *J. Biol. Chem.* **174**, 979 (1948).
129. L. P. Vernon and M. D. Kamen, *Arch. Biochem. Biophys.* **44**, 298 (1953).
130. S.-C. Cheng. *Plant Physiol.* **29**, 458 (1954).
131. S. Korkes, see S. Ochoa, *Physiol. Revs.* **31**, 56 (1951).
132. E. M. Gal, *Arch. Biochem. Biophys.* **73**, 279 (1958).
133. J. H. Quastel and P. G. Scholefield, *J. Biol. Chem.* **214**, 245 (1955).
134. D. T. O. Wong and S. J. Ajl, *J. Am. Chem. Soc.* **78**, 3230 (1956).
135. H. L. Kornberg and S. R. Elsden, *Advances in Enzymol.* **23**, 401 (1961).
136. R. A. Smith and I. C. Gunsalus, *J. Am. Chem. Soc.* **76**, 5002 (1954).
137. R. A. Smith and I. C. Gunsalus, *J. Biol. Chem.* **229**, 305 (1957).
138. H. E. Umbarger, *Federation Proc.* **19**, 52 (1960).
139. E. A. Evans, B. Vennesland, and L. Slotin, *J. Biol. Chem.* **147**, 771 (1943).
140. C. Liebecq and R. A. Peters, *Biochim. et Biophys. Acta* **3**, 215 (1949).
141. J. B. Veiga Salles and S. Ochoa, *J. Biol. Chem.* **187**, 849 (1950).
142. F. L. Breusch, *Z. physiol. Chem. Hoppe-Seyler's* **250**, 262 (1937).
143. C. Martius, *Z. physiol. Chem. Hoppe-Seyler's* **257**, 29 (1938).
144. H. A. Krebs, *Advances in Enzymol.* **3**, 191 (1943).
145. H. G. Wood, *Physiol. Revs.* **26**, 198 (1946).

146. J. R. Stern and S. Ochoa, *J. Biol. Chem.* 172, 491 (1949).
147. J. A. Shepherd and G. Kalnitzky, *J. Biol. Chem.* 207, 605 (1954).
148. H. A. Krebs and L. V. Eggleston, *Biochem. J.* 38, 426 (1944).
149. M. Saffran and J. L. Prado, *J. Biol. Chem.* 180, 1301 (1949).
150. R. A. Peters, *Advances in Enzymol.* 18, 113 (1957).
151. M. B. Chenoweth, *Pharmacol. Revs.* 1, 383 (1949).
152. G. R. Bartlett and E. S. G. Barron, *J. Biol. Chem.* 170, 67 (1947).
153. G. Kalnitsky and E. S. G. Barron, *Arch. Biochem.* 19, 75 (1948).
154. G. Kalnitsky, *J. Biol. Chem.* 179, 1015 (1949).
155. P. Buffa and R. A. Peters, *J. Physiol.* (*London*) 110, 488 (1949).
156. P. Buffa and R. A. Peters, *Nature* 163, 914 (1949).
157. C. Liebecq and R. A. Peters, *Biochim. et Biophys. Acta* 3, 215 (1949).
158. C. Martius, *Ann.* 561, 227 (1949).
159. W. B. Elliott and G. Kalnitsky, *J. Biol. Chem.* 186, 487 (1950).
160. R. A. Peters, R. W. Wakelin, D. E. A. Rivett, and L. C. Thomas, *Nature* 171, 1111 (1953).
161. J. F. Morrison and R. A. Peters, *Biochem. J.* 58, 473 (1954).
162. W. D. Lotspeich, R. A. Peters, and T. H. Wilson, *Biochem J.* 51, 20 (1952).
163. R. A. Peters, *Proc. Roy. Soc.* B139, 143 (1952).
164. R. O. Brady, *J. Biol. Chem.* 217, 213 (1955).
165. R. A. Peters and R. W. Wakelin, *J. Physiol.* (*London*) 119, 421 (1953).
166. J. O. Hutchens, H. Wagner, B. Podolsky, and T. M. McMahon, *J. Pharmacol. Exptl. Therap.* 95, 62 (1949).
167. M. B. Chenoweth, A. Kandel, L. B. Johnson, and D. R. Bennett, *J. Pharmacol. Exptl. Therap.* 102, 31 (1951).
168. S. Gitter, *Biochem. J.* 63, 182 (1956).
169. H. Busch and V. R. Potter, *Proc. Soc. Exptl. Biol. Med.* 81, 172 (1952).
170. W. B. Elliott and A. H. Phillips, *Arch. Biochem.* 49, 389 (1954).
171. F. L. Engel, K. Hewson, B. T. Cole. *Am. J. Physiol.* 179, 325 (1954).
172. M. Jowett and J. H. Quastel, *Biochem. J.* 29, 2181 (1935).
173. J. H. Quastel and A. H. M. Wheatley, *Biochem. J.* 29, 2773 (1935).
174. L. C. Hendershot and M. B. Chenoweth, *J. Pharmacol. Exptl. Therap.* 110, 344 (1954); 113, 160 (1955).
175. N. Eeg-Larsen and K. Naeso, *Acta Pharmacol. Toxicol.* 7, 331 (1951).
176. A. H. Mehler and Y. T. Chang, *Arch. Biochem. Biophys.* 62, 293 (1956).
177. M. Wollemann and G. Feuer, *Acta Physiol. Acad. Sci. Hung.* 11, 165 (1957).
178. J. L. Webb and K. A. C. Elliott, *J. Pharmacol. Exptl. Therap.* 103, 24 (1951).
179. J. L. Webb and K. A. C. Elliott, *Can. J. Research* 26, 239 (1948).
180. D. Benitez, G. R. Pscheidt, and W. E. Stone, "Neurochemistry" (K. A. C. Elliott, I. H. Page, and J. H. Quastel, eds.), p. 503. C. C. Thomas, Springfield, Illinois, 1955.
181. D. Benitez, G. R. Pscheidt, and W. E. Stone, *Am. J. Physiol.* 176, 488 (1954).
182. S. Lahiri and J. H. Quastel, *Proc. Can. Fed. Biol. Soc.* 4, 38 (1961); *Biochem. J.* 88 (1963).
183. S. R. Elsden and J. G. Ormerod, *Biochem. J.* 63, 91 (1956).

184. J. H. Brummer, *Biochem. Biophys. Research Communs.* 7, 53 (1962).
185. K. E. Eimhjellen and H. Larsen, *Biochem. J.* 60, 139 (1955).
186. A. Ruffo, M. Romano, and A. Adinolfi, *Biochem. J.* 72, 613 (1959).
187. A. Ruffo, A. Adinolfi, G. Budillon, and G. Capobianco, *Biochem. J.* 84, 82P (1962).
188. C. M. Montgomery, A. S. Fairhurst, and J. L. Webb, *J. Biol. Chem.* 221, 369 (1956).
189. C. M. Montgomery and J. L. Webb, *J. Biol. Chem.* 221, 359 (1956).
190. H. A. Krebs, *"Symposium on Regulation of Respiration,"* Ciba Foundation Symposium, p. 1. Churchill, London, 1959.
191. D. R. Sanadi, M. Langley, and R. White, *J. Biol. Chem.* 234, 183 (1959).
192. C. Veeger and V. Massey, *Biochim. et Biophys. Acta* 37, 181 (1960).
193. M. Webb, *Biochem. J.* 84, 116P (1962).
193a. J. D. Judah, *Biochem. J.* 49, 271 (1951).
193b. P. Borst and E. C. Slater, *Biochim. et Biophys. Acta* 48, 362 (1961).
193c. L. Danielson and L. Ernster, *Biochem. Biophys. Research Communs.* 10, 85 (1963).
194. C. A. Villee and D. D. Hagerman, *in* "Proceedings of the International Symposium on Enzyme Chemistry," Tokyo and Kyoto, 1957, p. 317. Academic Press, New York, 1958.
195. C. A. Villee and E. E. Gordon, *J. Biol. Chem.* 216, 203, 215 (1955).
196. E. F. Neufeld, N. O. Kaplan, and S. P. Colowick, *Biochim. et Biophys. Acta* 17, 525 (1955).
197. C. V. Ramakrishnan, R. Steel, and C. P. Lentz, *Arch. Biochem. Biophys.* 55, 270 (1955).
198. W. C. Hülsmann and C. Benckhuijsen, *Biochem J.* 84, 63P (1962).

CHAPTER 32

Uncouplers and Inhibitors of Oxidative Phosphorylation

E. C. Slater

I. INTRODUCTION: DEFINITIONS

The energy made available by intracellular respiration, catalyzed by the mitochondria, is largely utilized for the synthesis of ATP, brought about by a process known as *oxidative phosphorylation.*

All oxidative phosphorylation reactions can be described by Eq. (1).

$$AH_2 + B + ADP + P_i \rightleftharpoons A + BH_2 + ATP \tag{1}$$

The energy required for the phosphorylation of ADP by P_i [Eq. (1a)]

$$ADP + P_i \rightleftharpoons ATP - 8000 \text{ cal } (\Delta G_0') \tag{1a}$$

is supplied by the hydrogen or electron transfer from the $AH_2 \rightleftharpoons A$ system at lower oxidation-reduction potential to $BH_2 \rightleftharpoons B$ at higher potential.

We distinguish between two types of oxidative phosphorylation: (*a*) *substrate-linked,* where AH_2 is one of the substrates—phosphoglyceraldehyde, pyruvate or α-ketoglutarate; and (*b*) *respiratory-chain,* where AH_2 and B are both members of the respiratory chain.

An *uncoupler of oxidative phosphorylation* permits the oxidation of AH_2 by B to proceed without net phosphorylation [Eq. (2)]

$$AH_2 + B \rightarrow A + BH_2 \tag{2}$$

Although the concept of uncoupling is quite general, the term will be restricted in this article to uncoupling of respiratory-chain phosphorylation.

An *inhibitor of oxidative phosphorylation* acts on the link between the oxidation reaction and the phosphorylation. In consequence reaction (1) is completely inhibited. Inhibition of the oxidation reaction can be relieved by addition of certain uncouplers.

II. UNCOUPLERS

A. Historical

The stimulatory effects of nitrophenols on the over-all metabolism of the animal were known to the pharmacologists as long ago as 1885, when Cazeneuve and Lepine (1) found that ingestion of dinitro-a-naphthol by the dog caused a high fever. This finding was confirmed and extended to other species and to different dinitrophenols by a number of workers, notably Mathews and Longfellow (2), Heymans and Bouchaert (3), Magne, Mayer, and Plantefol (4, 5), and Plantefol (6). Heymans and Bouchaert (3) and Magne et al. (4, 5) clearly demonstrated that the dinitrophenols acted directly on the tissues and not by stimulating the heat-regulating center. They showed, moreover, that the increased heat production was not due to increased muscular activity.

The first detailed biochemical study of the mechanism of action of these compounds was made by Van Uytvanck (7), who found that injection of dinitro-a-naphthol increased the amount of phosphate (presumably inorganic phosphate) in the blood and muscle of pigeons and increased the lactate content of the muscle. Cahn (8) obtained similar results with dinitrophenol. Isolated tissues were first used in the important work of Euler (9, 10), Ehrenfest and Ronzoni (11), Dodds and Greville (12), and Ronzoni and Ehrenfest (13), which showed that nitrophenols caused a marked stimulation of the respiration of a number of tissues [Ehrenfest and Ronzoni (11) obtained a sevenfold stimulation with frog muscle]. In addition, Dodds and Greville (14) found that 4,6-dinitro-o-cresol increased aerobic glycolysis, while Ronzoni and Ehrenfest (13) showed that 2,4-dinitrophenol increased the rate of hydrolysis of creatine phosphate. Further studies led to the generalization that nitrophenols stimulated intracellular respiration, whereas energy-requiring functions, such as cell division in sea urchin eggs (15, 16), growth of yeast (17), assimilation in microorganisms (18), sperm motility (19), and phosphate uptake by yeast (20), were inhibited.

Greville (21, 22) showed that the stimulation of respiration by dinitrophenol was not due to its acting as an artificial hydrogen carrier like methylene blue. A new idea came from De Meio and Barron (23), who suggested that dinitrophenol acts by combining with some of the substances acting as agents for the control of the speed of cellular oxidations, thus increasing the activity of oxidizing enzymes. Lardy and Elvehjem (24) suggested that dinitrophenol and other uncoupling compounds acted either by allowing oxidation to occur without phosphorylation or by catalyzing the hydrolysis of an intermediate phosphate compound. In either case, oxidation would proceed without phosphorylation. This idea was first given direct experimental support by Loomis and Lipmann (25) and Cross, Taggart, Covo, and Green (26) when they found that 2,4-dinitrophenol and a number of other compounds inhibited the synthesis of ATP by mitochondrial preparations without affecting respiration. Since ATP is required for many energy-utilizing functions of the cell, the earlier findings were explained.

B. Characteristics of Uncouplers

Uncouplers have the following properties:

(1) They stimulate the respiration of isolated mitochondria suspended in a medium deficient in phosphate acceptor[1] (27–32) or deficient in phosphate[1] (25, 33), or sometimes even in a medium containing phosphate and acceptor (34).

(2) They completely abolish the synthesis of ATP normally coupled with mitochondrial respiration, except the substrate-linked phosphorylation in the oxidation step α-ketoglutarate $\rightarrow$ succinate.

(3) They promote the hydrolysis of ATP added to mitochondria (24, 27, 30, 35).

(4) They inhibit the P_i-ATP (36) and the ADP-ATP exchange reactions (37) and the exchange of oxygen atoms of P_i and water (38) and of ATP and water (39), catalyzed by mitochondria in the absence of added substrate.

[1] Except when the rate of respiration is limited by the rate of the substrate-linked phosphorylation associated with succinyl CoA.

C. Mechanism of Action of Uncouplers

No final decision can be made between the two possible mechanisms of action suggested by Lardy and Elvehjem (24). Ernster and his co-workers (40–42) favor the view that dinitrophenol acts by allowing the oxidation reaction to proceed without phosphorylation. Most workers favor the view that dinitrophenol promotes the hydrolysis of an intermediate high-energy compound. However, it is now clear that this cannot be a phosphate compound, as suggested by Lardy and Wellman (29, 30), since dinitrophenol abolishes the need for phosphate for maximal rates of respiration (25, 33).

Ernster's theory is described by Eqs. (3) and (4)

$$DPNH + fp + P_i \rightleftharpoons DPN^+ + fpH \sim P + OH^- \tag{3}$$

$$fpH \sim P + 2\ Fe^{3+} + ADP \rightleftharpoons fp + 2\ Fe^{2+} + ATP + 2\ H^+ \tag{4}$$

Sum: $DPNH + 2\ Fe^{3+} + ADP + P_i \rightleftharpoons DPN^+ + 2\ Fe^{2+} + ATP + H^+$

where fp stands for the DPNH-oxidizing flavoprotein, and Fe^{3+} and Fe^{2+} for the oxidized and reduced carrier next to the flavoprotein in the cytochrome region. The dinitrophenol-induced ATPase is explained by Eqs. (5)–(7).

$$ATP + fpH_2 \rightleftharpoons ADP + fpH \sim P \tag{5}$$

$$fpH \sim P + DPN^+ + OH^- \rightleftharpoons fp + P_i + DPNH \tag{6}$$

$$DPNH + fp + H^+ \xrightarrow{\text{(Dinitrophenol)}} DPN^+ + fpH_2 \tag{7}$$

Sum: $ATP + H_2O \xrightarrow{\text{(Dinitrophenol)}} ADP + P_i$

The alternative theory can be formulated (43) by the reaction scheme

$$Respiration \rightarrow \sim_1 \rightleftharpoons \sim_2 \rightleftharpoons \sim P \rightleftharpoons ATP$$

$$\downarrow \text{(Dinitrophenol)}$$

where $\sim_1$ is the dinitrophenol-sensitive high-energy compound, $\sim_2$ is a second high-energy compound which is sensitive to oligomycin (see later), while $\sim P$ is a high-energy phosphate compound. One possibility (but not the only one), written in the form of chemical equations, is shown in Eqs. (8)–(13).

$$AH_2 + B + I \rightleftharpoons A \sim I + BH_2 \tag{8}$$

$$A \sim I + X \rightleftharpoons X \sim I + A \tag{9}$$

$$X \sim I + P_i \rightleftharpoons X \sim P + I \tag{10}$$

$$X \sim P + ADP \rightleftharpoons X + ATP \tag{11}$$

$$A \sim I + H_2O \xrightarrow{\text{(Dinitrophenol)}} A + I \tag{12}$$

$$X \sim I + \text{oligomycin} \rightarrow X \sim I - \text{oligomycin} \tag{13}$$

where AH_2 and B are components of the respiratory chain, and I and X are unknown intermediates. The dinitrophenol-induced ATPase is here given by the reverse of Eqs. (11), (10), and (9), followed by Eq. (12), the P_i-ATP exchange reactions by Eqs. (10) and (11), and the ADP-ATP exchange reaction by Eq. (11).

D. Classification of Uncouplers

Very many different types of compounds have the property of uncoupling phosphorylation from respiration [see, e.g., list given by Lehninger (44)]. In fact, any substance which disrupts the mitochondrial structure, such as deoxycholate or Ca^{++}, will have this effect. The most useful uncouplers, however, are those which act more specifically without disrupting the mitochondrial structure. The two types can be roughly distinguished by their effect on the ATPase in the absence of added Mg^{++}. More specific compounds such as dinitrophenol stimulate the ATPase maximally without the addition of Mg^{++}. On the other hand, Mg^{++} is required to elicit maximum ATPase induced by deoxycholate. Uncouplers can be classified into six groups: (1) nitrophenols, (2) halophenols, (3) dicoumarol and related compounds, (4) antibiotics, (5) unsaturated fatty acids, (6) arsenate.

1. NITROPHENOLS

The relative effectiveness as uncouplers of various nitrophenols has been studied by Cross et al. (26), Parker (45), and Gladtke and Liss (46). Parker emphasized the role of pK and Gladtke and Liss that of the lipid solubility in determining the activity of an uncoupler. Hemker and Hülsmann (47) have shown that both factors are important. The optimal concentrations of different nitrophenols at various pH's for stimulation of the ATPase activity of rat liver mitochondria are given in Table I.

Accurate determinations of the form of the curve relating ATPase activity to concentration of dinitrophenol have revealed a double maxi-

TABLE I

COMPARISON OF OPTIMAL CONCENTRATIONS OF DIFFERENT NITROPHENOLS AT
VARIOUS pH'S FOR INDUCTION OF ATPASE ACTIVITY OF RAT LIVER MITOCHONDRIA[a]

Compound	pK	pQ[b]	pC_{opt}[c] at pH's				
			5	6	7	8	9
p-Nitrophenol	7.2	+0.45	3.30	3.37	3.51	3.39	—
2,6-Dinitrophenol	3.7	−2.35	4.77	4.22	3.68	3.12	—
2,6-Dinitro-3,4-dimethylphenol	[d]	[d]	4.92	4.51	4.36	3.95	3.60
2,6-Dinitro-4-isobutylphenol	4.3	−3.54	5.16	4.88	4.71	4.48	4.26
2,6-Dinitro-4-isoamylphenol	4.1	−4.15	5.55	5.42	5.18	4.92	4.71
2,6-Dinitro-4-isooctylphenol	4.05	−4.75	6.08	5.89	5.64	5.41	5.24

[a] From Hemker and Hülsmann (47).

[b] $pQ = -\log_{10} \dfrac{\text{concentration of undissociated phenol in xylene}}{\text{concentration of undissociated phenol in water}}$.

For the dinitrophenols at pH's >5,

$$pQ = pK - pH - \log_{10} \frac{\text{concentration of undissociated phenol in xylene}}{\text{concentration of total phenol in water}}.$$

[c] $pC_{opt} = -\log_{10} C_{opt}$; C_{opt} = concentration of phenol giving maximum ATPase activity.

[d] $pK - pQ = 7.44$.

mum, indicating that there may be at least two different dinitrophenol-induced ATPases, differing in the concentration of dinitrophenol giving maximum activity. Amytal appears to inhibit preferentially the ATPase activated by the higher concentrations of dinitrophenol, and antimycin at the lower concentrations (Hemker, unpublished).

When allowance is made for the small differences in pK and the large differences in lipid solubility, no difference is found among four alkyl-substituted 2,6-dinitrophenols (3,4-dimethyl, 4-isobutyl, 4-isoamyl, and 4-isooctyl) with respect to their ability to induce ATPase in rat liver mitochondria, if the concentrations are calculated on the basis of the amounts of undissociated phenol dissolved in the mitochondrial lipid (Table II).

From Table I, it can be calculated that maximum ATPase in rat liver mitochondria at pH 7 is obtained with 310 μM p-nitrophenol, 210 μM 2,6-dinitrophenol,[2] 44 μM 2,6-dinitro-3,4-dimethylphenol, 19 μM 2,6-

[2] About the same concentration of 2,4-dinitrophenol is also necessary for maximal ATPase activity, which in this case is about 33% higher than that obtained with the 2,6-dinitrophenols.

TABLE II

CALCULATION FROM DATA IN TABLE I OF CONCENTRATION IN MITOCHONDRIAL LIPID (C_L) OF DIFFERENT NITROPHENOLS NECESSARY FOR OPTIMUM ATPASE ACTIVITY AT VARIOUS pH'S[a]

Compound	pK	pQ	pC_L[b] at pH's				
			5	6	7	8	9
p-Nitrophenol	7.2	+0.45	3.55	3.62	4.06	4.62	—
2,4-Dinitrophenol[c]	4.1	−2.06	3.61	4.06	4.52	4.96	—
2,6-Dinitrophenol	3.7	−2.35	3.72	4.17	4.63	5.07	—
2,6-Dinitro-3,4-dimethylphenol	[d]	[d]	2.48	3.07	3.82	4.51	5.16
2,6-Dinitro-4-isobutylphenol	4.3	−3.54	2.33	3.05	3.88	4.65	5.43
2,6-Dinitro-4-isoamylphenol	4.1	−4.15	2.30	3.04	3.93	4.67	5.56
2,6-Dinitro-4-isooctylphenol	4.05	−4.75	2.28	3.09	3.84	4.61	5.44

[a] From Hemker and Hülsmann (47).
[b] $pC_L = pC_{opt} + pQ + pH + \log(K + [H^+])$.
[c] This compound was not so extensively investigated as the 2,6-dinitrophenol, but no significant difference was found between the values of pC_{opt} for the two compounds. For purposes of calculation, it has been assumed that they were identical.
[d] $pK - pQ = 7.44$.

dinitro-4-isobutylphenol, 6.6 μM 2,6-dinitro-4-isoamylphenol, and 2.3 μM 2,6-dinitro-4-isooctylphenol. Virtually complete inhibition of phosphate esterification is, however, obtained at considerably lower concentrations. For most experiments it is immaterial which compound is used. However, the nitrophenols are strongly yellow in neutral solution, which can be a disadvantage if spectrophotometric measurements are also to be undertaken. Under these circumstances, the highly lipid-soluble isooctyl compound is to be preferred.

The amount required for complete uncoupling depends not only on the lipid solubility and the pK of the uncoupler, and on the pH of the medium, but also on the nature of the mitochondria (e.g., less 2,4-dinitrophenol was required with the preparations of blowfly sarcosomes used by Slater and Lewis (48) than with rat heart sarcosomes) and on the concentration of the mitochondria and of extraneous material. Jongejans-Sickler et al. (49) have measured the relative affinities of uncoupling agents for protein by filtering a solution of each compound in ascites fluid through cellophane under pressure, and measuring the concentration of the uncoupling agent in the protein-free filtrate. Under these conditions the following values were obtained for the percentage of uncoupling agent bound by the ascites fluid: p-nitrophenol, 57%; 2,4-dinitrophenol, 76%;

2-methyl-4,6-dinitro-5-isopropylphenol (4,6-dinitrocarvacrol), 95%; 2-isopropyl-4,6-dinitro-5-methylphenol (2,4-dinitrothymol), 98%. In consequence of this binding, the activities of all four compounds in ascites fluid *in vitro* are of the same order of magnitude, whereas their activities differ markedly when tested in Krebs-Ringer bicarbonate. It has also been shown that serum albumin can protect against uncoupling by 2,4-dinitrophenol (*50, 51*).

2. HALOPHENOLS

Loomis (*52*) showed that di- and trihalophenols uncouple oxidative phosphorylation. Weinbach (*53, 54*) has made a special study of the uncoupling action of pentachlorophenol. Since it has a high pK, this compound (as well as the other halophenols) has the advantage of being colorless at neutral pH's. It has the serious disadvantage, however, that, at concentrations only a little higher than necessary for complete uncoupling, it inhibits many of the reactions catalyzed by the mitochondria and, at somewhat higher concentrations, solubilizes the mitochondria.

3. DICOUMAROL

Martius and Nitz-Litzow (*55*) showed that dicoumarol [3,3′-methylenebis(4-hydroxycoumarin)] and related compounds are active uncouplers. Dicoumarol is also a powerful inhibitor of a flavoprotein, which has been called variously menadione reductase (*56*), phylloquinone reductase (*57*), vitamin K reductase (*58*), and DT diaphorase (*59*). It appears, however, that this inhibition is unrelated to the uncoupling activity. Furthermore, there is little evidence that the uncoupling activity is related to the well-known antiblood-clotting activity of dicoumarol.

4. ANTIBIOTICS

Many antibiotics, both phenols and polypeptides, are active uncouplers. This was first shown by Hotchkiss (*60*) and Cross *et al.* (*26*) for gramicidin. Aureomycin (*61*) and valinomycin (*62*) are also uncouplers.

5. UNSATURATED FATTY ACIDS

The uncoupling activity of long-chain fatty acids was discovered by Pressman and Lardy (*63–65*). Hülsmann *et al.* (*66–68*) showed that the active principle of a protein fraction isolated from disintegrated, aged mitochondria by Polis and Shmukler (*69*) and Pullman and Racker (*70*), called mitochrome by the former workers, consisted of a mixture of long-chain unsaturated fatty acids, which could be separated from the hemo-protein by extraction with isooctane. Borst and Loos (71) showed that unsaturated fatty acids are much more potent uncouplers than the saturated. The degree of unsaturation is less important, e.g., oleic, linoleic, linolenic, and elaidic acids are all about equally effective. Lehninger and Remmert (72) found also that an uncoupling factor (called U factor) could be extracted with isooctane from aged mitochondria or mitochon-drial fragments and suggested that this factor may be a long-chain fatty acid.

Unsaturated fatty acids produced by enzymic hydrolysis of neutral lipids or phospholipids in the mitochondrial preparation are probably at least partly responsible for the high ATPase activity of aged mitochon-dria. The formation of uncoupling fatty acids during incubation of mitochondria can be inhibited by EDTA, ATP, or DFP (68), or by ATP + CoA (72).

Two characteristic properties of fatty acids make it easy to test whether an uncoupling preparation isolated from natural materials owes its activity to unsaturated fatty acids. Firstly, the uncoupling activity is extracted into isooctane; secondly, the activity is counteracted by serum albumin, which binds unsaturated fatty acids very strongly, especially oleic acid (73). The beneficial effects of serum albumin on the oxidative phosphorylation of isolated insect sarcosomes (74–76) has been shown to be due to the presence of unsaturated fatty acids in these preparations (77, 78). This is also probably the reason why albumin increases the P/O ratio of mitochondria isolated from tumors (79, 80). Unsaturated fatty acids are also the active principles in the inhibitor produced by *Tetra-hymena pyriformis* (81).

Uncoupling by unsaturated fatty acids may be distinguished from that brought about by other anionic detergents in that it is readily reversible by the subsequent addition of serum albumin.

6. ARSENATE

Arsenate differs from the uncoupling agents mentioned above in that it also uncouples the substrate-linked phosphorylation linked with the oxidation of phosphoglyceraldehyde (82) and α-ketoglutarate (83). Crane and Lipmann (84) showed that it also uncoupled respiratory chain phos-phorylation. Like other such uncouplers it induces an ATPase (85, 86) and inhibits the P_i-ATP exchange reaction (86, 87), the ADP-ATP exchange reaction (85), and the exchange of oxygen atoms between P_i and water (87).

As an uncoupler of respiratory chain phosphorylation, arsenate is much less useful than the compounds mentioned above. High concentrations are necessary, the degree of uncoupling increases with time (*84, 86*), and uncoupling is usually incomplete. The main use of arsenate is in combination with dinitrophenol when it is necessary to uncouple substrate-linked as well as respiratory chain phosphorylation.

III. INHIBITORS

In 1955, Hollunger (*88*) introduced a new type of respiratory inhibitor, guanidine, which inhibits respiration coupled with phosphorylation, without having any effect on the nonphosphorylating respiration of mitochondrial fragments or of mitochondria in the presence of dinitrophenol. Guanidine was not widely used, probably because the mitochondria must be preincubated with rather high concentrations for complete inhibition. In 1958, Lardy *et al.* (*89*) introduced the fungicide oligomycin which, in very low concentrations, has effects similar to those brought about by guanidine. Oligomycin is a neutral, unsaturated, optically active alcohol which may also contain ketone groups (*90, 91*). No elements besides carbon, hydrogen, and oxygen are present. It is a very useful inhibitor of oxidative phosphorylation.

Oligomycin has no effect on the respiration of rat liver mitochondria in the absence of either phosphate or phosphate acceptor, but inhibits completely the increment of the respiration brought about by the addition of phosphate or phosphate acceptor, respectively (*43*). The inhibition of the respiration of mitochondria, measured in the presence of both phosphate and phosphate acceptor, is usually not complete, amounting to about 90% with glutamate as substrate and 60% with succinate (*43, 89*). In both cases, however, phosphorylation is completely inhibited, except for the substrate-linked phosphorylation step of α-ketoglutarate oxidation. The residual respiration is due to the fact that, in isolated mitochondria, respiration is not completely coupled to phosphorylation, the degree of "loose coupling" being greater for succinate than for glutamate. The degree of inhibition by oligomycin is a good measure of the tightness of the coupling. Inhibition of respiration by oligomycin is completely relieved by dinitrophenol (*43, 89*) but not by arsenate (*43, 92*). The respiration of nonphosphorylating mitochondrial fragments is not inhibited by oligomycin (*43, 89*).

Oligomycin preparations used are a mixture of three structurally related compounds (A, B, and C) of molecular weights 424, 394, and 478, respectively (*90, 91*). The relative proportions of the three components can be determined by paper chromatography (*91*). Oligomycin is usually added as an ethanolic solution.

Using a preparation consisting mainly of oligomycin B, 0.75 μg oligomycin/ml (1.4 μmoles/mg mitochondrial protein) was found sufficient for maximal inhibition of respiration (*43*). The amount required is proportional to the protein concentration (unpublished).

Oligomycin also inhibits completely the dinitrophenol-induced ATPase of mitochondria and also the ATPase of mitochondrial fragments (*89*). Chappell and Greville (*93*) have used oligomycin to prevent the hydrolysis of ATP induced by dinitrophenol, while still retaining its uncoupling activity. Since it is without effect on the ATPase of microsomes, oligomycin can be used to measure the degree of contamination of mitochondria by microsomes (*43, 94*).

Although low concentrations of oligomycin (about 1 μg/mg protein) are sufficient to inhibit the dinitrophenol-induced ATPase of mitochondria by about 50%, very high concentrations (about 50 μg/mg protein) are required for complete inhibition (unpublished). Apparently, part of the dinitrophenol-induced ATPase is much more resistant to oligomycin than the rest.

Oligomycin inhibits the $P_i \leftrightharpoons ATP$ reaction (*89*). According to Lardy (*89*) and Huijing and Slater (*43*), it has no effect on the ADP $\leftrightharpoons$ ATP reaction, but Cooper (*95*) and Wadkins (*96*) have found extensive inhibition.

The action of oligomycin can be explained by Eqs. (8)–(13), shown above, if it is further assumed that the noncoupled oxidation, in the presence of oligomycin, proceeds by hydrolysis of A$\sim$I. If the concentration of X does not exceed that of I, the inhibition of the ADP-ATP exchange reaction [Eq. (11)] is explained.

It should be noted that, according to this scheme, oligomycin does not inhibit the formation of all high-energy compounds but only the conversion of these compounds to ATP. This is in contrast to uncouplers which lead to the complete discharge of all high-energy compounds. Thus, oligomycin is a useful reagent for testing whether the high-energy intermediates of oxidative phosphorylation can be directly utilized for energy-requiring reactions in the mitochondria, without having first to be converted to ATP. An example is the succinate-induced reduction of DPN$^+$, which is inhibited by dinitrophenol, but not by oligomycin (*97*).

REFERENCES

1. P. Cazeneuve and R. Lepine, *Compt. rend. acad. sci.* **101**, 1167 (1885).
2. A. P. Mathews and E. Longfellow, *J. Pharmacol.* **2**, 200 (1910).

3. C. Heymans and J. J. Bouchaert, *Arch. intern. pharmacodynamie* **35**, 63 (1928).

4. H. Magne, A. Mayer, and L. Plantefol, *Ann. physiol. physicochim. biol.* **7**, 269 (1931).

5. H. Magne, A. Mayer, and L. Plantefol, *Ann. physiol. physicochim. biol.* **8**, 1, 51, 70, 157 (1932).

6. L. Plantefol, *Ann. physiol. physicochim. biol.* **8**, 127 (1932).

7. P. Van Uytvanck, *Arch. intern. pharmacodynamie* **41**, 160 (1931).

8. T. Cahn, *Ann. physiol. physicochim. biol.* **9**, 393 (1933).

9. U. S. von Euler, *Arch. intern. pharmacodynamie* **43**, 67 (1932).

10. U. S. von Euler, *Arch. intern. pharmacodynamie* **44**, 464 (1933).

11. E. Ehrenfest and E. Ronzoni, *Proc. Soc. Exptl. Biol. Med.* **31**, 318 (1933).

12. E. C. Dodds and G. D. Greville, *Nature* **132**, 966 (1933).

13. E. Ronzoni and E. Ehrenfest, *J. Biol. Chem.* **115**, 749 (1936).

14. E. C. Dodds and G. D. Greville, *Lancet* **112** (1), 398 (1934).

15. G. H. A. Clowes and M. E. Krahl, *J. Gen. Physiol.* **20**, 145 (1936).

16. G. H. A. Clowes, *Ann. N.Y. Acad. Sci.* **51**, 1409 (1948–51).

17. A. W. Martin and J. Field, *Proc. Soc. Exptl. Biol. Med.* **32**, 54 (1934).

18. M. J. Pickett and C. E. Clifton, *J. Cellular Comp. Physiol.* **22**, 147 (1943).

19. H. A. Lardy and P. H. Phillips, *J. Biol. Chem.* **149**, 177 (1943).

20. R. D. Hotchkiss, *Advances in Enzymol.* **4**, 153 (1944).

21. G. D. Greville, Ph.D. Thesis, University of London (1939).

22. G. D. Greville, *Nature* **148**, 320 (1941).

23. R. H. De Meio and E. S. G. Barron, *Proc. Soc. Exptl. Biol. Med.* **32**, 36 (1934–1935).

24. H. A. Lardy and C. A. Elvehjem, *Ann. Rev. Biochem.* **14**, 1 (1945).

25. W. F. Loomis and F. Lipmann, *J. Biol. Chem.* **173**, 807 (1948).

26. R. J. Cross, J. V. Taggart, G. A. Covo, and D. E. Green, *J. Biol. Chem.* **177**, 655 (1949).

27. V. R. Potter and R. O. Recknagel, *in* "Phosphorus Metabolism" (B. Glass, ed.), Vol. I, p. 377. Johns Hopkins Press, Baltimore, Maryland, 1951.

28. M. Rabinovitz, M. P. Stulberg, and P. D. Boyer, *Science* **114**, 641 (1951).

29. H. A. Lardy and H. Wellman, *J. Biol. Chem.* **195**, 215 (1952).

30. H. A. Lardy and H. Wellman, *J. Biol. Chem.* **201**, 357 (1953).

31. W. A. Engelhardt, *Biochem. Z.* **227**, 16 (1930).

32. W. A. Engelhardt, *Biochem. Z.* **251**, 343 (1932).

33. P. Borst and E. C. Slater, *Biochim. et Biophys. Acta* **48**, 362 (1961).

34. E. C. Slater and S. Lewis, *Biochem. J.* **58**, 337 (1954).

35. F. Hunter, *in* "Phosphorus Metabolism" (B. Glass, ed.), Vol. I, p. 297. Johns Hopkins Press, Baltimore, Maryland, 1951.

36. P. D. Boyer, A. B. Falcone, and W. H. Harrison, *Nature* **174**, 401 (1954).

37. A. L. Lehninger, C. L. Wadkins, C. Cooper, T. M. Devlin, and J. L. Gamble, *Science* **128**, 450 (1958).

38. M. Cohn, *J. Biol. Chem.* **201**, 735 (1953).

39. M. Cohn and G. R. Drysdale, *J. Biol. Chem.* **216**, 831 (1955).

40. H. Löw, P. Siekevitz, L. Ernster, and O. Lindberg, *Biochim. et Biophys. Acta* **29**, 392 (1958).

41. B. Grabe, *Biochim. et Biophys. Acta* **30**, 560 (1958).

42. H. Löw, *Biochim. et Biophys. Acta* **32**, 1 (1959).

43. F. Huijing and E. C. Slater, *J. Biochem. (Tokyo)* **49**, 493 (1961).
44. A. L. Lehninger, *Harvey Lectures Ser.* **49**, 176 (1955).
45. V. H. Parker, *Biochem. J.* **69**, 306 (1958).
46. E. Gladtke and E. Liss, *Biochem. Z.* **331**, 65 (1959).
47. H. C. Hemker and W. C. Hülsmann, *Biochim. et Biophys. Acta* **48**, 221 (1961).
48. E. C. Slater and S. E. Lewis, *Biochem. J.* **58**, 207 (1954).
49. N. E. Jongejans-Sickler, A. Kemp, and J. van Noordwijk, *J. Biochem. Pharmacol.* **6**, 263 (1961).
50. D. K. Myers and E. C. Slater, *Biochem. J.* **67**, 572 (1957).
51. G. F. Azzone, O. Eeg-Olofsson, L. Ernster, R. Luft, and G. Szabolesi, *Exptl. Cell Research* **22**, 415 (1961).
52. W. F. Loomis, *Federation Proc.* **8**, 220 (1949).
53. E. C. Weinbach, *J. Biol. Chem.* **210**, 545 (1954).
54. E. C. Weinbach, *J. Biol. Chem.* **221**, 609 (1956).
55. C. Martius and D. Nitz-Litzow, *Biochim. et Biophys. Acta* **12**, 134 (1953).
56. W. D. Wosilait and A. Nason, *J. Biol. Chem.* **208**, 785 (1954).
57. C. Martius and R. Strufe, *Biochem. Z.* **326**, 24 (1954).
58. F. Märki and C. Martius, *Biochem. Z.* **333**, 111 (1960).
59. L. Ernster, M. Ljunggren, and L. Danielson, *Biochem. Biophys. Research Communs.* **2**, 88 (1960).
60. R. D. Hotchkiss, *in* "Currents in Biochemical Research" (D. E. Green, ed.), p. 379. Interscience, New York, 1946.
61. W. F. Loomis, *Science* **111**, 474 (1950).
62. W. C. McMurray and R. W. Begg, *Arch. Biochem. Biophys.* **84**, 546 (1959).
63. B. C. Pressman and H. A. Lardy, *J. Biol. Chem.* **197**, 547 (1952).
64. B. C. Pressman and H. A. Lardy, *Biochim. et Biophys. Acta* **18**, 482 (1955).
65. B. C. Pressman and H. A. Lardy, *Biochim. et Biophys. Acta* **21**, 458 (1956).
66. W. C. Hülsmann, W. B. Elliott and H. Rudney, *Biochim. et Biophys. Acta* **27**, 663 (1958).
67. W. B. Elliott, W. C. Hülsmann, and E. C. Slater, *Biochim. et Biophys. Acta* **33**, 509 (1959).
68. W. C. Hülsmann, W. B. Elliott, and E. C. Slater, *Biochim. et Biophys. Acta* **39**, 267 (1960).
69. B. D. Polis and H. W. Shmukler, *J. Biol. Chem.* **227**, 419 (1957).
70. M. E. Pullman and E. Racker, *Science* **123**, 1105 (1956).
71. P. Borst and J. Loos, *Rec. trav. chim.* **78**, 874 (1959).
72. A. L. Lehninger and F. L. Remmert, *J. Biol. Chem.* **234**, 2459 (1959).
73. D. S. Goodman, *J. Am. Chem. Soc.* **80**, 3892 (1958).
74. B. Sacktor, *J. Gen. Physiol.* **37**, 343 (1954).
75. S. E. Lewis and E. C. Slater, *Biochem. J.* **58**, 207 (1954).
76. B. Sacktor, J. J. O'Neill, and D. G. Cochran, *J. Biol. Chem.* **233**, 1233 (1958).
77. L. Wojtczak and A. B. Wojtczak, *Biochim. et Biophys. Acta* **39**, 277 (1960).
78. S. E. Lewis and K. E. Fowler, *Biochim. et Biophys. Acta* **38**, 564 (1960).
79. T. M. Devlin and M. P. Pruss, *Federation Proc.* **17**, 211 (1958).

80. P. Borst, *J. Biophys. Biochem. Cytol.* 7, 381 (1960).
81. H. J. Eichel, *Biochim. et Biophys. Acta* 43, 364 (1960).
82. D. M. Needham and R. K. Pillai, *Biochem. J.* 31, 1837 (1937).
83. D. R. Sanadi, D. M. Gibson, P. Ayengar, and L. Ouellet, *Biochim. et Biophys. Acta* 13, 146 (1954).
84. R. K. Crane and F. Lipmann, *J. Biol. Chem.* 201, 235 (1953).
85. C. L. Wadkins, *J. Biol. Chem.* 235, 3300 (1960).
86. G. F. Azzone and L. Ernster, *J. Biol. Chem.* 236, 1510 (1961).
87. P. C. Chan, A. L. Lehninger, and T. Enns, *J. Biol. Chem.* 235, 1790 (1960).
88. G. Hollunger, *Acta Pharmacol. Toxicol.* 11, Suppl., 1 (1955).
89. H. A. Lardy, D. Johnson, and W. C. McMurray, *Arch. Biochem. Biophys.* 78, 587 (1958).
90. S. Masamune, J. M. Sehgal, E. E. Van Tameleu, F. M. Strong, and W. H. Peterson, *J. Am. Chem. Soc.* 80, 6092 (1958).
91. J. Visser, D. E. Weinauer, R. C. Davis, W. H. Peterson, W. Nazarewicz and H. Ordway, *J. Biochem. Microbiol. Technol. Eng.* 2, 31 (1960).
92. R. W. Estabrook, *Biochem. Biophys. Research Communs.* 4, 89 (1961).
93. J. B. Chappell and G. D. Greville, *Nature* 190, 502 (1961).
94. E. C. Slater, *Proc. 5th Intern. Congr. Biochem., Moscow, 1961*, p. 325. Pergamon Press, New York, 1963.
95. C. Cooper and R. G. Kulka. *J. Biol. Chem.* 236, 2351 (1961).
96. C. L. Wadkins, *Proc. 5th Intern. Congr. Biochem., Moscow, 1961*, p. 363. Pergamon Press, New York, 1963.
97. A. M. Snoswell, *Biochim. et Biophys. Acta* 52, 216 (1961).

CHAPTER 33

Effects of Anesthetics, Depressants, and Tranquilizers on Cerebral Metabolism

J. H. Quastel

I. INTRODUCTION

Narcotics and anesthetics include a large variety of structural types, such as hydrocarbons, alcohols, ethers, urethans, sulfones, amides, ureides, barbiturates, and nitrous oxide. Their common property of inducing narcosis in animals evidently depends on certain physicochemical characters that they have in common rather than on the possession of any special chemical constitution.

It has long been known that narcotics, such as the urethans, as a general rule inhibit enzymic and respiratory processes. It was early shown (1) that when yeast cells or a cell-free heart preparation are aerated in the presence of a substrate and a narcotic, cytochrome b is reduced and cytochromes c and a remain in the oxidized form. Ethylurethan (0.36 M) inhibits the oxidation of succinate mediated through the cytochrome system by about 90% and through phenothiazine methosulfate by about 40%. It thus has two effects on a succinic oxidase system in a heart muscle preparation. It breaks a link between cytochrome b and c, and to a lesser degree it inhibits the enzymic activity of succinic dehydrogenase (2). A concentration of 0.02 M ethylurethan only inhibits unstimulated rat brain cortex respiration *in vitro* by 6% (3), while 0.03 M ethylurethan inhibits guinea pig brain respiration by 20% and does not inhibit yeast respiration at all (4). At the latter concentration it inhibits the oxygen consumption of a guinea pig brain preparation in the presence of glucose by 17% and has no effect in presence of succinate (4). The narcotizing concentration of ethylurethan in the rat is about 0.022 M (3), and there can be no doubt that, as a general rule, the concentrations of anesthetics required to induce narcosis in an animal are usually of a far smaller order than those required to inhibit most enzymic reactions.

In the narcotic state, induced by a variety of anesthetics, there is diminished cerebral consumption of oxygen. Anoxia, for example (5), exists in the central nervous system during the anesthesia brought about by barbiturates and other narcotics. Under Pentothal, oxygen consumption of the cerebral cortex is decreased more than that of the lower centers (6). With thiopental anesthesia, the average oxygen intake is lowered about 35% (7). Ether anesthesia is associated with a decrease in the difference between the oxygen contents of arterial and venous bloods (8). In the human subject under the influence of Amytal there is a small but definite inhibition of oxygen uptake and dextrose utilization by the brain (9). The depression of cerebral function by barbiturates indeed parallels the reduction of oxygen uptake. This fall in oxygen uptake *in vivo*, however, may be only a reflection of the diminished cerebral activity obtained under narcosis (19).

It should be pointed out in this connection that the physiological facts point to a very high degree of dependence of mental function on the maintenance of oxygen and glucose supply to the central nervous system. Any interference with the respiratory activity of the nervous system, or with some important aspect of this, by the action of the drug would be expected to disturb its functional activity. The action of the metabolic inhibitor, i.e., its biochemical effect, may be highly localized even if its distribution in the brain as a whole is uniform. Accessibilty of the substance to the enzyme systems affected must be dependent on the chemical constition of the cell structures in which these enzyme systems are located.

II. ANESTHETICS AND RESPIRATION OF THE BRAIN *IN VITRO*

Anesthetics inhibit, at low concentrations, the respiration of brain tissue either in the form of a mince or of intact thin slices (*10, 27*). Studies (*4*) of the effects of seven alkylbarbiturates on the oxygen uptake of minced guinea pig brain respiring in the presence of glucose have shown that there is a rough parallelism in this series of barbiturates between hypnotic power and inhibitive effect on brain respiration. This parallelism takes place among narcotics of different chemical types (*11*).

Results shown in Table I, obtained by using brain cortex slices (*10*), make it clear that a variety of anesthetics, at their narcotizing concentrations, produces inhibitions of cerebral respiration varying from 6 to 32%. The data indicate that a small but definite inhibition of respiration is produced by concentrations of the order of those producing deep narcosis. The inhibitions recorded represent the effects of the narcotics on the respiration of the entire brain cortex of the animal. Local inhibition will be much higher if the narcotic is localized or specifically absorbed at particular centers. It is known that narcotics have differential effects on the neurons in brain (*12*). The addition of pentobarbital (0.002 *M*) brings about a large inhibition of oxygen uptake of human cerebral cortex slices in the presence of glucose, human brain cortex being a little more sensitive than rat brain cortex (*13*). When very dilute concentrations of an anesthetic are investigated, the effect sometimes, e.g., with phenobarbital (*14*), is to bring about a small increase of respiration (about 5–10%) of the brain cortex slice, the effect being dependent on the calcium and magnesium concentrations.

The results of experiments which combined a dog brain biopsy method and the manometric technique of measuring respiration showed that the oxygen consumption *in vitro* of brain cortex, basal ganglion, or hypothalamus may be depressed to the extent of 70% in the presence of 0.04% pentobarbital (*15*). Moreover, the measurements of the rate of oxygen consumption of rat brain cortex slices in which the suspension medium

TABLE I

ANESTHETIC CONCENTRATION AND EFFECTS ON THE RESPIRATION OF BRAIN CORTEX
SLICES IN A GLUCOSE MEDIUM

Anesthetic	Animal	Estimated narcotic dose (gm/kg)	Narcotizing concentration (M)	Per cent inhibition of brain tissue respiration by narcotizing concentration
Ethylurethan	Rat	2	0.022	6
Magnesium ions	Rat	—	0.005	13
Chloral hydrate	Rat	0.22	0.0013	10
Luminal	Rat	0.2	0.0008	15
Chloretone	Rat	0.18	0.001	20
Evipan	Guinea pig	0.16	0.00062	17
Avertin	Rat	0.3	0.0011	31
Chloretone	Guinea pig	0.18	0.0010	32

consisted of whole blood drawn from a dog before and at given intervals after the administration of 36 mg/kg Nembutal showed significant inhibitions (25–33%) of brain respiration with blood drawn 3, 15, 30, and 60 minutes after administration of the narcotic (16).

III. ANESTHETICS AND SPECIFICITY OF OXIDATIVE INHIBITION

Anesthetics do not inhibit all oxidative processes to the same extent. Sen (17), for example, showed that urethan, at the high concentrations that inhibit succinic dehydrogenase, has no effect on xanthine oxidase. The oxidations of glucose, lactate, and pyruvate are most affected by relatively small concentrations of the anesthetics, while those of succinate and p-phenylenediamine are undisturbed (4).

The rate of oxygen consumption of tissues other than brain is also affected by anesthetics, though not to the same extent. Examination of the inhibitive action of narcotics on the respiration of a variety of tissues in the presence of different substances has shown (10) that anesthetics inhibit the oxidation of glucose, lactate, and pyruvate in tissues such as liver, kidney, or diaphragm to about the same extent as in brain. Anesthetics will also inhibit the oxidation of fatty acids and amino acids by isolated liver (10). Narcotic inhibition of oxidations is not, therefore, restricted to glucose and its breakdown products.

IV. REVERSIBILITY OF NARCOTIC ACTION *IN VITRO*

The effects of anesthetics such as the barbiturates and chloretone on the respiration of brain slices are reversible. This is shown simply by washing the brain slices in an anesthetic-free medium after their immersion for an hour at 37° in the anesthetic solution. The slow constant rate of oxygen uptake found in the presence of the anesthetic is raised immediately to a high level, which remains constant (*18*). High concentrations of anesthetics, however, produce irreversible effects.

There are two effects of an anesthetic on brain respiration *in vitro*:

1. Rapid attainment of an equilibrium between the anesthetic and a constituent of the respiratory system. The inhibition of respiration is that to be expected from a simple mass action equation (*3*), as observed with small concentrations of anesthetic producing inhibitions not greater than 40%. This applies to anesthetics such as urethan, chloral, chloretone, barbiturates, Avertin (tribromoethyl alcohol), and magnesium ions.

2. Relatively slow development of irreversible changes, leading to increased inhibitions of respiration that cannot be restored to normal by removal of the anesthetic. This takes place with most anesthetics, such as barbiturates or chloretone at relatively high concentrations. It occurs, however, at low concentrations with ether (*20*). Irreversibility of action also occurs with indole, which is a powerful inhibitor of brain respiration (*18*). Conceivably, this is due to gradual irreversible denaturation of the proteins with which these narcotics become associated.

V. STIMULATED BRAIN METABOLISM

The respiration of isolated brain cortex slices in a normal physiological (glucose-containing) medium is about half that found *in vivo*. It may be increased by two methods to values approximating those found *in vivo*: (*a*) alteration of the cationic composition, particularly the K^+ and Ca^{++} content, of the medium in which the brain slice is incubated; and (*b*) application of electrical impulses.

It was shown many years ago (*21, 22*) that increasing the potassium ion concentration of the medium in which a brain slice is immersed to 100 meq/liter (which is approximately the concentration of potassium ions in the nerve cell) brings about a marked increase in the rate of respiration, approaching double that of the normal in a glucose medium. That the stimulating effect is due to the balance between potassium and calcium ions rather than to the absolute magnitude of the potassium ion concentration is demonstrated by the fact that a considerable stimulation may occur by removal of calcium ions from a medium containing the usual (5 meq/liter) concentration of potassium ions (23). This phenomenon does not occur in a brain homogenate or mince; it is evident that it is linked with the integrity of the brain cell membranes.

It was equally well known that the respiration of isolated muscle and peripheral nerve is increased on electrical stimulation. Winterstein (24) showed that application of electrical impulses to isolated frog spinal cord led to an increase in its respiration. Bronk and Brink (25), in fact, demonstrated that the increment in the rate of oxygen uptake of frog nerve carrying impulses at the rate of 50 impulses/second is highly anesthetic sensitive. McIlwain (26) showed that application of electrical impulses to the isolated brain tissue (in the form of slices), in a physiological medium, brings about an increased rate of respiration, approximately double the normal value.

There is little doubt that both methods of respiratory stimulation have a common basis, namely, cationic displacements at the brain cell membrane. What is important, however, is the fact that the stimulated respiration of isolated brain tissue has the magnitude of brain respiration *in vivo* and possesses some of the characteristic features of brain *in vivo*, such as response to drug action. It may be considered a working hypothesis that the stimulated brain slice is an approximation, so far as its biochemical characteristics are concerned, to the functioning brain, that is, to brain tissue *in vivo*, stimulated by sensory impulses. It must be borne in mind, however, that brain slices, under the best experimental conditions obtained so far, do not show all the electrophysiological responses to stimulation, or the spontaneous activity associated with brain *in vivo*. Nevertheless, even as an approximation to the *in vivo* condition, they are able to yield valuable biochemical data that bear upon the properties of the functioning brain (19).

A. Effects of Anesthetics, etc., on Stimulated Brain Metabolism

The steady state of the diminished respiration of brain slices brought about by small concentrations of anesthetics, such as phenobarbital or chloretone, is greatly dependent on the K^+ concentration of the medium (10). The presence of 12.8 meq/liter K^+ secures a steady inhibition of respiration by chloretone, lower concentrations of K^+ producing a fluctuating and unstable state, possibly due to loss of K^+ from the brain cells. This unstable state depends on the temperature and is less evident at 29° than at 39°.

Anesthetics (as well as depressants and tranquilizers) exercise much larger inhibitory effects on the respiration of nerve tissue, stimulated either electrically or by the presence of a high content of K^+ or diminished Ca^{++}, than on that of the unstimulated preparation. The rate of oxygen uptake by resting frog nerve is reduced 15% by 2 mM chloretone but the increment in the rate of oxygen uptake by nerves carrying impulses at the rate of 50 impulses/second is decreased by 50% by the same quantity of the narcotic (25). Anesthetics such as the barbiturates and chloral inhibit the respiration of electrically stimulated brain cortex slices at concentrations having relatively little effect on the respiration

TABLE II

EFFECTS OF LUMINAL ON RAT BRAIN CORTEX RESPIRATION IN THE PRESENCE OF
POTASSIUM CHLORIDE (27)

Additions	Q_{O_2} without added KCl	Q_{O_2} with added KCl (0.1 M)	Average % increase due to KCl
Glucose	14.2, 12.6, 11.5	24.5, 20.0, 21.0	70
Glucose + 3.3 mM Luminal	9.5, 7.4, 6.9	10.5, 8.5, 7.8	12

TABLE III

EFFECTS OF CHLORETONE ON THE KCL-STIMULATED RESPIRATION OF RAT BRAIN
CORTEX SLICES IN THE PRESENCE OF DIFFERENT SUBSTRATES (10 MM) (27)

Substrate	Condition	Q_{O_2} No chloretone present	Q_{O_2} In the presence of 3.3 mM chloretone
Glucose	Without added KCl	12.5	8.3
	With 0.1 M KCl	20.5	9.2
Sodium pyruvate	Without added KCl	13.2	10.1
	With 0.1 M KCl	18.8	11.2
Sodium L-glutamate	Without added KCl	7.5	5.0
	With 0.1 M KCl	7.0	5.0
Sodium succinate	Without added KCl	10.8	10.5
	With 0.1 M KCl	9.0	8.5

of the unstimulated tissue (26). Moreover, potassium-stimulated respiration is more sensitive to the action of barbiturates and chloral than unstimulated respiration. Luminal inhibition, it was already known, is greater in the absence of Ca^{++} than in its presence (10). Removal of Ca^{++} has effects on anesthetic sensitivity similar to that due to added K^+ (23). It is, however, the increased aspect of brain respiration due to cationic stimulation which is highly sensitive to luminal, chloretone, and ethanol (27), and, in fact, the anesthetic suppresses the K^+ stimulation (see Tables II and III).

The largest effects of cationic stimulation on rates of oxygen consumption are with the substrates glucose, fructose, pyruvate, and lactate, and little is seen with L-glutamate or succinate. The presence of increased potassium ion concentrations or decreased calcium ion concentrations does not affect the action of anesthetics on oxygen consumption in the presence of glutamate or succinate. The enhanced inhibitory effect of anesthetics is restricted to the substrates whose oxidation is accelerated by the increased ratio of K^+ to Ca^{++}. Recent evidence (28, 28a–28c) indicates that the cationic stimulation of respiration is due to the increased rate of operation of the citric acid cycle in the brain cell, the rate-limiting step that is (indirectly) affected being the conversion of pyruvate into acetyl CoA.

Investigations using radioactive glucose and estimating the rates of formation of $C^{14}O_2$ instead of oxygen consumption show very clearly the inhibiting effects, at low concentrations, of Amytal (0.5 mM), Doriden (a-ethyl-a-phenylglutarimide) (2.5 mM), and ethanol on potassium-stimulated cerebral respiration (29).

B. Anesthetics and Uncoupling of Phosphorylation

Anesthetics at low concentrations will dissociate phosphorylations from oxidations, sometimes without any apparent effect on the respiratory rate. It is well known that certain drugs, such as dinitrophenol and gramicidin, will exhibit this phenomenon. It has been shown (30) that barbiturates at low concentrations will also bring about the same phenomenon. Definite decreases of the P/O ratio may, however, accompany decreases of the rate of oxygen uptake, contrary to what occurs with low concentrations of dinitrophenol. The evidence (31) makes it clear that the behavior of narcotics on metabolic processes in the brain differs from that of a typical uncoupling agent, such as 2,4-dinitrophenol (31b). With liver mitochondria the oxybarbiturates do not depress phosphorylation more than they depress respiration (31a; see also 31c). These drugs do not activate ATPase in contrast to the effect of 2 : 4 dinitrophenol (*31a, b, d*).

Experiments with cell preparations gave rise to the conclusion (*32*) that the site of action of anesthetics (e.g. chloretone) on brain respiration is located with a process playing an intermediate role between cytochrome oxidase and a flavoprotein concerned with the oxidation of diphosphopyridine nucleotide ($NADH_2$). This conclusion is confirmed for oxybarbiturates by results of work on mitochondria (*31b*). In accordance with this conclusion, it has been found (*33, 34*) that Amytal or chloretone (*35*) is a highly effective inhibitor of the oxidation of $NADH_2$. As it is now well known that the biological oxidation of $NADH_2$ is accompanied by the phosphorylation of adenosine diphosphate (ADP) to adenosine triphosphate (ATP), it follows that the anesthetic is also inhibitory to oxidative phosphorylation. This is shown in the following reaction [Eq. (1)]:

$$NADH_2 + ADP + Pi + O \xrightarrow[\text{Amytal or Chloretone}]{\text{Inhibited by}} NAD + ATP + H_2O \quad (1)$$

The suppression of $NADH_2$ oxidation by Amytal thus has the double effect of suppressing the citric acid cycle (as pyruvate oxidation requires NAD for the formation of acetyl CoA) and ATP production. In this connection it may be noted that when the oxidation of pyruvate by liver mitochondria is stimulated by the addition of a pyrase (which releases ADP) it is the stimulated oxidation which is more inhibited by barbiturates than the unstimulated (*31a, b*). Chloretone is an effective inhibitor of $NADH_2$ oxidation in a rat brain homogenate (60% inhibition with 2 mM chloretone) and in dog liver mitochondria (*35*).

It is of importance to note that succinate reduces intramitochondrial pyridine nucleotide (PN) and that Amytal (1.6 mM) not only suppresses the oxidation of PNH_2 but slows the rate of reduction (*35a*).

The effects of anesthetics on ATP synthesis in the brain are shown by their suppression of acetylcholine synthesis (*36–38*) and by their inhibitory effects (e.g., those of 4 mM chloretone or 1 mM Nembutal) on P^{32} incorporation (from phosphate) into phosphoproteins and organic phosphorus compounds in cat brain slices respiring in presence of glucose (*38a*). A striking demonstration (*28*) of the action of a low concentration of anesthetic (0.5 mM Amytal) on ATP formation in brain slices is shown by its ability to suppress glutamine synthesis, a reaction that requires the participation of ATP in the condensation of glutamate and ammonia. Other changes also take place, and these can be satisfactorily explained by the conclusion that Amytal has a twofold effect (see also *39*): (*a*) diminution of NAD formation from NADH$_2$, and (*b*) diminution of ATP formation. Reduced triphosphopyridine nucleotide oxidation in brain is not affected by Amytal (*40*). Amytal has little or no effect, it should be noted, on certain other NADH oxidizing systems (*41–43*).

C. Anesthetics and Incorporation of Phosphate (P^{32}) into Phospholipids

It is known that the incorporation of labeled phosphate (P^{32}) into phospholipids of rat brain preparations is dependent on the supply of metabolic energy and that the isotope is incorporated into ATP prior to its entry into phospholipids (*43a*). The presence of high concentrations of K$^+$ results in an increase of incorporation of P^{32} into phospholipids of rat brain cortex slices in an incubation time of 30 minutes (*43b, c*) (although continued incubation for 4 hours leads to a decreased incorporation (*43d*) possibly due to irreversible effects gradually occurring in the high K$^+$ medium). Both Amytal (0.5 mM) and chloretone (2mM) almost abolish the potassium-stimulated incorporation of P^{32} into phospholipids in rat brain cortex (*43b*). Moreover, these anesthetics at the concentrations quoted, as well as ethanol (0.2 M), suppress the incorporation of P^{32} into phospholipids in rat brain cortex slices stimulated either by acetylcholine or by potassium ions (*43b, 43c*). These results are consistent with the conclusion that the anesthetics reduce the ability of brain cortex *in vitro*, when stimulated by K$^+$, to form ATP and therefore to bring about, at normal rates, the incorporation of phosphate into phospholipids.

D. Anesthetics and Brain Diaphorases

It has been pointed out in experiments with brain homogenates that anesthetics, such as the barbiturates and chloretone, suppress anaerobic reduction of methylene blue by the brain dehydrogenases, particularly those concerned with the breakdown of carbohydrates, lactate, and pyruvate. They have less effect on the dehydrogenases concerned with succinate or glycerophosphate (*44*). Moreover, some competition with the anesthetic is evident, as the inhibitory effect of the drug diminishes with increasing concentration of the substrate (e.g. lactate). With a sheep brain preparation, 23 mM chloretone produces 50% inhibition of brain lactic acid oxidation with 20 mM lactate as substrate (*44*).

The activities of purified preparations from ox brain of diaphorases that catalyze the anerobic oxidation of NADH and NADPH by a number of electron acceptors, including menadione and methylene blue, are suppressed by Amytal in a competitive manner (45, 46). However, 55% inhibition of activity by Amytal required the relatively high concentration of 6.6 mM (46). The purified preparation of NADH diaphorase is inhibited competitively by a number of barbiturates and other depressants, including chloretone, which gave a 20% inhibition at 3.3 mM with a concentration of $NADH_2$ as low as 0.019 mM (47). Possibly these diaphorase inhibitions are responsible for the recorded earlier observations on narcotic-inhibited brain dehydrogenases (44).

While these inhibitions are likely to play a role in the mechanisms involved in the suppression of brain respiration *in vitro* by anesthetics, it is to be noted (10) that the respiration of brain cortex slices is not only much more susceptible to the drug than a brain homogenate, but that increase of the concentration of the substrate in the medium in which the cortex slices are incubated does not diminish the percentage inhibition (10). Increase of the substrate concentration may be expected to increase the NADH (as it presumably does in a brain homogenate) (44), and this should diminish the anesthetic inhibition. It may be concluded, therefore, that anesthetic inhibition of brain cortex respiration will involve more than a simple suppression of the activity of the NADH diaphorase system.

Spectrophotometric evidence (47a, b) obtained with intact mitochondria have confirmed the conclusion (32) that Amytal acts upon the site of the respiratory chain concerned with the oxidation of $NADH_2$. Purified NADH dehydrogenase is not sensitive to Amytal (47c). NADH diaphorase, using dichlorophenol-indophenol, ferricyanide, and some quinones, is not affected by Amytal (47d; see also 32, 47f), in contrast with highly sensitive NADH oxidase which can be extracted from mitochondria (47d). It has been suggested (47e) that chloretone, which inhibits the activity of pyridine nucleotide-dependent oxidases, brings about some destruction of endogenous pyridine nucleotide.

Inhibitive effects of narcotics, anesthetics, or a tranquilizer, such as chlorpromazine, on ATP synthesis in the brain do not necessarily involve an immediate fall in respiration in the brain cells affected. A situation may arise where the increased concentration of ADP, which has a rate-limiting effect on metabolic reactions involved in glucose breakdown, can give rise to an increased rate of oxygen consumption. This is a frequent effect of the addition of respiratory "uncouplers." Nevertheless, this effect may be transient, depending on a variety of conditions, and the ultimate effect of suppression of so important a process as $NADH_2$ oxidation must be a suppression of respiration.

Narcotics, such as pentobarbital and ethanol, exercise a larger inhibitory effect on respiration in the adult than in the young rat brain (48), a result that is to be expected from the fact that the activity of the citric acid cycle increases with age during the early days of postnatal life and that the effect of K^+ on aerobic nerve metabolism is greatly decreased in very young animal brain. There is a significant positive correlation between rate of brain respiration at different ages and sensitivity to barbiturates (49). The inhibitory effects of barbiturates on respiration diminish in old age, the maximum effects occurring in the young adult.

E. Effects of Chlorpromazine on Brain Metabolism *in vitro*

Chlorpromazine at low concentrations reduces the enhanced respiration due to electrical excitation (50, 50a) just as it reduces the increased oxygen uptake found with potassium ion stimulation (51). The electrical-stimulated respiration is apparently more sensitive than the potassium-stimulated respiration. It also brings about some inhibition *in vitro* of incorporation of glycine-1-C^{14} into rat brain cortex proteins, a process that is ATP dependent, at concentrations (0.2 mM) that have little or no effect on the respiration of brain or on the breakdown of glycine-1-$C^{14}O_2$ into $C^{14}O_2$ (51). The inhibitory effect (50% inhibition) is also brought about by 0.5 mM Amytal and 0.4 M ethanol. Thus, it is possible that chlorpromazine may affect physiological action by an inhibitive or uncoupling action on ATP synthesis at the particular site in the brain where it gains access most easily to the relevant enzyme systems. The addition of chlorpromazine (0.1 mM) to guinea pig brain slices brings about changes in labeling of lipid phosphorus in the presence of P^{32}, namely, decreases of phosphatidylethanolamine and phosphatidylcholine and an increase of phosphoinositide; with higher concentrations of the drug there is a considerable decrease in labeling of lipid phosphorus (52, 52a). Chlorpromazine also exerts an inhibitory activity on the respiration of brain cortex slices in the presence of glucose, pyruvate, or L-glutamate but not succinate. This inhibitory effect is greatly increased with brain cortex slices stimulated by the presence of potassium ions, a definite inhibition occurring with 0.2 mM chlorpromazine.

Recent results (53) indicate that chlorpromazine uncouples phosphorylation coupled to the oxidation of ferrocytochrome c and inhibits NADH-cytochrome c reductase, the effect being mainly due to an effect on the coupled phosphorylation reaction.

Thus, chlorpromazine, like Amytal, brings about an inhibition of oxidative phosphorylation in brain cortex respiration *in vitro*. However, the action of chlorpromazine *in vitro* differs from that of the barbiturates in bringing about progressive inhibitions and in its high binding power with tissue proteins (probably lipoproteins). The drug, after combining with tissue components, gradually diffuses into the brain cell bringing about its metabolic inhibitions (*51*). The conclusion that chlorpromazine affects $NADH_2$ oxidation (in phosphorylating systems, such as those in brain cortex *in vitro*) has been confirmed with the use of liver mitochondrial systems (*53*). Chlorpromazine 0.2 mM brings about in liver mitochondria a marked inhibition of incorporation of P^{32} into ATP (see also *53a*). These facts do not imply that chlorpromazine and Amytal act at the same locations in the nervous system. The differences between the clinical effects of these two drugs may be due more to their different sites of action than to essential differences in biochemical mechanism.

Chlorpromazine appears to affect cell permeability (*53b, c*). It diminishes the uptake of circulating labeled noradrenaline into heart and adrenal medulla (*53d*). Possibly, these effects are due either to combination with membrane constituents or to depression of ATP that may control transport at the cell membrane. Combinations of chlorpromazine with manganese ions (*53e*) or the strong electron-donor properties of chlorpromazine (*53f*) have been suggested as possible explanations for its activity in the nervous system.

F. Effects of Aliphatic Alcohols on Brain Metabolism

The addition of ethanol at small concentrations diminishes (*27, 54*) the oxygen consumption of rat brain cortex slices respiring in a glucose-phosphate medium when this has been stimulated by the presence of 100 meq/liter K^+. Potassium-stimulated respiration of rat brain slices is much more affected by ethanol at low concentration than normal respiration, the concentration being of the same order as that necessary to bring about the narcotic state in the rat. The behavior with ethanol is similar in this respect to that brought about by anesthetics such as the barbiturates or chloretone (*54–57*). Ethanol also causes a decrease in the respiration of electrically stimulated brain tissue in the presence of glucose (*57*).

The inhibitory effects of the alcohols increase markedly as the length of the carbon chain increases and with increase in concentration, and the potassium ion stimulation of brain cortex respiration is diminished or abolished by concentrations of alcohols that have little effect on the unstimulated respiration (*54*). *n*-Pentanol is much more effective than ethanol in effecting an inhibition of the stimulated respiration, and there seems to take place a rapid establishment of equilibria between the alcohols and the components that influence the brain respiratory system. It has been found (*54*, *58*) that brain mitochondrial respiration is relatively insensitive to concentrations of alcohols that considerably depress stimulated rat-brain slice respiration. In this respect, the alcohols differ from the barbiturates but resemble, perhaps, the action of chlorpromazine (*59*). The results support the conclusion that the alcohols exercise their inhibitory effects on brain respiration at some site located in the brain cell membranes. If this is true, it must be concluded that a significant proportion of the brain cell respiration is controlled by the cell membrane, where presumably the potassium ion stimulation takes place. The alternative explanation, that the effects are due to oxidation of the alcohols to the highly toxic aldehydes or that the alcohols block the entry of substrates into the cell, is not supported by the available evidence.

It may therefore be concluded that anesthetics and cell depressants have a twofold mechanism of action on brain respiration and metabolism: (1) an action at the cell membrane, affecting cationic equilibria there and thereby diminishing cationic stimulation of respiration and (2) an action within the cell, once penetration has occurred, affecting NADH oxidation in the manner already visualized. The two mechanisms are apparently independent, and the first may occur without the second.

G. Effects of Salicylates on Brain Metabolism

Salicylates, like 2,4-dinitrophenol, suppress the formation of radioactive glutamine from radioactive glucose in the presence of rat brain cortex slices. Representative results are shown in Table IV (*60*). There can be little doubt that the inhibition is due to the suppression of oxidative phosphorylation (*61*, *62*). The effect, however, is more pronounced with the cation-stimulated metabolism than with the unstimulated metabolism. The effects of acetylsalicylate and 2,4-dinitrophenol are not identical. The former strongly depresses labeled alanine formation with but little effect on that of labeled γ-aminobutyrate, whereas the latter has the reverse effect (Table IV). A noteworthy effect of acetylsalicylates (and DNP) is their bringing about a greatly increased leakage of amino acids from the brain tissue, an effect greatly enhanced under conditions where cell ATP is already diminished (e.g., in the presence of high K^+). They also suppress uptake of amino acids and of creatine into the brain tissue (*60*). These results indicate that the major effect of the two drugs is that of uncoupling phosphorylation from respiration, the loss of ATP resulting in changed transport velocities at the cell membrane and in retarded ATP-dependent reactions. The different clinical effects are

TABLE IV

EFFECTS OF ACETYLSALICYLATE AND 2,4-DINITROPHENOL (DNP) ON RADIOACTIVE
AMINO ACID FORMATION[a] FROM GLUCOSE-U-C^{14} (5 mM) IN RAT BRAIN CORTEX
SLICES[a] (60)

| Amino acid | 5 mM KCl | 105 mM KCl | 0.05 mM DNP | | 5 mM Acetyl-salicylate | |
			5 mM KCl	105 mM KCl	5 mM KCl	105 mM KCl
Glutamate	1032	1078	1140	935	890	770
Glutamine	370	732	254	45	255	40
γ-Aminobutyrate	270	467	400	270	234	350
Aspartate	280	280	520	265	227	135
Alanine	215	233	154	125	57	82
O$_2$	10.2	15.1	18.2	16.4	14.4	11.5

[a] Amounts expressed as mμ atom C^{14} incorporated/hour/100 mg wet weight tissue.

presumably to be attributed to the different sites of action in the body (62a).

H. Effects of Amytal on the Incorporation of P^{32} into Adenosine Triphosphate (ATP), Adenosine Diphosphate (ADP), and Phosphocreatine (CrP)

It has been shown (63) that electrical stimulation of the brain causes a drop in the content of ATP and a rise in inorganic phosphate, while there is evidence that excitation of the brain increases the ADP/ATP ratio (64). It is now well known that concentrations of ADP (or phosphate ions) may be rate limiting in mitochondrial respiration. Hence, stimulation of the brain in vitro by reactions increasing ADP (or phosphate) may result in acceleration of oxygen consumption and other dependent metabolic events.

The organic phosphates of brain slices undergo considerable changes in the presence of increased K$^+$. There is a fall of ATP and CrP (65–67). This effect of cationic stimulation is shown in Table V (60a), where it is seen that the incorporation of P^{32} from radioactive phosphate is diminished in ATP and CrP, and increased in ADP. This would be expected if cationic stimulation causes an increased rate of conversion of ATP to ADP, with resultant fall in CrP according to the reaction [Eq. (2)]

$$ADP + CrP \rightleftarrows ATP + Cr \qquad (2)$$

TABLE V

EFFECTS OF AMYTAL ON THE INCORPORATION OF P[32] INTO ATP, ADP, AND CrP
IN RAT BRAIN CORTEX SLICES INCUBATED AEROBICALLY IN GLUCOSE-RINGER
MEDIUM CONTAINING 10 mM NA$_2$HP^{32}O$_4$ (10[7] COUNTS/MINUTE)

Addition	KCl present (mM)	ATP[a]	ADP[a]	CrP[a]
Nil	5	3100	100	1900
Nil	105	2150	550	950
Amytal (0.5 mM)	5	2950	150	1450
Amytal (0.5 mM)	105	1250	50	400

[a] Counts/minute/100 mg wet tissue.

In the presence of Amytal (0.5 mM), however, there is, with the normal (5 mM) KCl concentration, a fall in the labeled CrP which is larger than that of labeled ATP. These effects are greatly increased in the presence of 105 mM KCl. It is evident that at normal concentrations of K$^+$ the fall in ATP due to Amytal is diminished by the transphosphorylation due to CrP present. With high concentrations of K$^+$, there is less CrP available to react with ADP (whose phosphorylation is suppressed by Amytal), and hence there is a diminished ATP level.

VI. MODE OF ACTION OF ANESTHETICS AND ALLIED SUBSTANCES

It is possible to understand the effects of anesthetics, depressants, and tranquilizers so far studied by their effects on (a) mitochondrial oxidations (NADH$_2$ oxidation) and/or (b) cation equilibria at the brain cell membrane. It is known that, so far as the barbiturates are concerned, there is a reasonable correlation between the anesthetic concentration and those required to give 20% inhibition of mitochondrial respiration (31a, b). The effects on mitochondrial respiration may be summarized in the following reactions [Eqs. (3) and (4)]:

Pyruvate + NAD + CoA

$\downarrow$ Stimulated by increased K$^+$ or decreased Ca^{++} (or electrically) by cytoplasmic increase of ADP (at expense of ATP and CrP)   (3)

Acetyl CoA + NADH$_2$ + CO$_2$

$NADH_2 + ADP + P_i$

$$\downarrow \quad O \text{ Inhibited by Amytal, etc.} \qquad\qquad (4)$$

$NAD + ATP + H_2O$

The effects at the brain cell membrane may be understood if the transport carriers at the membrane that are responsible for cation movements (essential for the changes of ATP and ADP, with increased K^+ or diminished Ca^{++} in the medium) associate with or are rendered inert by the responsible drugs. Such effects would result in the diminution or abolition of cationic or electrical stimulation and, hence, would ultimately have an effect similar to that of a respiratory inhibitor acting on the mitochondria. Substances affecting the cell membrane in the manner visualized would not necessarily be "uncouplers" of respiration. It is possible that chlorpromazine and the aliphatic alcohols act primarily in this manner, whereas the barbiturates or chloretone act primarily on mitochondrial $NADH_2$ oxidation.

It is justifiable to conclude that the anesthetics influence both mitochondrial and nerve cell respiration by their adsorption or combination with lipid groups present in the membrane, these groups being involved in the establishment of ionic gradients and respiratory metabolism of the cells.

VII. ANESTHETICS AND GLYCOLYSIS

The mechanism of anaerobic breakdown of glucose in brain involves the interplay of dehydrogenases that are also involved in the aerobic breakdown of the sugars. The absence of any effect of chloretone (*32*) indicates that the narcotic-sensitive oxidative system, important in the aerobic breakdown of glucose, is either absent from or is without influence on the reactions involved in the anaerobic breakdown of glucose by brain. There is now evidence, indeed, to show that anesthetics increase aerobic glycolysis by suppression of the Pasteur effect. Possibly, this is the explanation for the observation (*69*) that anesthetics at low concentrations accelerate glucose consumption by excised rat superior cervical ganglia. This conclusion would account for earlier observations (*70–72*) that in the presence of anesthetics there is an increased rate of breakdown of glucose, though there is suppression of respiration.

VIII. EFFECTS OF ANESTHETICS ON BIOLOGICAL ACETYLATIONS

Anesthetics that suppress respiration also suppress acetylcholine synthesis by brain. This was first shown using ether (*36*). Depression of synthesis by brain slices is obtained by various drugs (*37*, *38*). There is always a concomitant drop in rate of respiration, but this need not necessarily be as large.

Anesthetics do not diminish, or only slightly diminish (*37*, *38*), the anaerobic synthesis of acetylcholine by ATP in the presence of brain extracts. The known phosphorylations by ATP (e.g., those involved in hexokinase activity and in glycolysis) are not impeded by anesthetics at low concentrations. No inhibitory effect by anesthetics is found on the acetylation of sulfanilamide by enzymes present in the liver.

When the acetylating system is linked with a respiratory system such as that present in brain, the ATP necessary for the acetylation by these systems being formed by the energy of respiration, the presence of anesthetics secures large inhibitory effects on the acetylation (*38*). Thus, Nembutal (0.5 mM) and chloretone (4 mM), at concentrations that do not affect anaerobic synthesis of acetyl sulfanilamide in the presence of ATP, exert marked effects on the aerobic synthesis in the absence of added ATP. Moreover, the addition of ATP to the aerobic system brings about a considerable alleviation of the inhibitory effect of the narcotic. The most obvious explanation of the inhibitory phenomena that take place aerobically is that the narcotics inhibit those links in the respiratory chain (e.g., $NADH_2$ oxidation) that are responsible for the oxidative synthesis of ATP.

IX. STEROIDS

Steroids that have anesthetic potency also affect rat brain (homogenate) respiration in the presence of glucose but not in the presence of succinate (*73*, *74*). The inhibitions parallel anesthetic activities. There is evidence (*75*) to indicate that the site of action of corticosterone, and possibly other steroids, lies in the respiratory chain between the flavoproteins and cytochrome c, a site already suggested as a point of action of a variety of anesthetics (*32*).

X. RESERPINE

The well-known tranquilizing effect of reserpine seems to be associated with its ability to diminish the content of amines in the cell, e.g., of serotonin, from the brain (rabbit, cat) *(68)* or from other tissues [e.g., rabbit intestine *(68a)*, blood platelets *(63b)*], or of catechol amines [e.g., from cat hypothalamus *(68c)*, or adrenergic neurons of rabbits, cats, and dogs *(68d)*, or adrenal medulla *(68e)*]. Reserpine has the power to release serotonin and noradrenaline wherever they are found in the brain *(68f)*.

Reserpine inhibits uptake of noradrenaline, adrenaline, and serotonin by blood platelets *(68b)*. It seems likely that this inhibition is due to an affinity of the drug for the transport carrier concerned with uptake of the amines and is not due to interference with the energetics of the cells concerned. Such inhibition could account for the depleting action of reserpine.

The conclusion that the sedative action of the reserpine group of drugs is due to lowered brain levels of certain amines seems to be supported by the fact that drugs that raise these levels (e.g., monamine oxidase inhibitors) may act as antidepressants *(68f)*. Out of a large number of monamine oxidase inhibitors, those that are active in this respect *in vitro* and *in vivo* are usually stimulatory to the central nervous system *(68g)*, a conclusion put forward over 20 years ago *(68h)*. However, there still exists conflicting evidence that must be explained before the relation between amine content and sedation (or excitement) is made clear *(68g)*.

References

1. D. Keilin, *Proc. Roy. Soc.* **B98**, 312 (1925) ; **B104**, 206 (1929).
2. D. Keilin and T. E. King, *Proc. Roy. Soc.* **B152**, 163 (1960).
3. M. Jowett, *J. Physiol.* (*London*) **92**, 322 (1938).
4. J. H. Quastel and A. H. M. Wheatley, *Proc. Roy. Soc.* **B112**, 60 (1932).
5. R. D. McClure, F. W. Hartmann, J. G. Schnedorf, and V. Schelling, *Ann. Surg.* **110**, 836, 1939.
6. W. A. Himwich, E. Homburger, R. Maresca, and H. E. Himwich, *Am. J. Psychiat.* **103**, 689 (1947).
7. H. E. Himwich, "Brain Metabolism and Cerebral Disorders." Williams & Wilkins, Baltimore, Maryland, 1951.
8. J. L. Shaw, B. F. Steele, and C. A. Lamb, *Arch. Surg.* **35**, 1 (1937).
9. W. Dameschek, A. Myerson, and J. Loman, *Am. J. Psychiat.* **91**, 113 (1934).
10. M. Jowett and J. H. Quastel, *Biochem. J.* **31**, 565 (1937).
11. F. A. Fuhrman and J. Field, *J. Pharmacol. Exptl. Therap.* **77**, 392 (1943).
12. R. Swank and Cammermeyer, *J. Cellular Comp. Physiol.* **34**, 43 (1949).
13. H. W. Elliott and V. C. Sutherland, *J. Cellular Comp. Physiol.* **40**, 221 (1952).

14. B. A. Westfall, *J. Pharmacol. Exptl. Therap.* **96**, 193 (1949).
15. D. S. Wilkins, R. M. Featherstone, J. T. Schwidde, and M. Brotman, *J. Pharmacol. Exptl. Therap.* **98**, 36 (1950).
16. F. W. Schueler and E. G. Gross, *J. Pharmacol. Exptl. Therap.* **98**, 28, (1950).
17. K. C. Sen, *Biochem. J.* **25**, 849 (1931).
18. J. H. Quastel and A. H. M. Wheatley, *Biochem. J.* **28**, 1521 (1934).
19. J. H. Quastel, *in* "Neurochemistry." (K. A. C. Elliott, I. H. Page, and J. H. Quastel, ed.), 2nd edition, p. 790. Thomas, Springfield, Illinois, 1962.
20. M. Jowett and J. H. Quastel, *Biochem. J.,* **31**, 1101 (1937).
21. F. Dickens and G. C. Greville, *Biochem. J.* **29**, 1468 (1935).
22. C. A. Ashford and K. C. Dixon, *Biochem. J.* **29**, 157 (1935).
23. L. Buchel, *Anesthésie et analgésie* **10**, No. 1, 1 (1953).
24. H. Winterstein, Handbuch der normalen und pathologischen Physiologie (A. Bethe *et al.*, eds.), Vol 9. Springer, Berlin, 1929.
25. D. W. Bronk and F. Brink, *Federation Proc.* **10**, 19 (1951).
26. H. McIlwain, *Biochem. J.* **53**, 403 (1953).
27. J. J. Ghosh and J. H. Quastel, *Nature* **174**, 28 (1954).
28. M. M. Kini and J. H. Quastel, *Nature* **184**, 252 (1959).
28a. Y. Kimura and T. Niwa, *Nature* **171**, 881 (1953).
28b. Y. Tsukada and G. Takagaki, *Nature* **175**, 725 (1955).
28c. G. Takagaki, S. Hirano, and Y. Tsukada, *J. Biochem. (Tokyo)* **45**, 41 (1958).
29. S. S. Parmar and J. H. Quastel, in J. H. Quastel, *Proc. 4th Intern. Congr. Biochem., Vienna* **3**, 90 (1959).
30. T. M. Brody and J. A. Bain, *Proc. Soc. Exptl. Biol. Med.* **77**, 50 (1951).
31. W. J. Johnson and J. H. Quastel, *J. Biol. Chem.* **205**, 163 (1953).
31a. W. N. Aldridge and V. H. Parker, *Biochem. J.* **76**, 47 (1960).
31b. W. N. Aldridge, *in* "Enzymes and Drug Action." Ciba Foundation Symposium, p. 155. Churchill, London, 1962.
31c. J. J. Eiler and W. K. McEwen, *Arch. Biochem.* **20**, 163 (1949).
31d. A. Andrejew and A. J. Rosenberg, *Compt. rend. soc. biol.* **150**, 681 (1956).
32. M. Michaelis and J. H. Quastel, *Biochem. J.* **35**, 918 (1941).
33. L. Ernster, H. Löw, and O. Lindberg, *Acta Chem. Scand.* **9**, 200 (1955).
34. L. Ernster, O. Jalling, H. Löw, and O. Lindberg, *Exptl. Cell Research Suppl.* **3**, 124 (1955).
35. M. Michaelis and S. Hashimoto, *Nature* **194**, 680 (1962).
35a. B. Chance and G. Hollinger, *Federation Proc.* **16**, 163 (1957).
36. P. J. G. Mann, M. Tennenbaum, and J. H. Quastel, *Biochem. J.* **32**, 343 (1938).
37. H. McLennan and K. A. C. Elliott, *J. Pharmacol. Exptl. Therap.* **103**, 35 (1951).
38. W. J. Johnson and J. H. Quastel, *Nature* **171**, 602 (1953).
38a. M. Findlay, K. P. Strickland, and R. J. Rossiter, *Can. J. Biochem. Physiol.* **32**, 504 (1954).
39. B. Chance, *in* "Enzymes." (O. Gaebler, ed.), p. 447. Academic Press, New York, 1956.
40. A. Giuditta and H. J. Strecker, *J. Neurochem.* **5**, 50 (1959).

41. B. De Bernhard, *Biochim. et Biophys. Acta* **23**, 510 (1957).
42. H. R. Mahler, I. Raw, R. Molinari, and D. F. DoAmaral, *J. Biol. Chem.* **233**, 230 (1958).
43. R. L. Ringler, S. Minakami, and T. P. Singer, *Biochem. Biophys. Research Communs.* **3**, 417 (1960).
43a. R. J. Rossiter and K. P. Strickland, *in* "Lipid Metabolism." (K. Bloch, ed.), p. 69. Wiley, New York, 1960.
43b. H. Yoshida and J. H. Quastel, *Biochim. et Biophys. Acta* **57**, 67 (1962).
43c. M. Brossard and J. H. Quastel, *Can. J. Biochem. Physiol.* **41**, 1243 (1963).
43d. M. Findlay, W. L. Magee, and R. J. Rossiter, *Biochem J.* **58**, 236 (1954).
44. D. R. Davies and J. H. Quastel, *Biochem. J.* **26**, 1672 (1932).
45. A. Giuditta and H. J. Strecker, *Nature* **193**, 979 (1962).
46. A. Giuditta and H. J. Strecker, *Biochim. et Biophys. Acta* **48**, 10 (1961).
47. A. Giuditta, *J. Neurochem.* **9**, 329 (1962).
47a. B. Chance, *in* "Enzymes: Units of Biological Structure and Function." (O. H. Gaebler, ed.), p. 447. Academic Press, New York, 1956.
47b. M. Klingenberg and T. Bücher, *Biochem. Z.* **334**, 1 (1961).
47c. R. L. Ringler, S. Minakami, and T. P. Singer, *Biochem. Biophys. Res. Commun.* **3**, 417 (1960).
47d. T. E. Conover, L. Danielson, and L. Ernster, *Biochem. et Biophys. Acta* **67**, 254 (1963).
47e. J. Mager and Y. Avi Dor, *Arch. Biochem. Biophys.* **62**, 40 (1956).
47f. Y. Hatefi, A. G. Haavik, and D. E. Griffiths, *J. Biol. Chem.* **237**, 1676 (1962).
48. H. E. Himwich, P. Sykowski, and J. F. Fazekas, *Am. J. Physiol.* **132**, 640, (1941).
49. M. L. Desbarats-Schonbaum and M. K. Birmingham, *J. Gerontol.* **14**, 284 (1959).
50. H. McIlwain and O. Greengard, *J. Neurochem.* **1**, 348 (1957).
50a. H. McIlwain, *in* "Enzymes and Drug Action." Ciba Foundation Symposium, p. 170. Churchill, London, 1962.
51. O. Lindan, J. H. Quastel, and S. Sved, *Can. J. Biochem. Physiol.*, **35**, 1135, 1145 (1957).
52. W. L. Magee, J. F. Berry, and R. J. Rossiter, *Biochim. et Biophys. Acta* **21**, 408 (1956).
52a. W. L. Magee and R. J. Rossiter, *Can. J. Biochem. Physiol.* **41**, 1155 (1963).
53. M. Dawkins, Jr., J. D. Judah, and K. R. Rees, *Biochem. J.* **73**, 16 (1959).
53a. P. N. Abadom, K. Ahmed, and P. G. Scholefield, *Can. J. Biochem. Physiol.* **39**, 551 (1961).
53b. P. H. Bulle, *Proc. Soc. Exptl. Biol. Med.* **94**, 553 (1957).
53c. J. Christensen, Y. S. L. Feng, E. Polley, and A. W. Wa, *Federation Proc.* **17**, 538 (1958).
53d. J. Axelrod, L. G. Whitby, and G. Hertting, *Science* **133**, 383 (1961).
53e. G. C. Gotzias and D. C. Borg, *Research Publs. Assoc. Research Nervous Mental Disease* **40**, 337 (1962).
53f. G. Karreman, I. Isenberg, and A. Szent-Gyorgyi, *Science* **130**, 1191 (1959).
54. C. T. Beer and J. H. Quastel, *Can. J. Biochem. Physiol.* **36**, 531, 543 (1958).
55. E. Fischer, "Alcoholism," p. 19. Am. Assoc. Advance Sci., Washington, D. C., 1957.

56. V. C. Sutherland, C. H. Hine, and T. N. Burbridge, *J. Pharmacol. Exptl. Therap.* 116, 469 (1956).
57. H. Wallgren and E. Kulonen, *Biochem. J.* 75, 150 (1960).
58. A. Wolpert, E. B. Truitt, F. K. Bell, and J. L. Krautz, *J. Pharmacol. Exptl. Therap.* 117, 358 (1956).
59. M. Berger, H. J. Strecker, and H. Waelsch, *Nature* 177, 1234 (1956); *Ann. N. Y. Acad. Sci.* 66, 806 (1957).
60. O. Gonda and J. H. Quastel, *Can. J. Biochem. Physiol.* 41, 435 (1963).
60a. O. Gonda and J. H. Quastel, cited in reference 19.
61. M. J. H. Smith, and S. W. Jeffrey, *Biochem. J.* 64, 589 (1956).
62. K. L. Manchester, P. J. Randall, and G. H. Smith, *Brit. Med. J.* 1028 (1958).
62a. J. H. Quastel, *Appl. Therap.* 5, 252 (1963).
63. R. M. C. Dawson and D. Richter, *Am. J. Physiol.* 160, 203 (1950).
64. V. S. Shapot, *in* "Metabolism of the Nervous System" (D. Richter, ed.), p. 257. Pergamon Press, New York, 1957.
65. H. McIlwain, *Biochem. J.* 52, 289 (1952).
66. M. B. R. Gore and H. McIlwain, *J. Physiol.* (*London*) 117, 471 (1952).
67. P. J. Heald, *Biochem. J.* 57, 673 (1954).
68. A. Pletscher, P. A. Shore, and B. B. Brodie, *J. Pharmacol. Exptl. Therap.* 116, 84 (1956).
68a. A. Pletscher, P. A. Shore, and B. B. Brodie, *Science* 122, 374 (1955).
68b. F. B. Hughes and B. B. Brodie, *J. Pharmacol. Exptl. Therap.* 127, 96 (1959).
68c. M. Holzbauer and M. Vogt, *J. Neurochem.* 1, 8 (1956–1957).
68d. E. Muscholl and M. Vogt, *J. Physiol.* 141, 132 (1958).
68e. N. A. Hillarp, *Acta Physiol. Scand.* 49, 376 (1960).
68f. H. Himwich, *in* "Neurochemistry." (K. A. C. Elliott, I. H. Page, and J. H. Quastel, eds.), 2nd edition, p. 766. Thomas, Illinois, 1962.
68g. S. S. Kety, *Research Publs. Assoc. Research Nervous Mental Disease* 40, 311 (1962).
68h. P. J. G. Mann and J. H. Quastel, *Biochem. J.* 34, 414 (1940).
69. C. Edwards and M. G. Larrabee, *Federation Proc.* 12, 37 (1953).
70. M. E. Greig, *J. Pharmacol. Exptl. Therap.* 91, 317 (1947).
71. A. J. Rosenberg, L. Buchel, N. Etling, and J. Levi, *Compt. rend. acad. sci.* 230, 480 (1950).
72. J. L. Webb and K. A. C. Elliott, *J. Pharmacol. Exptl. Therap.* 103, 24, (1951).
73. G. S. Gordan and H. W. Elliott, *Endocrinology* 41, 517 (1947).
74. E. Eisenberg, G. S. Gordan, H. W. Elliott, and J. Talbot, *Proc. Soc. Exptl. Biol. Med.* 73, 140 (1950).
75. P. K. Jensen, *Nature* 184, Suppl. 1, 451 (1959).

CHAPTER 34

Inhibitors of Gas Transport

Q. H. Gibson

I. INTRODUCTION

Inhibitors of gas transport differ from other metabolic inhibitors because they act by making the physical separation of the lungs and tissues into an effective barrier and have, ideally, little or no direct effect on individual metabolic processes. It follows that their action must be discussed in terms of physiological rather than biochemical systems. Quite apart from their theoretical interest, one of them, carbon monoxide, is of practical importance, since something of the order of 1000 deaths are due to it each year in Britain alone. These deaths are for the greater part due to the use of poisonous illuminating gas and could be avoided by burning hydrocarbons or using electrical power. In addition, incomplete combustion of fuels in heating appliances or in engines creates a further hazard, while the dangers to coal miners have been recognized for very many years. There is, naturally, a large literature dealing with every aspect of the problem. In this article no attempt has been made at compilation, but a brief account of the mechanism of action has been given, and an attempt has been made to correlate laboratory and clinical findings.

Conversion of hemoglobin to methemoglobin or sulfhemoglobin is much less common and is a rare cause of death. The mechanism of the formation and removal of methemoglobin is interesting biochemically, and both processes have been extensively studied.

Interference with CO_2 transport by inhibitors of carbonic anhydrase is chiefly of academic interest and has a shorter history than the study of inhibitors of oxygen transport. The subject is still developing actively, and some problems remain to be worked out, especially those relating to the gas tensions in the blood, where the static extracorporeal methods of analysis commonly used are not directly applicable.

II. POISONING BY CARBON MONOXIDE

A. Preliminary

This inhibitor acts on hemoglobin and myoglobin, and a word about the functions of these proteins under normal conditions is necessary. The oxygen requirement of the tissues in man is substantially independent of the supply over any appreciable period and at rest is, say, 0.25 liters/min. Given an alveolar gas tension of oxygen of 100 mm Hg, blood free from hemoglobin would contain about 3 ml O_2/liter. Thus, even if the tissues could remove all of this in a single passage, it would be necessary for the heart to circulate 83 liters of blood to the tissues each minute. This volume is about 15 times larger than the normal resting cardiac output; and even if the heart were enlarged and adapted to deal with the great volumes required, it would itself use up most of the oxygen in the blood, leaving the tissues still without provision. The need for a respiratory carrier is obvious. The detailed study of hemoglobin and of the way in which its behavior fits into the economy of the animal was carried out chiefly by the Cambridge school of physiology under Sir Joseph Barcroft (1) and has been described by him in his classic books "The Respiratory Function of the Blood," Part 1, Lessons from High Altitudes; Part 2,

Hemoglobin, published in 1928. He pointed out that an efficient oxygen-transporting pigment should have the properties of becoming fully saturated, or nearly so, at the gas tensions ruling in the alveoli and should give up the greater part of its oxygen at a tension of 40 mm Hg or thereabouts. This unloading tension is important in providing the oxygen concentration gradient between the capillary and the tissue necessary for the final distribution of oxygen to the points at which it is to enter into metabolism. The sigmoid oxygen dissociation curve of many hemoglobins makes them well adapted to perform these functions and provides also a reserve of transporting capacity which can come into play in exercise when, in response to a moderate fall in the venous partial pressure of oxygen, a large increase in oxygen removal from the blood can occur. In mammals, myoglobin is found in skeletal muscle and is believed to act as a short-term oxygen store, maintaining the supply during the interruption of the circulation associated with vigorous muscular contraction. Its combination with carbon monoxide is not very important physiologically, but must be taken into account in critical studies of such procedures as the determination of corpuscular volume by the carbon monoxide method and in detailed studies of the uptake and removal processes in the animal.

B. Absorption of the Gas

The affinity of hemoglobin for carbon monoxide is much greater than for oxygen, and, under conditions where sufficient quantities of these gases are present so that little uncombined hemoglobin remains, the distribution of hemoglobin between the ligands is given by Eq. (1)

$$M \cdot pCO \cdot O_2Hb = pO_2 \cdot COHb \tag{1}$$

where M is the partition coefficient and has a value of about 210 for man (2). As air contains 21% O_2, it appears that a concentration in the inspired air of only 0.085% would be sufficient, at equilibrium, to give 50% conversion of the hemoglobin to COHb. This concentration is so small that the quantity inspired is often of more importance than the equilibrium conversion to COHb which would be attained after indefinite exposure to a given gas mixture. Thus, at 50% saturation the hemoglobin will be combined with about 500 ml carbon monoxide. If the total ventilation is 7 liters/min with a dead space of 0.15 liters, then, at 20 breaths/min, 4 liters/min of air will be presented for respiratory exchange. Assuming 0.085% CO, this air will contain 3.4 ml CO or about 0.7% of the total equilibrium content of the body. Thus, even if all the CO presented for respiratory exchange were absorbed, only about 0.4%/min of the hemoglobin could be converted to COHb. Detailed studies by Pace *et al.* (*3*) have shown that over the first 30% of the way to equilibrium the rate of uptake may be taken as linear and that the

$$\% \text{ COHb} = \frac{[\text{parts CO per 10,000}][\text{exposure time (min)}] \times [\text{minute volume (liters)}]}{20 \, [\text{blood volume (liters)}]} \quad (2)$$

where the minute volume is reduced to STP. They found that about 40% of the inspired CO is retained in the blood.

As equilibrium is approached, the rate of uptake declines. Fairly extensive experiments using gasometric methods for the determination of COHb were carried out by Forbes, Sargent, and Roughton (*4*), who found that their results could be described by the semiempirical equation (3).

$$\frac{d\text{CO}}{dt} = k \, \text{pCO} \, \frac{\% \text{ COHb at equilibrium} - \% \text{ COHb at time } t}{\% \text{ COHb at equilibrium} - \% \text{ COHb at time zero}} \quad (3)$$

Recently, much attention has been given to the uptake of CO from the lungs as a tool in the determination of the diffusing capacity in health and disease, and Forster, Fowler, and Bates (*5*) have treated the case (among others) where a small concentration of CO is inhaled over a prolonged period. They assume, essentially, that the rate of CO uptake is proportional to the difference in pCO between the blood and the alveoli and that the blood is sufficiently nearly saturated at all times to allow the relation of Eq. (1) to be used together with the alveolar pO_2 to estimate pCO in the pulmonary capillary. The original should be consulted for details.

C. Toxicity of Carbon Monoxide

It has been recognized for many years that the toxic effects of conversion of a part of the hemoglobin into COHb are more severe than those produced by the same loss of gas-transporting capacity in anemia. Thus, Haldane (*6*) expressed the difference forcibly, pointing out that a man who had lost 50% of his hemoglobin through anemia might readily go about his daily work, while a similar loss of oxygen capacity through the formation of COHb would incapacitate him and might well render him unconscious. The main reasons for the difference between CO poisoning and anemia appear to be the alteration of the oxygen dissociation curve produced by partial conversion of hemoglobin to COHb and the lack of adaptive cardiorespiratory adjustment in CO poisoning.

The effect on the oxygen dissociation curve has been studied by Roughton and Darling (7), who have shown that, to a fair approximation, the pressures of oxygen and carbon monoxide required to bind a particular total amount of reduced hemoglobin may be treated as additive, the pressures of carbon monoxide being first multiplied by M', where the prime is introduced to make it clear that the shapes of the oxygen and carbon monoxide dissociation curves should not be regarded as identical but only as agreeing to a good approximation. The agreement they found is illustrated in Fig. 1, which is taken from their paper. Figure 1 also

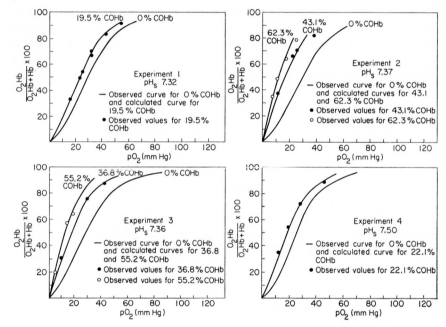

FIG. 1. Observed and calculated oxyhemoglobin dissociation curves of human blood containing varying amounts of carboxyhemoglobin. (From *Am. J. Physiol.* 141, p. 23, Fig. 3)

shows clearly the change in the oxygen dissociation curve of the remaining free hemoglobin. It is shifted to the left of the normal curve and is less strongly inflected. The simple rule for determining the distribution of oxy- and carboxyhemoglobin, which has just been given, can only be regarded as an approximation. As Roughton and Darling (7) point out in discussing their results in terms of Adair's (8) model for hemoglobin, the rule would only be exactly true if all four equilibrium constants for the combination of carbon monoxide could be derived from the corresponding constants for oxygen by multiplication by M. This can be expressed in another way by saying that if the rule were exactly true there would be no difference between M and the M' introduced previously. Although Joels and Pugh (9) have shown that the dissociation curves for carbon monoxide and for oxygen are, for human hemoglobin, quite nearly superposable, the precision of the measurements and their range of saturations are not sufficient to allow conclusions to be drawn about the values which the individual equilibrium constants would have if the equilibrium were described in terms of Adair's model.

Whatever their exact theoretical interpretation, there is no doubt about the effect of the change in affinity and shape shown in the oxygen dissociation curves reproduced in Fig. 1. Their meaning is, perhaps, most clearly illustrated by Fig. 2, again taken from Roughton and Darling (7). The actual amounts of oxygen held by the blood are plotted against pO_2 for several degrees of conversion to COHb and one example of severe anemia.

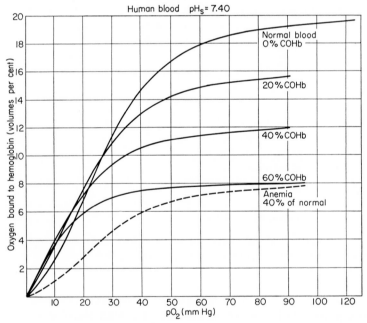

FIG. 2. Calculated O_2-dissociation curves of human blood containing varying amounts of carboxyhemoglobin, plotting the absolute amounts of bound O_2 rather than the percentage of available hemoglobin bound to O_2. (From the *Am. J. Physiol.* **141**, p. 28, Fig. 4.)

If the oxygen consumption of a man at rest is taken as 250 ml/min and the cardiac output is 5 liters/min, then the arterial blood oxygen content of 19 ml/100 ml for the normal case in Fig. 2 must fall to 14 ml/100 ml in the mixed venous blood. In the curve of Fig. 2 this content of oxygen corresponds to a partial pressure of 37 mm Hg. It should be noted that the curves in the figure are taken at a constant pH and so neglect the favorable influence of CO_2 transport on O_2 transport. Proceeding in the same way, the oxygen tensions found for the mixed venous blood for 20, 40, and 60% conversion of the hemoglobin to COHb are 27, 18, and 8 mm Hg, respectively, whereas in the case of anemia with 40% of the hemoglobin remaining the oxygen tension would be 20 mm Hg.

To interpret these figures it is necessary to consider the blood supply to the brain, the organ most susceptible to damage from oxygen lack. The subject has been thoroughly reviewed by Opitz and Schneider (10). The data important for the present purpose are as follows. (1) The oxygen uptake of the brain is independent of the partial pressure of oxygen supplied to it in the animal down to the point at which the circulation fails. It may be regarded as constant for purposes of calculation and is 3.3 ml/100 gm/min. (2) The blood flow through the brain amounts to 50 ml/100 gm/min. It appears to be regulated by the oxygen tension in the venous blood leaving the brain; the flow begins to increase at an oxygen tension of 25–28 mm Hg and increases rapidly from 20 mm Hg downward. The flow can be increased by 50–100% at most. (3) The venous tension at rest in man is normally 35 mm Hg. The threshold for the compensatory increase of blood flow is at a venous O_2 tension of 25 mm Hg. Serious disturbance of function with loss of consciousness results below 20 mm Hg, whereas the lethal threshold is about 12 mm Hg. All these values are time dependent and can be regarded only as averages. (4) Not all parts of the brain are alike in their oxygen supply and degree of vascularity. Thus, most parts of the grey matter have an oxygen consumption and a degree of vascularity such that their oxygen need can be covered with a tissue gradient of about 4 mm Hg, as shown by diffusion calculations. The corpus striatum, however, has a less favorable relation between oxygen uptake and vascularity and would require a gradient of at least 7 mm Hg to satisfy its needs.

Using these data, the oxygen tension in the blood coming from the brain can be estimated, as the rate of O_2 use, blood flow, arterial oxygen content, and oxygen dissociation curve have all been specified. The results, read graphically from the curves of Fig. 2, have been collected in Table I. These figures suggest that no important symptoms should be found below 30% saturation, but that beyond 40% saturation a serious and rapidly

TABLE I

Effect of Various Degrees of Conversion of Hb to COHb on the Venous pO_2

Condition	COHb (%)	Blood flow (ml/100 gm/min)	Venous pO_2 (mm Hg)
	0	50	35
	20	50	27
	40	75	22
	60	75	8
Breathing 1 atm O_2			
	60	75	17
Anemia sparing 40% of normal hemoglobin	0	75	27

progressing intoxication should occur. Having regard to the scatter of the observations on the toxicity and to the crudity of the calculations of the venous oxygen tensions, the agreement between expectation and observation is excellent. It appears possible to account for the toxicity of CO solely in terms of its action on hemoglobin.

Although this conclusion fits in well with the work of Haldane (11), who showed that the primary effect of CO was due to its combination with hemoglobin in the celebrated experiment in which he exposed mice to 1 atm CO + 2 atm O_2 without killing them so long as the excess pressure was maintained, there are good reasons for examining other possibilities. Thus, it is known that CO will form a compound with the cytochrome oxidase which prevents its action with oxygen, but this possibility is usually discounted because of the relatively low affinity of the enzyme for CO as compared with O_2. Haldane (12) was able to show a direct effect by varying the conditions of his father's experiment, comparing the effect on rats of breathing a mixture of 1 atm CO + 3 atm O_2 with the effect of 3 atm CO + 3 atm O_2. In the first mixture they behaved substantially normally, whereas in the second they developed convulsions after a short time. The conditions of this experiment were so extreme, however, that they seemed to reinforce the arguments for neglecting any direct influence of carbon monoxide on the tissue enzymes. Bänder and Kiese (12a) have re-examined the matter and have pointed out that in severe CO poisoning the tissue O_2 tensions are much reduced and that under conditions of low O_2 tension the simple hyperbolic relation between pCO and enzyme inhibition does not hold good, the inhibition exceeding that predicted from experiments conducted with higher gas tensions. Against this is the fact that, as found by Argyll Campbell (13), the CO tension in the tissues is below that in the alveoli. This is due to the sharp drop in the equilibrium CO tension as the blood gives up O_2 during its passage through the tissue capillary, so that a CO diffusion gradient exists from the arterial to the venous end of the capillary, and the mean tissue CO is below that in the arterial blood. Bänder and Kiese conclude, nevertheless, that a significant inhibition of the cytochrome oxidase may occur in the terminal stages of CO poisoning and may exceed 10%.

D. Circulatory and Respiratory Responses to CO Poisoning

There is general agreement that in man and in the dog there is little change either in cardiac output or respiration until the level of COHb in the blood is of the order of 40%. Beyond this level Chiodi et al. (14) found a small increase in cardiac output. There was no increase in total ventilation, and experiments with added CO_2 showed diminished excitability of the respiratory center. There is no evidence of stimulation of the chemoreceptors of the carotid body, and in electrophysiological experiments Duke, Green, and Neil (15) have found that even with 70% or more COHb in the blood of anesthetized cats no discharges take place so long as the blood pressure is maintained. Daly, Lambertsen, and Schweitzer (16) point out that this result is not easily reconciled with their measurements of the blood flow and metabolic rate of the carotid body. They found the very high flow of 2 liters/100 gm/min at normal arterial pressure. The arteriovenous difference was not great enough to allow an estimate of the O_2 consumption at full flow, but when the flow was reduced to about one-quarter by lowering the arterial pressure, an arteriovenous difference of 2.5 vols% was found, giving an O_2 consumption of 9 ml/100 gm/min. The conditions under which this arteriovenous difference was determined are similar to those in which a strong response can be elicited from the chemoreceptors. If this response is determined by the venous pO_2 in the blood draining the carotid body, the threshold must lie at a high value of pO_2, and stimulation would be predicted in CO poisoning. As already stated, all the evidence suggests that no such stimulation occurs. It seems certain that CO does not inactivate the chemoreceptors of the cat, which will give a strong response after exposure to it. The explanation which is sometimes offered, that chemoreceptor stimulation depends on arterial pO_2 and not on venous pO_2 and that since arterial pO_2 is not lowered in CO poisoning no stimulation would be expected, does not appear to fit the experiments in which strong stimulation of the chemoreceptors is obtained on lowering the arterial blood pressure. It may be that some special factor operates in CO poisoning.

E. Elimination of CO from the Blood and Treatment of CO Poisoning

Experiments on the rate of removal of CO from the blood have given conflicting results even when carried out by expert observers using adequate methods. Thus, Roughton and Root (*17*) found a half-time much longer than Lillienthal and Pine (quoted in *18*). There is agreement, however, that breathing O_2 as opposed to air gives a sixfold increase in rate of elimination and that the addition of CO_2 to the oxygen will increase the rate still further. This further increase has varied considerably from one group of workers to another.

The details of treatment have been much discussed. It is generally agreed that:

(1) The patient should be removed at once from the CO-containing atmosphere; (2) artificial respiration, if required, should be given at once; and (3) oxygen should be given, using a mask to obtain the greatest possible increase in alveolar pO_2.

Controversy has arisen about the use of CO_2-O_2 mixtures for resuscitation. Although there is no doubt that mixtures allow faster removal of CO from the blood than does O_2 alone, this speed of removal is not especially important. The outcome of CO poisoning depends on the pO_2 in the brain and on the duration of hypoxia, and, provided the alveolar pO_2 is raised *promptly* by giving oxygen with or without artificial respiration, the later stages of recovery are unimportant. The immediate effect of giving O_2 is to provide a bonus of about 1.5 ml O_2/100 ml blood, which is sufficient, as shown in Table I, to raise the venous pO_2 by about 8 mm Hg. This is enough to transfer a patient from the lethal threshold of 12 mm Hg to the comparative security of 20 mm Hg. It is doubtful if the controversy about gas mixtures can readily be settled by experiment, as so many variables are involved. The balance of evidence seems to suggest that CO_2-O_2 mixtures are certainly as good as plain O_2, and may be superior, but their superiority is less than has been claimed by their more enthusiastic supporters. References include McDonald and Paton (*19, 20*), Henderson and Haggard (*21*), Nicloux *et al.* (*22*), and Schwerma *et al.* (*23*).

Although some exotic treatments have from time to time been proposed and applied [see (*18*) for references], no use seems to have been made of cardiorespiratory stimulants acting through the carotid body, such as nikethamide. As brain blood flow is directly dependent on pressure, such drugs might in a severe case provide a little additional oxygen immediately at the time when it is most needed.

F. The Use of Carbon Monoxide as a Tool in Studies of Respiratory Carriers

The dramatic effects of CO on mammals have suggested its use to diagnose the function of hemoglobin in nonmammalian organisms. If its application produces a dramatic effect on the animal, then it seems fair to conclude that the hemoglobin acts as a respiratory carrier. The converse should not, however, be assumed without careful study of the animal and of its normal environment. The capacity to survive by means of anaerobic metabolic mechanisms, and so to show little obvious sign of disturbance on treatment with CO, is not necessarily an indication that hemoglobin present in an animal does not normally function as a respiratory carrier. Exercise tolerance tests, which would often be of value in this respect, are difficult to apply in many species. The subject has been discussed by Manwell (24) in a recent review.

III. METHEMOGLOBINEMIA

The various aspects of the subject have been reviewed in recent years; and so far as its effect on oxygen transport is concerned, there is little to add. The literature on compounds inducing methemoglobin formation and the mechanism of their action was reviewed by Heubner (25), and a wider review with 246 references by Bodansky (26) deals with all aspects of the problem. The mechanism of reduction of methemoglobin in erythrocytes has been considered by Gibson (27). In the account which follows these sources will be drawn upon freely without further reference.

A. The Effect of Methemoglobin on the Oxygen Dissociation Curve

Recent experiments *in vitro* and *in vivo* have been made by Darling and Roughton (28) and confirmed by Kiese and Klingmüller (29). They found that the curve was shifted to the left and was less inflected than normal. The effect is analogous to that found with carbon monoxide and has been discussed theoretically from this point of view by Wyman and Allen (30). Quantitatively, however, the effect of conversion to methemoglobin is smaller; and so far as affinity and shape of dissociation curve are concerned, COHb formation has about twice the effect of conversion of a similar percentage of the total pigment to methemoglobin. It has been shown in animal experiments that the shift of the dissociation curve observed *in vitro* occurs *in vivo* and that methemoglobin is less toxic than an equivalent amount of carboxyhemoglobin (31).

B. Effects of Methemoglobinemia on Transport of Oxygen in Tissues

These are similar to, but less severe than, those produced by the same percentage conversion to COHb. Chronic methemoglobinemia, although rare, is a well-recognized condition [see (27) for references]. In untreated cases up to 45% conversion of the hemoglobin has been observed, often without any apparent disability. In these patients it seems that the compensatory polycythemia often found covers much of the deficit in oxygen-transporting capacity. Several of the cases reported have been in heavy manual laborers, while one was a member of a hockey team. Determinations of the form and position of the oxygen dissociation curve have given discordant results. Thus, Hitzenberger (32) and Gibson and Harrison (33) found a shift and change in shape, whereas Eder, Finch, and McKee (34), in repeated careful determinations, could detect no deviation from the normal. The existence or otherwise of a shift is of great theoretical interest, since if it could be shown, preferably by examination of the same sample of blood before and after removal of the methemoglobin, that there was not any change in the form and position of the curve, the presumption would be strong that the blood sample contained two types of erythrocyte, one containing methemoglobin, the other free from the pigment. It should be pointed out that the important region of the curve is from 0 to 10% saturation and that the precise gasometric methods developed by Roughton and his co-workers are appropriate (see 35). The lack of points at the foot of the dissociation curve greatly diminishes the value of all the observations in which an apparent lack of effect of methemoglobinemia has been found because other compensatory mechanisms might well shift the curve bodily to the right. With the advance of spectrophotometric techniques it may well become possible to settle this question by investigating the light absorption of single cells.

C. Formation of Methemoglobin

1. Compounds Reacting Directly with Hemoglobin

An example is sodium nitrite. On injection of nitrite the blood methemoglobin rises rapidly, reaches a maximum within about half an hour, and, in nonfatal poisoning, disappears again in the course of a few hours. The time course varies a good deal from one species to another because of interspecific differences in the efficiency of the enzymic mechanisms for methemoglobin reduction. Nitrite will react directly with hemoglobin *in vitro*, the products depending on the conditions. When pO_2 is high, conversion to methemoglobin is almost quantitative, but at low pO_2 nitric oxide hemoglobin is also formed. Chlorates are also believed to react directly with hemoglobin, but the reaction has many unusual features. There appears to be a threshold concentration, but once the reaction has started, it is autocatalytic. Quinones may also react directly with hemoglobin, and Fishberg (*36*) has described a patient who excreted benzoquinoneacetic acid and had methemoglobinemia. Rapid regeneration of hemoglobin was obtained on giving ascorbic acid, which presumably acted by reducing the quinone.

2. COMPOUNDS ACTING INDIRECTLY

One of the most thoroughly studied is aniline, where the mechanism has been worked out in detail by Kiese and his co-workers (*37–41*). They have shown that aniline is oxidized to phenylhydroxylamine, which in turn reacts with hemoglobin in the presence of oxygen to give nitrosobenzene and methemoglobin. The nitrosobenzene is reduced back to phenylhydroxylamine by an enzyme system in the erythrocyte (the methemoglobin reductase of Kiese), setting up a catalytic cycle of methemoglobin formation. This cycle explains the observation that phenylhydroxylamine is capable of converting many equivalents of hemoglobin to methemoglobin *in vivo*, whereas with drugs such as nitrite approximately stoichiometric relations are found.

In addition to qualitative demonstrations that the series of reactions aniline ⇌ phenylhydroxylamine ⇌ nitrosobenzene can take place in the blood, quantitative determinations of the amount of circulating nitrosobenzene have been made after the administration of aniline to dogs. These levels have been reproduced by continuing infusion of nitrosobenzene, and it has been shown that the same rate of methemoglobin formation is observed whether the nitrosobenzene is formed indirectly from aniline or is injected directly into the blood stream. Although it is not strictly relevant to the topic of oxygen transport, it should be pointed out that the complexities of the system have by no means been exhausted by the description given above; and in the absence of the enzyme system, quite different reactions between hemoglobin and nitrosobenzene occur, with the formation of a comparatively stable hemoglobin-ligand complex.

Many organic compounds are able to cause methemoglobin formation, and aniline has been chosen for discussion solely because the mechanism of its action has been so thoroughly worked out. It is likely that similarly complex transformations occur with other compounds which have not yet been so fully studied.

D. Treatment of Methemoglobinemia

Except in the idiopathic variety the tendency is towards recovery. The methemoglobin is reduced to hemoglobin by the enzyme systems within the erythrocyte. In man, the system active with nitrite-hemoglobin in the absence of carriers such as methylene blue appears to depend on DPN-reducing dehydrogenases, and can deal with 5–10% of the total pigment per hour.

When the pigment has been formed by the action of phenylhy-droxylamine, the chemical reactions are more complicated and involve TPN-reducing dehydrogenases, including enzymes able to decarboxylate glucose-6-phosphate. In this rather special case a continuing oxygen uptake by the blood occurs, but the methemoglobin does not become reduced, though it will become reduced and will remain so in the presence of carbon monoxide *in vitro*.

With several redox dyes, such as methylene blue, the chemical changes are similar to those found with phenylhydroxylamine, but as the reoxidation of the dyes is not coupled to the oxidation of hemoglobin, the methemoglobin becomes reduced even in the presence of oxygen. With methylene blue, for example, the reactions occur as in Eqs. (4)–(6).

$$MB + TPN \text{ enzyme system} + glucose \rightarrow LeucoMB + oxidation\ products + CO_2 \quad (4)$$

$$LeucoMB + O_2 \rightarrow MB + H_2O_2 \quad (5)$$

$$LeucoMB + methemoglobin \rightleftharpoons MB + hemoglobin \quad (6)$$

In this system, in the presence of oxygen, which keeps the concentration of free hemoglobin very low, the equilibrium is in favor of methemoglobin reduction; and as the dehydrogenase systems are very active, the net result is that methylene blue acts as an effective redox carrier, allowing methemoglobin to be reduced at the expense of glucose oxidation. As the TPN enzyme systems do not react readily with methemoglobin in the absence of carrier, the addition of methylene blue speeds methemoglobin reduction by as much as fiftyfold.

Other substrates, such as malate, fumarate, and pentose sugars, have been shown to reduce methemoglobin *in vitro*. Their importance under ordinary circumstances is uncertain. Nonenzymic reduction occurs with ascorbic acid, glyceraldehyde, and glutathione. This may be important in chronic idiopathic methemoglobinemia, where the accumulation of the pigment is due to a hereditary defect in the reducing systems within the erythrocyte and the rate of formation and of reduction are both very low. Ascorbic acid has been studied in this connection, and it has been calculated that the concentrations reached in the blood could give a reduction of perhaps 2–3% of total pigment per day. The uncertainties involved in these calculations are, however, considerable.

The treatment of acute methemoglobinemia is therefore as follows:

(1) If the patient is so severely poisoned as to be comatose, oxygen should be given at once just as for CO poisoning.

(2) An intravenous injection of 0.1 gm methylene blue in 10 ml should be given. This is just as urgent as giving oxygen, as it will produce worthwhile effects in as little as 10 minutes and will usually clear the blood within 30 minutes.

(3) If the patient is cyanosed but not seriously ill, no treatment is necessary. In the case of some poisons the maximum blood level continues to rise for several hours. It is important to watch the patient to make sure that a seriously toxic level in the blood is not being reached. Methylene blue may be given by mouth and will be effective in about 30 minutes.

(4) Idiopathic methemoglobinemia. Treatment is required for cosmetic reasons only. It may be deferred until any scientific investigations have been carried out. Ascorbic acid in large doses is cheap, nontoxic, and effective in reducing, but not eliminating, cyanosis. Methylene blue will virtually clear the blood of methemoglobin, but may be less desirable for long-continued administration. The treatment of choice is perhaps to give ascorbic acid regularly, reserving methylene blue to remove the last traces of cyanosis for special occasions.

IV. CARBON DIOXIDE TRANSPORT

Although carbon dioxide is much more soluble than oxygen and will pass more readily through membranes, a specialized transport mechanism is required to deal with its properties as an acid. Most of the carbonic acid formed by reaction with water is buffered within the red cell by reaction with hemoglobin in two ways: (1) Oxyhemoglobin is a stronger acid than reduced hemoglobin and is able to bind base more strongly. When a solution containing oxyhemoglobin is reduced, it gives up base and the solution becomes more alkaline. In the tissues, the base released by the reduction of hemoglobin is taken up by carbonic acid, which is thereby carried without change in pH. (2) Carbonic acid and hemoglobin react together to form bicarbonate and a more acid hemoglobin. This mechanism buffers the carbonic acid with a small change in pH.

In addition, carbon dioxide is able to react directly with amino groups in hemoglobin to form carbaminohemoglobin. In this case carbonic acid is not formed at all. Since mechanisms (1) and (2) start with carbonic acid, transport is preceded by the reactions

$$CO_2 + H_2O \rightleftharpoons H_2CO_3 \rightleftharpoons H^+ + HCO_3{}^-$$

whereas the reverse changes take place in the lungs. Although the ionization of carbonic acid is instantaneous, the hydration of CO_2 and the dehydration of carbonic acid are not especially rapid. Quantitative calculations by Henriques (42) showed that the dehydration of carbonic acid is not fast enough to allow for the unloading of CO_2 in the lungs if all transport were by mechanisms (1) and (2). He showed, further, that the exchange of CO_2 with a gas phase was much more rapid in whole blood than in blood plasma. These considerations and experiments set in train a series of investigations leading to the recognition and purification of the enzyme carbonic anhydrase and to the recognition of the place of carbamino compounds in CO_2 transport. This work has been dealt with by Roughton (43) in a review which retains, after 25 years, all its original interest.

A. Inhibitors of Carbonic Anhydrase

Many compounds have been shown to inhibit carbonic anhydrase, though because of the technical difficulties few detailed studies have been made. Keller (44) has recently reviewed the inhibitors and activators of carbonic anhydrase and gives references to the original work. Although there are so many inhibitors, and although some of them, like the sulfonamides, have been widely used in medicine for a long time, the literature affords little indication of effects which might be put down to disturbance of CO_2 transport. There are two reasons for this apparent lack of effect, of which the first is the great excess of enzyme available in the blood. Thus, Roughton et al. (45) have estimated that there is about 7500 times as much in the erythrocyte as would be needed to deal with normal CO_2 transport in man, so that a very high degree of inhibition is required before interference with CO_2 transport can be expected. The second is that compensatory changes in respiration allow CO_2 transport to be maintained even when marked inhibition of carbonic anhydrase has been achieved. Some of the difficulties in analyzing the effects of carbonic anhydrase inhibitors have been pointed out by Mithoefer (46). They are chiefly due to the occurrence of adaptive physiological responses which mask the primary effects of the inhibitors and allow CO_2 transport to be carried on even when carbonic anhydrase has been powerfully inhibited.

B. Effects of Inhibition of Carbonic Anhydrase

The principal findings may be exemplified by data taken from the careful observations of Carter and Clark (47) on unanesthetized dogs. These animals received a single intravenous dose of acetazolamide sufficient to produce at least 97% inhibition of carbonic anhydrase. As compared with control periods for the same animals, total ventilation rose from 2.7 liters/min to 5.0 liters/min after 30 minutes; CO_2 output was unchanged at 67 and 66 ml/min before and after injection, while the corresponding figures for O_2 were 84 and 82 ml/min. As a result of the increase in total ventilation, alveolar pCO_2 fell from 37 to 19 mm Hg, and pO_2 rose from 103 to 123 mm Hg. The effect of the respiratory changes was to maintain the normal CO_2 output with a tissue CO_2 tension just sufficiently above normal to maintain the stimulus to the respiratory center.

Serious difficulty is met in attempting to determine the gas tensions in the blood. The method of aerotonometry outside the body requires that a gas bubble be rotated in a larger volume of blood until equilibrium is reached. The period of rotation, however, also allows the CO_2-bicarbonate reactions to go to equilibrium and consequently invalidates the CO_2 tension determinations. Indirect methods of calculation by use of the Henderson-Hasselbalch equation are equally inapplicable because the equation assumes equilibrium between CO_2, HCO_3^- and H^+. As a result, conflicting reports have appeared on the gas tensions in the alveolar air and the arterial blood. For example, in the paper of Carter and Clark (47) the alveolar pCO_2 is quoted as 19 mm Hg, while the arterial pCO_2 was 42 mm Hg by aerotonometry and 39 mm Hg by calculation from the Henderson-Hasselbalch equation. It seems probable, however, that the arterial pCO_2 as the blood left the lungs was really 19 mm, though it would be expected to rise during the passage to the tissues as bicarbonate and CO_2 approached equilibrium. In the tissues the venous pCO_2 would be expected to rise to about normal values, but would fall as equilibrium was approached during the passage to the lungs. The net effect would be to accentuate the part played by carbaminohemoglobin and to increase the amount of CO_2 transported in physical solution. It does not appear easy to express these effects quantitatively because of the shifts which should occur during the circulation time of the blood.

The experiments of Carter and Clark (47) were carried out with unanesthetized dogs at rest; similar experiments conducted with anesthetized animals have yielded essentially similar results (48). In man the effect of large doses of sulfanilamide has been investigated by Roughton et al. (45), who found that although the largest doses of sulfanilamide they gave were well tolerated at rest, the limits of physiological adjustment were exceeded when severe exercise was attempted, and the subjects treated with sulfanilamide had a reduced work capacity, associated with subjective feelings of choking, presumably due to CO_2 retention in the tissues.

It should perhaps be pointed out that the practical importance of inhibitors of carbonic anhydrase derives less from their action in the erythrocyte than from their action on the kidney. This matter, however, lies outside the scope of the present article. One other effect involving carbonic anhydrase is also, strictly, irrelevant to the present discussion, but offers so attractive an application in biochemistry as to deserve brief mention. This is the use of carbonic anhydrase as a tool for determining whether carbon dioxide is liberated as such in an enzyme reaction or whether it appears as bicarbonate. Thus, Krebs and Roughton (49) showed that if urease is allowed to act on urea in such quantity that the whole of the substrate is consumed in a period of a minute or so, and at a pH such that at equilibrium most of the CO_2 is converted to bicarbonate, and if the reaction is followed manometrically with vigorous shaking, then in the absence of carbonic anhydrase the pCO_2 in the liquid phase can reach a value well above the equilibrium level, and CO_2 is first shaken out into the gas phase and absorbed again later as equilibrium is approached. In the presence of carbonic anhydrase CO_2 is maintained almost in equilibrium with bicarbonate, and no excess CO_2 is shaken into the gas phase at any stage of the reaction. It is thus shown that CO_2 and not bicarbonate is the immediate product of the enzyme reaction.

References

1. Sir J. Barcroft, "The Respiratory Function of the Blood," Part 1, Lessons from High Altitudes; Part 2, Haemoglobin. 1928. Cambridge Univ. Press, London and New York.
2. J. Sendroy, S. H. Liu, and D. D. Van Slyke, *Am. J. Physiol.* **90,** 511 (1929).
3. N. Pace, W. V. Consolazio, W. A. White, Jr., and A. R. Behnke, *Am. J. Physiol.* 147, 352 (1946).
4. W. H. Forbes, F. Sargent, and F. J. W. Roughton, *Am. J. Physiol.* 143, 594 (1945).
5. R. E. Forster, W. S. Fowler, and D. V. Bates, *J. Clin. Invest.* 33, 1128 (1954).
6. J. B. S. Haldane, *J. Physiol. (London)* 45, xxii (1912).

7. F. J. W. Roughton, and R. C. Darling, *Am. J. Physiol.* 141, 17 (1944).
8. G. S. Adair, *J. Biol. Chem.* 63, 529 (1925).
9. N. Joels and L. G. C. E. Pugh, *J. Physiol. (London)* 142, 63 (1958).
10. E. Opitz and M. Schneider, *Ergeb. Physiol. biol. Chem. u. exptl. Pharmakol.* 46, 126 (1950).
11. J. S. Haldane, *J. Physiol. (London)* 18, 201 (1895).
12. J. B. S. Haldane, *Biochem. J.* 21, 1068 (1927).
12a. A. Bänder and M. Kiese, *Klin. Wochschr.* 33, 152 (1955).
13. J. Argyll Campbell, *J. Physiol. (London)* 68, 81 (1929–1930).
14. H. Chiodi, D. B. Dill, F. Consolazio, and S. M. Horvath, *Am. J. Physiol.* 134, 683 (1941).
15. H. N. Duke, J. H. Green, and E. Neil, *J. Physiol. (London)* 118, 520 (1952).
16. M. de B. Daly, C. J. Lambertsen, and A. Schweitzer, *J. Physiol. (London)* 125, 67 (1954).
17. F. J. W. Roughton, and R. W. Root, *Am. J. Physiol.* 145, 239 (1945).
18. J. L. Lillienthal, *Pharmacol. Revs.* 2, 324 (1950).
19. K. W. McDonald and W. D. M. Paton, *Brit. Med. J.* I, 313 (1955).
20. K. W. McDonald and W. D. M. Paton, *Brit. Med. J.* I, 664 (1955).
21. Y. E. Henderson and H. W. Haggard, *J. Pharmacol. Exptl. Therap.* 16, 11 (1920).
22. M. Nicloux, H. Nerson, J. Stahl, and J. Weill, *Compt. rend. soc. biol.* 92, 174 and 178 (1925).
23. H. Schwerma, A. C. Ivy, H. Friedmann, and E. La Brosse, *Occupational Med.* 5, 24 (1948).
24. C. Manwell, *Ann. Rev. Physiol.* 22, 191 (1960).
25. W. Heubner, *Ergeb. Physiol. biol. Chem. u. exptl. Pharmakol.* 43, 9, (1940).
26. O. Bodansky, *Pharmacol. Revs.* 3, 144 (1951).
27. Q. H. Gibson, *Biochem. Soc. Symposia (Cambridge, Engl.)* No. 12, 55 (1955).
28. R. C. Darling and F. J. W. Roughton, *Am. J. Physiol.* 137, 56 (1942).
29. M. Kiese and G. Klingmüller, *Arch. exptl. Pathol. u. Pharmakol. Naunyn-Schmiedeberg's* 207, 655 (1949).
30. J. J. Wyman, Jr. and D. W. Allen, *J. Polymer Sci.* 7, 499 (1951).
31. O. Lester and L. A. Greenberg, *J. Pharmacol. Exptl. Therap.* 81, 182 (1944).
32. K. Hitzenberger, *Wien. Arch. inn. Med.* 23, 85 (1931).
33. Q. H. Gibson and D. C. Harrison, *Lancet* ii, 941 (1947).
34. H. A. Eder, C. Finch, and R. W. McKee, *J. Clin. Invest.* 28, 265 (1948).
35. A. B. Otis, F. J. W. Roughton, and R. L. J. Lyster, *Proc. Roy. Soc.* B144, 29 (1955).
36. E. H. Fishberg, *J. Biol. Chem.* 172, 155 (1948).
37. M. Kiese, D. Reinwein, and H. D. Waller, *Arch. exptl. Pathol. u. Pharmakol. Naunyn-Schmiedeberg's* 210, 393 (1950).
38. M. Kiese and D. Reinwein. *Arch. exptl. Pathol. u. Pharmakol. Naunyn-Schmiedeberg's* 211, 392 (1950).
39. H. Dannenberg and M. Kiese, *Arch. exptl. Pathol. u. Pharmakol. Naunyn-Schmiedeberg's* 211, 410 (1950).

40. M. Kiese, *Arch. exptl. Pathol. u. Pharmakol. Naunyn-Schmiedeberg's* **235,** 360 (1959).
41. J. Haan, M. Kiese, and A. Werner, *Arch. exptl. Pathol. u. Pharmakol. Naunyn-Schmiedeberg's* **235,** 365 (1959).
42. O. M. Henriques, *Biochem. Z.* **200,** 1 (1928).
43. F. J. W. Roughton, *Physiol. Revs.* **15,** 241 (1935).
44. H. Keller, *Z. Vitamin- Hormon- u. Fermentforsch.* **9,** 297 (1959).
45. F. J. W. Roughton, A. B. Dill, R. C. Darling, A. Graybiel, C. A. Knehr, and J. H. Talbott, *Am. J. Physiol.* **135,** 77 (1941).
46. J. C. Mithoefer, *J. Appl. Physiol.* **14,** 109 (1959).
47. E. T. Carter and R. T. Clark, *J. Appl. Physiol.* **13,** 42 (1958).
48. J. F. Tomashevski, H. I. Chinn, and R. T. Clark, *Am. J. Physiol.* **177,** 451 (1954).
49. H. A. Krebs and F. J. W. Roughton, *Biochem. J.* **43,** 550 (1948).

CHAPTER 35

Selective Inhibitors of Photosynthesis

Manuel Losada and Daniel I. Arnon

I. INTRODUCTION[1]

Inhibitors of photosynthesis have been discussed in monographs and

---

[1] The following abbreviations will be used: ATP, adenosine triphosphate; PN, PNH₂, oxidized and reduced di- or triphosphopyridine nucleotide; DPN, DPNH₂, oxidized and reduced forms of diphosphopyridine nucleotide; TPN, TPNH₂, oxidized and reduced forms of triphosphopyridine nucleotide; PGA, 3-phosphoglyceric acid; RuDP, ribulose diphosphate; FMN, flavin mononucleotide; P$_i$, orthophosphate; ADP, adenosine diphosphate.

recent reviews[2] (*1–3*). Our purpose in undertaking this review is not to survey once more the extensive literature of the subject but to discuss selected investigations, mainly of subcellular systems, in which inhibitors were used for the study of component reactions of photosynthesis. We will attempt to show how the effects of inhibitors have been traced to component reactions of photosynthesis and how these effects support the unified concept of the mechanism of this process that has recently emerged from investigations of photosynthesis in subcellular particles (*4*).

The emphasis in our discussion will be placed on inhibitors of those reactions that are directly concerned with the unique feat of photosynthesis, the conversion of radiant energy into chemical energy. These reactions have long been the subject of conjecture, but in the last decade work with subcellular particles (isolated chloroplasts and bacterial chromatophores) has provided experimental evidence that the conversion of solar radiant energy into cellular energy involves the formation of adenosine triphosphate (ATP) and reduced pyridine nucleotide (PNH_2). These two compounds are now known to be the first stable, chemically defined molecular species formed by photosynthetic cells at the expense of absorbed radiant energy (cf. *5*).

The reduction of CO_2 to carbohydrates consists exclusively of dark reactions that are driven by ATP and PNH_2. The same reactions are now known to occur widely in nonphotosynthetic cells (*6–8*). The distinction between photosynthetic and nonphotosynthetic cells seems to lie, therefore, in the manner in which ATP and PNH_2 are formed. Photosynthetic cells form these compounds at the expense of radiant energy, whereas nonphotosynthetic cells form them at the expense of energy released by dark chemical reactions.

Although the photochemically generated ATP and PNH_2 (jointly termed assimilatory power) are most often used for the reduction of CO_2 to carbohydrates, they may also be used for other types of cellular syntheses that proceed at the expense of ATP or PNH_2, or both. Thus, in photosynthetic cells, inhibitors of photochemically generated assimilatory power may also indirectly inhibit the whole gamut of those synthetic reactions of cellular metabolism that are driven by ATP or PNH_2. Since no review of this scope is intended here, we will mainly stress the inhibitors of those reactions in which ATP and PNH_2 are formed and consider only a few of the reactions in which they are used by photosynthetic cells. Inhibitors of oxygen evolution will also be included, since oxygen evolu-

---

[2] An extensive survey by N. E. Good of inhibitors of the Hill Reaction (*Plant Physiol.* **36**, 788, 1961) has recently appeared after the review of literature pertaining to this article was concluded.

tion is an important part of the over-all photosynthetic process in green plants, even though it is now known to be fundamentally independent of the photochemical formation of ATP and PNH_2 (9–12).

Apart from inhibitors of photochemical reactions, we will discuss inhibitors of those dark enzymic reactions that are involved in the initial incorporation of CO_2 in photosynthesis. These enzymes were first found in photosynthetic tissues and, for a time, were thought to be peculiar to photosynthesis. As already stated, they are now known, along with all other reactions of CO_2 assimilation, to function also in nonphotosynthetic cells (cf. reviews 7, 8), but they continue to hold special interest for students of photosynthesis.

II. INHIBITORS OF CO₂ ASSIMILATION

A. Sites of ATP and PNH₂ Utilization in Photosynthesis

The notion that ATP and PNH_2 represent the sum total of the photochemically generated assimilatory power sprang from the realization that, fundamentally, the synthesis of carbohydrate in photosynthesis may proceed by a reversal of the reactions of carbohydrate breakdown. These degradative reactions, particularly the glycolytic pathway, were mapped out in detail in the 1930's and the early 1940's. The main energy barrier in the reversal of the glycolytic pathway would be the reversal of the oxidation of glyceraldehyde-3-phosphate to 3-phosphoglyceric acid, a reaction which in the forward direction generates ATP and PNH_2. Thus, to reverse this reaction an input of ATP and PNH_2 would be required.

The first complete hypothesis of this sort was put forward in 1943 by Ruben (13), who, elaborating on earlier suggestions by Thimann (14) and Lipmann (15), proposed that sugar formation in photosynthesis is a completely dark, chemosynthetic process which depends on only two products formed by light reactions: PNH_2 and ATP. Ruben's theoretical proposal (there was then no experimental evidence to support it) distinguished two phases of sugar synthesis in the dark: a special carboxylative phase, dependent on ATP only, in which CO_2 enters cellular metabolism by carboxylating an acceptor molecule, and a reductive phase, analogous to the reversal of the glyceraldehyde-3-phosphate oxidation in glycolysis, in which a carboxyl group is reduced by PNH_2 with the aid of ATP.

In the ensuing years, Ruben's scheme received experimental support from several directions: (a) Calvin, Horecker, Ochoa, Racker, and their associates (16–19) have identified the ATP-dependent carboxylative phase in CO_2 assimilation. They have shown that the entry of CO_2 into the metabolism of photosynthetic cells depends on the phosphorylation of ribulose monophosphate by ATP to ribulose diphosphate, which is then carboxylated by CO_2 and cleaved to give 2 molecules of PGA. Thus, the consumption of 1 mole of ATP at this stage would result in the incorporation of 1 mole of CO_2 and the formation of 2 moles of PGA. (b) The kinetic studies of Calvin's group (20) suggested that the reductive phase of CO_2 assimilation is indeed the reduction of PGA to triose phosphate by a reversal of the glyceraldehyde-3-phosphate oxidation reaction of glycolysis. Since 1 mole of ATP and 1 mole of PNH_2 are required for the reduction of 1 mole of PGA to triose, 2 moles of ATP and 2 moles of PNH_2 are required to reduce the 2 moles of PGA that are formed for each mole of CO_2 taken up in phase (a). (c) In addition to a carboxylative and a reductive phase, the finding in photosynthetic tissues of components of the pentose cycle (cf. review 7) afforded a mechanism for the regeneration of the CO_2 acceptor in photosynthesis, in what might be designated as a third, regenerative phase of CO_2 assimilation. No ATP or PNH_2 are required here since this phase proceeds without any additional input of energy.

The carboxylative, reductive, and regenerative phases constitute a cyclic sequence of dark reactions (20) which Racker has termed a reductive pentose phosphate cycle (19). A complete turn of the cycle requires 3 moles of ATP and 2 moles of $TPNH_2$ per mole of CO_2. The distinctive reactions of this cycle, whether it operates in photosynthetic or nonphotosynthetic cells, are those of the carboxylative phase, i.e., the phosphorylation of ribulose monophosphate to a diphosphate, followed by the carboxylation and subsequent cleavage of the adduct to give two moles of PGA (cf. 7, 8). It will be shown that some of the inhibitors of the carboxylative phase of CO_2 assimilation are among the best-known inhibitors of photosynthesis at the cellular level, for example, cyanide. Only the inhibitors of this phase of the carbon cycle will be discussed here, since the other two phases, the reductive and the regenerative, comprise the well-known reactions of glycolysis and of the pentose cycle—two topics that are discussed elsewhere in the volume.

B. Phosphoribulokinase

Phosphoribulokinase (18, 19, 21) catalyzes the phosphorylation of Ru-5-P in accordance with Eq. (1).

$$\text{Ru-5-P} + \text{ATP} \xrightarrow{\text{Mg}^{++}} \text{RuDP} + \text{ADP} \tag{1}$$

The enzyme is activated by divalent metal ions, of which Mg^{++} is the most effective. Phosphoribulokinase appears to be a sulfhydryl enzyme. It is inhibited by the addition of heavy metals (Cu^{++} or Hg^{++}) and by p-chloromercuribenzoate. Hurwitz et al. (21) showed that the inhibition by metals and by p-chloromercuribenzoate was completely reversed by cysteine.

In an investigation of CO_2 assimilation by a reconstituted chloroplast system, which yielded evidence for the operation of the reductive pentose phosphate cycle in isolated chloroplasts, Trebst, Losada, and Arnon (22) found that iodoacetamide strongly inhibited the carboxylative phase, but only mildly inhibited the reductive phase, i.e., that phase which involves the reduction of 1,3-PGA by glyceraldehyde-3-phosphate dehydrogenase, an enzyme known to be inhibited by iodoacetamide. Trebst et al. (22) interpreted their results as probably due to an inhibition of phosphoribulo-kinase, although they did not exclude the possibility that iodoacetamide may have inhibited pentose phosphate isomerase, the enzyme which catalyzes the conversion of ribose-5-P to ribulose-5-P.

Similar conclusions were reached by Calo and Gibbs (23), who found that low concentrations of iodoacetamide (5×10^{-5} M), which inhibit CO_2 fixation by isolated chloroplasts, are also inhibitory to phosphoribulo-kinase but not to pentose phosphate isomerase or to glyceraldehyde-3-phosphate dehydrogenase. It would appear, therefore, that in isolated chloroplasts, iodoacetamide affects photosynthetic CO_2 fixation by in-hibiting phosphoribulokinase.

Different conclusions, however, were reached by investigators of the effects of iodoacetate on photosynthetic CO_2 assimilation by intact cells. Simonis and Weichart (24) found that iodoacetate inhibition of photo-synthesis in Elodea leaves resulted in an accumulation of PGA and phosphoenolpyruvate and a decrease in sugar phosphates. They concluded from this that the site of the inhibition was the glyceraldehyde-3-phos-phate dehydrogenase reaction. Likewise, Kandler, Liesenkotter, and Oaks (25) observed an accumulation of PGA and a decrease in sugar phosphates in iodoacetate-inhibited Chlorella cells.

Kandler et al. (25) also ascribed the effect of iodoacetate to the inhibi-tion of the reductive step in CO_2 assimilation, but they postulated that the reductive step is not the well-known reduction of phosphoglyceric acid by glyceraldehydephosphate dehydrogenase but a reduction, directly to sugar (by an as yet unknown enzyme), of a keto acid formed by the carboxylation of ribulose diphosphate. Kandler et al. suggested that their postulated pathway is the physiological one in whole cells. The reduction of 1,3-PGA to triosephosphate by reversal of the glyceraldehyde-3-

phosphate dehydrogenase reaction, is, according to Kandler *et al.*, an artifact occurring only in isolated chloroplasts (*22, 25a*). No meaningful evaluation of Kandler's suggestions can be made without more direct experimental evidence for the postulated enzyme and its substrate (the keto acid) in photosynthetic cells.

C. The Carboxylation Enzyme (Carboxydismutase)

The carboxylation enzyme (ribulosediphosphate carboxylase) was first purified from spinach leaves (*17–19*) and was found to catalyze the reaction shown in Eq. (2).

$$RuDP + CO_2 \rightarrow 2\ PGA \tag{2}$$

The carboxylation enzyme is activated by sulfhydryl compounds (cysteine, glutathione) and is inhibited by sulfhydryl-binding agents. $HgCl_2$ at $2 \times 10^{-4}\ M$ completely inhibited the activity of the enzyme, whereas *p*-chloromercuribenzoate at the same concentration inhibited 50%. Arsenite at $10^{-3}\ M$ was without effect, showing that a dithiol is not involved (*85*). The enzyme requires Mg^{++}, but this may be replaced by other divalent ions such as Ni^{++} or Co^{++}.

The carboxylation enzyme was reported to be inhibited by arsenate and by relatively low concentrations of phosphate. In the presence of 0.03 M and 0.01 M phosphate, Weissbach, Horecker, and Hurwitz (*17*) found that the activity of the enzyme was only 10 and 30% of the control value, respectively. Arsenate at 0.02 M gave complete inhibition.

By contrast, Trebst *et al.* (*22*) found little inhibition by arsenate or phosphate of the carboxylative phase of CO_2 assimilation in a reconstituted chloroplast system. However, the reductive phase of CO_2 assimilation by chloroplasts was strongly inhibited in their experiments by the addition of arsenate (but not of phosphate). In the presence of arsenate, CO_2 assimilation did not go beyond PGA, which accumulated as the main product.

Gibbs and Calo (*26, 27*) observed a difference in the effect of phosphate on CO_2 assimilation between intact and fragmented and reconstituted chloroplasts. In the reconstituted chloroplast system, increasing the concentration of phosphate from $5 \times 10^{-6}\ M$ to $10^{-2}\ M$ stimulated CO_2 fixation approximately fourteenfold. No inhibition occurred until the phosphate concentration exceeded $5 \times 10^{-2}\ M$. By contrast, CO_2 fixation by intact chloroplasts was strongly inhibited (60%) by $2 \times 10^{-3}\ M$ phosphate. Gibbs and Calo (*27*) found also an inhibition of CO_2 fixation by arsenate, but again at high concentrations, viz., 0.03 M and 0.05 M. Arsenate did not inhibit at concentrations below 10^{-2} M.

The high concentrations of phosphate and arsenate needed to demonstrate inhibition of CO_2 fixation by the reconstituted chloroplast system, and the reported differences between intact and reconstituted chloroplasts, make it difficult to assess the significance of the reported phosphate and arsenate inhibition of the purified carboxylation enzyme (17).

Cyanide inhibition of photosynthesis has been the subject of many investigations (cf. 1) ever since it was first observed by Warburg (28). Trebst, Tsujimoto, and Arnon (29) found that cyanide inhibited the dark CO_2 assimilation in isolated chloroplasts, but the site of this inhibition was not known. It was of special interest to find, therefore, that cyanide was a strong and, so far, the only known effective inhibitor of the carboxylation enzyme in chloroplasts (22). This effect of cyanide is in harmony with other considerations (cf. 1) which indicate that cyanide inhibition of photosynthesis results from inhibition of CO_2 assimilation proper.

III. CYCLIC AND NONCYCLIC PHOTOPHOSPHORYLATION

As already stated, the contribution of the photochemical reactions of photosynthesis to carbon assimilation is the production of ATP and PNH_2. Since these reactions and their presently envisaged mechanisms will form the main basis for our interpretation of inhibitor action in photosynthesis, it might be useful first to discuss them briefly.

Photosynthetic phosphorylation (photophosphorylation) is a term introduced by Arnon, Allen, and Whatley (30) to describe a light-induced ATP formation which they discovered in isolated chloroplasts. Photosynthetic phosphorylation was distinct from oxidative phosphorylation, since it occurred without the aid of mitochondria and without a net consumption of molecular oxygen or chemical substrate. A similar reaction was found in subcellular preparations of photosynthetic bacteria by Frenkel (31). The over-all reaction is represented by Eq. (3).

$$\text{ADP} + \text{P} \xrightarrow{\text{Light}} \text{ATP} \qquad (3)$$

Reaction (3), in which the sole product is ATP, was subsequently renamed cyclic photophosphorylation (9) to distinguish it from noncyclic photophosphorylation, a second photophosphorylation reaction, which Arnon, Whatley, and Allen (9) found later in chloroplasts and which Nozaki, Tagawa, and Arnon (32) recently demonstrated in chromatophores of photosynthetic bacteria. A generalized representation of non-cyclic photophosphorylation is given by Eq. (4). (The donors of the electrons shown on the left side of the equation will be discussed later.)

$$\text{ADP} + \text{P} + \text{PN} + 2e^- + 2\text{H}^+ \xrightarrow{\text{Light}} \text{ATP} + \text{PNH}_2 \tag{4}$$

We still retain the term photosynthetic phosphorylation, but we use it now more broadly as a collective term for both cyclic and noncyclic photophosphorylation. In cyclic photophosphorylation all of the biochemically effective radiant energy is used for ATP formation. In noncyclic photophosphorylation only a portion of the biochemically effective radiant energy is used for ATP formation; the remainder is used for the formation of a strong reductant, PNH_2, and, in green plants, for oxygen evolution. There is evidence (33) to support the view that both cyclic and noncyclic photophosphorylation are needed for the synthesis of carbohydrates from CO_2. The noncyclic process by itself does not supply enough ATP to run the reductive carbon cycle.

Photosynthetic phosphorylation was first discovered in a single species of green plants (spinach). The process has now been observed in every major class of photosynthetic organisms. The discovery of cyclic and noncyclic photophosphorylation by isolated chloroplasts was confirmed and extended in other laboratories, notably those of Jagendorf (34–38), Wessels (39, 40), Vennesland (41, 42), and Hill (43). Whatley et al. (44) have demonstrated both cyclic and noncyclic photophosphorylation in chloroplasts isolated from several other species of plants. Frenkel's (31) finding of cyclic photophosphorylation in subcellular preparations of a purple nonsulfur photosynthetic bacterium, R. rubrum, was confirmed by Geller (45) and was followed by Williams' demonstration of the same process in the anaerobic photosynthetic sulfur bacteria, Chromatium and Chlorobium (46). Cyclic photophosphorylation by Chromatium particles was further investigated by Kamen and Newton (47) and Anderson and Fuller (48). In algal preparations, cyclic photophosphorylation was demonstrated by Thomas and Haans (49) and Petrack and Lipmann (50).

The widespread occurrence of photosynthetic phosphorylation has emphasized the fundamental nature of this process in energy conversion during photosynthesis. It is, therefore, of considerable interest to examine the effects of various inhibitors on this process.

A. Mechanism of Cyclic Photophosphorylation

A mechanism for cyclic photophosphorylation must account for the unique features of this process that distinguish it from oxidative phosphorylation by mitochondria: ATP is formed without the consumption of either an external electron donor (substrate) or an electron acceptor (oxygen) and hence cannot be formed at the expense of free energy released during electron transport from substrate to oxygen. The mechanism postulated in 1959 by Arnon and his associates (5, 51, 52) envisages that the formation of the high-energy pyrophosphate bond of ATP in cyclic photophosphorylation occurs at the expense of free energy released during an endogenous electron transfer that is set in motion by the capture of radiant energy by the chlorophyll pigment system.

According to this theory, during the primary photochemical act a chlorophyll molecule within the chloroplast or chromatophore system becomes excited by an absorbed photon. This excited state leads to an "expulsion" of an electron that has been raised to a high energy level. The excited chlorophyll thus becomes the electron donor. On losing an electron, chlorophyll becomes also the electron acceptor $(Chl)^+$ to which the expelled electron returns with a resultant release of free energy. This "downhill" return of the electron proceeds in a stepwise manner, via a "closed circuit" of electron carriers, the terminal member of which is a cytochrome that adjoins the chlorophyll molecule. In the final step, the electron is transferred from reduced cytochrome to the adjoining "electron-deficient" chlorophyll molecule $(Chl)^+$, which is thereby restored to the ground state and becomes ready to accept another photon to initiate the cyclic electron flow again.

This theory (51, 5) envisages a phosphorylation step coupled with electron transfer within the chloroplast from a reduced cytochrome to $(Chl)^+$. The phosphorylation that accompanies the oxidation of the cytochrome in chloroplasts would be analogous to the phosphorylation that accompanies the oxidation of the cytochromes in mitochondria by oxygen. Thus, chlorophyll with the aid of light is the ultimate oxidant in photophosphorylation and plays a part which corresponds to molecular oxygen in oxidative phosphorylation. Earlier members of the photosynthetic electron carrier system, those that precede the cytochromes, are quinones (vitamin K), flavins (FMN), or related physiological equivalents. Additional phosphorylations are probably coupled with the oxidation-reduction of these cofactors (51, 5). A diagram illustrating this mechanism is shown in Fig. 1.

These physiological cofactors (electron carriers) can be replaced by certain nonphysiological agents, such as phenazine methosulfate, which apparently act by providing an artificial "shortcut" that bypasses one or more phosphorylation sites (45). A diagram illustrating a shortened cyclic electron flow mechanism of this type is shown in Fig. 2.

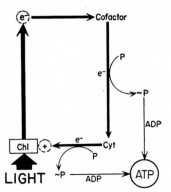

FIG. 1. Scheme for cyclic photophosphorylation catalyzed by a physiological cofactor (a quinone or a flavin). The chlorophyll (Chl) molecule (bound to a protein in the chloroplast) becomes excited by the absorption of a photon. The excited chlorophyll donates its high energy electron to the oxidized cofactor and accepts an electron from reduced cytochrome (Cyt). The cycle is completed when the cofactor, after becoming reduced, in turn transfers an electron to cytochrome, which has become oxidized by its transfer of an electron to chlorophyll. The phosphorylation steps are envisaged as being linked with the transfer of electrons from cofactor to cytochrome and from the cytochrome chain to chlorophyll. [From (5).]

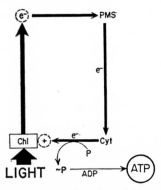

FIG. 2. Scheme for cyclic photophosphorylation catalyzed by phenazine methosulfate (PMS). The envisaged mechanism here differs from that in Fig. 1, in that PMS serves as a shortcut bypassing the site of the physiological cofactor. This bypass is not coupled with phosphorylation. The phosphorylation coupled with electron transfer in the sector between cytochromes and chlorophyll remains the same as in Fig. 1 [From (5).]

The salient feature of the proposed cyclic mechanism (Figs. 1 and 2) is that electrons, "activated" by light energy, travel in a "closed circuit" from which they are not removed. The stepwise interaction of the high-energy electron with the intermediate electron acceptors and the coupled phosphorylating system constitutes the energy conversion process in cyclic photophosphorylation.

Granted the validity of this mechanism [for a review of supporting evidence see (5)], an inhibitor of cyclic photophosphorylation may be effective by impeding one of the three main phases of the process: (a) the light-induced generation of a high-energy electron and the ultimate electron acceptor (Chl)+, (b) electron transport by the photosynthetic electron transport chain, and (c) phosphorylation reactions coupled to electron transport. Phases (b) and (c) are analogous to, and at some points possibly identical with, their counterparts in oxidative phosphorylation, and hence there is considerable interest in comparing the inhibitors of these two processes. Phase (a) is peculiar to photosynthetic phosphorylation and involves physical events for which our knowledge of inhibitor action is only now beginning to emerge. Arnold and Clayton (52a) observed that phase (a) could be isolated from subsequent photosynthetic events by the use of sodium azide or hydroxylamine. In the presence of these inhibitors, intact cells of a carotenoidless mutant *Rhodopseudomonas spheroides* showed on illumination spectral changes near the absorption maxima of bacteriochlorophyll, similar to spectral changes seen on illuminating of chromatophores, either in suspension or as dried films. The spectral changes may result from an accumulation of a pool of electrons expelled from bacteriochlorophyll in the primary photochemical act [phase (a)]; the use of these electrons in phase (b) is prevented by the inhibitor.

B. Mechanism of Noncyclic Photophosphorylation

As summarized in Eq. (4), noncyclic photophosphorylation differs from the cyclic type in that the formation of ATP accompanies the reduction of pyridine nucleotide and the oxidation of an external electron donor. In the mechanisms for noncyclic photophosphorylation proposed by Arnon and his co-workers (11, 12, 51), the primary photochemical act remains the same as in cyclic photophosphorylation. Photon capture by chlorophyll results in the generation of a high-energy electron and of an electron acceptor (Chl)+. However, the cyclic path of the electron is interrupted; the high-energy electron removed from the excited chlorophyll molecule is transferred to pyridine nucleotide which, in the intact cell, is used for CO_2 assimilation.

As the electrons from excited chlorophyll are transferred to pyridine nucleotide, they must be replaced by an external electron donor. The "closed" circuit of cyclic photophosphorylation thus gives way in non-cyclic photophosphorylation to an "open" circuit for the transport of electrons from an external electron donor to pyridine nucleotide. This noncyclic electron transport also requires an input of light energy, since the electron donor is at a potential less reducing than the electron acceptor. A diagrammatic representation of this concept is given in Fig. 3.

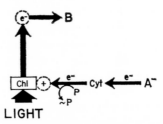

LIGHT

FIG. 3. Scheme for noncyclic photophosphorylation of the bacterial type. The chlorophyll molecule (Chl) becomes excited by the absorption of a quantum of light. The excited chlorophyll donates its high energy electron (e^-) to the electron acceptor (B) and accepts, via the cytochrome system (Cyt), an electron from an external electron donor (A^-). The phosphorylation step is envisaged as linked with the transfer of the electron from cytochrome to chlorophyll. B represents pyridine nucleotide. [From (11).]

Noncyclic and cyclic photophosphorylation are thus envisaged as sharing the primary photochemical act, i.e., chlorophyll excitation by photon capture, and the related oxidation of cytochromes with an accompanying phosphorylation step. Noncyclic photophosphorylation would, therefore, be expected to be equally sensitive to inhibitors which inhibit these steps in cyclic photophosphorylation. But the proposed mechanism for noncyclic photophosphorylation provides two additional sites for inhibitor action: (a) the transfer of electrons from the external electron donor to the photosynthetic apparatus and (b) the transfer of electrons from excited chlorophyll to pyridine nucleotides.

Noncyclic phosphorylation in green plants is distinguished from that in photosynthetic bacteria by its electron donor system (11, 52). In green plants, water,[3] i.e., OH^- ions, supplies the electrons required in reaction (4). However, photosynthetic bacteria cannot use hydroxyl ions but use inorganic or organic electron donors, such as thiosulfate or succinate. It now appears that plants, but not photosynthetic bacteria, are able to use

[3] OH^- will be used here interchangeably with water and represents hydroxyl ions at neutral pH as in the reaction:

$$4 \ OH^- \ (10^{-7} \ M) \longrightarrow O_2 + 2 \ H_2O + 4e^-; \ E_0' = 0.815V \ (pH \ 7)$$

hydroxyl ions as electron donors because plants have evolved an additional pigment system (*11, 12, 53*)—chlorophyll b or equivalent accessory pigment—that catalyzes a special light-dependent reaction [Eq. (5)] for the photooxidation of hydroxyl ions (Fig. 4).

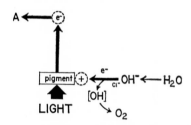

FIG. 4. Scheme for photooxidation of water by chloroplasts. This reaction is now visualized (Cf. *11, 12*) as an auxiliary photochemical reaction in chloroplasts, catalyzed by a photosynthetic pigment (chlorophyll b or equivalent) that does not occur in photosynthetic bacteria. The pigment molecule, when it becomes excited by the absorption of a photon, donates a high-energy electron (e^-) to an intermediate electron acceptor (A) and accepts an electron from an hydroxyl ion. The oxidation product (OH) of the hydroxyl ion is the precursor of molecular oxygen. [From (*11*).]

$$4 \text{ OH}^- \xrightarrow{\text{Light}} 4e^- + O_2 + 2 H_2O \tag{5}$$

To recapitulate, the proposed mechanisms for photosynthetic phosphorylation provide for several groups of inhibitors, each capable of inhibiting the over-all process of photosynthesis by affecting one of the following: (*a*) oxygen evolution (plants only), (*b*) electron transfer steps involved in cyclic and noncyclic photophosphorylation (plants or bacteria), or (*c*) the phosphorylation reactions themselves (plants or bacteria).

IV. INHIBITORS OF OXYGEN EVOLUTION

Prior to the recognition of oxygen evolution as a component of noncyclic photophosphorylation in chloroplasts, evidence for a specific action of certain inhibitors on oxygen evolution in photosynthesis came from experiments on hydrogen-adapted algae and on the Hill reaction. Gaffron (*54*) has shown that certain green algae can be adapted to hydrogen gas to perform a type of light-dependent CO_2 assimilation, resembling bacterial photosynthesis, in which hydrogen consumption replaces oxygen evolution. This kind of photosynthesis, which he called photoreduction, was much more resistant to hydroxylamine, o-phenanthroline, vitamin K derivatives, and hydrogen sulfide inhibition than the conventional photosynthesis in which oxygen was evolved, leading to the conclusion that these agents affect primarily the reaction(s) responsible for oxygen evolution (55, 56).

This conclusion was supported by evidence that the same inhibitors also inhibit the Hill reaction, under conditions when CO_2 assimilation or photophosphorylation are excluded. Warburg found (57) that o-phenanthroline was a powerful inhibitor of oxygen evolution in the Hill reaction, and this was confirmed by other investigators (see review 3). Among other inhibitors of the Hill reaction are hydroxylamine, sodium azide, and phenylurethan; cyanide was found to be without effect (cf. 58).

A. Effect of Phenylurethan and Substituted Phenylureas

Urethans have been widely used as poisons ("narcotics") of photosynthesis since they were first introduced by Warburg in 1919. In 1956, Wessels and van der Veen (59), investigating the mode of action of the herbicide CMU [3-(4-chlorophenyl)-1,1-dimethylurea], discovered that this substance and other substituted ureas were extremely powerful inhibitors of the Hill reaction (as measured by the photoreduction of 2,6-dichlorophenolindophenol), exceeding greatly in effectiveness the structurally related phenylurethan (Table I).

These findings were confirmed by Spikes (60) and extended by Bishop (61) to hydrogen-adapted cells. Bishop compared the effect of DCMU (for abbreviations see Table I) on photosynthesis and photoreduction in *Scenedesmus*. Photosynthesis was reduced to half by 5×10^{-7} M DCMU and became completely inhibited in the presence of 3×10^{-6} M DCMU. The inhibitory effect of DCMU disappeared if the alga was adapted to hydrogen; photoreduction was not inhibited.

High light intensities are known to "deadapt" algae adapted to hydrogen gas and to restore conventional photosynthesis in them (54–56). This reversion of photoreduction to photosynthesis by the use of higher light intensities was prevented at 3×10^{-6} M DCMU, indicating again that conventional photosynthesis of green plants of which oxygen evolution is an essential part, cannot proceed in the presence of DCMU (61).

The substituted urea compounds have provided for the first time photosynthetic inhibitors which are effective at concentrations lower (by a hundredfold) than that of chlorophyll (59, 60). Moreover, this powerful inhibitory action seems to be affecting a specific photochemical reaction,

TABLE I

PHENYLURETHAN AND SUBSTITUTED PHENYLUREAS

Name	Formula
Phenylurethan	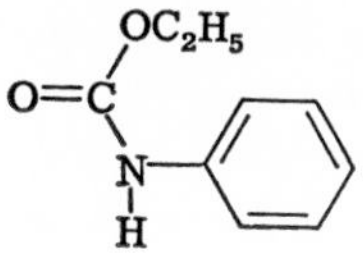 $O=C$ with OC_2H_5 and N—H—phenyl
3-Phenyl-1,1-dimethylurea	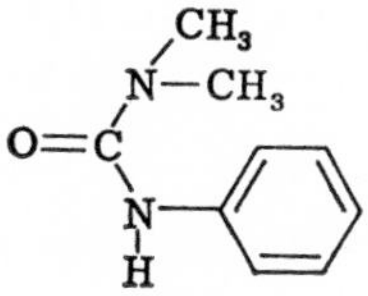 $O=C$ with $N(CH_3)$—CH_3 and N—H—phenyl
3-(4'-Chlorophenyl)-1,1-dimethylurea (CMU)	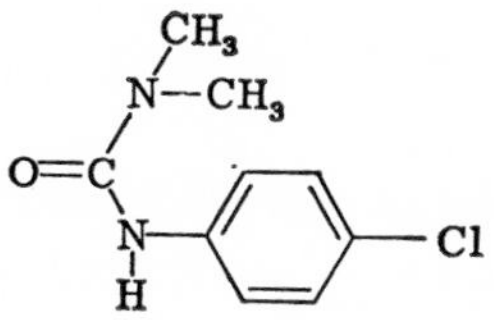 $O=C$ with $N(CH_3)$—CH_3 and N—H—phenyl—Cl
3-(3',4'-Dichlorophenyl)-1,1-dimethylurea (DCMU)	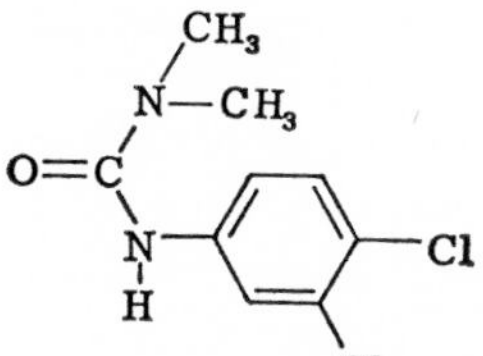 $O=C$ with $N(CH_3)$—CH_3 and N—H—phenyl—Cl, Cl
3-(3'-Chlorophenyl)-1,1-dimethylurea	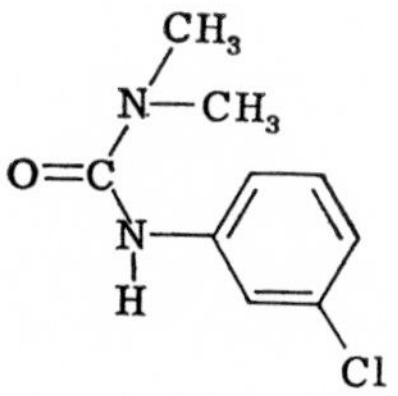 $O=C$ with $N(CH_3)$—CH_3 and N—H—phenyl—Cl

the photooxidation of OH$^-$ that gives rise to oxygen evolution (Fig. 4), a reaction which Losada et al. (11, 12) have experimentally separated in isolated chloroplasts from the other photochemical reactions of photosynthesis.

If the proposed reaction mechanisms were valid, it would be expected that substituted ureas, and other inhibitors of oxygen evolution, such as o-phenanthroline, would not inhibit those photosynthetic reactions in which OH$^-$ does not serve as an electron donor, viz., (a) an experimentally modified noncyclic photophosphorylation in chloroplasts in which the physiological electron donor OH$^-$ is replaced (11) by an ascorbate-dye system (A$^-$ in Fig. 3), (b) noncyclic photophosphorylation in bacterial chromatophores (Fig. 3), and (c) cyclic photophosphorylation, either in chloroplasts or in chromatophores, since in both these cases an endogenous electron flow is being set in motion by light without the involvement of any external electron donor (Fig. 1). As will be shown below, these expectations have been experimentally verified.

B. Insensitivity of Cyclic and Noncyclic Photophosphorylation to Inhibitors of Oxygen Evolution

1. NONCYCLIC PHOTOPHOSPHORYLATION

Vernon and Zaugg (62) have shown that in the presence of 10^{-5} M DCMU, freshly prepared chloroplasts, which have lost completely (98%) the capacity to reduce TPN with electrons donated by OH$^-$, are nevertheless able to reduce TPN photochemically by electrons donated by a reduced dye, 2,6-dichlorophenolindophenol. (In practice, the dye is supplied in catalytic amounts and kept in a reduced form by substrate amounts of added ascorbate.) Similar effects were observed in the presence of 10^{-3} M hydroxylamine (62).

Losada, Whatley, and Arnon (11) have recently shown that in isolated chloroplasts the light-dependent noncyclic electron transfer from ascorbate to TPN (via 2,6-dichlorophenolindophenol) is coupled with the formation of ATP. The phosphorylation accompanying this TPN reduction was not accompanied by oxygen evolution, and hence, as predicted by the working hypothesis, it was not inhibited by CMU (Table 1 in ref. 11). This provided evidence that in chloroplasts, as in photosynthetic bacteria, (32) the essential events of noncyclic photophosphorylation, (i.e., ATP formation coupled with photoreduction of PN) are basically independent of oxygen evolution. By blocking the photoproduction of oxygen, Losada *et al.* (*11*) have shown that chloroplasts can be experimentally induced to give the bacterial type of noncyclic photophosphorylation described by Nozaki *et al.* (*32*).

These findings are in agreement with the earlier ones of Vernon and Ash (*63*) with chromatophores of *R. rubrum*, that DCMU had little effect on bacterial photoreduction of pyridine nucleotide, photophosphorylation, or photooxidation of ascorbate.

2. Cyclic Photophosphorylation

There is general agreement among different investigators (*12*, *64–69*) that cyclic photophosphorylation in chloroplasts catalyzed by phenazine methosulfate (or pyocanin) is a truly anaerobic process in which no oxygen is produced or consumed. This view is supported by the consistent evidence from different laboratories that this type of cyclic photophosphorylation is resistant to inhibition by inhibitors of oxygen evolution. However, in the case of cyclic photophosphorylations catalyzed by vitamin K or FMN, the effects of inhibitors of oxygen evolution seemed less clear-cut.

Whatley *et al.* (*65*) and Trebst and Eck (*66*) found that cyclic photophosphorylation catalyzed by FMN was more sensitive to *o*-phenanthroline than that catalyzed by vitamin K or phenazine methosulfate, and this observation served, among others, to support a case for two parallel pathways of cyclic photophosphorylation: one catalyzed by FMN and another, by vitamin K or phenazine methosulfate (*65*). Jagendorf and Margulies (*67*) found that, under their experimental conditions, cyclic photophosphorylation catalyzed either by vitamin K or FMN was equally inhibited by CMU. They therefore put both these photophosphorylations in the same category and suggested that both depend on an oxygen-evolving step that is missing in the CMU-resistant cyclic photophosphorylation catalyzed by phenazine methosulfate. Similar conclusions were reached by Vennesland (*68*) and Krall *et al.* (*69*).

The effect of CMU on cyclic photophosphorylation by chloroplasts has recently been reinvestigated by Arnon *et al.* (*5*, *12*). They confirmed the resistance of cyclic photophosphorylation catalyzed by phenazine methosulfate to CMU, but, in addition, they have shown that under appropriately controlled experimental conditions cyclic photophosphorylation catalyzed by vitamin K or FMN is also resistant to inhibition by CMU. The required experimental conditions include an absence of oxygen, higher concentrations (catalytic versus "microcatalytic") of vitamin K and FMN, low light intensity, and, particularly for the FMN system.

high concentrations of the chloroplast material. The need for a relatively high concentration of chloroplast material suggested that the CMU-resistant, anaerobic FMN and vitamin K systems require more chloroplast factor(s) than the anaerobic phenazine methosulfate system.

Arnon et al. (12) found that, unless the necessary experimental conditions were maintained, cyclic photophosphorylation catalyzed by FMN or vitamin K became converted into a pseudocyclic type, i.e., a special case of noncyclic photophosphorylation in which molecular oxygen replaces pyridine nucleotide as the electron acceptor [cf. Eq. (4)]. The pseudocyclic process is dependent on oxygen evolution by chloroplasts [Eq. (5)] and hence is sensitive to CMU, o-phenanthroline, and other oxygen inhibitors. Thus, these inhibitors of oxygen evolution provide an experimental device for distinguishing the pseudocyclic, oxygen-dependent photophosphorylation catalyzed by vitamin K or FMN from the corresponding cyclic type (also catalyzed by vitamin K or FMN) which is truly anaerobic and involves neither the consumption nor the evolution of oxygen (see Table 2 in ref. 12).

Similar conclusions about the anaerobic nature of cyclic photophosphorylation by chloroplasts were independently reached by Trebst and Eck (66). In their experiments, cyclic photophosphorylation catalyzed either by vitamin K or by phenazine methosulfate was independent of molecular oxygen and resistant to inhibition by DCMU and o-phenanthroline. In agreement with the earlier results of Whatley et al. (65), Trebst and Eck (66) found that cyclic photophosphorylation catalyzed by FMN was sensitive to these inhibitors and thus seemingly dependent on oxygen. However, the experimental conditions that are now known to be necessary for demonstrating the anaerobic nature of cyclic photophosphorylation catalyzed by FMN (5, 12) were not used in the experiments of Whatley et al. (65) and Trebst and Eck (66).

In bacterial preparations, the independence of photosynthetic phosphorylation from oxygen evolution and its inhibitors was to be expected in view of the strictly anaerobic nature of bacterial photosynthesis. In isolated chloroplasts, where oxygen evolution is normally an integral part of photosynthesis, special experimental techniques, including the use of inhibitors, have been used to demonstrate the basic independence of cyclic and noncyclic photophosphorylation from oxygen evolution or consumption. The elucidation of the important but nevertheless special role of oxygen evolution in noncyclic photophosphorylation in chloroplasts has revealed the basic similarity of this process in green plants and photosynthetic bacteria; this basic similarity was also shown for cyclic photophosphorylation.

V. INHIBITORS OF PHOTOSYNTHETIC ELECTRON TRANSPORT

We will now consider inhibitors of photosynthetic electron transport pathways unrelated to oxygen evolution. The discussion will include (a) electron flow in cyclic photophosphorylation by chloroplasts and bacterial chromatophores and (b) electron flow in noncyclic photophosphorylation of the bacterial type, i.e., the type in which oxygen evolution does not occur. As already stated, the bacterial type of noncyclic photophosphorylation has recently been demonstrated in chromatophores of *R. rubrum* (*32*) and has also been shown to be an experimentally separable component of noncyclic photophosphorylation in isolated chloroplasts (*11, 12*).

A. Inhibitors of Cyclic Electron Flow

In bacterial preparations, cyclic photophosphorylation proceeds without the addition of external cofactors. Chromatophores of *Chromatium*, when prepared under anaerobic conditions, give a vigorous cyclic photophosphorylation which is not increased by the addition of cofactors. On aging the isolated chromatophores, this "physiological" cyclic photophosphorylation progressively decreases but is restorable by the addition of phenazine methosulfate and vitamin K analogues (see Table 2 in ref. *5*).

These results suggest that aging of chromatophores brings about a progressive inactivation of some physiological cofactor of electron transport and that this may be overcome by the addition of exogenous cofactors. Phenazine methosulfate and vitamin K analogues are also effective in catalyzing cyclic photophosphorylation in isolated chloroplasts, but here they must be added even to freshly prepared chloroplasts if a vigorous rate of cyclic photophosphorylation is to be obtained. It seems likely that loss or inactivation of the endogenous cofactor(s) of cyclic photophosphorylation is inherent in the present methods for isolating chloroplasts but is avoided in preparing bacterial chromatophores.

With bacterial chromatophores the effect of inhibitors on cyclic photophosphorylation may, therefore, be investigated either in an endogenous (physiological) system to which no cofactors are added or in a system fortified by the addition of exogenous cofactors. In isolated chloroplasts investigations of inhibitors have usually been carried out not in endogenous systems but in the presence of added cofactors because, as already mentioned, without them the rate of cyclic photophosphorylation is very low. These experimental differences between chloroplasts and chromatophores must be kept in mind when comparing the effects of inhibitors on the two systems.

1. EFFECT OF FERRICYANIDE

In oxidative phosphorylation by mitochondria oxygen uptake gives a measure of electron transport both under conditions when ATP is formed or when it is experimentally abolished (uncoupled). There is no similar direct procedure for measuring electron flow in cyclic photophosphorylation independent of ATP formation. ATP formation is a measure of both electron flow and phosphorylation. If phosphorylation is abolished, a cyclic electron flow would, by definition, produce no other measurable chemical change in the system. Special experimental devices have, therefore, been used for distinguishing between the effect of a given treatment on the phosphorylation reaction proper and on cyclic electron flow. Some of these, going beyond conventional inhibitors, will now be reviewed.

The key premise in the proposed mechanisms for cyclic photophosphorylation is that the electron expelled from the chloroplast molecule in the primary photochemical act is not removed from the closed circuit within which it travels before it returns to the chlorophyll $(Chl)^+$. If this basic postulation is correct, it follows that cyclic photophosphorylation should be abolished if electrons are prevented from completing the cycle because of capture by an external electron acceptor. To be convincing, such an experiment should be carried out with an electron "trap" which would be free from the suspicion that it prevented ATP formation by acting as an uncoupler or an inhibitor of phosphorylation.

An electron acceptor that fulfills these requirements is ferricyanide. As shown by Avron and Jagendorf (37) and confirmed in this laboratory, ferricyanide has a great affinity for trapping electrons during cyclic photophosphorylation without acting as an uncoupler or inhibitor of ATP formation. Because of these properties it may be used as a terminal electron acceptor in noncyclic photophosphorylation by chloroplasts (9, 10) to replace TPN (see B in Fig. 5). In the conventional noncyclic photophosphorylation by chloroplasts, electrons trapped by ferricyanide are continuously replaced by electrons donated by OH^-, with a resultant evolution of oxygen that is accompanied by photoreduction of substrate amounts of ferricyanide (Fig. 5). When the flow of electrons from OH^- is prevented by the omission of chloride (5, 51), ferricyanide ceases to act as a terminal electron acceptor in noncyclic photophosphorylation and acts instead as an electron trap which breaks the closed circuit of cyclic electron flow. In chromatophores ferricyanide always acts as an electron

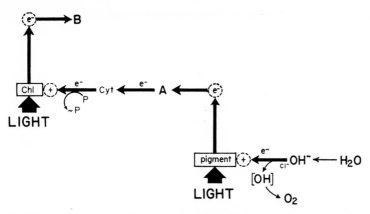

FIG. 5. Scheme for noncyclic photophosphorylation of the green plant type. This scheme combines the photooxidation of water (Fig. 4), as the first light reaction, with the noncyclic photophosphorylation of the bacterial type (Fig. 3), as the second light reaction (cf. *11*, *12*). The intermediate electron acceptor (A) from the first light reaction serves, in its reduced form (A⁻), as the electron donor for the second light reaction. [From (*11*).]

trap, since OH^- cannot serve as an electron donor, whether chloride is present or not.

The addition of ferricyanide (in the absence of chloride) had indeed abolished cyclic photophosphorylation both in chloroplasts and in chromatophores (see Table 2 in ref. *51*). Adding this ion in its reduced form as ferrocyanide was without effect. The reduction of ferricyanide with ascorbate either prior to or during illumination of chloroplasts or chromatophores restored in full their capacity for cyclic photophosphorylation. The conclusion seemed justified, therefore, that the inhibitory effect of ferricyanide resulted from the capture by this ion (in its oxidized form) of electrons which would normally have traveled the cyclic electron transport route. This conclusion was strengthened by the finding that the inhibition was produced by very low concentrations of ferricyanide. This would be expected if, as demanded by the hypothesis, the quantity of ferricyanide necessary to capture electrons from the cyclic system need only be sufficient to leave the catalytic components of the system in an oxidized form.

2. EFFECT OF INHIBITORS OF RESPIRATORY ELECTRON TRANSPORT

From the standpoint of comparative biochemistry, special interest centers on the effects on photosynthetic phosphorylation of inhibitors of oxidative phosphorylation in mitochondria, especially those that have been identified with a particular site in the electron transport chain.

a. *Antimycin A and HOQNO.* Antimycin A and 2-heptyl-4-hydroxy-quinoline-*N*-oxide (HOQNO) are two inhibitors of electron transport in oxidative phosphorylation whose site of inhibition is generally considered to lie between cytochromes b and c (70–72). Geller (45, 73) and Smith and Baltscheffsky (74) found, respectively, that antimycin A and HOQNO inhibit cyclic photophosphorylation in chromatophores of *R. rubrum.* Similar effects of these two inhibitors were observed by Nozaki *et al.* on cyclic photophosphorylation with chromatophores of *Chromatium* (32). In the experiments of Nozaki *et al.* (32) the inhibition was particularly pronounced in washed chromatophores.

The inhibition of cyclic photophosphorylation in chromatophores does not occur in the presence of catalytic amounts of phenazine methosulfate (45, 73, 75), which evidently serves as a bypass around the site of inhibition. These findings are of interest, since cyclic photophosphorylation in chloroplasts—measured, as will be recalled, in the presence of added cofactors—was found to be resistant to antimycin A [Arnon *et al.* (76), Whatley *et al.* (65)] and to HOQNO [Avron (77)]. Baltscheffsky (78, 79) reported that the inhibition of cyclic photophosphorylation in chloroplasts required a 1000 times higher concentration of each of these two inhibitors than in chromatophores.

On present evidence, it remains unsettled whether chloroplasts have or have not an endogenous cyclic photophosphorylation that is sensitive to these two inhibitors. The possibility cannot be ruled out that chloroplasts also have an antimycin- and HOQNO-sensitive site (i.e., one lying between cytochromes of the b and c types) which is lost by the present methods of isolating chloroplasts and is experimentally bypassed by the addition of exogenous cofactors of cyclic photophosphorylation.

Further support for the "bypass" effect of phenazine methosulfate in cyclic electron transport in chromatophores, and a suggestion that the site of inhibition of antimycin A in the photosynthetic electron transport chain lies between cytochromes b and c, has come from a recent report of Rudney (80). He found that chromatophores obtained from *R. rubrum* cells grown in the presence of diphenylamine (DPA), an inhibitor of carotenoid synthesis, had a lower cyclic photophosphorylation activity than chromatophores obtained from normal cells. Phosphorylation in both types of chromatophores (from normal or DPA-treated cells) was equally stimulated by the addition of phenazine methosulfate. Moreover, the phosphorylating activity of chromatophores from the DPA-treated cells, but not from normal cells, was increased by the addition of isoprenologues of coenzyme Q. Antimycin A blocked completely the increased phosphorylation obtained by adding isoprenologues of coenzyme Q, whereas the phosphorylation in the phenazine methosulfate treatment was relatively insensitive to antimycin A. These observations again support the view that antimycin A inhibits a site between cytochromes b and c. This is the region of the respiratory electron transport chain in which coenzyme Q is placed [Green (81)].

b. *Gramicidin, Oligomycin, Methylene Blue and Other Dyes.* Gramicidin was found to inhibit cyclic photophosphorylation in isolated chloroplasts (65, 79) and in extracts of *R. rubrum* (82) but not in *Chromatium* chromatophores (see Table 3 in ref. 5). Baltscheffsky and Baltscheffsky (82) found that oligomycin inhibited cyclic photophosphorylation in extracts of *R. rubrum* in concentrations similar to those necessary to inhibit oxidative phosphorylation in mitochondria.

Methylene blue, a dye that is known to be a strong inhibitor of oxidative phosphorylation (83), was found by Arnon et al. to be also a strong inhibitor of cyclic photophosphorylation in chloroplasts (65, 76) but not in *Chromatium* chromatophores (see Table 3 in ref. 5). However, Geller and Lipmann (73) obtained a strong inhibition of photophosphorylation in *R. rubrum* by 10^{-4} M methylene blue as well as by other dyes, namely, brilliant blue, thionine, and dichlorophenolindophenol.

c. *Arsenite and the Question of Lipoic Acid.* Interest in the effect of arsenite on photosynthetic phosphorylation stems from the proposal of Calvin and his associates (84) that lipoic (thioctic) acid is a key compound in photosynthesis, the one concerned in the primary conversion into chemical energy of the radiant energy absorbed by chlorophyll. This suggestion has recently been brought forward again by Racker (71).

Reactions in which lipoic acid is a cofactor are very sensitive to arsenite inhibition (85). For example, the pyruvic oxidation system, in which lipoic acid is a cofactor, is inhibited by concentrations of arsenite of the order of 3×10^{-5} M (85, 86). In chloroplasts, Arnon et al. (76) and Whatley et al. (65) found that 10^{-3} M arsenite failed to inhibit either cyclic or noncyclic photophosphorylation. The improbability of lipoic acid as a participant in photosynthetic phosphorylation is also indicated by the results of Geller and Lipmann (73); 10^{-2} M arsenite failed to inhibit phosphorylation by illuminated particles of *R. rubrum*.

d. *p-Chloromercuribenzoate.* Cyclic photophosphorylation by chloroplasts, whether catalyzed by FMN or vitamin K is sensitive to p-chloromercuribenzoate inhibition (64, 65, 76). Cyclic photophosphorylation in chloroplasts, when catalyzed by phenazine methosulfate, is also inhibited

by *p*-chloromercuribenzoate (*64*). The inhibition of cyclic photophosphorylation was reversed by the addition of glutathione (*65, 76*). These
results suggest that sulfhydryl compounds, in enzymes or cofactors, or
both, participate in photosynthetic phosphorylation.

e. Cyanide. Cyanide, the classic inhibitor of respiration, [and of the
carboxylation enzyme (see Section II, B)] is noted for its inhibition of
cytochrome oxidase (see review, *87*). Since this enzyme is not involved
in the strictly anaerobic reactions of bacterial photosynthesis and is
absent from chloroplasts (*88, 89*), the effect of cyanide on the photosynthetic electron transport chain would be expected to differ from that on
the respiratory electron transport chain. Thus, Smith and Baltscheffsky
(*74*) found that in cell-free extracts of *R. rubrum* cyanide inhibited
respiration but had no inhibitory effect on photophosphorylation.

Geller and Lipmann (*73*) observed that photophosphorylation in
R. rubrum was not appreciably affected by 10^{-2} *M* cyanide or azide. In
chloroplasts, Wessels (*39*) found the addition of 10^{-3} *M* KCN increased
by over 100% cyclic photophosphorylation catalyzed by vitamin K_3 but
severely inhibited cyclic photophosphorylation catalyzed by FMN.
Whatley *et al.* (*65*) have also observed a cyanide inhibition of an FMN-
catalyzed cyclic photophosphorylation in chloroplasts, but no stimulation of the vitamin K system. In fact, Whatley *et al.* (*65*) found that,
depending on the pH and the form of vitamin K used, cyanide also
inhibited the vitamin K system. These conflicting observations cannot, as
yet, be reconciled by any cogent theory as to a possible mode of action
of cyanide in photosynthetic phosphorylation.

f. Other Inhibitors. Among other inhibitors, Baltscheffsky (*79*) found
that Amytal gave only a weak inhibition of cyclic photophosphorylation
in chloroplasts, even at concentrations several times higher than those
which inhibit oxidative photophosphorylation in mitochondria. Geller and
Lipmann (*73*) obtained inhibition of cyclic photophosphorylation in
R. rubrum by butyl-3,5-diodo-4-hydroxybenzoate and the alkylated
naphthoquinone, Compound SN 5949.

B. Inhibitors of Noncyclic Electron Flow

As was already stated (Section III, B), the proposed mechanism of
noncyclic photophosphorylation provides for two sites of inhibitor action
which are not encountered in cyclic photophosphorylation: (*a*) the transfer of electrons from the external electron donor to the photosynthetic
apparatus and (*b*) transfer of electrons from excited chlorophyll to pyri-

dine nucleotide. In both isolated chloroplasts and chromatophores the physiological electron acceptor is pyridine nucleotide; experimentally, in isolated chloroplasts pyridine nucleotide may be replaced by ferricyanide or some other Hill reagent.

The physiological external electron donor for chloroplasts is OH^- (water); and since oxidation of this ion must be accompanied by oxygen evolution, the previously discussed (Section IV) inhibitors of oxygen evolution necessarily prevent electron transfer from the external donor, OH^-, to the photosynthetic apparatus. These inhibitors do not affect either the bacterial type of noncyclic photophosphorylation where OH^- is not the electron donor or the strictly anaerobic cyclic electron flow (either in chromatophores or in isolated chloroplasts) in which molecular oxygen does not participate (12).

The use of inhibitors provides an experimental technique for comparing the electron transport chain in cyclic and noncyclic photophosphorylation. Similar sensitivity to the inhibitors would point to similar components in the two pathways. Thus, in the case of *R. rubrum* chromatophores, Nozaki *et al.* (32) found that the noncyclic electron flow from succinate (a physiological electron donor for this organism) was also inhibited by antimycin A and HOQNO, two inhibitors of the cyclic electron flow. Nozaki *et al.* (32) have, therefore, concluded that the cyclic and noncyclic electron pathways in *R. rubrum* share the same site of inhibition (*X* in Fig. 6), lying between cytochromes b and c, which is bypassed by using ascorbate as the electron donor.

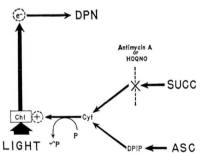

FIG. 6. Site of antimycin A or HOQNO inhibition in noncyclic photophosphorylation of *R. rubrum* chromatophores, with succinate as the electron donor. Electrons from ascorbate bypass [via 2,6-dichlorophenolindophenol (DPIP)] the site of inhibition. [From (32).]

1. PHENYLMERCURIC ACETATE

Smith and Baltscheffsky (74) found that phenylmercuric acetate (PMA) inhibited photophosphorylation by *R. rubrum* in the presence of substrate amounts of succinate. The inhibitory effect of PMA might have resulted either from inhibition of a site that is common to both the cyclic and noncyclic electron pathway in *R. rubrum* (as is the case with antimycin A on HOQNO) or from inhibition of a site that is peculiar to the noncyclic electron pathway. Nozaki *et al.* (*32*) obtained evidence in favor of the second possibility. PMA completely inhibited noncyclic electron flow in *R. rubrum* chromatophores at concentrations which gave only partial inhibition of the cyclic electron flow.

2. *p*-Chloromercuribenzoate

This sulfhydryl group inhibitor, which was cited earlier as inhibiting cyclic photophosphorylation, also inhibits noncyclic photophosphorylation in chloroplasts when TPN is used as the electron acceptor (*90*). This is consistent with the evidence (*91*) that *p*-chloromercuribenzoate inhibits the chloroplast pyridine nucleotide reductase, which is necessary for the photoreduction of TPN. *p*-Chloromercuribenzoate does not inhibit the noncyclic electron flow where the pyridine nucleotide reductase is not involved; for example, the Hill reaction with benzoquinone as the hydrogen acceptor (*76*).

3. 2-Alkyl-4-hydroxyquinoline

Inhibition by quinoline-*N*-oxide (HOQNO) compounds has already been discussed under cyclic photophosphorylation (Section V, A, 2). Avron (*77*) has recently reported that 2-heptyl-4-hydroxyquinoline-*N*-oxide and 2-nonyl-4-hydroxyquinoline-*N*-oxide are very effective inhibitors of noncyclic photophosphorylation in isolated chloroplasts when the electron acceptor is ferricyanide. The inhibition was less pronounced when TPN was the electron acceptor and almost nonexistent in cyclic photophosphorylation with phenazine methosulfate as the catalyst.

By analogy with the effect of substituted ureas (Section A, 1), Avron (*77*) ascribed the inhibitory effect of HOQNO to the suppression of oxygen evolution. However, it is difficult to account on this basis for the greater inhibition of the noncyclic photophosphorylation with ferricyanide than with TPN; in his experiments oxygen evolution occurred in both cases.

VI. INHIBITORS OF ATP FORMATION

In this category special interest centers on uncouplers, i.e., agents which at appropriate concentrations inhibit ATP formation and either stimulate or do not affect electron transport. In oxidative phosphorylation by mitochondria, uncouplers, particularly dinitrophenol, have been widely used for separating the electron flow in respiration (measured by oxygen uptake) from its normally associated phosphorylation. The application of true uncouplers to photosynthetic phosphorylation became possible only with the discovery of noncyclic photophosphorylation (9). Only then could a light-induced electron flow be uncoupled from its normally associated phosphorylation and be measured independently either by oxygen evolution or by the reduction of the terminal electron acceptor.

Noncyclic photophosphorylation afforded the first experimental demonstration that phosphorylation is, in fact, coupled with a light-induced electron flow in photosynthesis. Prior to this, the proposed (92) dependence of photosynthetic phosphorylation on a light-induced electron flow was a hypothesis, supported only by analogy with the electron flow and its coupled phosphorylation in respiration and glycolysis. There was no experimental evidence then linking ATP formation with an experimentally demonstrable, light-induced, electron flow in isolated chloroplasts, e.g., a Hill reaction.

A. Dinitrophenol and Other Substituted Phenols

Oxidative phosphorylation by mitochondria is completely uncoupled by 5×10^{-5} M dinitrophenol (cf. review, 71), a concentration at which dinitrophenol does not affect photosynthetic phosphorylation at all, either cyclic or noncyclic. In the first phosphorylation experiments with chloroplasts (30), strong inhibition of ATP formation was obtained only at a dinitrophenol concentration of about 10^{-3} M, a concentration that is high by comparison with oxidative phosphorylation. This was also found to be the case for chromatophores of $R.$ $rubrum$ (31, 45, 73). In later experiments with chloroplasts (65) even this high concentration of dinitrophenol was ineffective in inhibiting cyclic photophosphorylation catalyzed by phenazine methosulfate or menadione.

Although dinitrophenol may be classified as a weak inhibitor of photosynthetic phosphorplation, the evidence speaks against its being an uncoupler in this process. When, at high concentrations, dinitrophenol inhibits ATP formation with TPN (90) or ferricyanide (93), it also inhibits to the same degree the electron flow (measured by oxygen evolution or the photoreduction of TPN or ferricyanide). The failure of dinitrophenol to act as an uncoupler of photosynthetic phosphorylation shows that this process resembles more closely the substrate-level phosphorylation in glycolysis than the oxidative phosphorylation in mitochondria.

Krogmann *et al.* (*93*) have shown a parallel case for another uncoupler of oxidative photophosphorylation, pentachlorophenol. It also acts not as an uncoupler but as an inhibitor of noncyclic photophosphorylation. It inhibits equally electron flow and ATP formation.

The earlier literature on the effects of dinitrophenol on photosynthesis in whole cells has been reviewed elsewhere (*94*). A more recent contribution is that of Simonis and Urbach (*95*), who have reported that in cells of the green alga *Ankistrodesmus braunii* concentrations of dinitrophenol which inhibit oxidative phosphorylation in the dark do not inhibit photosynthetic phosphorylation in the light. They have concluded that the two phosphorylation processes in the green cell are independent of each other, a view that is in accord with phosphorylation experiments on subcellular particles of green leaves [Arnon (*90*)].

The difference between the effect of dinitrophenol on photosynthetic and oxidative phosphorylation is underlined by the unexpected finding of Wessels (*96*), which places nitrophenols, and several other aromatic nitro and nitroso compounds, among catalysts of cyclic photophosphorylation that can act in a manner similar to that of FMN or vitamin K. The optimal concentration of dinitrophenol for catalyzing cyclic photophosphorylation under anaerobic conditions was about 3×10^{-4} M. The catalytic activity of nitrophenols is apparently due to the photoreduction of these compounds to the corresponding nitrosophenols (*97*).

B. Arsenate

Arsenate has long been known to disrupt phosphorylation reactions by substituting for phosphate and thus causing the formation of unstable arsenyl compounds in place of the physiologically stable phosphoryl intermediate. This is clearly exemplified by the uncoupling effect of arsenate on the substrate-level phosphorylation which accompanies the oxidation of glyceraldehyde-3-phosphate (*98*). Crane and Lipmann (*99*) have shown that arsenate may also replace phosphate, and thus act as an uncoupler, in oxidative phosphorylation by mitochondria.

Krogmann, Avron, and Jagendorf (*93, 100*) concluded that arsenate acts as an uncoupler of the noncyclic photophosphorylation that is linked with ferricyanide reduction. At a concentration of arsenate which seriously inhibited ATP formation, electron flow (ferricyanide reduction) remained unaffected. However, it should be noted that in these experiments high concentrations of arsenate (3.3×10^{-2} M) were required to give a marked inhibition of phosphorylation; 10^{-2} M arsenate had almost no effect. In the presence of ADP and Mg^{++}, arsenate stimulated ferricyanide reduction while inhibiting phosphorylation, thus showing under these conditions a common feature of uncouplers: a stimulation of electron flow concomitant with a suppression of phosphorylation.

C. Ammonia

Krogmann, Jagendorf, and Avron (93) discovered that ammonium ion at a concentration of about 10^{-3} M is an effective uncoupler of noncyclic photophosphorylation with ferricyanide, i.e., ATP formation was inhibited, while ferricyanide reduction was increased. The phosphorylation was restored by washing the ammonium salt out. The effect was specific for ammonium ions and was not shared, at similar concentrations, by potassium, sodium, calcium, or magnesium ions. Good (101) has reported a similar uncoupling effect by a number of amines.

Trebst et al. (22) have extended the investigation of the uncoupling effect of ammonia to noncyclic photophosphorylation linked with TPN reduction and to cyclic photophosphorylation. In the presence of ammonia, phosphorylation was suppressed and the carboxylative and reductive phases of CO_2 assimilation, both of which depend on ATP formation, were sharply curtailed (22).

An inhibitory effect of ammonium sulfate on mitochondrial respiration, as measured by oxygen uptake, was reported by Gatt and Racker (102). High concentrations of ammonia (2.5×10^{-1} M) greatly reduced the rate of respiration, and at these concentrations phosphorylation was more sharply reduced than oxygen uptake. Racker (71) has therefore classified ammonia as a weak uncoupler of oxidative phosphorylation.

The marked difference between the uncoupling effect of ammonia on oxidative and photosynthetic phosphorylation deserves stressing. In photosynthetic phosphorylation ammonia inhibits ATP formation at a relatively low concentration without inhibiting the uncoupled electron flow, which, in fact, is increased (93). The way in which ammonia uncouples photosynthetic phosphorylation cannot be now satisfactorily explained.

D. Atebrin

Baltscheffsky found that atebrin, often used as a flavin antagonist in inhibiting electron flow in oxidative phosphorylation, inhibits cyclic photophosphorylation in R. rubrum (103) and in chloroplasts (79). The inhibition occurred in the presence of phenazine methosulfate or menadione. Thus, in the case of atebrin inhibition, in contrast to antimycin A and HOQNO, phenazine methosulfate failed to provide in bacterial chromatophores a bypass around the site of inhibitor action.

In *R. rubrum* atebrin inhibition was completely overcome by the addition of FAD but only partly by the addition of FMN (*103*). In chloroplasts, however, atebrin inhibition was not reversed by high concentrations of flavin nucleotide. Here, in fact, FAD ($2 \times 10^{-2}\ M$) gave almost complete, and FMN ($5 \times 10^{-3}\ M$) partial, inhibition of photophosphorylation (*79*).

On the basis of these results, Baltscheffsky has assigned to flavins the role of obligatory electron carriers in photosynthetic phosphorylation. However, in recent experiments in this laboratory, Losada, Mitsui, and Paneque have found that in chloroplasts atebrin is not an inhibitor of electron flow but is an effective uncoupler of photophosphorylation. Atebrin suppressed ATP formation without inhibiting the photoreduction of TPN or ferricyanide. Atebrin also inhibited cyclic photophosphorylation catalyzed by one of several cofactors, including phenazine methosulfate.

The assessment of the significance of the uncoupling effect of atebrin on cyclic and noncyclic photophosphorylation in chloroplasts must await further experimentation. If atebrin is indeed a specific flavin antagonist in electron transport, then the failure of atebrin to inhibit electron flow in noncyclic photophosphorylation by chloroplasts would argue against the participation of flavins in that pathway. However, as Hemker and Hülsmann (*104*) have recently stressed, atebrin is not a specific flavin antagonist.

E. Valinomycin

McMurray and Begg (*105*) found that low concentrations of the antibiotic valinomycin uncoupled oxidative phosphorylation in animal mitochondria. Baltscheffsky (*106*) investigated the effects of this antibiotic on photosynthetic phosphorylation in chromatophores and chloroplasts with the following results.

Low concentrations of valinomycin gave a partial inhibition of the endogenous cyclic photophosphorylation in chromatophores of *R. rubrum*. At higher concentrations of valinomycin the inhibition leveled off at around 50%. Valinomycin gave no significant inhibition of the bypass pathway, i.e., when cyclic photophosphorylation was catalyzed by phenazine methosulfate. By contrast, in chloroplasts, low concentrations of valinomycin gave no significant inhibition of cyclic photophosphorylation, whether it was catalyzed by phenazine methosulfate, menadione, FMN, or FAD.

Baltscheffsky (*106*) interpreted these findings as supporting the existence of two sites of ATP formation in bacterial cyclic photophosphorylation, only one of which is sensitive to valinomycin inhibition—hence, the leveling off of the inhibition at 50%. Phenazine methosulfate, by providing a bypass around the valinomycin sensitive site, would catalyze a cyclic photophosphorylation pathway with only a single site for photophosphorylation that is resistant to valinomycin inhibition. Likewise, in chloroplasts, Baltscheffsky (*106*) explains the resistance to valinomycin inhibition by the existence of only a single, valinomycin-resistant phosphorylation site which operates whether the system is catalyzed by vitamin K or FMN or phenazine methosulfate.

The existence of more than one phosphorylating site in the endogenous cyclic photophosphorylation of chromatophores is supported by other lines of evidence (*106*). However, Baltscheffsky's suggestion that cyclic photophosphorylation in isolated chloroplasts has always only one site of ATP formation runs counter to other evidence (*5*). Although no final conclusions are possible at this time, it seems likely that in chloroplasts as in chromatophores the cyclic electron flow is normally coupled with more than one site of ATP formation and that in both types of particles, phenazine methosulfate provides a "shortcut" which bypasses one or more phosphorylation sites.

VII. CONCLUDING REMARKS

The use of selective inhibitors in subcellular particles of photosynthetic cells has served as an important tool in testing and elucidating proposed mechanisms for the component reactions of photosynthesis. Certain inhibitors of photosynthesis come close to meeting the biochemist's specifications for an ideal inhibitor; they selectively inhibit, at very low concentrations, a well-defined component reaction of the over-all process.

A case in point is the inhibition of oxygen evolution by substituted ureas. They inhibit the oxygen evolution component of photosynthesis in chloroplasts, and, accordingly, they inhibit noncyclic photophosphorylation in chloroplasts only when it is coupled with oxygen evolution. At low concentrations they do not inhibit noncyclic photophosphorylation in chloroplasts when it is modified experimentally so that oxygen evolution is prevented; neither do they inhibit noncyclic photophosphorylation in bacterial particles in which oxygen evolution never occurs.

In another instance the use of inhibitors was found helpful in evaluating alternative proposals for the mechanism of noncyclic photophosphorylation. Chance and Olson (*106a*) proposed that the photoreduction of pyridine nucleotide may be driven by ATP, formed by photophosphorylation. However, this proposal is rendered unlikely, since ammonia or atebrin uncouples photophosphorylation; thus, electron transport, resulting in TPN reduction, occurs in the presence of ammonia or atebrin when ATP formation, either by cyclic or noncyclic photophosphorylation, is excluded.

In the case of oxygen evolution the enzyme(s) concerned is still unknown. But in other cases the action of the inhibitor on photosynthesis in subcellular particles is in good agreement with its action on photosynthesis in the intact cell and can also be traced to the selective inhibition of a single enzyme. For example, the inhibitory action of cyanide on photosynthesis can now be accounted for by its inhibition of ribulose di-P carboxylase, even if cyanide were to inhibit secondarily other enzymes within or without the chloroplast or chromatophore. In other cases, although the photosynthetic component affected by the inhibitor is not known for certain, the site of inhibition may be defined and marked for further investigation by comparing its effect with the known action of the same inhibitor in other systems. For example, the inhibitory effect of antimycin A on photophosphorylation in chromatophores strongly supports the conclusion that cytochromes of the b and c type participate in the photosynthetic electron transport chain to which ATP formation is coupled.

Perhaps the most significant conclusion to which this survey leads is that the action of inhibitors on the partial reactions of chloroplasts and chromatophores adds substantial support to the proposed mechanisms of photosynthetic phosphorylation—a process of energy conversion that is a common denominator of photosynthesis in green plants and photosynthetic bacteria (*5, 107*).

REFERENCES

1. E. Rabinowitch, "Photosynthesis and Related Processes," Vol. I, 1945. Vol. II, Part 2, 1956. Interscience, New York.
2. M. G. Stålfelt, *in* "Handbuch der Pflanzenphysiologie" (W. Ruhland, ed.), Vol. V, Part 2, p. 152. Springer, Berlin, 1960.
3. K. A. Clendenning, *in* "Handbuch der Pflanzenphysiologie" (W. Ruhland, ed.), Vol. VI, Part 1, p. 761. Springer, Berlin, 1958.
4. D. I. Arnon, *Bull. Torrey Botan. Club* 88, 215 (1961).
5. D. I. Arnon, *in* "Light and Life" (W. D. McElroy and B. Glass, eds.), p. 489. Johns Hopkins Press, Baltimore, Maryland, 1961.
6. M. Calvin, *Science* 130, 1170 (1959).

7. W. Vishniac, B. L. Horecker, and S. Ochoa, *Advances in Enzymol.* **19**, 1 (1957).

8. J. R. Quayle, *Ann. Rev. Microbiol.* **15**, 119 (1961).

9. D. I. Arnon, F. R. Whatley, and M. B. Allen, *Science* **127**, 1026 (1958).

10. A. T. Jagendorf, *Brookhaven Symposia Biol.* **11**, 236 (1958).

11. M. Losada, F. R. Whatley, and D. I. Arnon, *Nature* **190**, 601 (1961).

12. D. I. Arnon, M. Losada, F. R. Whatley, H. Y. Tsujimoto, D. O. Hall, and A. A. Horton, *Proc. Natl. Acad. Sci. U.S.* **47**, 1314 (1961).

13. S. Ruben, *J. Am. Chem. Soc.* **65**, 279 (1943).

14. K. V. Thimann, *Science* **88**, 506 (1938).

15. F. Lipmann, *Advances in Enzymol.* **1**, 148 (1941).

16. J. R. Quayle, R. C. Fuller, A. A. Benson, and M. Calvin, *J. Am. Chem. Soc.* **76**, 3610 (1954).

17. A. Weissbach, B. L. Horecker, and J. Hurwitz, *J. Biol. Chem.* **218**, 795 (1956).

18. W. B. Jakoby, D. O. Brummond, and S. Ochoa, *J. Biol. Chem.* **218**, 811 (1956).

19. E. Racker, *Arch. Biochem. Biophys.* **69**, 300 (1957).

20. M. Calvin, *Proc. 3d Intern. Congr. Biochem., Brussels, 1955*, p. 211 (1956).

21. J. Hurwitz, A. Weissbach, B. L. Horecker, and P. Z. Smyrniotis, *J. Biol. Chem.* **218**, 769 (1956).

22. A. V. Trebst. M. Losada, and D. I. Arnon, *J. Biol. Chem.* **235**, 840 (1960).

23. N. Calo and M. Gibbs, *Z. Naturforsch.* **15b**, 287 (1960).

24. W. Simonis and G. Weichart, *Z. Naturforsch.* **13b**, 694 (1958).

25. O. Kandler, I. Liesenkotter, and B. A. Oaks, *Z. Naturforsch.* **16b**, 50 (1961).

25a. R. B. Park, N. G. Pon, K. P. Louvrier, and M. Calvin, *Biochim. et Biophys. Acta* **42**, 27 (1960).

26. M. Gibbs and N. Calo, *Plant Physiol.* **34**, 318 (1959).

27. M. Gibbs and N. Calo, *Biochim. et Biophys. Acta* **44**, 341 (1960).

28. O. Warburg, *Biochem. Z.* **100**, 230 (1919).

29. A. V. Trebst, H. Y. Tsujimoto, and D. I. Arnon, *Nature* **182**, 351 (1958).

30. D. I. Arnon, M. B. Allen, and F. R. Whatley, *Nature* **174**, 394 (1954).

31. A. W. Frenkel, *J. Am. Chem. Soc.* **76**, 5568 (1954).

32. M. Nozaki, K. Tagawa, and D. I. Arnon, *Proc. Natl. Acad. Sci.* **47**, 1314 (1961).

33. A. V. Trebst, M. Losada, and D. I. Arnon, *J. Biol. Chem.* **234**, 3055 (1959).

34. M. Avron and A. T. Jagendorf, *Nature* **179**, 428 (1957).

35. M. Avron, A. T. Jagendorf, and M. Evans, *Biochim. et Biophys. Acta* **26**, 262 (1957).

36. A. T. Jagendorf and M. Avron, *J. Biol. Chem.* **231**, 277 (1958).

37. M. Avron and A. T. Jagendorf, *J. Biol. Chem.* **234**, 1315 (1959).

38. A. T. Jagendorf, *Federation Proc.* **18**, 974 (1959).

39. J. S. C. Wessels, *Biochim. et Biophys. Acta* **25**, 97 (1957).

40. J. S. C. Wessels, *Biochim. et Biophys. Acta* **29**, 113 (1958).

41. C. T. Chow and B. Vennesland, *Plant Physiol.* **32**, Suppl., iv (1957).

42. T. Nakamoto, D. W. Krogmann, and B. Vennesland, *J. Biol. Chem.* **234**, 2783 (1959).

592 M. LOSADA AND D. I. ARNON

43. R. Hill and D. A. Walker, *Plant Physiol.* **34**, 240 (1959).

44. F. R. Whatley, M. B. Allen, A. V. Trebst, and D. I. Arnon, *Plant Physiol.* **35**, 188 (1960).

45. D. H. Geller, Photophosphorylation by *Rhodospirillum rubrum* Preparations, Doctoral Dissertation, Div. Med. Sci., Harvard University (1957).

46. A. M. Williams, *Biochim. et Biophys. Acta* **19**, 570 (1956).

47. M. Kamen and J. W. Newton, *Biochim. et Biophys. Acta* **25**, 462 (1957).

48. I. C. Anderson and R. C. Fuller, *Arch. Biochem. Biophys.* **76**, 168 (1958).

49. J. B. Thomas and A. M. Haans, *Biochim. et Biophys. Acta* **18**, 286 (1955).

50. B. Petrack and F. Lipmann, *in* "Light and Life," (W. D. McElroy and B. Glass, eds.), p. 621. Johns Hopkins Press, Baltimore, Maryland, 1961.

51. D. I. Arnon, *Nature* **184**, 10 (1959).

52. D. I. Arnon, M. Losada, M. Nozaki, and K. Tagawa, *Nature* **190**, 601 (1961).

52a. W. Arnold and R. K. Clayton, *Proc. Natl. Acad. Sci. U.S.* **46**, 769 (1960).

53. L. N. M. Duysens, J. Amesz, and B. M. Kamp, *Nature* **190**, 510 (1961).

54. H. Gaffron, *Biol. Revs.* **19**, 1 (1944).

55. H. Gaffron, *J. Gen. Physiol.* **28**, 269 (1945).

56. A. Frenkel, H. Gaffron, and E. H. Battley, *Biol. Bull.* **97**, 269 (1949).

57. O. Warburg, "Heavy Metal Prosthetic Groups and Enzyme Action," Oxford Univ. Press (Clarendon), London and New York, 1944.

58. D. I. Arnon and F. R. Whatley, *Arch. Biochem.* **23**, 141 (1949).

59. J. S. C. Wessels and R. van der Veen, *Biochim. et Biophys. Acta* **19**, 548 (1956).

60. J. D. Spikes, *Plant Physiol.* **31**, Suppl., xxxii (1956).

61. N. I. Bishop, *Biochim. et Biophys. Acta* **27**, 205 (1958).

62. L. P. Vernon and W. S. Zaugg, *J. Biol. Chem.* **235**, 2728 (1960).

63. L. P. Vernon and O. K. Ash, *J. Biol. Chem.* **235**, 2721 (1960).

64. A. T. Jagendorf and M. Avron, *Arch. Biochem. Biophys.* **80**, 246 (1959).

65. F. R. Whatley, M. B. Allen, and D. I. Arnon, *Biochim. et Biophys. Acta* **32**, 32 (1959).

66. A. V. Trebst and H. Eck, *Z. Naturforsch.* **16b**, 455 (1961).

67. A. T. Jagendorf and M. Margulies, *Arch. Biochem. Biophys.* **90**, 184 (1960).

68. B. Vennesland, T. Nakamoto, and B. Stern, *in* "Light and Life," (W. D. McElroy and B. Glass, eds.), p. 609. Johns Hopkins University Press, Baltimore, Maryland, 1961.

69. A. R. Krall, N. E. Good, and B. C. Mayne, *Plant Physiol.* **36**, 44 (1961).

70. B. Chance and G. R. Williams, *Advances in Enzymol.* **17**, 65 (1956).

71. E. Racker, *Advances in Enzymol.* **23**, 323 (1961).

72. F. L. Jackson and J. W. Lightbown, *Biochem. J.* **69**, 3 (1958).

73. D. M. Geller and F. Lipmann, *J. Biol. Chem.* **235**, 2478 (1960).

74. L. Smith and M. Baltscheffsky, *J. Biol. Chem.* **234**, 1575 (1959).

75. H. Baltscheffsky and M. Baltscheffsky, *Acta Chem. Scand.* **12**, 1333 (1958).

76. D. I. Arnon, M. B. Allen and F. R. Whatley, *Biochim. et Biophys. Acta* **20**, 449 (1956).

77. M. Avron, *Biochem. J.* **78**, 735 (1961).
78. H. Baltscheffsky, *Acta Chem. Scand.* **13**, 2130 (1959).
79. H. Baltscheffsky, *Acta Chem. Scand.* **14**, 264 (1960).
80. H. Rudney, *J. Biol. Chem.* **236**, PC39 (1961).
81. D. E. Green, *in* "Quinones in Electron Transport," Ciba Foundation Symposium (G. E. Wolstenholme and C. M. O'Connor, eds.), p. 130. Little, Brown, Boston, Massachusetts, 1960.
82. H. Baltscheffsky and M. Baltscheffsky, *Acta Chem. Scand.* **14**, 257 (1960).
83. J. D. Judah and G. Williams-Ashman, *Biochem. J.* **48**, 33 (1951).
84. J. A. Barltrop, P. M. Hayes, and M. Calvin, *J. Am. Chem. Soc.* **76**, 4348 (1954).
85. R. A. Peters, H. M. Sinclair, and R. S. Thompson, *Biochem. J.* **40**, 516 (1946).
86. I. C. Gunsalus, *J. Cellular Comp. Physiol.* **41**, Suppl., 113 (1953).
87. W. W. Wainio and S. J. Cooperstein, *Advances in Enzymol.* **17**, 329 (1956).
88. J. H. McClendon, *Am. J. Botany* **40**, 260 (1953).
89. R. Hill, *Proc. 3rd Intern. Congr. Biochem., Brussels, 1955* p. 225 (1956).
90. D. I. Arnon, F. R. Whatley, and M. B. Allen, *Biochim. et Biophys. Acta* **32**, 47 (1959).
91. A. San Pietro and H. M. Lang, *J. Biol. Chem.* **231**, 211 (1958).
92. D. I. Arnon, *Science* **122**, 9 (1955).
93. D. W. Krogmann, A. T. Jagendorf, and M. Avron, *Plant Physiol.* **34**, 272 (1959).
94. D. I. Arnon, *Ann. Rev. Plant Physiol.* **7**, 325 (1956).
95. W. Simonis and W. Urbach, *Z. Naturforsch.* **15b**, 816 (1960).
96. J. S. C. Wessels, *Biochim. et Biophys. Acta* **36**, 264 (1959).
97. J. S. C. Wessels, *5th Intern. Congr. Biochem. Moscow, 1961. Symposium No. VI.*
98. O. Warburg and W. Christian, *Biochem. Z.* **303**, 40 (1939).
99. R. K. Crane and F. Lipmann, *J. Biol. Chem.* **201**, 235 (1953).
100. M. Avron and A. T. Jagendorf, *J. Biol. Chem.* **234**, 967 (1959).
101. N. Good, *Biochim. et Biophys. Acta* **40**, 502 (1960).
102. S. Gatt and E. Racker, *J. Biol. Chem.* **234**, 1015 (1959).
103. H. Baltscheffsky, *Biochim. et Biophys. Acta* **40**, 1 (1960).
104. H. C. Hemker and W. C. Hülsmann, *Biochim. et Biophys. Acta* **44**, 175 (1960).
105. W. C. McMurray and R. W. Begg, *Arch. Biochem. Biophys.* **84**, 546 (1959).
106. H. Baltscheffsky, *in* "Biological Structure and Function" (T. W. Goodwin and O. Lindberg, eds.), p. 431. Academic Press, New York, 1961.
106a. B. Chance and J. M. Olson, *Arch. Biochem. Biophys.* **88**, 54 (1960).
107. R. Y. Stanier, *Bacteriol. Revs.* **25**, 1 (1961).

CHAPTER 36

Inhibitors of Nitrogen Fixation

Clive Bradbeer and P. W. Wilson

I. INTRODUCTION

Early investigation of biological nitrogen fixation furnished results that strongly suggested interference with the process by combined forms of nitrogen, such as ammonia or nitrates. Historically then, these may be regarded as the first observed specific inhibitors, but it should be recognized that unequivocal data with these substances, especially data concerned with the quantitative aspects, were not obtained until the tracer N^{15} became available. Since, in the meantime, several gases had been shown to be important inhibitors, our discussion will begin with them.

II. MOLECULAR GASES AS INHIBITORS

A. Hydrogen

While studying the effect of the physicochemical environment on red clover plants inoculated with an effective strain of *Rhizobium trifolii*, workers at the University of Wisconsin established that molecular hydrogen acted as a specific competitive inhibitor of nitrogen fixation by this symbiotic system. Wilson (*1–3*) has furnished complete and detailed discussions of this early research. *Specific* is used here in the sense that the criteria proposed by Burk (*4*) were met, although Wilson (*2*) later suggested that insistence on rigid application of these criteria might be not only too limiting but also illogical. The criteria are:

(1) Comparative studies should include cultures growing, and likewise previously grown, in free and fixed nitrogen.
(2) Different forms of combined nitrogen should be used, such as nitrate (oxidized), ammonia (reduced), asparagine (organic).
(3) Differences obtained with free and fixed nitrogen should be interpreted with due allowance for unspecific effects caused by differences in rates and amounts of growth.
(4) N_2 at times should be replaced with an inert gas to demonstrate its true necessity in relation to some process claimed to be specific.

At first, it appeared that this inhibition was uniquely associated with the symbiotic system (and possibly only with that in red clover), but in 1941 Wyss and Wilson (*5*) extended the observations to *Azotobacter*. This discovery had far-reaching effects; now studies could be readily and rapidly made in the laboratory, whereas with the symbiotic system time-consuming, laborious greenhouse experiments had been necessary. Soon these studies included some made with cell-free enzyme preparations (hydrogenase), constituting a great advance in the technique. Of the many investigations that have been made during the past 20 years, two types will be discussed here: (*a*) those dealing with the comparative biochemistry of the inhibition, i.e., its occurrence among the agents known to fix nitrogen, together with an analogous reaction, the inhibition of hydrogen evolution by molecular nitrogen and (*b*) the biochemical basis of the inhibition.

1. OCCURRENCE OF H_2 INHIBITION IN VARIOUS AGENTS OF N_2 FIXATION

Burris and Wilson (*6*) obtained evidence that nitrogen fixation by the blue-green alga, *Nostoc muscorum*, could be inhibited by H_2, but the effect appeared to be less definite than that observed with species of *Azotobacter* and with the red clover system. This difference undoubtedly was due to the slow rate and extent of fixation by the alga. For this reason criterion 3 must be considered in interpreting the results. However, this limitation was overcome in part by use of N^{15} as a tracer, thus allowing for relatively short-time experiments. Thus, as early as 1946, it had been demonstrated that nitrogen fixation by representatives of all the aerobic agents known at that time was competitively inhibited by molecular hydrogen. Attempts to extend the findings to the anaerobic fixer *Clostridium pasteurianum* were unsuccessful when rates as well as extent of fixation were considered (7). This result did not appear to be surprising, since the organism produces H_2 in its fermentation of carbohydrates, and it would appear to be a metabolic error for it to form a product that would inhibit a function seemingly so advantageous as nitrogen fixation. This reasoning appeared to be confirmed when Gest *et al.* (8) could detect no hydrogen inhibition of nitrogen fixation by the photosynthetic nitrogen fixer, *Rhodospirillum rubrum*.

In 1957, however, Hiai *et al.* (9) reported inhibition by hydrogen of nitrogen fixation in an anaerobe isolated from a soil in Japan. Although originally this organism was believed to be a species of *Clostridium*, Hino and Wilson (10) concluded that it probably was *Bacillus polymyxa*, a view supported by the survey made by Grau and Wilson (11). Pengra and Wilson (12) extended this important observation to another facultative anaerobe, *Aerobacter aerogenes*. Recently, Pratt and Frenkel (13), using a sensitive recording mass spectrographic technique, readily demonstrated hydrogen inhibition of nitrogen fixation by *R. rubrum*. Meanwhile, Shug *et al.* (14) obtained spectroscopic evidence of competition between H_2 and N_2 in an enzyme preparation from *C. pasteurianum*.

The results of these various investigations suggested that another look at the clostridia was in order. Westlake and Wilson (15) found that inhibition of nitrogen fixation by hydrogen in the strain previously used by Rosenblum and Wilson (7) could be detected when relatively high partial pressures of hydrogen were used. The observed value of K_{H_2} was considerably higher than those noted in the other systems (red clover, *Azotobacter vinelandii*, *B. polymyxa*). Nevertheless, when careful control was exerted, inhibition could be observed in experiments in which either total nitrogen or the isotopic tracer was used as the measure of fixation. Also, Goerz and Pengra (16) report definite inhibition by H_2 of nitrogen fixation by *Achromobacter* sp. which even anaerobically does not evolve this gas.

2. Effect of N_2 on H_2 Evolution

From the point of view of the mechanism of H_2 inhibition of nitrogen fixation it is important to determine the existence of the "reverse" reaction, i.e., the effect of N_2 on enzyme systems involving H_2. During the more than 20 years that we have studied hydrogenase activity in cell-free preparations of *Azotobacter*, this point has been repeatedly investigated.

Although some evidence of inhibition has been obtained occasionally, it has been neither impressive nor consistent. As will be discussed later, technical errors may account for the occasional positive results obtained. Likewise, the data of Stadtman and Barker (*17*) suggest that N_2 does not affect hydrogenase in the anaerobic nitrogen fixer, *Clostridium kluyveri*.

Mortenson and Wilson (*18*) investigated the effect of N_2 on a reaction carried out by *C. pasteurianum*—the so-called phosphoroclastic split of pyruvate with the liberation of H_2 and CO_2. Evolution of H_2 was the same when helium, argon, or nitrogen was used as the inert gas, but hydrogen inhibited, as had been previously observed by Kubowitz with *Clostridium butyricum* (*19*). However, photoevolution of H_2 by the photosynthetic nitrogen fixers *R. rubrum* and *Chromatium* sp. can be suppressed by molecular nitrogen (*20, 21*). Hoch *et al.* (*22*) observed a more complicated relationship between the two gases in the excised nodules of the soybean; N_2 inhibited H_2 evolution but stimulated the exchange reaction (see next section).

Hino (*23*) reported an inhibition by nitrogen of hydrogen production from glucose by washed cells of *B. polymyxa*; no inhibition occurred with pyruvate or formate as substrates. To date, attempts to repeat these observations in our own laboratory have been unsuccessful. Hydrogen evolution by washed cells metabolizing mannitol, glucose, pyruvate, or formate was the same under helium as under nitrogen. The inhibition reported by Hino seems to be associated with a lag phase before hydrogen evolution becomes maximal. This lag may be a recovery from an oxygen poisoning occurring during cell washing. In our experiments this lag has been much shorter—only a few minutes. For example, Hino (*23*, fig. 7) obtains only about 50 μl hydrogen evolved after 60 minutes; under the same conditions we observed 4–5 times this quantity. When the gases were not further purified, N_2 often showed a slightly longer lag period than did helium. However, on sparging through chromous chloride, hydrogen evolution under nitrogen and under helium did not differ. By using growing cultures rather than washed cells the influence of oxygen might be lessened and the effect of nitrogen observed more easily, but again, in our hands, nitrogen did not inhibit hydrogen evolution.

Another example of a technical error that can mislead was obtained by our studies in which evolution of H_2 was followed in a mass spectrometer. A measured volume of growing cells was shaken under various gas mixtures of helium and nitrogen; gas samples were taken at hourly intervals and examined in the mass spectrometer. Cultures of *B. polymyxa*, grown on N_2 and ammonia, *C. pasteurianum* and *A. aerogenes*, grown on N_2, and *Escherichia coli*, grown on glucose-peptone-beef extract, were examined by this technique. In all organisms, the rate of hydrogen and carbon dioxide evolution was decreased by nitrogen; a pN_2 of one atmosphere inhibited about 50%. However, when these experiments were repeated using a manometric technique, no inhibition of hydrogen evolution could be detected. It was then established that the apparent inhibition obtained in the mass spectrometer arose from an effect of nitrogen or helium on the peak heights of hydrogen and carbon dioxide.

3. MECHANISM OF H_2 INHIBITION

Two explanations of the action of H_2 on nitrogen fixation, one purely physical, the second physiological, have been experimentally examined. If H_2 and N_2 compete physically for a site on an enzyme surface associated with the fixation reaction, then the ratio of the dissociation constants K_{H2}/K_{N2}, should approximate that of the corresponding van der Waals' constants a. This was found to be true, both being equal to 5.5 (24). However, this purely physico chemical explanation does not appear to be sufficient, since an examination of other gases with appropriate a constants reveals no activity (25).

A hypothesis that has been more experimentally fruitful is that nitrogenase and hydrogenase, the specific enzymes for activation of molecular nitrogen and hydrogen, respectively, are related. Considerable evidence has been reported in favor of this view:

1. Species of the strictly aerobic *Azotobacter* contain a powerful hydrogenase, although normally it does not evolve or utilize H_2 in its metabolism.

2. The level of hydrogenase in species of *Azotobacter* is consistently higher when the organism is grown on N_2 than when grown on combined types, such as ammonia or nitrate, even in the presence of H_2. Hydrogenase thus appears to be a quantitatively inducible enzyme which responds to the presence of N_2 rather than H_2. However, even in the absence of N_2 some hydrogenase appears.

3. Mutants of *Azotobacter* unable to fix nitrogen ("N_2-less") have a lowered content of hydrogenase.

4. The following agents of fixation are known to contain a hydrogenase: *Azotobacter* spp., *Clostridium* spp., *A. aerogenes*, *B. polymyxa*, *Methanobacterium omelianskii*, *Desulfovibrio desulfuricans*, and all the photosynthetic bacteria. Its presence in the nitrogen-fixing blue-green algae is obscure, but at least some blue-green species are known to have the enzyme (26).

5. As has been discussed, N_2 inhibits the activity of hydrogenase in some, though not all, agents of fixation.

A thorough discussion of the experimental bases for these conclusions can be found in the reviews of Gest (27) and Wilson (28). Although the supporting evidence is impressive, certain reservations must be admitted. Certainly, the relationship is not complete, since many organisms possessing hydrogenase apparently cannot fix N_2 (29); also, the mineral requirements for functioning of the two enzyme systems appear to differ (30).

It is not clear that all organisms that do fix nitrogen possess hydrogenase. Inability to demonstrate the enzyme, however, is not always convincing, since the various methods for its assay do not give concordant results. No one method has been demonstrated to be completely reliable, although the physical methods—the exchange reaction between D_2 and H_2 and that involving the ortho-para interconversion of H_2—would appear to be least subject to error. Surprisingly, these do not always indicate the maximum activity in a specific organism (31, 32).

The oustanding example of the limitations imposed by the methodology is that of the symbiotic system. Although hydrogen inhibits fixation by the intact red clover plant (1) as well as by excised nodules from the soybean (33), attempts to demonstrate a hydrogenase in either the free, living cultures of the root nodule bacteria or in nodular preparations met with failure. Hamilton et al. (34) obtained spectroscopic evidence for a hydrogenase in preparations from the soybean nodules, a demonstration that was soon confirmed by Hoch et al. (35), who obtained under appropriate conditions evolution of H_2 from such preparations.

Finally, it should be emphasized that hydrogenase and nitrogenase may be associated in some but not in all agents of fixation. In view of the diversity in the physiological properties of the many organisms now known to fix nitrogen, it would be surprising if precisely the same enzymic patterns were found in all.

B. Carbon Monoxide

Unlike hydrogen, which is qualitatively a specific inhibitor of biological nitrogen fixation, inhibition by carbon monoxide is specific in a quantitative sense only. Low concentrations of carbon monoxide (0.01–1%), which inhibit nitrogen fixation, have virtually no effect on the utilization of combined forms of nitrogen; higher concentrations, however, inhibit the utilization of both free and combined nitrogen.

1. INHIBITION IN VARIOUS AGENTS

a. *Symbiotic Systems.* Lind and Wilson (36) demonstrated inhibition of nitrogen fixation in red clover with as little as 0.01% of carbon monoxide;

almost complete inhibition was obtained with 0.05%. Uptake of ammonium nitrate was unaffected by these levels of carbon monoxide; but when the CO concentration was raised to 0.05–2%, small decreases in the rate of uptake of the combined nitrogen were observed. However, 2% carbon monoxide gave only a 25% decrease in the specific rate constant for the assimilation of ammonium nitrate, whereas 68% inhibition of nitrogen fixation was obtained with 0.05% CO.

More recently, Bond (37) has shown that the symbiotic nitrogen fixation systems in excised nodules from the nonlegumes, *Alnus* and *Myrica*, are inhibited by both hydrogen and carbon monoxide. The observed sensitivity of these systems to the inhibitors was of the same order as that of legume nitrogen fixation. Nodules from *Casuarina* behaved similarly towards hydrogen, but the effect of carbon monoxide on nitrogen fixation by this plant was not reported. Although the microbial partner in these nonlegume symbioses has yet to be identified, the essential biochemical similarity between the nitrogen fixation processes in legume and nonlegume nodules is stressed by similarities in behavior toward inhibitors and also by the recent demonstration of Davenport (38) that hemoglobin is also present in nonlegume nodules.

b. *Free-Living Aerobic Organisms*. Lind and Wilson (39) extended their studies to the nitrogen-fixing system of the free-living *Azotobacter*. This organism was more suitable for obtaining precise, detailed information on the nature of the carbon monoxide inhibition, since much greater control of the experimental conditions was possible and the experiments could be completed within a few hours, as compared with the months required in some of the red clover experiments. They observed inhibition of nitrogen fixation in *A. vinelandii* with 0.2% carbon monoxide; 0.6% seemed to be about the critical level of the inhibitor, since this concentration almost completely suppressed fixation of nitrogen but had little effect on the assimilation of ammonium nitrogen. Although the pCO necessary to inhibit nitrogen fixation by *A. vinelandii* is about ten times that effective with the symbiotic system, the responses of the two types of biological nitrogen fixation are parallel. Likewise, Burris and Wilson (6) found that the response of nitrogen fixation by *N. muscorum* to carbon monoxide is essentially the same as those observed with red clover and *A. vinelandii*; however, the levels that inhibit assimilation of N_2 but not combined nitrogen, are intermediate between the effective levels of the red clover and *Azotobacter* systems.

Investigating the sensitivity of the anaerobic nitrogen-fixing system of *C. pasteurianum* towards carbon monoxide, Virtanen *et al.* (40) reported about 80% inhibition of nitrogen fixation by 0.3% CO; this level had no appreciable effect on the uptake of ammonium nitrogen. Hino (41) noted that anaerobic fixation of nitrogen by an organism later identified as *B. polymyxa* was appreciably inhibited by 0.1% CO and almost completely inhibited by 1% CO; 50% inhibition was observed with 0.3–0.7% carbon monoxide, which is similar to the values reported by Lind and Wilson (39) for aerobic nitrogen fixation by *Azotobacter*. Uptake of ammonium nitrogen by the *Bacillus* was also inhibited but to a lesser extent, 50–60% inhibition obtaining in 1% CO. The inhibition of ammonium uptake was not further increased above this level, even in 100% CO.

2. Mechanism of CO Inhibition of Nitrogen Fixation

The type of inhibition which carbon monoxide exerts on nitrogen fixation has been investigated in red clover and in *Azotobacter*. Since carbon monoxide is an isostere of nitrogen, the inhibition might be regarded as a consequence of the competition between these two gases for adsorption on the surface of the responsible enzyme. Lind and Wilson (36) concluded from their studies with red clover plants that the inhibition by carbon monoxide is noncompetitive. More detailed studies were carried out by Ebersole et al. (42), who used the microrespiration method to investigate the nature of the CO inhibition of nitrogen fixation in *Azotobacter*. The results of over 40 experiments, in which both the pN_2 and the pCO were varied, were subjected to the appropriate mathematical analysis. When $1/k$ (k, the specific rate constant for nitrogen fixation) was plotted against $1/pN_2$, both the slope and the y intercept increased with the concentration of inhibitor, in agreement with the theory of noncompetitive inhibition. The slope, however, increased somewhat more than did the intercept, as was shown by the small but consistent rise in the K_{N_2}, suggesting a small amount of competitive inhibition. Consideration of all the data leads to the conclusion that the carbon monoxide inhibition of biological nitrogen fixation is primarily noncompetitive, but that there is also an element of competitive inhibition.

Obviously, any discussion of carbon monoxide inhibition of nitrogen fixation should consider the possible role of hemoglobin in the symbiotic system. Virtanen et al. (43) have shown that a close correlation exists between the nitrogen-fixing capacity of a plant and the hemoglobin concentration in its root nodules. The high sensitivity of the symbiotic nitrogen fixation system towards carbon monoxide is in keeping with the high affinity of hemoglobin for carbon monoxide. Although substantial evidence is available that hemoglobin participates in some way in nitrogen fixation in root nodules, there is disagreement regarding its precise role. Burris and Wilson (44) suggested that hemoglobin may aid in oxygen transport within the nodule and thus enhance nitrogen fixation by increasing the respiratory activity. Smith (45) rejected this proposal when he found that concentrations of carbon monoxide which completely inhibited nitrogen fixation and which were sufficient to convert all the pigment to CO-hemoglobin did not affect the respiratory activity of the whole nodules. Spectrographic observations (46, 47) of preparations from soybean nodules under various gases have led Bergersen (48) to propose a mechanism for symbiotic nitrogen fixation in which hemoglobin functions as an intermediary electron carrier in the coupling of nodule respiration to nitrogen fixation. The hemoglobin is reduced by reduced cytochrome and then becomes reoxidized during the reduction of nitrogen in the fixation process.

The absence of hemoglobin from the cells of the free-living nitrogen fixers, *Azotobacter*, *Clostridium*, and *Nostoc*, may be related to the lower sensitivity toward carbon monoxide of the nitrogen-fixing systems in these agents. The function of hemoglobin in the nodules may be replaced in these by some other compound which has a lower affinity for carbon monoxide.

C. Oxygen

Burk (49) made the first quantitative investigation of the effect of O_2 on biological nitrogen fixation. He found that growth of the *Azotobacter* was maximal at 2–4% oxygen and decreased with both higher and lower partial pressures. Since this effect of O_2 was independent of the source of nitrogen, he concluded that the oxygen pressure function furnished no clues regarding the nature of the chemical mechanism of nitrogen fixation. In a similar study, Wilson and Fred (50) showed that neither fixation of free nitrogen nor assimilation of combined nitrogen by red clover plants is significantly affected by changes in the pO_2 between 0.05 and 0.4 atmospheres. On either side of this plateau in the pO_2 function the uptake of either free or combined nitrogen declined rapidly with changes in the oxygen pressure. These studies likewise gave no support for the suggestion that oxygen may play a direct role in the symbiotic nitrogen fixation process. More recently, Burris et al. (51) demonstrated that no significant incorporation of N_2^{15} by slices of excised soybean nodules occurs at partial pressures of oxygen below 0.05 atmosphere. Fixation increased with increasing pO_2 until a maximum was reached at about 0.5 atmosphere. Above 0.65 atmosphere, oxygen became increasingly inhibitory. As might be expected, oxygen also inhibits the nitrogen fixation process in the anaerobic nitrogen fixers. Pratt and Frenkel (13) found that 4% oxygen completely inhibits nitrogen fixation by *R. rubrum*, and Hino and Wilson (*10*) reported that nitrogen fixation by *B. polymyxa* is significantly reduced by 1% oxygen.

In spite of the earlier negative conclusion of Burk (*49*), Parker (*52*) has reinvestigated the possibility of a specific oxygen inhibition of nitrogen fixation by *A. vinelandii*. Parker and Scutt (*53*) measured the growth of this organism with N_2 as the sole source of nitrogen under oxygen concentrations of 10, 20, and 30%, and under nitrogen concentrations of 2, 4, 8, and 16%. By assuming that the growth of the *Azotobacter* was exponential throughout their experiments and that nitrogen fixation was the limiting rate reaction, they calculated the velocity constant k, the specific rate constant of nitrogen fixation. When $1/k$ was plotted against $1/pN_2$ at 10% and at 20% oxygen, the resulting two lines had different slopes but essentially the same intercept on the vertical axis, indicating a competitive inhibition by oxygen. The Michaelis constants were 0.0107 atmospheres N_2 at 10% oxygen and 0.0229 at 20% oxygen. Higher oxygen tensions had, in addition to the specific effect on nitrogen fixation, a general effect on growth. At about 30% O_2, some mechanism other than nitrogen fixation was inhibited sufficiently to become a limiting factor for growth, and this nonspecific effect masked the competitive inhibition of nitrogen fixation by O_2. On the basis of these results, Parker and Scutt suggested that nitrogen fixation can be regarded as a form of respiration and that oxygen and nitrogen compete as alternative respiratory acceptors.

It should be noted that the effect of oxygen on biological nitrogen fixation may be only another aspect of the relationship of hydrogenase and nitrogenase. Hydrogenase activity in all organisms investigated is more or less sensitive to O_2, independent of their ability to fix nitrogen. If hydrogenase and nitrogenase are closely associated, the somewhat equivocal experimental results reported concerning the inhibition by oxygen may reflect an indirect effect.

D. Nitrous Oxide

Although the hypothesis being tested by Molnar *et al.* (*25*) failed to be substantiated, this research did provide an important positive finding—nitrous oxide was shown to be a specific inhibitor for nitrogen fixation by *A. vinelandii*. Since this compound is the anhydride of hyponitrous acid, an often-proposed intermediate, this result assumed particular significance. Following the initial discovery, Repaske and Wilson (*54*) demonstrated that the inhibition was competitive, a result confirmed independently by Wilson and Roberts (55, 56). Virtanen and Lundbom (57) extended the observations to the anaerobe C. butyricum (C. pasteuri-anum), and Hino (41) to the facultative aerobe later shown to be B. polymyxa.

The fact of inhibition is well established, but two important aspects have been subjects of dispute. Although all workers agree that uptake of ammonium nitrogen is unaffected by N_2O, Virtanen and Lundbom (57) in their long-term growth experiments with both A. vinelandii and C. butyricum reported an inhibition of the assimilation of nitrate nitrogen similar to that noted with N_2. Because of the implication of this result for the chemical mechanism, a joint experiment was made by Virtanen, Burris, and their co-workers (58) in which a short-time manometric technique was used—a method that enables the estimation of rates, as well as final total uptake, of different forms of nitrogen. In these trials with A. vinelandii no inhibition of assimilation of nitrate nitrogen by N_2O was observed. This result was confirmed using the tracer N^{15}; again, rate as well as total assimilation was measured. Lundbom (59) later published what might be regarded as a minority report in which con-firmation of the earlier inhibition was claimed. No explanation for the difference between the short-time and long-term experiments was offered. In general, as has been discussed elsewhere (2, 4, 28, 60), the short-time trial in which rate of reaction is measured is to be preferred for study of biochemical mechanisms including the action of inhibitors.

A second point at issue, significant for the chemical mechanism, is whether nitrogen-fixing agents can use N_2O as a source of nitrogen. In total nitrogen macroexperiments Lind and Wilson (39) could detect no uptake. Employing the more sensitive manometric technique, Wilson and Roberts (56) reached a similar conclusion. This result was verified in experiments in which cells of Azotobacter were labeled with N^{15} and then exposed to unlabeled N_2O. Mozen and Burris (61, 62), however, did detect a small but consistent uptake by this organism as well as by sliced soy-bean nodules when labeled N_2O was supplied. Assimilation of N_2O by A. vinelandii was inhibited both by N_2 and H_2 (62). The explanation, at least with the nodules, may be that the N_2O is first converted to N_2; interestingly, also, N_2O as well as N_2 inhibits evolution of H_2 by the nodules (22).

Finally, mention should be made of the limited information on hyponi-trite itself. From their studies of the influence of this compound on respi-ration and nitrogen fixation in A. vinelandii, Chaudhary et al. (63) concluded that hyponitrous acid is an irreversible noncompetitive inhibi-tor, which is not specific for fixation. Since it was not utilized by the

Azotobacter, they rejected the view that it is a direct intermediate in the assimilation of N_2.

E. Nitric Oxide

Mozen (*64*) found that 0.1–1% nitric oxide completely blocked nitrogen fixation by *C. pasteurianum*. This inhibition was not specific for nitrogen fixation, since the same level of the inhibitor prevented growth of the organisms on ammonia. Burris (*62*) has suggested, however, that nitric oxide should be studied further at even lower concentrations than 0.1%, to discover whether a level can be reached at which it will exhibit a specific inhibition of nitrogen fixation, since like carbon monoxide it has a high affinity for hemoglobin (*65*) and is a powerful inhibitor of hydrogenase (*66*).

III. COMBINED NITROGEN COMPOUNDS AS INHIBITORS

A. Ammonia and Nitrate

As was previously mentioned, early workers postulated that little or no assimilation of molecular nitrogen occurred either symbiotically or asymbiotically in the presence of combined inorganic nitrogen; there was less certainty regarding organic forms (for reviews of early work see *1, 67*). Because of their agronomic importance, most of the early studies were primarily concerned with the effects of ammonium and nitrate. Later, the interest in this question shifted to the significance of the results for the chemical mechanism (*2, 28*).

Burk and Lineweaver (*68*) in 1930 made an estimate of the quantitative aspects of inhibition of nitrogen fixation in *Azotobacter* by NH_4^+ and NO_3^-. They emphasized the obvious technical limitations of the early studies; with the improved methodolgy afforded by short-time trials in the microrespirometer, they constructed a curve which indicated that 5–10 ppm of either ion would inhibit completely nitrogen fixation by this organism. Wilson and co-workers (*69, 70*) introduced the use of an isotopic tracer, which greatly improved the reliability of the results but led to essentially the same conclusion with regard to ammonia. Nitrate (or nitrite), however, in reasonably high concentrations (50–100 ppm) was much less effective. Inhibition by urea was practically the same as with ammonia; asparagine was only partially inhibitory; aspartate and glutamate were without effect. They concluded that inhibition by a source of combined nitrogen depended on the readiness of its conversion to ammonia. Zelitch (71) found that ammonia inhibition of the assimilation of N_2 by C. pasteurianum, although marked, was incomplete even with 20 ppm combined nitrogen. The isotopic inhibition experiments thus provided initial support for the view that ammonia was the key intermediate in biological nitrogen fixation (for discussion of this aspect, see 62, 70).

B. Nitrite

Although nitrite has long been regarded as the initial reduction product of nitrate, little attention has been directed toward a possible specific action of this ion, except to note its toxicity in rather low concentrations in comparison with its precursor (60, 72). More recently, Azim and Saraf (73) have provided evidence that nitrite is indeed an intermediate in reduction of nitrate by A. vinelandii, and Azim and Roberts (74) demonstrated that, at concentrations above 10^{-4} M, nitrite inhibited both respiration and nitrogen fixation. Lower concentrations had virtually no effect on the rate of respiration but markedly stimulated nitrogen fixation. In these experiments, in which the total fixation after 4 hours was determined, the lower the concentration of nitrite (down to 10^{-7} M) the higher the stimulation of nitrogen fixation. In a more detailed study of the inhibition by 10^{-5} M nitrite, Roberts (75) showed that during the first half hour, during which the cells utilized the nitrite, nitrogen fixation was inhibited. After 30 minutes, however, no nitrite was left in the medium; and at the end of 4 hours, the fixation of nitrogen had been stimulated 40% in comparison with the controls which had not been supplied with nitrite. This stimulation resembles that observed by Green and Wilson (76), who found that the hydrogenase activity of A. vinelandii supplied with ammonia or nitrate was lower than that in nitrogen-fixing cultures. However, when the supply of combined nitrogen was exhausted and these cultures began fixing nitrogen, the hydrogenase activity was stimulated to a level well above that in cultures which had been fixing nitrogen throughout. These results provide another example of the parallelism that has been noted on several occasions between the activities of hydrogenase and nitrogenase in nitrogen-fixing organisms.

C. Hydroxylamine

Hydroxylamine is of interest as a possible inhibitor of nitrogen fixation, since it, too, has often been postulated to be an intermediate in the fixation process (*1, 2, 28*). Several workers (*77–79*) have studied the effect of this compound on the growth of *A. vinelandii*; the data suggest that *A. vinelandii* cannot utilize hydroxylamine, nor is it a specific inhibitor. From these results, together with those from an investigation of the exchange reaction between N_2 and NH_2OH, Pethica *et al.* (*80*) rejected the suggestion that nitrogen fixation in legumes can occur by a reversal of the reaction between NH_2OH and hemoglobin (for further discussion of this point see ref. *81*).

D. Hydrazine

Bach's (*82*) proposal that hydrazine rather than hydroxylamine is a more likely intermediate in biological nitrogen fixation has led to renewed interest in its role as an inhibitor. For some time it had been regarded merely as a nonspecific toxic reagent (*83*). More recently, Azim and Roberts (*84*) have shown that at hydrazine concentrations below 2×10^{-5} *M*, nitrogen fixation was stimulated, although some inhibition of respiration occurred. However, at higher concentrations which completely suppressed nitrogen fixation, only 40% inhibition of respiration was obtained. These results suggest that nitrogen fixation is not entirely governed by the respiratory rate. The *Azotobacter* cells were apparently unable to utilize the hydrazine as a source of nitrogen, and Roberts (*75*) has reported that the disappearance of hydrazine from the culture medium is due to its sequestration by some compound produced by the bacterium. After removal of the bacterial cells from the culture medium by centrifugation, almost 100% of the hydrazine could be recovered from the supernatant liquid following acid hydrolysis. The sequestrating agent has still to be identified, though it is not pyruvate or a-ketoglutarate.

IV. METABOLIC INHIBITORS

Initial studies on the mechanism of biological nitrogen fixation in the early 1930's included examination of many of the common metabolic inhibitors (*60, 85*). Among these were KCN, NaF, NaN_3, H_2S, $KClO_3$, $SnCl_2$, oxalate, iodoacetate, sulfite, benzoate, urethan, selenate, and toluene. Since almost without exception no specific influence on assimilation of N_2 was detected, this approach was discontinued. In recent years, with a better understanding of their mode of action and with the availability of new inhibitors, interest has been revived.

Hino (41) has reported that cyanide, azide, monoiodoacetate, p-chloromercuribenzoate, and o-phenanthroline were powerful inhibitors of a clostridial nitrogen-fixing system, although this inhibition was apparently nonspecific. A more detailed investigation has been carried out by Rakestraw and Roberts (86), who compared azide inhibition of nitrogen fixation by A. vinelandii with that of cyanate and nitrous oxide. Azide was found to be a specific, reversible inhibitor of nitrogen fixation, and is apparently not utilized by the organism—a type of inhibition qualitatively similar to that of nitrous oxide. Quantitatively, however, azide is a much more powerful inhibitor of nitrogen fixation than nitrous oxide and is, of course, a well-known general inhibitor of metal-enzyme systems. In contrast, cyanate, which has similar physical properties to those of azide, i.e., similar bond lengths, molecular shape, and electron distribution, is a weak, nonspecific, noncompetitive, irreversible inhibitor of nitrogen fixation. From these great differences of behavior among such physically similar molecules as nitrous oxide, azide, and cyanate, Rakestraw and Roberts point out the dangers of postulating similar biological activity from purely structural and dimensional similarities of compounds. Furthermore, they suggest that the view that the inhibition of nitrogen fixation by these compounds is due to their physical similarity to the nitrogen molecule should be reconsidered.

Carnahan et al. (87) have searched for further examples of selective inhibitors of nitrogen fixation with the purpose of using them to identify substances involved in the fixation process. The compounds were tested for specific action on nitrogen fixation by comparing their relative growth-restricting effects on parallel cultures of C. pasteurianum growing on nitrogen gas and on ammonia. Compounds which restricted growth in nitrogen-fixing cultures but not in ammonia-assimilating cultures were tentatively accepted as specific inhibitors of nitrogen fixation. Six such specific compounds were found. They are lipoic acid, 3-(6-carboxyhexyl)-1,2-dithiolane, dihydrolipoic acid, 1,2-diacetylethylene, N,N'-dioctylacetamidine, and trichloromethylsulfenyl benzoate. The first five apparently attacked components of the nitrogen-fixing system that depend upon biotin, since the inhibition by these five compounds could be relieved by added biotin. The inhibition by the sixth compound could be counteracted by sodium molybdate. It was of interest that this compound also inhibited hydrogenase activity, and this inhibition was also reversed by sodium molybdate.

The interesting inhibition of nitrogen fixation and nitrate reduction by tungstate (*88, 89*), acting as an antagonist for molybdenum, provides what should be a valuable tool for study of the mode of action of the latter metal on nitrogen fixation. This type of inhibition recalls the early observations with oxalate, whose inhibitory action was ascribed to precipitation of the calcium ion (*60*). Oxalate might be useful for investigations of one of the perennial questions in this field: Is calcium uniquely required for nitrogen fixation? (*90, 91*).

Finally, mention should be made of perhaps the least-expected influence whose action might be regarded as that of an inhibitor—meteorological conditions (*92*). Full discussion of the claims regarding this would take us too far afield, but the interested reader may find such a discussion together with relevant bibliography in the paper by Jensen (*93*).

V. RETROSPECT AND PROSPECT

The progress made on preparation of cell-free enzyme systems capable of fixing nitrogen (*94–96*) and the prospects of success in applying new methods of analysis, such as the ultraviolet-visible scanning and electron spin resonance spectrometers (*46, 47, 97*), for use with these preparations suggest that one era in this research is about over and that a new, exciting one is beginning.

Mortenson *et al.* (*98*) demonstrated that nitrogen fixation by cell-free extracts of *C. pasteurianum* was sensitive to the phosphate ion, an optimum being observed at 0.01–0.02 M. Lockshin's (*99*) data indicated that when the concentration of phosphate was sufficiently high to induce a lag in fixation, the inhibition by H_2 was uncompetitive; however, the inhibition was competitive when the phosphate concentration was low, so that a linear time course was obtained. This finding is of special interest in view of the recent claim that H_2 inhibition in growing cultures of *A. vinelandii* is noncompetitive (*100*).

Investigating the effect of CO on the components of the cell-free system, Mortenson *et al.* (*101*) found that treatment of the hydrogen-donating component produced only a temporary, reversible lag in fixation, whereas treatment of the nitrogen-activating component resulted in an irreversible decrease in the rate of fixation. CO inhibited hydrogenase, but apparently had no effect on the pyruvate metabolism as measured by reduction of methylene blue. Mortenson *et al.* (*98*) likewise observed that CO did not affect the activity of the recently discovered electron carrier, ferredoxin. Lockshin's (*99*) investigations of the clostridial system revealed that CO inhibited N_2 fixation competitively in contrast with results reported earlier with red clover and *Azotobacter*, but in agreement with the observations on the blue-green alga, *Nostoc muscorum;* also, both N_2O and NO inhibited competitively. McNary and Burris (*102*) reported that arsenate was a potent inhibitor of nitrogen fixation by the cell-free system from the clostridia; Grau and Wilson (*103*) noted a similar result using a preparation of *B. polymyxa*. Details of these and other studies of the effect of inhibitors on the cell-free systems are provided in the authoritative summaries recently compiled (*101, 104, 105*).

In retrospect, it appears that the chief contribution of the various studies discussed in the text has been the information they have furnished for construction of schemes for the physicochemical mechanism of this biological process. From the proposals of Wilson and Burris (*81*) in 1947 through Winfield's (*106*) provocative discussion in 1955 to the recent stimulating speculations of the late Norman Bauer (*107*), the observations made regarding the action of H_2, N_2O, CO, $NH_4{}^+$, and others have provided the flesh to clothe the various skeletons.

In prospect, it appears to be a safe prediction that, with the new tools and agents available, future researches will discard, modify, refine, and extend our present ideas arising from the inhibition studies and that new schemes for the enzymic mechanisms will be forthcoming, based on additional and more exact data. A second prediction is that this attractive new edifice already beginning to take shape will likely be supported by the foundations of the past research discussed here.

REFERENCES

1. P. W. Wilson, "Biochemistry of Symbiotic Nitrogen Fixation." University of Wisconsin Press, Madison, Wisconsin, 1940. (Out of print, but obtainable in microfilm from University Microfilms, Ann Arbor, Michigan.)
2. P. W. Wilson, *in* "Bacterial Physiology" (C. H. Werkman and P. W. Wilson, eds.), pp. 483–488. Academic Press, New York, 1951.
3. P. W. Wilson, *in* "Perspectives and Horizons in Microbiology" (S. A. Waksman, ed.), pp. 110–120. Rutgers Univ. Press, New Brunswick, New Jersey, 1955.
4. D. Burk, *Proc. 2nd Intern. Congr. Microbiol., London*, 1937 pp. 264–265.
5. O. Wyss and P. W. Wilson, *Proc. Natl. Acad. Sci. U.S.* 27, 162 (1941).
6. R. H. Burris and P. W. Wilson, *Botan. Gaz.* 108, 254 (1946).
7. E. D. Rosenblum and P. W. Wilson, *J. Bacteriol.* 59, 83 (1950).
8. H. Gest, M. D. Kamen, and H. M. Bregoff, *J. Biol. Chem.* 182, 153 (1950).
9. S. Hiai, T. Mori, S. Hino, and T. Mori, *J. Biochem. (Tokyo)* 44, 839 (1957).
10. S. Hino and P. W. Wilson, *J. Bacteriol.* 75, 403 (1958).
11. F. Grau and P. W. Wilson, *J. Bacteriol.* 83, 490 (1962).
12. R. M. Pengra and P. W. Wilson, *J. Bacteriol.* 75, 21 (1958).

13. D. C. Pratt and A. W. Frenkel, *Plant Physiol.* **34**, 333 (1959).
14. A. L. Shug, P. B. Hamilton, and P. W. Wilson, in "Inorganic Nitrogen Metabolism" (W. D. McElroy and B. Glass, eds.), pp. 344–360. Johns Hopkins Press, Baltimore, Maryland, 1956.
15. D. W. S. Westlake and P. W. Wilson, *Can. J. Microbiol.* **5**, 617 (1959).
16. R. D. Goerz and R. M. Pengra, *Bacteriol. Proc.* p. 13 (1960).
17. E. R. Stadtman and H. A. Barker, *J. Biol. Chem.* **181**, 221 (1949).
18. L. E. Mortenson and P. W. Wilson, *J. Bacteriol.* **62**, 513 (1951).
19. F. Kubowitz, *Biochem. Z.* **274**, 285 (1934).
20. H. Gest and M. D. Kamen, *Science* **109**, 558 (1949).
21. J. W. Newton and P. W. Wilson, *Antonie van Leeuwenhoek J. Microbiol. Serol.* **19**, 71 (1953).
22. G. E. Hoch, K. C. Schneider, and R. H. Burris, *Biochim. et Biophys. Acta* **37**, 273 (1960).
23. S. Hino, *J. Biochem. (Tokyo)* **47**, 482 (1960).
24. D. Burk and R. H. Burris, *Ann. Rev. Biochem.* **10**, 587 (1941).
25. D. M. Molnar, R. H. Burris, and P. W. Wilson, *J. Am. Chem. Soc.* **70**, 1713 (1948).
26. A. Frenkel, H. Gaffron, and E. H. Battley, *Biol. Bull.* **99**, 157 (1950).
27. H. Gest, *Bacteriol. Revs.* **18**, 43 (1954).
28. P. W. Wilson, in "Handbuch der Pflanzenphysiologie" (W. Ruhland, ed.), Vol. VIII, pp. 9–47, Springer, Berlin, 1958.
29. E. S. Lindstrom, S. M. Lewis, and M. J. Pinsky, *J. Bacteriol.* **61**, 481 (1951).
30. D. J. D. Nicholas, D. J. Fisher, W. J. Redmond, and M. Wright, *J. Gen. Microbiol.* **22**, 191 (1960).
31. H. D. Peck, Jr., and H. Gest, *J. Bacteriol.* **71**, 70 (1956).
32. A. I. Krasna and D. Rittenberg, *Proc. Natl. Acad. Sci. U.S.* **42**, 180 (1956).
33. R. H. Burris, in "A Conference on Radioactive Isotopes in Agriculture," pp. 361–369, U. S. Government Printing Office, Washington, D. C. (1956). AEC Report TID-7512.
34. P. B. Hamilton, A. L. Shug, and P. W. Wilson, *Proc. Natl. Acad. Sci. U.S.* **43**, 297 (1957).
35. G. E. Hoch, H. N. Little, and R. H. Burris, *Nature* **179**, 430 (1957).
36. C. J. Lind and P. W. Wilson, *J. Am. Chem. Soc.* **63**, 3511 (1941).
37. G. Bond, *J. Exptl. Botany* **11**, 91 (1960).
38. H. E. Davenport, *Nature* **186**, 653 (1960).
39. C. J. Lind and P. W. Wilson, *Arch. Biochem.* **1**, 59 (1942).
40. A. I. Virtanen, H. Mustakallio, and H. Strandström, *Suomen Kemistilehti* **26B**, 6 (1953).
41. S. Hino, *J. Biochem. (Tokyo)* **42**, 775 (1955).
42. E. R. Ebersole, C. Guttentag, and P. W. Wilson, *Arch. Biochem.* **3**, 399 (1944).
43. A. I. Virtanen, J. Erkama, and H. Linkola, *Acta Chem. Scand.* **1**, 861 (1947).
44. R. H. Burris and P. W. Wilson, *Biochem. J.* **51**, 90 (1951).
45. J. D. Smith, *Biochem. J.* **44**, 591 (1949).
46. P. B. Hamilton, A. L. Shug and P. W. Wilson, *Proc. Natl. Acad. Sci. U.S.* **43**, 297 (1957).

47. F. J. Bergersen and P. W. Wilson, *Proc. Natl. Acad. Sci. U.S.* 45, 1641 (1959).
48. F. J. Bergersen, *Bacteriol. Revs.* 24, 246 (1960).
49. D. Burk, *J. Phys. Chem.* 34, 1195 (1930).
50. P. W. Wilson and E. B. Fred, *Proc. Natl. Acad. Sci. U.S.* 23, 503 (1937).
51. R. H. Burris, W. E. Magee and M. K. Bach, *in* "Biochemistry of Nitrogen," Virtanen Homage Volume, pp 190–199. Helsinki, 1955.
52. C. A. Parker, *Nature* 173, 780 (1954).
53. C. A. Parker and P. B. Scutt, *Biochim. et Biophys. Acta* 38, 230 (1960).
54. R. Repaske and P. W. Wilson, *J. Am. Chem. Soc.* 74, 3101 (1952).
55. T. G. G. Wilson and E. R. Roberts, *Chem. & Ind. (London)* p. 87 (1952).
56. T. G. G. Wilson and E. R. Roberts, *Biochim. et Biophys. Acta* 15, 568 (1954).
57. A. I. Virtanen and S. Lundbom, *Acta Chem. Scand.* 7, 1223 (1953).
58. M. M. Mozen, R. H. Burris, S. Lundbom, and A. I. Virtanen, *Acta Chem. Scand.* 9, 1232 (1955).
59. S. Lundbom, *Acta Chem. Scand.* 12, 589 (1958).
60. D. Burk, *Ergeb. Enzymforsch.* 3, 23 (1934).
61. M. M. Mozen and R. H. Burris, *Biochim. et Biophys. Acta* 14, 577 (1954).
62. R. H. Burris, *in* "Inorganic Nitrogen Metabolism" (W. D. McElroy and B. Glass, eds.), pp. 316–343. Johns Hopkins Press, Baltimore, Maryland, 1956.
63. M. T. Chaudhary, T. G. G. Wilson, and E. R. Roberts, *Biochim. et Biophys. Acta* 14, 507 (1954).
64. M. M. Mozen, Ph.D. Thesis, University of Wisconsin (1955).
65. J. Keilin, *Biochem. J.* 59, 571 (1955).
66. A. I. Krasna and D. Rittenberg, *Proc. Natl. Acad. Sci. U.S.* 40, 225 (1954).
67. C. K. Horner and F. E. Allison, *J. Bacteriol.* 47, 1 (1944).
68. D. Burk and H. Lineweaver, *J. Bacteriol.* 19, 389 (1930).
69. P. W. Wilson, J. F. Hull, and R. H. Burris, *Proc. Natl. Acad. Sci. U.S.* 29, 289 (1943).
70. R. H. Burris and P. W. Wilson, *J. Bacteriol.* 52, 505 (1946).
71. I. Zelitch, *Proc. Natl. Acad. Sci. U.S.* 37, 559 (1951).
72. P. W. Wilson and C. J. Lind, *J. Bacteriol.* 45, 219 (1943).
73. M. A. Azim and S. D. Saraf, *Biochim. et Biophys. Acta* 21, 321 (1956).
74. M. A. Azim and E. R. Roberts, *Biochim. et Biophys. Acta* 21, 308 (1956).
75. E. R. Roberts, *Symposium Soc. Exptl. Biol.* 13, 24–41 (1959).
76. M. Green and P. W. Wilson, *J. Bacteriol.* 65, 511 (1953).
77. R. Novak and P. W. Wilson, *J. Bacteriol.* 55, 517 (1948).
78. W. Segal and P. W. Wilson, *J. Bacteriol.* 57, 55 (1949).
79. B. A. Pethica, E. R. Roberts, and E. R. S. Winter, *Biochim. et Biophys. Acta* 14, 85 (1954).
80. B. A. Pethica, E. R. Roberts, and E. R. S. Winter, *J. Chem. Phys.* 18, 996 (1950).
81. P. W. Wilson and R. H. Burris, *Bacteriol. Revs.* 11, 41 (1947).
82. M. K. Bach, *Biochim. et Biophys. Acta* 26, 104 (1957).
83. D. Burk and C. K. Horner, *Naturwissenschaften* 23, 259 (1935).
84. M. A. Azim and E. R. Roberts, *Biochim. et Biophys. Acta* 21, 562 (1956).
85. P. W. Wilson, *Ergeb. Enzymforsch.* 8, 13 (1939).

86. J. A. Rakestraw and E. R. Roberts, *Biochim. et Biophys. Acta* 24, 555 (1957).
87. J. E. Carnahan, L. E. Mortenson, and J. E. Castle, *J. Bacteriol.* 80, 311 (1960).
88. H. Takahashi and A. Nason, *Biochim. et Biophys. Acta* 23, 433 (1952).
89. R. F. Keeler and J. E. Varner, *Arch. Biochem. Biophys.* 70, 585 (1957).
90. G. L. Bullock, J. A. Bush, and P. W. Wilson, *Proc. Exptl. Biol. Med.* 105, 26 (1960).
91. A. Jakobsons, E. A. Zell, and P. W. Wilson, *Arch. Mikrobiol.* 41, 1 (1962).
92. H. Bortels, *Zentr. Bakteriol. Parasitenk. Abt. II* 102, 129 (1940).
93. H. L. Jensen, *Plant and Soil* 2, 301 (1950).
94. J. E. Carnahan, L. E. Mortenson, H. F. Mower, and J. E. Castle, *Biochim. et Biophys. Acta* 38, 188 (1960).
95. K. C. Schneider, C. Bradbeer, R. N. Singh, L. C. Wang, P. W. Wilson, and R. H. Burris, *Proc. Natl. Acad. Sci. U.S.* 46, 726 (1960).
96. D. J. D. Nicholas and D. J. Fisher, *Nature* 186, 735 (1960).
97. D. J. D. Nicholas, P. W. Wilson, W. Heinen, G. Palmer, and H. Beinert, *Nature* 196, 433 (1962).
98. L. E. Mortenson, R. C. Valentine, and J. E. Carnahan, *J. Biol. Chem.* 238, 794 (1963).
99. A. Lockshin, M.S. Thesis, University of Wisconsin (1963).
100. C. A. Parker and M. J. Dilworth, *Biochim. et Biophys. Acta* 69, 152 (1963).
101. L. E. Mortenson, H. F. Mower, and J. E. Carnahan, *Bacteriol. Revs.* 26, 42 (1963).
102. J. E. McNary and R. H. Burris, *J. Bacteriol.* 84, 598 (1962).
103. F. H. Grau and P. W. Wilson, *J. Bacteriol.* 85, 446 (1963).
104. L. E. Mortenson, *in* "The Bacteria" (I. C. Gunsalus and R. Y. Stanier, eds.), Vol. III, pp. 119–166. Academic Press, New York, 1962.
105. J. E. Carnahan and J. E. Castle, *Ann. Rev. Plant Physiol.* 14, 125 (1963).
106. M. E. Winfield, *Rev. Pure Appl. Chem.* (*Australia*) 5, 217 (1955).
107. N. Bauer, *Nature* 188, 471 (1960).

CHAPTER 37

Inhibitors of Nitrification

H. Lees

I. INTRODUCTION

Nitrification is a process whereby the ammonium ion is converted to nitrate that takes place in all fertile soils. It is usually supposed, in soils of more-or-less neutral reaction at least, to be mediated by two types of microorganisms working sequentially: *Nitrosomonas* (which oxidizes the ammonium ion to nitrite) and *Nitrobacter* (which oxidizes the nitrite so formed to nitrate). These two genera constitute the classic group of "nitrifying organisms," and it is on these two that attention will be concentrated here. It should not be forgotten, however, that some nitrification, i.e., conversion of ammonium to nitrate, may be carried out by other organisms (*1, 2*), although it is usually assumed, perhaps wrongly, that the contribution of the "nonclassic" nitrifiers to the total nitrification in soil is quantitatively small.

Both *Nitrosomonas* and *Nitrobacter* are chemosynthetic autotrophic microorganisms, elaborating all their cellular material from carbon dioxide and using as a source of energy for the reductive assimilation of carbon dioxide the energy generated by the primary oxidation of ammonium to nitrite or of nitrite to nitrate. The processes may be outlined as in Eqs. (1)–(3), where Eq. (1) refers to *Nitrosomonas*, Eq. (2) to *Nitrobacter*, and Eq. (3) to the reductive assimilation of carbon dioxide common to both.

$$NH_4^+ + 1.5\,O_2 = NO_2^- + H_2O + 2\,H^+ + 66\,kcal \qquad (1)$$

$$NO_2^- + 0.5\,O_2 = NO_3^- + 17\,kcal \qquad (2)$$

$$CO_2 + H_2O + energy\ from\ (1)\ or\ (2) = CH_2O + O_2 \qquad (3)$$

$$(CH_2O\ represents\ cell\ material)$$

Nitrification may, therefore, be inhibited at either stage in two different ways: (a) The primary oxidation may be inhibited. In this case the oxidation will stop regardless of whether a large population of the appropriate organism is present in the system or not. (b) The reductive assimilation of carbon dioxide may be inhibited. In this case the oxidation will continue if a large population of the appropriate organism is present in the system but will virtually stop if the population is small. It so happens that the primary oxidation systems summarized in Eqs. (1) and (2) are currently more interesting biochemically than the assimilatory systems of Eq. (3), since it is in their abilities to carry out these inorganic oxidations with the production of negotiable energy (high energy phosphate bonds, for instance) that the organisms are distinctive if not unique. All autotrophes can carry out the reductive assimilation of carbon dioxide; this assimilation probably proceeds in *Nitrobacter*, partially at least, by the Calvin cycle (*3*), and there is little doubt that the same will be found true for *Nitrosomonas*. It therefore turns out that most recent biochemical studies on the inhibition of nitrification have been aimed at discovering selective inhibitors of the primary oxidation reactions, since the action of such inhibitors might be expected to throw light on the mechanisms of the primary oxidations. Very great interest also centers on the coupling mechanisms that must exist between Eqs. (1) and (3) and Eqs. (2) and (3). There are reasons for believing that Eq. (1) represents the generation of, at most, three high energy bonds while Eq. (2) represents the generation of probably not more than one. The operation of Eq. (3), however, requires an energy supply of some 120 kcal/carbon atom—a supply, in other words, of about a dozen high energy bonds. The coupling between primary oxidation and reductive assimilation must, therefore, be multistage and complex, but, as yet, there has been little opportunity to study the effects of inhibitors of this coupling, largely because no active cell-free extract of either organism has been available until recently. It may be confidently expected, however, that the use of selective inhibitors on the coupling mechanisms will yield information of great value; this is an area of autotrophic metabolism well worthy of exploration.

Another, nonacademic, reason for studying methods of inhibiting the nitrifiers, especially in their natural habitat, is that too intensive a nitrifying activity in a cropped soil may be disadvantageous. Although most plants thrive better on nitrate than on ammonium as a source of nitrogen, nitrate is easily leached down through soil profiles by rain water and thus removed from the reach of the plant roots. Ammonium, on the other hand, is held by the base exchange complexes of the soil and is not so susceptible to removal by leaching. The ammonium so held, however, is available to plants, since the respiratory activities of the roots generate hydrogen ions which can enter the base exchange complexes of the soil and there displace ammonium ions which are thus made available to the plant roots. Any cheap and reliable inhibitor of the nitrifiers that could be used in the field would thus almost certainly enhance the efficiency of utilization of nitrogenous fertilizers in tropical regions where rainfall and microbial activity are high.

There are two main ways in which nitrification, and the effects of various inhibitors of the process, have been studied. One is to study the process as it actually occurs in soil, and for this type of study the technique that has proved to be biochemically the most useful and adaptable is the "soil perfusion" or "soil percolation" technique (4–6). A solution of ammonium salts is percolated and repercolated through a column of soil that is kept in an aerated condition by air dragged through the column by the percolating solution. Small samples of the solution are taken from time to time and analyzed for ammonium ions, nitrite, and nitrate; these analyses show the course of the nitrification as it is proceeding in the soil column. Inhibitions of the process are followed by comparing the rate of nitrification in a soil percolated with a solution of ammonium salts containing inhibitor with the rate in a soil percolated with a similar solution free of inhibitor. If the soil is a "fresh" soil, i.e., one that has not recently carried out any appreciable nitrification, there is likely to be a lag period before any ammonium is nitrified because the nitrifying population is small; then small amounts of nitrite appear as the population of *Nitrosomonas* builds up. The appearance of this nitrite stimulates the growth of *Nitrobacter*, with consequent oxidation of the nitrite to nitrate. Thereafter, since the *Nitrobacter* population can usually oxidize the nitrite as fast as it is formed, the oxidation of the ammonium yields nitrate alone. When an appreciable population of nitrifiers has been built up in this way in a soil and the soil is repercolated with a fresh solution of ammonium salts, oxidation of ammonium to nitrate takes place without any lag period and usually at a linear rate, since the nitrifying population of the soil is as great as the soil will bear; such soils are said to be "stimulated," "enriched," or "bacteria saturated" (5, 6). It is also possible to remove the soil from the percolator after stimulation and follow nitrification in it by transferring samples to a Warburg vessel and observing oxygen uptakes in the presence of ammonium ions with or without the addition of any inhibitor under investigation (6).

This brief description of the technique has been based on the percolation of ammonium ions and the resultant build-up of populations of both *Nitrosomonas* and *Nitrobacter* in the soil. It is, however, possible to stimulate a soil to nitrite oxidation alone by percolating nitrite instead of ammonium; it is also possible to stimulate to ammonium oxidation alone by percolating ammonium salts in the presence of chlorate, which specifically inhibits the growth of *Nitrobacter* under such conditions (*vide infra*). The advantage of the technique in studies of inhibitors of nitrification is that inhibitions take place under conditions approximating those obtaining in the field, and it is thus of considerable practical value. On the other hand, there is no guarantee that any substance X, which is found to inhibit nitrification in a soil percolator, will necessarily inhibit nitrification as studied in pure cultures of the nitrifying organisms, since there is always the possibility that X is changed into some other compound Y in the soil by the activities of various soil organisms and that Y, not X, is the actual inhibitor.

Studies of inhibitors of nitrification in pure cultures of *Nitrosomonas* and *Nitrobacter* are free of this drawback but have the disadvantage that they are tedious to carry out. The organisms are slow to grow in pure culture, and *Nitrosomonas*, at least, apparently cannot at present be cultured continuously for long periods under strictly autotrophic conditions when it is pure.

This brief survey of techniques has been given in order to allow those not familiar with nitrification studies to assess the value of the different results presented here and as a map of the pitfalls for those who might be tempted to explore this particular area of biochemistry.

II. GENERAL INHIBITORS OF NITRIFICATION

Probably the earliest biochemical study proper on the nitrifying organisms was that carried out by Schloesing and Muntz (7–9), in which they showed unequivocally that nitrification in sewage and soil was a biological process. A column of quartz sand containing 2% lime was percolated with sewage. For the first 20 days of the experiment the ammonia content of the issuing fluid was the same as that running into the column; then nitrate began to appear in the issuing fluid and "sa quantité croissant très vite" soon replaced all ammonia. After 4 months of such percolation, during which all ammonia entering the column was steadily oxidized to nitrate during passage, a small dish of chloroform was placed on the top of the column and its vapor was forced down the column by a stream of air. For 15 days after this treatment a smell of chloroform persisted in the issuing fluid, and no further nitrate appeared, all ammonia entering the column now passing through unchanged. This state of affairs persisted for 2 months, and nitrification was not re-established until fresh soil suspension was poured into the column. This was a clear demonstration that the nitrifiers were inhibited or killed by the chloroform. Parallel experiments with samples of soil in closed vessels also showed that nitrification in soil itself was inhibited by chloroform vapor.

Warington, in a remarkable series of experiments that clarified a great deal of the gross physiology of the nitrifying organisms (10–13), showed that carbon disulfide, chloroform, and phenol were all inhibitory to nitrification. He also showed that light inhibited the second stage of nitrification and that crude mixed cultures of the nitrifiers exposed to light and supplied with ammonia accumulated only nitrite. The inhibitory action of light was subsequently noted by other workers; it may be due to some light-induced malfunctioning of a biologically active pigment system such as the cytochrome system known to be concerned in nitrite oxidation by *Nitrobacter*. Warington also showed that ammonia was inhibitory to *Nitrobacter*, a notion at first dismissed by Winogradsky (14) but later accepted (15). Of this very early work on inhibitors of nitrification, none is more significant than that of Munro (16), who investigated what substances could be nitrified by soil suspensions and waters from wells and rivers. Among the many substances he tested were ammonium thiocyanate and thiourea, prepared from the ammonium thiocyanate by heating. Whereas the ammonium thiocyanate was readily nitrified, thiourea was not: "After three seedings, and a period of trial extending over three years, we may conclude that thiocarbamide is not nitrifiable." Sixty years were to pass before the full significance of this conclusion was appreciated. Munro had, in fact, discovered the highly specific toxic effect of the thioureas on *Nitrosomonas*, later reinvestigated by Lees (17, 18), and Quastel and Scholefield (6).

Following the classic researches of Winogradsky on the autotrophic nature of *Nitrosomonas* and *Nitrobacter*, Winogradsky and Omeliansky (15, 19) published an investigation whose initial fame has been transmuted to notoriety. This purported to show that not only were *Nitrosomonas* and *Nitrobacter* independent of any external supply of organic materials but that they were actually inhibited by various organic compounds (e.g., glucose, peptone, urea, asparagine, glycerol, straw extract, etc.). As a result, there arose the belief, still expressed in textbooks, that the nitrifying organisms are "inhibited by organic matter." This belief is, in fact, quite unfounded: In the first place, the results of Winogradsky and Omeliansky would scarcely bear any modern statistical analysis; insofar as they show anything, they show only indications of some effect by some of the compounds tested. In the second place, nitrification takes place very readily in soils rich in organic matter, in sewage, and in dung heaps. Beijerinck (20), however, thought that exposure of *Nitrobacter* to certain organic substances caused a loss of nitrite-oxidizing power but did not necessarily kill the organisms.

Of all the different types of "organic material" that have been alleged to affect the nitrifiers, the following probably have the best-attested inhibitory actions.

Peptone. There is fairly general agreement that peptone is inhibitory to the growth of one or both of the nitrifiers (19–21). Beef infusion, or an alcohol extract thereof, was also found to be inhibitory by Beijerinck (20). Kingma Boltjes (21) showed that the inhibition by peptone was due to free amino acids therein, and the inhibitions noted by Beijerinck are presumably explicable on the same basis. Why free amino acids should have such an action is not clear. Possible explanations are: (a) they bind essential trace elements [this may explain the inhibitory action of histidine (18)], and (b) they specifically block some key reaction in the cells; a specific inhibition of glutamine synthetase presumably explains why methionine sulfoxide retards the growth of *Nitrosomonas* in the soil percolator (6). It is most unlikely that amino acids ever inhibit the nitrifiers under field conditions because amino acids (with the possible exceptions of threonine and methionine) are rapidly destroyed by soil microflora (22) and are normally found in soil and humus only in minute traces (23).

Glucose. Although Winogradsky and Omeliansky found glucose to be toxic to the nitrifiers, this conclusion has not been generally confirmed. Jensen (24) thought that, where glucose had been found toxic, the toxicity could probably be ascribed to the formation of mannose during autoclaving. Glucose sterilized by filtration he found not to be inhibitory to *Nitrosomonas* up to concentrations of 10%, whereas mannose was inhibitory at concentrations greater than 0.2%. The basis of the mannose inhibition is unknown.

Urea. Where urea has been found to be toxic (15, 25) to the nitrifiers, its action, at least on *Nitrobacter*, is explicable on the grounds that any urea solution is likely to contain traces of cyanate (26), which is now known (27) to be highly toxic to *Nitrobacter* and possibly to other organisms too (28).

Organic Acids. Simple organic acids, such as formate, acetate, and butyrate, have been found toxic to the nitrifiers by many independent workers (*15, 24, 25*), usually at fairly high (decimolar) concentrations. There is no known reason for the effect of the organic acids, although it might seem worth while to reinvestigate their action in order to ascertain whether they induce wasteful carboxylations in the organisms, as does succinic acid in the autotrophic green sulfur bacterium *Chlorobium* (*29*).

Urethans and Ammonia. Meyerhof (*25*) showed, with cultures of the nitrifiers, that various urethans were very inhibitory to substrate oxidation, and that *Nitrosomonas* was especially sensitive to mixtures of urethans. He suggested that the toxicity of the urethans was related to their lipid solubility, a conclusion that was supported by his finding that ammonium salts became more toxic to *Nitrobacter* as the pH was increased (i.e., as the concentration of lipid-soluble NH_3 rose and that of the lipid-insoluble NH_4^+ fell). Soil experiments (*6, 30*) have confirmed the inhibitory action of urethans, and it has been found, moreover, that ammonia oxidation by *Nitrosomonas* growing in a fresh soil is more sensitive to ethylurethan poisoning than is ammonia oxidation by *Nitrosomonas* already established in an enriched soil. It was therefore concluded that ammonia assimilation rather than ammonia oxidation was the process affected by the urethan (*6*). That ammonia toxicity, especially towards *Nitrobacter*, increases as the pH increases has recently been substantiated (*31, 32*).

Guanidine. Meyerhof's observation (*25*) that guanidine was highly toxic to the nitrifiers has been confirmed (*6*). The basis of its action is unknown, but it may well be similar to that of ammonia.

Borate. Borate presents a puzzle. Boullanger and Massol (*33*) found that ammonium borate was easily oxidized by *Nitrosomonas*, and they comment on the fact that salts usually looked on as antiseptics (fluoride and borate) are apparently not inhibitory to *Nitrosomonas*. Porteous and Lees (unpublished) found that 10^{-2} *M* borate increased the rate of nitrification in several tropical soils. On the other hand, Meyerhof (*25*) found that approximately 10^{-1} *M* borate inhibited oxidation by *Nitrobacter*. Recent work in the writer's laboratory has appeared to show that 5×10^{-3} *M* borate, whatever the effect of the ion in soil, inhibits growth of *Nitrosomonas* in enrichment cultures.

III. SPECIFIC INHIBITORS OF NITRIFICATION

The inhibitors considered so far are general ones; their action has revealed only the broad types of compounds to which the nitrifiers are sensitive. In recent years, however, a number of inhibitors with quite specific actions have been discovered, and elucidation of their modes of action has begun to yield a clearer picture of the actual functioning of the biochemical mechanisms of the nitrifiers. It is to these inhibitors that attention will now be directed.

A. Inhibitors of *Nitrobacter*

In 1945 Lees and Quastel (*34*) reported that potassium chlorate had "a remarkable inhibitory effect on the conversion of ammonia to nitrate" in soils (this was a piece of serendipity, since the effect was originally noted, in an attenuated way, with iodate, which was being tested as an eel-worm inhibitor at the time). The effect was that if a fresh soil, with a consequently low population of nitrifying organisms, was treated with ammonium sulfate and potassium chlorate, the oxidation of ammonia went on unhindered, but the oxidation of the nitrite formed was considerably delayed; as a consequence there was, for a time, an appreciable accumulation of nitrite in the soil. Such accumulation did not occur if the soil was first treated with ammonium salts or nitrite and left until a population of *Nitrobacter* had built up in it. Such "enriched" soils oxidized nitrite almost as well in the presence of chlorate as in its absence. From these results Lees and Quastel concluded: "Potassium chlorate at low concentrations (c. $M \times 10^{-5}$ to $M \times 10^{-6}$) exercises a bacteriostatic action on soil organisms oxidizing nitrite to nitrate. . . . Chlorate has little or no effect on nitrite oxidation in a soil which is rich in nitrite-oxidizing organisms. Its effect at low concentrations seems almost wholly concerned with the inhibition of the proliferation of these organisms." They also noted that the effect of chlorate could be antagonized by nitrate, just as the well-known herbicidal effect of chlorate could also be antagonized by nitrate. Somewhat later, it was noted (*6*) that relatively high concentrations of chlorate (10^{-3} M) would suppress nitrite oxidation in a soil in which a population of *Nitrobacter* had, in fact, been established, thus showing that the chlorate was not entirely without effect on the primary nitrite oxidation. The mode of action of chlorate, however, remained obscure until chlorate was tested on suspensions of *Nitrobacter* (*27*). It was then found that concentrations of the order of 5×10^{-3} M were necessary before any chlorate effect manifested itself as an inhibition of nitrite oxidation. Various concentrations of chlorate were tested, and all gave the same result, an inhibition of nitrite oxidation that became more and more marked as oxidation proceeded. The inhibition was dependent upon the cell density of the suspension used, being more marked in weak suspensions than in stronger ones. It was then noticed that nitrite oxidation by *Nitrobacter* was accompanied by the appearance of reduced cytochrome absorption bands, a band at 551 mμ being particularly marked. This suggested that nitrite oxidation was mediated, directly or indirectly, by a cytochrome system. Furthermore, it was observed that if nitrite oxidation were allowed to proceed in the presence of chlorate these reduced bands gradually disappeared as oxidation proceeded. In the absence of chlorate the bands appeared when nitrite was added and persisted at constant intensity until all nitrite was oxidized, when they abruptly disappeared again. It therefore seemed likely that the chlorate somehow destroyed the cytochrome during nitrite oxidation and thus gradually eliminated the nitrite-oxidizing systems. If cells were suspended in chlorate in the absence of nitrite for extended periods and then washed free of chlorate, they oxidized nitrite as well as cells suspended in chlorate-free, nitrite-free media for the same period. Clearly, chlorate was inhibitory only when active nitrite oxidation was going on. Cells suspended in chlorate + nitrite for varying periods of time, and then washed and resuspended in nitrite, showed a decreased oxidizing ability according to the length of time they had oxidized nitrite in the presence of chlorate; moreover, the residual oxidizing ability after such treatment was linearly related to the relative intensity of the reduced cytochrome band at 551 mμ that remained after nitrite-chlorate treatment. It was also noticed that, although *Nitrobacter* is a strict aerobe, it would oxidize nitrite, at a steadily diminishing rate, under anaerobic conditions if chlorate were present; seemingly, the chlorate could act, to some extent, as an electron acceptor for the nitrite oxidation system. On the basis of these findings it was suggested that the oxidation of nitrite by *Nitrobacter* could be visualized as shown in Eqs. (4)–(7),

$$Fe_{cyt\ 551}^{3+} + NO_2^- \rightarrow Fe_{cyt\ 551}^{2+} + \underline{NO_2} \tag{4}$$

$$Fe_{cyt\ 551}^{2+} + \underline{NO_2} + \tfrac{1}{2}O_2 \rightarrow Fe_{cyt\ 551}^{3+} NO_3^- \tag{5}$$

$$Fe_{cyt\ 551}^{2+} + \underline{NO_2} + ClO_3^- \rightarrow Fe_{cyt\ 551}^{3+} + NO_3^- + ClO_2^- \tag{6}$$

$$Fe_{cyt\ 551}^{3+} + ClO_2 \rightarrow \text{inactivated cytochrome 551} \tag{7}$$

where $Fe^{3+}_{cyt\,551}$ and $Fe^{2+}_{cyt\,551}$ represent the oxidized and reduced forms of the 551 cytochrome and $\underline{NO_2}$ represents some compound, free or bound to a carrier, at the oxidation level of the nitrite radical. In presenting this scheme, in which cytochrome inactivation is brought about by reaction with chlorite (*35*) produced by Eq. (6), Lees and Simpson were careful to point out that "Although the reactions are depicted as taking place directly, this does not preclude the possibility that one or more of them may involve carrier systems." Unfortunately the high ultraviolet absorption of both nitrite and nitrate ions precludes the possibility of observing pyridine nucleotide carrier reduction by the usual spectroscopic or ultraviolet fluorescence methods, and if such reduction is involved in nitrite oxidation, some indirect demonstration will be necessary. As far as *Nitrobacter* is concerned, nothing presents a more urgent problem than the elucidation of the mechanisms whereby the oxidation of nitrite is coupled to the generation of negotiable reducing power and the production of high energy phosphate (?) bonds required for CO_2 assimilation. The problem here is twofold. The E'_0 of the system shown in Eq. (8)

$$NO_2^- + \tfrac{1}{2}O_2 = NO_3^- \tag{8}$$

is some $+0.32$ volt at pH 7, whereas even cytochrome c has an E'_0 no higher than 0.26 volt (the 551 cytochrome of *Nitrobacter*, which is of the "c" type (*36*), has an E'_0 of 0.25 volt), while the E'_0 of pyridine nucleotide carriers is about -0.28 volt at this pH. This means that the equilibria of the reactions shown in Eqs. (9) and (10)

$$2Fe_{cyt}^{3+} + H_2O + NO_2^- = 2Fe_{cyt}^{2+} + NO_3^- + 2H^+ \tag{9}$$

$$TPN + NO_2^- + H_2O = TPNH_2 + NO_3^- \tag{10}$$

must lie to the left and that, in particular, the generation of reduced pyridine nucleotide by the simple oxidation of nitrite is virtually impossible. This is, of course, only another way of stating the well-known fact that TPN-linked nitrate reductase catalyzes the virtually complete reduction of nitrate (*37*). It thus seems possible that Eq. (10) should be written:

$$TPN + NO_2^{-*} + H_2O = TPNH_2 + NO_3^- \tag{11}$$

where NO_2^{-*} represents some activated form of nitrite (adenyl nitrite?) capable of reducing oxidized TPN. It is also possible that the oxidation of nitrite according to Eq. (9) may demand some initial activation of the nitrite before the cytochrome system can function and thus generate more high energy bonds for the further activation of nitrite. In this respect it is interesting that with whole cells (*38*) and with some cell-free preparations (*39*), if not all (*3*), uncoupling agents such as 2,4-DNP merely prevent nitrite oxidation. The whole of this area of metabolism in *Nitrobacter* warrants much more study with selective inhibitors of the different stages involved in oxidation of nitrite, generation of high energy bonds, and generation of reducing power. An inhibitor that may prove of value here is cyanate. Quastel and Scholefield (*6*) reported that, among other potent inhibitors of nitrification in soil, they had noted nitrourea. When freshly prepared nitrourea was tested on cultures of Nitrobacter, however, it was found not to be inhibitory, but became so if it were allowed to stand at room temperature, especially under alkaline conditions (27). Alkaline degradation of nitrourea might be expected to yield cyanate, and, indeed, when cyanate was tested, it proved very toxic, being 50% inhibitory to nitrite oxidation at a concentration of 5×10^{-4} M. The inhibition was reversible by water washing, and, since in the presence of cyanate no reduced cytochrome bands appeared in the presence of nitrite, it seems likely that cyanate inhibits nitrite oxidation in the area covered by Eq. (4) above. A curious aspect of cyanate inhibition was found by Butt and Lees (40), who showed that if the oxygen tension in a culture of *Nitrobacter* oxidizing nitrite were decreased, inhibition by cyanate became less and that at very low oxygen tensions cyanate would stimulate oxidation at concentrations markedly inhibitory to oxidation at normal oxygen tensions. A similar dependence on oxygen tension was shown by the inhibitions due to arsenite and nitrate. Nitrite itself is known to be inhibitory to its own oxidation at concentrations much above 10^{-2} M and becomes more so as the oxygen tension is lowered. It thus seems possible that nitrate, cyanate, and arsenite, all of which have an ion structure somewhat similar to nitrite, inhibit by preventing access of nitrite to the surface of the oxidizing enzyme; at normal oxygen tensions, when the nitrite can be oxidized rapidly, these substances would thus act as inhibitors, but at low oxygen tensions they might well augment nitrite oxidation by preventing too great an accumulation of the (toxic) nitrite at the same enzyme surface. Whatever the mechanism, however, it seems likely that a study of the precise action of these compounds will throw some light on the mechanism of nitrite oxidation by *Nitrobacter*.

Aleem (41) showed that molybdate was necessary for proper oxidation of nitrite in growing cultures of *Nitrobacter*, whereas Zavarzin (42, 43) found that while iron was also necessary, molybdate could be replaced by tungstate. However, if both tungstate and molybdate were used together with iron, they antagonized one another. In view of the fact that the molybdate-tungstate effects were pH dependent, Zavarzin postulated that the biologically active form of the molybdate or tungstate is a "heteropoly" ion (presumably phosphomolybdate or phosphotungstate) but that in the presence of both ions a mixed, biologically inactive, heteropoly ion is formed. Whatever the explanation, it is clear that a marked imbalance in trace element supply may be inhibitory to *Nitrobacter*, which perhaps explains the high toxicity of various amines and citrate noted by Meyerhof (25), since such compounds might be expected to throw out normal trace element supply by chelation or to interfere with the working of the molybdeno-flavoprotein-cytochrome and respiration system outlined by Zavarzin. At one time it seemed possible that catalase was responsible for oxidation of nitrite by *Nitrobacter*; the organisms certainly possess a catalase activity sensitive to poisoning by azide, cyanide, and hydroxylamine. But when the inhibitions of catalase activity brought about by these poisons were compared quantitatively with the inhibitions the same poisons exerted on nitrite oxidation, no correlation was found (44). Azide was a weak inhibitor of catalase activity but a strong one of nitrite oxidation; with hydroxylamine the situation was reversed. Zavarzin (42, 43) concluded similarly that catalase was not involved in nitrite oxidation.

B. Inhibitors of *Nitrosomonas*

In 1946, experiments (17) on ammonia oxidation in soils already enriched with a population of nitrifying organisms showed that ammonia oxidation could be inhibited to an extent of 90–95% by percolation of the soils with potassium ethyl xanthate, salicylaldoxime, sodium diethyl-dithiocarbamate, or allylthiourea, all at concentrations of 0.004 M. These compounds are all known inhibitors of copper enzymes, and, since the ammonia oxidizing activity of soils treated with them could be to some extent restored by percolation with copper sulfate, it seemed possible that a copper enzyme was involved in ammonia oxidation by *Nitrosomonas*. Quastel and Scholefield (6) showed that 0.002 M allylthiourea or thiourea virtually prevented proliferation of ammonia-oxidizing organisms in a fresh soil. Work with several chelating agents (18) showed that all inhibited ammonia oxidation in cultures of *Nitrosomonas*, but there was still no indication of the site of their action. About this time it was shown, however, that hydroxylamine, which had often been suggested as an intermediate in ammonia oxidation but which had always failed to yield nitrite when tested on cultures of *Nitrosomonas*, was, in fact, an intermediate and that previous failures to establish it as such were in all probability due to the use of too high concentrations. When the hydroxylamine was tested at concentrations of some 10^{-4} M, it was oxidized to nitrite as fast, or faster, than was ammonium sulfate. This discovery (45) made it possible to start some investigations into the mechanism of ammonia oxidation, and it was found that allylthiourea was, in fact, a specific inhibitor of the system that oxidizes ammonia to hydroxylamine. Allylthiourea at 2 $\times$ 10^{-7} M was found to inhibit ammonia oxidation in washed suspensions of *Nitrosomonas* by some 50%, and there was no evidence of any competition between ammonia and the allylthiourea. At 10^{-3} M allylthiourea showed no inhibition whatever of the oxidation of hydroxylamine. It was then further noticed that hydrazine was also an inhibitor of ammonia oxidation and on investigation proved actually to be an inhibitor of hydroxylamine oxidation. At a concentration of 3×10^{-3} M, hydrazine prevented virtually all nitrite production from ammonia or hydroxylamine, but did not prevent the accumulation of small quantities of hydroxylamine in the presence of ammonia. Thus, the pathway of ammonia oxidation in *Nitrosomonas* can be formulated as in Eq. (12)

$$NH_4 \xrightarrow{(a)} NH_2OH \xrightarrow{(b)} (?) \xrightarrow{(c)} NO_2^- \qquad (12)$$

in which step (a) is inhibited by copper enzyme poisons and step (b) or (c) by hydrazine. Two steps are indicated between hydroxylamine and nitrite because a total of four electrons is involved, but there may be more than two steps, since we cannot be sure that part of the oxidation does not take place via one-electron transfers. It seems probable that at least one two-electron transfer is involved because under anaerobic conditions in the presence of methylene blue, cell-free extracts of *Nitrosomonas* oxidized hydroxylamine with consequent decolorization of the methylene blue (*46*). Nitrite was not formed, but there was a gas output. Under aerobic conditions, methylene blue increased the amount of nitrite produced from hydroxylamine by such extracts, but the oxygen uptake did not correspond to the amount of nitrite produced. Under aerobic conditions in the presence of cyanide and methylene blue, the hydroxyl-- amine disappeared, no nitrite was produced, and there was a gas output. It thus appears that cell-free extracts of *Nitrosomonas* were able to oxidize hydroxylamine to the unstable intermediate labeled "?" in Eq. (12) above and that this intermediate either decomposed to nitrogen (or some oxide of nitrogen) or was oxidized to nitrite by means of some enzyme system requiring molecular oxygen, since the cyanide poisons this system and converts the whole setup to a condition resembling anaerobiosis.

Much of Anderson's work (*46*) has been confirmed by Engel and Alexander (*47*), but here the matter rests for the moment. The intermediate(s) that must lie between hydroxylamine and nitrite remain unidentified, and the coupling between ammonia oxidation and carbon dioxide assimilation remains unexplored. Work in this field is continuing, however, and there is reason to hope that before long some light may be shed on problems that, at present, seem totally baffling.

REFERENCES

1. E. L. Schmidt, *Science* 119, 187 (1954).
2. O. R. Eylar, Jr. and E. L. Schmidt, *J. Gen. Microbiol.* 20, 473 (1959).
3. E. Malavolta, C. C. Delwiche, and W. D. Burge, *Biochem. Biophys. Research Communs.* 2, 445 (1960).
4. H. Lees and J. H. Quastel, *Chem. & Ind. (London)* 26, 238 (1944).
5. H. Lees, *Plant & Soil* 1, 221 (1949).
6. J. H. Quastel and P. G. Scholefield, *Bacteriol. Revs.* 15, 1 (1951).
7. J. H. Schloesing and C. A. Muntz, *Compt. rend. acad. sci.* 84, 301 (1877).
8. J. H. Schloesing and C. A. Muntz, *Compt. rend. acad. sci.* 85, 1018 (1878).
9. J. H. Schloesing and C. A. Muntz, *Compt. rend. acad. sci.* 86, 892 (1878).
10. R. Warington, *J. Chem. Soc.* 33, 44 (1878).
11. R. Warington, *J. Chem. Soc.* 35, 429 (1879).
12. R. Warington, *J. Chem. Soc.* 45, 637 (1884).
13. R. Warington, *J. Chem. Soc.* 59, 484 (1891).
14. S. Winogradsky, *Am. inst. Pasteur* 5, 577 (1891).
15. S. Winogradsky and V. Omeliansky, *Arch. sci. biol. (St. Petersburg)* 7 (3) (1899).
16. J. H. M. Munro, *J. Chem. Soc.* 49, 632 (1886).
17. H. Lees, *Nature* 158, 97 (1946).
18. H. Lees, *Biochem. J.* 52, 134 (1952).
19. S. Winogradsky and V. Omeliansky, *Zentr. Bakteriol., Parasitenk. Abt. II* 5, 329, 377, 429 (1899).
20. M. W. Beijerinck, *Folia Microbiol. (Delft)* 3, 91 (1914).
21. T. Y. Kingma Boltjes, *Arch. Mikrobiol.* 6, 79 (1935).
22. D. J. Greenwood and H. Lees, *Plant & Soil* 7, 253 (1956).
23. P. Simonart and F. Peeters, *Trans. Intern. Congr. Soil Sci. 5th Congr. Leopoldville, 1954,* 3, 132 (1954).
24. H. L. Jensen, *Tidsskr. Planteavl* 54, 62 (1950).
25. O. Meyerhof, *Arch. ges. Physiol. Pflüger's* 164, 353 (1916); 165, 229 (1916); 166, 240 (1917).
26. P. Dirnhuber and F. Schutz, *Biochem. J.* 42, 628 (1948).
27. H. Lees and J. R. Simpson, *Biochem. J.* 65, 297 (1957).
28. A. Taussig, *Can. J. Microbiol.* 6, 619 (1960).
29. H. Larsen, *Kgl. Norske Videnskab. Selskabs Strifter* 1 (1953).
30. H. Lees and J. H. Quastel, *Biochem. J.* 40, 803 (1946).
31. B. J. Stovanovic and M. Alexander, *Soil Sci.* 86, 208 (1958).
32. M. S. Engel and M. Alexander, *Soil Sci. Soc. Am. Proc.* 24, 48 (1960).
33. E. Boullanger and L. Massol, *Ann. inst. Pasteur* 18, 181 (1904).
34. H. Lees and J. H. Quastel, *Nature* 155, 276 (1945).
35. P. George and D. H. Irvine, *Biochem. J.* 58, 188 (1954).
36. W. D. Butt and H. Lees, *Nature* 182, 732 (1958).
37. A. Nason and H. J. Evans, *J. Biol. Chem.* 202, 655 (1953).
38. W. D. Butt and H. Lees, *Nature* 188, 147 (1960).
39. M. I. H. Aleem and A. Nason, *Proc. Natl. Acad. Sci. U.S.* 46, 763 (1960).
40. W. D. Butt and H. Lees, *Biochem. J.* 76, 425 (1960).
41. M. I. H. Aleem, The Physiology and Chemautotrophic Metabolism of *Nitrobacter agilis*, Doctoral Thesis, Cornell Univ., Ithaca, New York, 1959.

42. G. A. Zavarzin, *Mikrobiologiya* 27, 401 (1958).
43. G. A. Zavarzin, *Mikrobiologiya* 27, 542 (1958).
44. H. Lees, *in "Autotrophic Micro-organisms,"* 4th Symposium Soc. Gen. Microbiol., pp. 84–97. Cambridge Univ. Press, London and New York, 1954.
45. T. Hofman and H. Lees, *Biochem. J.* 54, 579 (1953).
46. J. H. Anderson, Studies on the Biochemistry of Ammonia Oxidation by the Autotrophic Nitrifying Organism, *Nitrosomonas*, Doctoral Thesis, Aberdeen, Scotland, 1959.
47. M. S. Engel and M. Alexander, *J. Bacteriol.* 78, 796 (1959).

CHAPTER 38

Inhibition Due to Radiation

R. Goutier and Z. M. Bacq

I. INTRODUCTION

The most conspicuous effect of ionizing radiation on living matter is the inhibition of mitotic activity. It was discovered 54 years ago and clearly depicted by Bergonié and Tribondeau (1), who noticed that the higher the rate of mitotic activity of living tissue, the higher the sensitivity to radiation.

In the last 20 years, a large number of publications appeared dealing with the action of radiation on enzymes involved in the diverse aspects of cell metabolism. Although we shall concern ourselves here mainly with the inhibitory action of radiation on enzymes, we must not forget that activation is by no means a rare event *in vivo* and in some cases leads to reinforcement of the deleterious effect of the inhibition of other enzyme systems on the cell's life.

631

II. EFFECTS *IN VITRO*

Activation of enzymes is essentially an *in vivo* effect of radiation, the reasons of which will be given in the following sections.

On the other hand, *in vitro* irradiation of purified enzymes always results in a decrease of enzyme activity. There is no exception to this rule. In Table I are listed a few examples of *in vitro* inhibition of enzymes by X- and γ-rays.

A. Direct and Indirect Action

The inhibition observed *in vitro* when dilute aqueous solutions of pure enzymes are irradiated is mainly due to indirect effects, that is to say, to the interaction of free radicals produced by ionization of water with the enzyme molecule. The direct hit of radiation on the enzyme molecule represents an increasing percentage of the total effect with increasing enzyme concentration, but still remains less important than the indirect effect. This has been shown by Dale (*9*) for carboxypeptidase.

Useful discussions of the relative importance of direct and indirect action of ionizing radiation on enzymes *in vitro* may be found in Bacq and Alexander's textbook (*10*) and in Dale's lecture (*11*). An example of enzyme inhibition *in vitro* is given in Fig. 1, where the decreas-

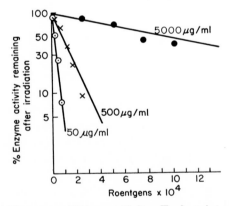

FIG. 1. Effect of X-rays on DNase activity. Each point on the curve represents the average of 5 experiments with a standard deviation from the mean of ± 10%. From Okada (*6*).

ing inhibitory effect with increasing enzyme concentration points to an indirect effect of radiation by way of free radicals originating from

TABLE I

INHIBITION OF PURIFIED ENZYMES BY RADIATION

Enzyme	Concentration	Kind of radiation and dose (r)	Inhibition (%)	Reference
Alcohol dehydrogenase	45 µg/ml	585 (X)	11	Pihl et al. (2)
		2340 (X)	46	
Phosphoglyceraldehyde dehydrogenase	70 µg/ml	585 (X)	8	Pihl et al. (2) ; see also (3)
		2340 (X)	31	
	70 µg/ml	500 (X)	94	Barron et al. (3) ; see also (2)
Adenosine triphosphatase				
Fresh	20 µg N/ml	10	10	Barron et al. (3)
Aged	20 µg N/ml	1	30	Barron et al. (3)
Urease				
Crude solution	20 mg/ml	17,000 (γ)	16	Tanaka et al. (4)
Pure solution	10 mg/ml	17,000 (γ)	100	Tanaka et al. (4)
Ribonuclease	50 µg/ml	13,500 (X)	50	Holmes (5)
Deoxyribonuclease (neutral)	0.5 µg/ml	100 (X)	20	Okada (6)
Cytochrome c	Dry	4×10^7 (X)	50	Rajewsky et al. (7)
Acetylcholinesterase (eel organ powder)	275 µg/ml	10^5 (X)	75	Serlin and Cotzias (8)

radiolysis of water. Indeed, at a given radiation dose the number of free radicals produced in the solvent is always the same, regardless of the concentration of the solute. Accordingly, the number of enzyme molecules attacked by these radicals will also be the same at any concentration, and therefore the percentage of inactivation of the enzyme decreases with increasing concentration (10).

B. Sulfhydryl Enzymes

The production of oxidizing radicals (OH$\bullet$ and HO$_2\bullet$) and hydrogen peroxide in irradiated water is liable to oxidize the sulfhydryl groups and to inactivate such enzymes as phosphoglyceraldehyde dehydrogenase, alcohol dehydrogenase, hexokinase, and adenosinetriphosphatase in which free SH groups are essential for enzymic activity. Barron (3, 12) performed experiments which pointed to a definitely greater sensitivity of SH enzymes to radiation in vitro. Two examples from his work are quoted in Table I; the greater sensitivity of aged solutions of adenosinetriphosphatase might be due to a decreased amount of free SH groups prior to irradiation. Unfortunately, these facts could not be confirmed by Pihl et al. (2), who observed that SH enzymes are inhibited by X-rays in vitro with the same ionic yield as non-SH enzymes (Table I). According to them, the ionic yield for the inhibition of phosphoglyceraldehyde dehydrogenase is 0.02, similar to that for non-SH enzymes, whereas Barron found an ionic yield equal to 1. They likewise did not confirm the reactivation of irradiated SH enzymes (phosphoglyceraldehyde dehydrogenase) by addition of glutathione, although glutathione protects urease (another SH enzyme) against inactivation by γ-rays (4), i.e., decreases the number of altered molecules, provided that glutathione is introduced into the system before irradiation.

Evidence, recently presented, shows that the inactivation of dry ribonuclease by irradiation is associated with the rupture of the S—S bond (12a).

At the present time, the idea of a preferential inhibition of SH enzymes by irradiation in vitro has been abandoned.

In vivo, inactivation of SH enzymes and coenzymes does not even seem to occur, unless at high doses after a long latent period.

Coenzyme A is not inactivated in the first hours following total body irradiation, as proved by the normal rate of acetylation of p-aminobenzoic acid (13). Other examples are presented and discussed by Errera (14), e.g., the lack of inhibition, or the weak inhibition of succinic dehydrogenase and hexokinase in tissues. Therefore, oxidation of

SH groups, even if it occurs to some extent *in vivo*, does not play a leading role in the eruption and the evolution of the radiolesion (*10, 15*).

C. Protection by Added Substances

By adding to a purified enzyme solution other substances, the molecules of which will compete with the enzyme molecules for the free radicals produced during irradiation, one decreases the probability of reaction between free radicals and enzyme molecules. Many examples are quoted in a recent review by Marples and Glew (*16*). The more purified an enzyme, the higher its sensitivity to radiation. Braams (*17*) found that different purification methods of invertase brought about different sensitivities of the enzyme to a-rays and protons.

Neutral deoxyribonuclease (DNase) can be protected against X-irradiation by addition of various compounds (*18*), but it is thought provoking that the best protection is afforded by deoxyribonucleic acid (DNA), the substrate of the enzyme, which is, indeed, the most likely substance to combine with the active sites of the enzyme molecule. Cellulose, Dowex, silicagel, and mitochondria all protect neutral DNase *in vitro*. The behavior of the dry enzyme is quite different; dry neutral DNase is more radiosensitive than wet DNase (the water molecules would seem to protect the enzyme), and adsorption of the dry enzyme on a solid support leads to an increased radiosensitivity, contrary to what happens to the wet enzyme. But, wet or dry, DNase is protected against radiation by complexing with its substrate, DNA (*19, 20*).

III. DIFFERENCES BETWEEN *IN VITRO* AND *IN VIVO* EFFECTS

A. Activation of Enzymic Activities

Two main factors determine the wide differences observed between the effects of irradiation on a given enzyme in solution and on the same enzyme in a living tissue: the presence of many other molecules in a cell and the possible adsorption of the enzyme on the cell substructure. Both factors afford protection; enzymes are much more resistant when irradiated *in vivo* than when purified and irradiated *in vitro*.

As we have already said, enzymic activity is often increased by irradiation of a living organism. This is, indeed, the main difference between *in vitro* and *in vivo* effects of irradiation. It deserves a short comment. The example of neutral DNase is striking in this respect; DNase is inhibited *in vitro* (see Table I) by doses which produce activation *in vivo* (*21*). *In vivo*, DNase (acid DNase, especially) always displays a sharp increase of activity in various tissues after irradiation [for references, see the review by Goutier (*22*).] Other enzymes, such as cathepsin (*23*) and ribonuclease (*24*), also undergo activation after *in vivo* irradiation. Together with acid DNase, they are located in the lysosomes (*25*). The activation of these enzymes may originate from the rupture of the granules by irradiation and the release of their contents into the cell sap. This has been shown to be the case for acid DNase (*26*) and ribonuclease (*27*) and has been considered by Bacq and Errera (*28*) as one of the main primary mechanisms by which radiation impairs cell life. This is the "enzyme release theory," according to which more enzyme comes into contact with its substrate. Acid DNase, for example, is concentrated in the lysosomes at a distance from any substrate. The distance, on the molecular scale, between this DNase and DNA in the nucleus is enormous. DNase, in order to be active, must (*a*) be released from its links in the lysosomes, (*b*) travel through submicroscopic structures in the cytoplasm, and (*c*) cross the nuclear membrane.

Other examples of increase of enzyme activity after irradiation of an animal may be found in Bacq and Alexander (*10*). Besides rupture of granules or lysosomes, activation of enzyme activity after *in vivo* irradiation may be due to the destruction of an inhibitor occurring naturally in normal tissues, as is the case for carboxypeptidase (*23*) and neutral DNase (*29*), to an endocrine reaction, such as the suprarenal cortex reaction inducing an increased synthesis of the tryptophan peroxidase in rat liver (*30*), or to an increase in cell membrane permeability, which is probably responsible for the increase of glutamic-oxalacetic transaminase activity in rabbit serum (*31, 32*).

The complexity of a living cell makes it difficult to predict the behavior of a particular enzymic activity after *in vivo* irradiation. For instance, it would be incorrect to assume that irradiation always inhibits syntheses and activates hydrolytic mechanisms. Although this is roughly true under certain conditions for DNA metabolism, it does not hold for hemin and globin syntheses, which are stimulated by *in vivo* irradiation, as found when bone marrow cells or reticulocytes were tested 30 minutes after irradiation (*33, 34*). Cholesterol synthesis, measured by incorporation of acetate-1-C^{14} and tritiated water into intact animals and into tissue slices, has also been shown to be enhanced to two times normal after 2400 r total body X-irradiation of rats (*35*). Cathepsin also seems to be synthesized at a higher rate in the thymus of irradiated rats; this increase, however, is associated with phagocytosis and may represent enzyme induction rather than enzyme activation (*35a*). Nevertheless, many syntheses, some of which are most important for cell mitosis and growth, are indeed inhibited.

B. Differences in Relative Biological Efficiency (RBE)

Fast neutrons and *a*-particles (densely ionizing radiations) kill cells more effectively than hard X-rays and γ-rays (sparsely ionizing radiations). If cell death originates from alteration of any particular chemical or enzymic reaction, one would expect this reaction to display *in vitro* the same relative sensitivities to different radiations as *in vivo*. But, in fact, for most radiochemical and enzymic *in vitro* reactions known so far, the RBE is higher for hard X-rays and γ-rays than for *a*-particles, contrary to what is observed *in vivo*.

On these grounds, the inactivation of enzymes observed *in vitro* can hardly be accepted as a possible primary lesion (*36, 37*).

The only case where the RBE's are qualitatively the same *in vitro* as *in vivo* for different radiations is the production of double breaks in the DNA molecule. The alteration of the DNA molecule might therefore be an acceptable candidate for the primary lesion. But, as pointed out by Bacq and Alexander (*38*), cells without DNA (red cells) or anucleated fragments of cells (*Amoeba, Acetabularia mediterranaea*) show typical radiolesions.

IV. INHIBITIONS *IN VIVO*

In the review by Errera (*14*) are listed the enzymes inhibited after *in vivo* irradiation (see also *38a*). We want to discuss some examples of inhibition of biologically important systems in which the inhibited enzymes or enzymic reactions have been clearly identified.

A. Inhibition of DNA Synthesis

A large number of publications describe the decrease in the incorporation of labeled precursors into DNA after *in vivo* irradiation. Recent reviews will provide the reader with the references: Bacq and Alexander (*10*), Errera (*14*), Howard (*39*), Kelly (*40*), Holmes (*41*), Stocken (*42*), and Goutier (22). The biological importance of this effect of radiation does not need to be emphasized.

Recent investigations have shown that in tissue cultures (42a) and in regenerating rat liver (42b), irradiation results in an inhibition of DNA synthesis in all cells in the synthetic phase and not in a decrease in the number of cells in the same phase.

Considering only the enzymological point of view, the radiolesion seems to be located at the end of the long sequence of events leading to the biosynthesis of DNA, when the nucleosides are converted to nucleoside triphosphates by specific kinases and then linked together to form the polynucleotide chain as a result of the intervention of a specific polymerase.

Since nucleosides accumulate in the tissues of an irradiated animal, it may be concluded that irradiation does not inhibit the nucleoside synthesis (43–49).

The first lesion that has been detected in the reaction sequence is a decreased rate of formation of the nucleoside triphosphates. Creasy and Stocken (50) observed that within 1 hour, the formation of high energy phosphorus compounds by nuclear suspensions of thymus tissue was suppressed by 100 r; it was only 20–50% of normal after 25 r total body irradiation. The inhibition can already be detected 3–5 minutes after 100 r. This is shown in Table II. Potter (49) observed that within a few

TABLE II

INHIBITION OF THE FORMATION OF LABILE PHOSPHATE IN NUCLEI ISOLATED FROM TISSUES OF RATS EXPOSED TO A WHOLE BODY X-IRRADIATION 1 HOUR PREVIOUSLY[a]

Tissue	Rate of phosphorylation for various doses of X-irradiation as percentage of control values		
	25 r	50 r	100 r
Spleen	18, 30	0, 0, 0	0, 0, 0
Thymus gland	45, 77	14, 23	0, 0, 0, 0, 0
Bone marrow	0, 0	0	0
Lymph node	0, 6	0	0

[a] From Creasey and Stocken (50).

hours, in vivo irradiation with 100–3200 rep gamma rays inhibited the incorporation of thymidine-C^{14} into thymine nucleotides and, to a still greater extent, into DNA.

That inhibition of the polymerization of nucleotides also occurs has been shown by Okada and Hempelmann (*51*) and by Bollum *et al.* (*52*) in regenerating livers of irradiated rats. The latter authors determined the activity of thymidine kinase (converting thymidine to thymidine monophosphate), of thymidylic kinase (converting thymidine monophosphate to thymidine triphosphate), and of polymerase (converting deoxyribonucleoside triphosphates into DNA). These enzymes are known to appear in the supernatant fraction of homogenates of regenerating liver in increasing amounts at the time that DNA synthesis begins *in vivo*, between 16 and 24 hours after partial hepatectomy (*53*). When the animals are irradiated 6 hours after hepatectomy, when DNA synthesis has not yet started, the appearance of the enzymes is delayed, and their activity is lower (depending on the radiation dose), as can be seen in Fig. 2. Since the inhibition of the over-all incorporation of thymidine-H³

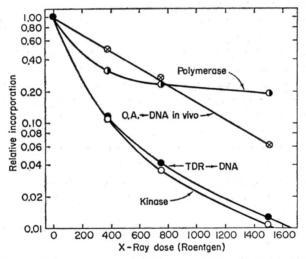

FIG. 2. Effect of X-ray dose given 6 hours after partial hepatectomy on the kinase and polymerase enzymes and on the over-all incorporation of thymidine-H³ into DNA, measured by *in vitro* assays 24 hours after the operation. The data are not corrected for the levels occurring in the tissues in the period 6–16 hours after the operation. Data on the X-ray inhibition of the *in vivo* incorporation of orotic acid-C¹⁴ into DNA of regenerating rat liver are shown for comparison. The latter data are from Beltz, Van Lancker, and Potter. O.A. = orotic acid; TDR = thymidine. From Bollum *et al.* (*52*).

into DNA closely parallels the inhibition of the kinase, it is clear that the kinase is the rate-limiting step. On the other hand, irradiation given 16 hours after hepatectomy does not slow down the ultimate increase in the enzyme activities which are normally present at that time, although incorporation of thymidine into DNA is still much depressed. In other words, in regenerating liver, irradiation prevents the synthesis of the enzymes rather than inhibits the activities of the enzymes themselves. This is an important point to note.

Van Lancker (*53a*), working with isolated nuclei of regenerating liver, came to the same conclusion. A similar delay has been found in the appearance of deoxycytidine deaminase activity in irradiated regenerating liver (*53b, 53c*).

As to our understanding of the inhibition of DNA synthesis by radiation, the experiments of Bollum *et al.* (*52, 53*) also show that, in liver at least, if the depressed synthesis of DNA may be explained by an inhibition of the synthetic enzymes in the early stages of liver regeneration, it must be ascribed to another still unknown cause when irradiation is given at later times, since the liver tissue is then incapable of synthesizing DNA *in vivo* despite the presence in the *in vitro* tests of a normal activity of synthetic enzymes and despite a slight decrease in DNase activity (*51, 54*).

The progressive inhibition of DNA synthesis observed *in vivo* when irradiation is given to rats 24 hours after partial hepatectomy is ascribed to a slowing down of the mitotic cycle because no change is observed in the capacity of isolated cells from irradiated livers to incorporate thymidine *in vitro* in DNA (*54a*). In rat spleen and small intestine, the radiosensitivity of the nucleotide polymerization process even seems doubtful, and the inhibition of the nucleotide-phosphorylating kinases is too small to account for the *in vivo* inhibition of DNA synthesis (*54b*). In these cases, losses of ions such as K or Ca by the nuclei of irradiated tissues (*54c*) perhaps cause important damage to the process of DNA synthesis (*54b*).

Other parameters, more recently investigated, may also be involved in the effect of irradiation on DNA synthesis.

Factors inhibiting the DNA-synthesizing enzymes have been described in the supernatant (*54d*) and microsomal fractions (*54e*) of normal rat liver homogenates. Induced regeneration of the liver leads to a decrease of the microsomal inhibiting factor; irradiation at lethal X-ray doses prior to partial hepatectomy prevents the normal decrease of the inhibiting factor (*54e*).

Macromolecules such as DNA, RNA, and proteins penetrate into cells in tissue culture (*54f, 54g*) and are translocated within plant tissues (*54h*) when added to the external medium. Although it is not known whether translocation of the plant's own DNA and RNA molecules also occurs under physiological conditions, irradiation depresses the translocation of added DNA and RNA in barley seedlings (*54h*).

B. Inhibition of Auxin Synthesis

In plant tissues, inhibition of DNA synthesis also occurs after irradiation (*55, 56*) and can reach 40% in terms of P^{32} incorporation, after moderate doses of 50–200 r X-rays (*55*). The same doses affect to an almost similar degree the synthesis of auxin which is also indispensable for plant growth.

The formation of auxin has been studied by Gordon (*57*). Tryptophan is the starting material, and, in the last step, oxidation of indoleacetaldehyde yields the indoleacetic acid which exerts the hormonal action. According to Gordon (*58*), it is this last conversion of acetaldehyde to the acid form that is inhibited by irradiation.

Figure 3, taken from Gordon (*58*), shows the accumulation of indole-

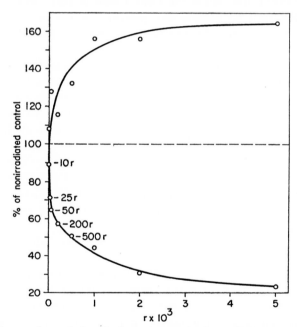

FIG. 3. Conversion of tryptophan to auxin by cell-free homogenates of X-irradiated mung bean seedlings. The lower curve gives the relative amount of indoleacetic acid formed; the upper curve, indoleacetaldehyde. From Gordon (*58*).

acetaldehyde with a corresponding decrease of indoleacetic acid in irradiated mung bean seedlings. It must be pointed out that this reaction is sensitive to very low doses of X-rays and that the inhibition can already be detected a few minutes after irradiation.

C. Inhibition of Oxidative and Glycolytic Processes

Here, again, much difference is observed between the effects of *in vivo* and *in vitro* irradiation. In isolated rat liver mitochondria, Fritz-Niggli (*59*) produced a 10% inhibition of the oxidation of citrate after *in vitro* X-irradiation by 50 r, when the mitochondria were isolated in 5.75% mannitol, and 60% inhibition, when they were isolated in 2.88% mannitol (the second medium is kept isotonic by means of phosphate buffer). The oxygen uptake by isolated mitochondria seems to be very radiosensitive, since, according to Fritz-Niggli (*60*), it displayed 60 and 74% inhibition $\frac{1}{2}$ and 1 hour, respectively, after *in vitro* irradiation with 0.1 r X-rays. The experiments of Fritz-Niggli have never been confirmed, a fact which suggests that an unknown important factor is introduced during the preparation of the mitochondria.

But, when oxidase activities are individually measured in irradiated liver slices, hardly any inhibition of succinic dehydrogenase, cytochrome oxidase, and succinoxidase is observed for X-ray doses below 10^6 r (*61*). In order to explain this discrepancy, one might think that the isolated mitochondria used by Fritz-Niggli had already been damaged by the isolation procedure and were, for this reason, more sensitive to external attack, whereas in the liver slices, used by Rajewsky, the mitochondria were still in a more physiological state.

The same phenomenon is observed with Tetrahymena. Whole cells given 3×10^5–6×10^5 r retain an almost normal level of oxidizing enzymes, whereas in irradiated cell-free homogenates, the oxidase activities are greatly depressed (*62, 63*). Here, too, the preservation of intact cell structures protects the enzymes against inactivation by irradiation.

After total body irradiation, the effects observed depend both on the radiation dose and the time lag between radiation and observation. The immediate effects were studied by Smith and Thomson (*64*), who irradiated rats, mice, hamsters, bats, fowls, and frogs continuously at 500 r/min until death; they did not observe any significant changes in aerobic and anaerobic glycolysis, oxidative phosphorylation, succinic dehydrogenase, cytochrome oxidase, adenosinetriphosphatase, and peroxidase in various tissues. In rats killed immediately after increasing doses of X-rays, Belokonsky and Rusev (*65*) found an increased O_2 demand, with an increase of cytochrome oxidase and a reduction of succinic dehydrogenase in various tissues after doses up to 500–1000 r. Higher doses (1000–20,000 r) produce a depression of oxidative processes with a reactivation of succinic dehydrogenase in the resistant tissues only.

Observations made several hours after irradiation do not always give concordant results. Ryser *et al.* (*66*) do not find any inhibition of succinic dehydrogenase in rat liver 1–3 days after 1000 r total body irradiation. In the rat thymus, likewise, negligible changes in succinic dehydrogenase, malic dehydrogenase, cytochrome oxidase, and adenosinetriphosphatase occur after 800 r X-rays (*67*). On the other hand, according to Di Bella (*68*), succinic dehydrogenase is inhibited by 50% in the liver and by 75% in the bone marrow 1–2 days after 800 r total body X-irradiation of rats.

Internal irradiation of rats by injection of 5 μc P^{32}/gm produces a 60% inhibition of anaerobic glycolysis in liver slices after 24 hours despite an increase in glycogen content. No change in succinic dehydrogenase, cytochrome oxidase, fumarase, and phosphorylase is observed (*69*).

Anaerobic glycolysis in Krebs ascites cells is 50% inhibited after 1000 r *in vitro* irradiation (*70, 71*). This effect can be mimicked by addition of H_2O_2 to the cell suspension. Addition of catalase protects the cells against inhibition of glycolysis by X-rays. Catalase itself is inhibited by total body irradiation of mice, where 850 r produce a 20% fall in liver catalase activity after 24 hours (*72*).

High doses of X-rays (>20 kr) given to ascites tumor cells *in vitro* produce an increase in O_2 consumption and in aerobic glycolysis and a depression in anaerobic glycolysis (*72a*) which is due to a dose-dependent decrease of ATP and DPN (*72b*). Inhibition of aerobic glycolysis seems, however, to occur in hepatoma cells after *in vitro* irradiation by 10–100 kr (*72c*).

In conclusion, despite the lack of consistency in the literature, oxidative enzymes and glycolytic processes seem to be less radiosensitive *in vivo* than other processes, such as DNA synthesis and nuclear phosphorylation.

The delayed inactivation by ionizing radiation of enzymes *in vivo* may also be interpreted by the enzyme-release theory. Enzymes linked to organelles are protected against inactivation and do not leak into all sap or circulating fluids; when they are set free by irradiation, they leak into the surrounding fluid and may be eliminated or become substrates for inactivating factors.

D. Inhibition of Phosphorylation

1. IN MITOCHONDRIA

Decreased P/O ratios were found by Potter and Bethell (*73*) in rat spleen mitochondria 1 hour after 800 r. This was confirmed by Hickman and Ashwell (74).

Van Bekkum et al. (75) showed that 4 hours after 1100 r total body irradiation, the phosphorylation, the oxygen uptake, and the P/O ratio were significantly decreased. In thymus, 50 r is able to inhibit oxidative phosphorylation. The mitochondrial damage brings about a release of cytochrome c, since cytochrome c added to mitochondria isolated after irradiation considerably enhances the P/O ratio as well as the phosphorylation and the oxygen uptake (76). Whether nuclear damage, which develops at the same time, has a bearing on the mitochondrial damage, is not known (77). When irradiated in vitro, isolated mitochondria possess normal levels of oxidative phosphorylation even after 20,000 r (76).

The inhibition of oxidative phosphorylation in rat spleen and liver 24 hours after 800 r total body irradiation is thought by Benjamin and Yost (78) to be an indirect effect of radiation, the inactivation being due in the spleen to an overproduction of thyroxine and in the liver to an overproduction of corticosteroids.

From a comparison between two mammary tumors, Goldfeder (78a) concludes that cells having a smaller number of mitochondria and, therefore, a lower level of phosphorylations are more radiosensitive.

2. IN THE NUCLEUS

Oxidative phosphorylation is an energy source common to all cells. Since some tissues are sensitive to radiation and others are not, it was interesting to look for a biochemical property which would be both sensitive to radiation and specific for radiosensitive tissues.

Creasy and Stocken (50) found that the formation of high energy phosphorus compounds by nuclear suspensions occurred in radiosensitive organs such as thymus, spleen, intestinal mucosa, and bone marrow and was lacking in liver, brain, kidney, and pancreas. The phosphorylation reaction is suppressed in the radiosensitive organ 1 hour after 50 r total body X-irradiation. No labile phosphate is formed in suspensions of spleen cell nuclei after 44 r γ-irradiation given to the nuclear suspension in vitro (see Table II). This seems to be a very sensitive test for early radiation damage. It has recently been confirmed and extended by Ord and Stocken (78b).

Maass (79) observed a decrease of ATP with a simultaneous increase of AMP in various tissues of rats irradiated with 800 r. He found the same phenomenon in the livers of dormice (Glis glis), provided the animals were irradiated awake. When irradiation was given during hibernation, no modification of AMP or ATP occurred. This is another indication that phosphorylation of nucleotides is related to the radio-sensitivity of a tissue.

E. Inhibition of Various Enzymes

1. CITRIC ACID SYNTHESIS

Injection of fluoroacetate into animals brings about an accumulation of citric acid (80, 81) due to inhibition of the oxidation of citrate by conversion of fluoroacetate to fluorocitrate (82). After 800 r X-irradiation (83) the accumulation of citric acid after fluoroacetate injection of rats is inhibited in spleen, thymus, ileum, pancreas, and testes; no effect is observed in heart and brain. Sublethal doses prevent the accumulation in spleen and thymus; this effect is reversible after sublethal doses only.

Normal male rats, injected with fluoroacetate, do not accumulate citrate in liver, in contrast to female rats. After irradiation, even injected male rats accumulate citrate in liver; sexual hormones may play a role in this effect of radiation on liver.

It is difficult to detect the specific cause of the inhibition by irradiation of citric acid accumulation in animals injected with fluoroacetate. As Potter (84) pointed out, the cause may be very remote from a direct interference with a reaction in the Krebs cycle. In any case, an inhibition of SH enzymes and coenzymes does not seem to be worth considering; succinic dehydrogenase is hardly inhibited by the X-ray doses used by Du Bois [see Thomson et al. (85)]. The inhibition of coenzyme A is a rather late phenomenon; a 37% inhibition has been observed in pigeon liver 6–7 days after doses of 3000 r (86).

2. CHOLINESTERASE

In intestinal loops of irradiated rats, Burn et al. (87) found that pseudocholinesterase is 50% inhibited 48 hours after 1000 r total body irradiation, whereas acetylcholinesterase (the "true" enzyme) is not. The changes observed 24 hours after irradiation are small (despite more important changes in intestinal motility).

One can only speculate about the mechanism of pseudocholinesterase inhibition. Since pseudocholinesterase is synthesized in liver, is the liver primarily affected by irradiation? Or if the synthesis in liver is controlled by the anterior pituitary gland, is the inhibition of pseudocholinesterase a part of the stress syndrome?

Conard (88) observed a significant depression of pseudocholinesterase in rat small intestine 20 hours after 500 r total body irradiation; on the fourth day, the inhibition was 60%. Nevertheless, according to Conard, these changes cannot be related to the changes observed in the motility of the intestine. In other organs, however, the activity of cholinesterases seems to be affected differently by irradiation. According to Lundin and Clemedson (88a), irradiation of the guinea pig by 400 r does not produce any change in liver pseudocholinesterase activity, whereas the enzyme activity is decreased in the plasma and increased in the bone marrow.

V. CONCLUSIONS

The earliest detected biochemical lesion in many irradiated tissues is the disturbance of nucleic acid metabolism and, especially, the inhibition of DNA synthesis, where polymerization rate and formation of nucleoside triphosphates are both decreased. This, however, does not account for the antimitotic action of radiation, since it has been possible in many instances to inhibit mitoses without inhibiting the DNA synthesis to the same extent (a phenomenon which leads to the formation of giant cells (89–91)). Some cases are known where mitosis occurs without DNA synthesis, as in *Tetrahymena* which can be forced to synthesize DNA without dividing and then to go through several mitoses in succession (92) without intermediate periods of DNA synthesis.

In plant tissues, irradiation may lead to increased cell growth or elongation without any mitotic activity present (93). At the present time, despite the broad insight gained on enzyme attack by radiation, we are still unable to offer a completely satisfactory explanation of the first observed effect of radiation, the mitotic block.

The mixture of inhibitions and activations of enzymes in irradiated tissues which we describe in this chapter reflects the complexity of the reaction of such a highly organized body as a living cell when energy is deposited by ionizing radiation.

Ionizing radiations, like other physical agents, do not inactivate a particular enzyme or series of enzymes in the tissues. After a short period of general metabolic stimulation, irradiation causes many aberrations in biochemical organization which lead to (1) mitotic arrest, (2) growth inhibition generally, and (3), if the dose has been large enough, cell death. The practical use of ionizing radiation in medicine is not restricted to cancer therapy, and many clinical observations about apparently contradictory effects of irradiation are now better understood.

Progress in fundamental radiobiology is critically linked with progress in cell biochemistry and biophysics, and an urgent need is felt for a deeper understanding of the metabolic relations between the nucleus and the cytoplasm.

REFERENCES

1. J. Bergonié and L. Tribondeau, *Compt. rend. acad. sci.* 143, 983 (1906).
2. A. Pihl, R. Lange, and L. Eldjarn, *Nature* 182, 1732 (1958).
3. E. S. G. Barron, S. Dickman, J. A. Muntz, and T. P. Singer, *J. Gen. Physiol.* 32, 537 (1949).
4. S. Tanaka, H. Hatano, and S. Ganno, *J. Biochem.* 46, 485 (1959).
5. B. Holmes, *Nature* 165, 266 (1950).
6. S. Okada, *Arch. Biochem. Biophys.* 67, 102 (1957).
7. B. Rajewsky, G. Gerber, and H. Pauly, *in* "Advances in Radiobiology" (G. C. de Hevesy, A. Forssberg and J. D. Abbatt, eds.), p. 25. C. C. Thomas, Springfield, Illinois, 1956.
8. I. Serlin and G. C. Cotzias, *Radiation Research* 6, 55 (1957).
9. W. M. Dale, *Brit. J. Radiol., Suppl.* 1, 46 (1947).
10. Z. M. Bacq and P. Alexander, "Fundamentals of Radiobiology," 2nd rev. ed. Pergamon Press, New York, 1961.
11. W. M. Dale, *in* "Ionizing Radiation and Cell Metabolism," Ciba Foundation Symposium (G. E. W. Wolstenholme and C. M. O'Connor, eds.), p. 25. Little, Brown, Boston, Massachusetts, 1956.
12. E. S. G. Barron, *Radiation Research* 1, 109 (1954).
12a. D. K. Ray, F. Hutchinson, and J. Morowitz, *Nature* 186, 312 (1960).
13. J. F. Thomson and E. T. Mikuta, *Proc. Soc. Exptl. Biol. Med.* 86, 487 (1954).
14. M. Errera, *in* "Protoplasmatologia" (L. V. Heilbrunn and F. Weber, eds.), Vol. 10, 3. Springer, Berlin, 1957.
15. M. Errera, *Am. Naturalist* 94, 111 (1950).
16. A. Marples and G. Glew, Atomic Energy Research Establishment Rept. AERE I/R 2726 (1958).
17. R. Braams, *Radiation Research* 12, 113 (1960).
18. S. Okada, *Arch. Biochem. Biophys.* 67, 113 (1957).
19. G. Fletcher and S. Okada, *Radiation Research* 11, 291 (1959).
20. S. Okada and G. L. Fletcher, *Radiation Research* 13, 92 (1960).
21. P. P. Weymouth, *Radiation Research* 8, 307 (1958).
22. R. Goutier, *Progr. in Biophys.* 11, 53 (1961).
23. R. N. Feinstein and J. C. Ballin, *Proc. Soc. Exptl. Biol. Med.* 53, 6 (1953).
24. J. S. Roth, *Arch. Biochem. Biophys.* 60, 7 (1956).
25. C. de Duve, B. C. Pressman, R. Gianetto, R. Wattiaux, and F. Appelmans, *Biochem. J.* 60, 604 (1955).
26. M. Goutier-Pirotte and A. Thonnard, *Biochim. et Biophys. Acta* 22, 396 (1956).
27. J. S. Roth, *Radiation Research* 9, 173 (1958).
28. Z. M. Bacq and M. Errera, Preliminary Report to the U.N. Scientific Committee on the Effects of Atomic Radiation. Document A (AC-82), 1210 (1958).

29. N. B. Kurnick, B. W. Massey, and G. Sandeen, *Radiation Research* **11**, 101 (1959).

30. J. E. Thomson and E. T. Mikuta, Argonne Natl. Lab., ANL-4794, p. 140; ANL-4840, p. 80; ANL-4932, p. 59 (1952).

31. R. L. Brent, M. M. McLaughlin, and J. N. Stabile, *Radiation Research* **9**, 24 (1958).

32. H. G. Albaum, *Radiation Research* **12**, 186 (1960).

33. J. E. Richmond, K. I. Altman, and K. Salomon, *J. Biol. Chem.* **190**, 817 (1951).

34. A. Nizet, S. Lambert, and Z. M. Bacq, *Arch. intern. physiol.* **62**, 129 (1954).

35. R. G. Gould, Los Alamos Sci. Lab., LA-2179 (1958).

35a. U. Hagen, *Strahlentherapie* **117**, 201 (1962).

36. P. Alexander, J. T. Lett, H. Moroson, and K. E. Stacey, *Intern. J. Rad. Biol. Suppl.* **1**, 47 (1960).

37. P. Alexander, *Proc. 8th Intern. Congr. Radiol., München, 1959*, publ. G. Thieme (1960).

38. Z. M. Bacq and P. Alexander, "The Initial Effects of Ionizing Radiations on Cells" (R. J. C. Harris, ed.), p. 301. Academic Press, New York, 1961.

38a. G. B. Gerber, *Klin. Physiol.* **1**, 244 (1960).

39. A. Howard, *in* "Ionizing Radiation and Cell Metabolism," Ciba Foundation Symposium (G. E. W. Wolstenholme and C. M. O'Connor, eds.), p. 196. Little, Brown, Boston, Massachusetts, 1956.

40. L. S. Kelly, *Progr. in Biophys.* **8**, 144 (1957).

41. B. E. Holmes, *Ann. Rev. Nuclear Sci.* **7**, 89 (1957).

42. L. A. Stocken, *Radiation Research Suppl.* **1**, 53 (1959).

42a. C. L. Smith, *IAEA Symposium on Tritium in the Physical and Biological Sciences* **2**, 381 (1962).

42b. W. B. Looney, R. C. Campbell, and B. E. Holmes, *Proc. Natl. Acad. Sci. U.S.* **46**, 698 (1960).

43. C. W. Bishop and J. N. Davidson, *Brit. J. Radiol.* **30**, 367 (1957).

44. M. G. Ord and L. A. Stocken, *Biochim. et Biophys. Acta* **29**, 201 (1958).

45. H. Maass and G. Schubert, *Proc. 2nd U.N. Intern. Conf. Peaceful Uses of Atomic Energy, Geneva, 1958* **22**, 449 (1959).

46. L. Cima, G. Fassina, and F. Pozza, *Exptl. Cell Research* **17**, 1 (1959).

47. P. Mandel and P. Chambon, *in* "Symposium on the Immediate and Low Level Effects of Ionizing Radiations, Venice, 1959" *Intern. J. Radiation Biol. Suppl.* **1**, 71 (1960).

48. J. J. Jaffa, L. G. Lajtha, G. Lascelles, M. G. Ord, and L. A. Stocken, *Intern. J. Radiation Biol.* **1**, 241 (1953).

49. R. L. Potter, *Federation Proc.* **18** (1959).

50. W. A. Creasey and L. A. Stocken, *Biochem. J.* **72**, 519 (1959).

51. S. Okada and L. H. Hempelmann, *Intern. J. Radiation Biol.* **1**, 305 (1959).

52. F. J. Bollum, J. W. Anderegg, A. B. McElya, and V. R. Potter, *Cancer Research*, **20**, 138 (1960).

53. F. J. Bollum and V. R. Potter, *Cancer Research* **19**, 561 (1959).

53a. J. L. van Lancker, *Biochim. et Biophys. Acta* **45**, 63 (1960).

53b. D. K. Myers, C. A. Hemphill, and C. M. Townsend, *Can. J. Biochem.* **39**, 1043 (1961).

53c. L. Stevens and L. A. Stocken, *Biochem. Biophys. Research Communs.* **7**, 315 (1962).

54. R. Goutier, M. Goutier-Pirotte, and P. Ciccarone, *in* "Symposium on the Immediate and Low Level Effects of Ionizing Radiations, Venice, 1959" *Intern. J. Radiation Biol. Suppl.* **1**, 93 (1960).

54a. S. M. Lehnert and S. Okada, *Intern. J. Rad. Biol.* **5**, 323 (1962).

54b. O. F. Nygaard and R. L. Potter, *Radiation Research* **16**, 243 (1962).

54c. W. A. Creasey, *Biochim. et Biophys. Acta* **38**, 181 (1960).

54d. E. D. Gray, S. M. Weissman, V. Richards, D. Bell, H. M. Keir, R. M. S. Smellie, and J. N. Davidson, *Biochim. et Biophys. Acta* **45**, 111 (1960).

54e. R. Goutier and I. Bologna, *IAEA Symposium on the Biological Effects of Ionizing Radiations at the Molecular Level, Brno, 1962,* p. 287.

54f. E. Borenfreund and A. Bendich, *J. Biophys. Biochem. Cytol.* **9**, 81 (1961).

54g. E. R. M. Kay, *Nature* **191**, 387 (1961).

54h. L. Ledoux, *IAEA Symposium on the Biological Effects of Ionizing Radiations at the Molecular Level, Brno, 1962,* p. 175.

55. S. R. Pelc and A. Howard, *Radiation Research* **3**, 135 (1955).

56. A. M. Kuzin and V. I. Tokarskaia-Merenova, *Biofizika* **4**, 446 (1959).

57. S. A. Gordon, *in* "The Chemistry and Mode of Action of Plant Growth Substances" (R. L. Wain and F. Wightman, eds.), p. 65. Academic Press, New York, 1956.

58. S. A. Gordon, *Quart. Rev. Biol.* **32**, 3 (1957).

59. H. Fritz-Niggli, *Naturwissenschaften* **43**, 113 (1956).

60. H. Fritz-Niggli, *Naturwissenschaften* **43**, 425 (1956).

61. B. Rajewsky, G. Gerber, and H. Pauly, *Strahlentherapie* **102**, 517 (1957).

62. H. J. Eichel and J. S. Roth, *Biol. Bull.* **104**, 351 (1953).

63. H. J. Eichel and J. S. Roth, *Biol. Bull.* **105**, 373 (1953).

64. D. E. Smith and J. F. Thomson, *Radiation Research* **11**, 198 (1959).

65. I. Belokonsky and G. Rusev, *Biofizika* **4**, 204 (1959).

66. H. Ryser, H. Aebi, and A. Zuppinger, *Experientia* **10**, 304 (1954).

67. J. F. Thomson, W. W. Tourtelotte, and M. S. Carttar, *Proc. Soc. Exptl. Biol. Med.* **80**, 268 (1952).

68. S. di Bella, *Boll. soc. ital. biol. sper.* **29**, 1147 (1953).

69. C. C. Irving and J. D. Perkinson, *Radiation Research* **12**, 597 (1960).

70. O. Warburg, K. Gawehn, A. W. Geissler, W. Schröder, H. S. Gewitz, and W. Völker, *Arch. Biochem. Biophys.* **78**, 573 (1958).

71. O. Warburg, W. Schröder, H. S. Gewitz, and W. Völker, *Z. Naturforsch.* **13b**, 591 (1958).

72. R. N. Feinstein, C. L. Butler, and D. D. Hendley, *Science* **111**, 149 (1950).

72a. A. Caputo and B. Giovanelli, *Radiation Research* **13**, 809 (1960).

72b. K. Dose and U. Dose, *Intern. J. Rad. Biol.* **4**, 85 (1961).

72c. P. Cammarano, *Nature* **194**, 591 (1962).

73. R. L. Potter and F. H. Bethell, *Federation Proc.* **11**, 270 (1952).

74. J. Hickman and G. Ashwell, *J. Biol. Chem.* **205**, 651 (1953).

75. D. W. van Bekkum, H. J. Jongepier, H. T. M. Nieuwerkerk, and J. A. Cohen, *Brit. J. Radiol.* **27**, 127 (1954).

76. D. W. van Bekkum, *in* "Ionizing Radiation and Cell Metabolism," Ciba Foundation Symposium (G. E. Wolstenholme and C. M. O'Connor, eds.), p. 77. Little, Brown, Boston, Massachusetts, 1956.

77. D. W. van Bekkum and O. Vos, *Brit. J. Exptl. Pathol.* 36, 432 (1955).
78. T. L. Benjamin and H. T. Yost, *Radiation Research* 12, 613 (1960).
78a. A. Goldfeder, *Intern. J. Rad. Biol.* 3, 155 (1961).
78b. M. G. Ord and L. A. Stocken, *Biochem. J.* 84, 600 (1962).
79. H. Maass, *Strahlentherapie* 112, 79 (1960).
80. P. Buffa and R. A. Peters, *Nature* 163, 914 (1949).
81. P. Buffa and R. A. Peters, *J. Physiol. (London)* 110, 488 (1950).
82. C. Liébecq and R. A. Peters, *Biochim. et Biophys. Acta* 3, 215 (1949).
83. K. P. Du Bois, K. W. Cochran, and J. Doull, *Proc. Soc. Exptl. Biol. Med.* 76, 422 (1951).
84. V. R. Potter, *Proc. Soc. Exptl. Biol. Med.* 76, 41 (1951).
85. J. F. Thomson, W. W. Tourtelotte, and M. G. Carttar, *Proc. Soc. Exptl. Biol. Med.* 80, 268 (1952).
86. V. N. Philippova and I. F. Seitz, *Biokhimiya* 23, 119 (1958).
87. J. H. Burn, P. Kordik, and R. H. Mole, *Brit. J. Pharmacol.* 7, 58 (1952).
88. R. A. Conard, *Am. J. Physiol.* 170, 418 (1952).
88a. J. Lundin and C. J. Clemedson, *Biochim. et Biophys. Acta* 42, 528 (1960).
89. T. T. Puck and P. I. Marcus, *J. Exptl. Med.* 103, 653 (1956).
90. M. Dickson, J. Paul, and J. N. Davidson, *Biochem. J.* 70, 18P (1958).
91. A. H. W. Nias and J. Paul, *Intern J. Radiation Biol.* 3, 431 (1961).
92. H. S. Ducoff, *Exptl. Cell Research* 11, 218 (1956).
93. J. Moutschen, *Experientia* 13, 240 (1957).

Author Index

Numbers in parentheses are reference numbers and indicate that an author's work is referred to although his name is not cited in the text.

Numbers in italics show the pages on which the complete references are listed.

651

Subject Index

Acetaldehyde
  arsenite and oxidation of, 103
3-Acetaminopyridine
  NAD analogues of, 9
Acetazolamide
  see 2-acetylamino-1,3,4-thiadiazole-5-
    sulfonamide
Acethion, 233, 234
Acetic acid
  catalase and, 385
  metal binding and, 121
  nitrification and, 621
  oxidation of,
    arsenicals and, 105
  synthesis of, 10
Acetic thiokinase
  alkali metals and, 343
  monovalent cations and, 367
Acetoacetate
  formation of
    6-aminonicotinamide and, 11
    arsenicals and, 103
    diethylstilbesterol and, 11
    succinate reduction and, 485
    testosterone and, 11
N-Acetyl-p-aminophenol, 88
2-Acetylamino-1,1,4 thiadiazole, 13
2-Acetylamino-1,3,4-thiadiazole-5-sulfo-
  namide, 13
Acetylation
  6-aminonicotinamide and, 9
Acetylcholine
  acetylcholinesterase inhibition by, 196
  dissociation of enzyme complex of, 210
  eserine and, 209
  nicotinamide and bronchospasm, 12
  synthesis by brain, 534
Acetylcholinesterase, 193–203
  acetyl form, 197, 199
  active sites of, 193, 203
  alkyl phosphates and, 198
  carbamates and, 201

carbamyl form of, 201
comparative action of carbamates on,
  213
distribution of, 206
esteratic site of, 194
hydrogen binding and, 197
hydrophobic bonds and, 194
hydroxylamine and, 200
kinetics of inhibition, 199
mechanism of action, 195
methanesulfonyl derivative of, 203
organophosphates and, 225
phosphoryl form, 199, 200
potency of inhibitors of, 199
prosthetic inhibitors of, 196
pyridine-2-aldoxime methiodide and,
  200
radiation and, 633, 645, 646
rate equation for, 195
reactivation by choline, 200, 202, 203
reactivation by hydroxylamine, 200,
  202, 203
reaction by pyridine-2-aldoxime methiodide, 200, 202
recovery from inhibition, 200
SDS and, 442
selective inhibition of, 211, 226
  carbamates and, 212
  species variation and, 227, 228
serine and, 202
substrate protection of, 202
taurocholate and, 448
tris (*o*-cresyl) phosphate and, 228
velocity constants for, 195, 199, 202
water and, 194
N-Acetyl-D-glucosamine
  cell walls and, 35, 36
  β-glucosides of, 36
  lysozyme and, 35
  muramic acid and, 36
  teichoic acids and, 32
Acetylglutathione
  binding of NAD and, 138

693